UK TABLES OF NUTRITIVE

VALUE AND CHEMICAL

COMPOSITION OF FEEDINGSTUFFS

MINISTRY OF AGRICULTURE, FISHERIES AND FOOD

STANDING COMMITTEE ON TABLES OF FEED COMPOSITION

MINISTRY OF AGRICULTURE FISHERIES AND FOOD

STANDING COMMITTEE ON TABLES OF FEED COMPOSITION

Representing:

Agricultural Development and Advisory Service
Rowett Research Institute
Scottish Agricultural Colleges
Department of Agriculture, Northern Ireland
Agricultural and Food Research Council
University of Nottingham
United Kingdom Agricultural Supply Trade Association

Published in the United Kingdom

by Rowett Research Services Ltd.

Greenburn Road, Bucksburn, Aberdeen, AB2 9SB, U.K.

First published 1990

Compiled by Blacklaws, Printers, Westhill, Aberdeen.
Printed in the U.K. by Holmes McDougal Ltd., Edinburgh.
Cover designed by Art Works Ltd., Aberdeen.

STANDING COMMITTEE ON TABLES OF FEED COMPOSITION

UK TABLES OF NUTRITIVE VALUE
AND CHEMICAL COMPOSITION
OF FEEDINGSTUFFS

Editors :   D I Givens,
                             Angela R Moss
                             ADAS Feed Evaluation Unit,
                             Stratford on Avon

Consultant Editors : J R Hopkins
                             ADAS, Northern Regional Office, Leeds

                             C A Morgan
                             Edinburgh School of Agriculture

                             M H Stranks
                             ADAS, South West Regional Office, Bristol

                             J H Topps
                             School of Agriculture, Aberdeen

                             J Wiseman
                             University of Nottingham School of
                             Agriculture

CONTENTS

This book is the second publication from the United Kingdom's Standing Committee on Tables of Feed Composition (SCTFC). The first book "Feed Composition" (MAFF, 1986) dealt solely with ruminants. The present publication includes not only data from other species but also a greater diversity of animal based measurements together with a much enlarged section dealing with laboratory measurements.

This publication was produced from a computer database held at the ADAS Feed Evaluation Unit at Stratford on Avon. The SCTFC wishes to gratefully acknowledge the efforts of this Unit. In particular the substantial contributions of Mrs J M Everington, Dr S Callikan, Mr R Dainton and Mr C Dyson in the development of the database and the associated software for publishing this book are noted.

INTRODUCTION

There is a continuing need, by all involved in animal production, for up-to-date information on the composition of feedingstuffs. Such information may be divided into two broad groupings: that derived from chemical analysis alone and that derived from animal trials coupled with chemical analysis. The latter is accepted as being more valuable, but it is more expensive to obtain, so this book contains data of both types.

To ensure that the Tables are of the highest quality, all data had to pass one of two tests. Either the data referred to samples with energy values determined in vivo by an accepted UK method, or, where such values were not available, a full range of chemical analysis had been carried out. Whilst this, inevitably, reduces the numbers of samples included in the Tables, it does ensure that the relationships between values reported are realistic.

Digestible or metabolisable energy values were determined by the most appropriate of the participating groups. Samples on which only analytical results are given were analysed in the ADAS Laboratories. Clearly, the Tables contained in this book were produced only as a result of extensive co-operation between all of the organisations listed. Thanks are expressed to all of the individuals who worked hard to transfer data to the ADAS Feed Evaluation Unit computer, and, in particular to Mr J Round who ably represented the United Kingdom Agricultural Supply Trade Association on the SCTFC, and who arranged the provision of a large number of the samples for chemical analysis.

M H STRANKS
Chairman, UK Standing Committee on
Tables of Feed Composition

Bristol, January 1990

GLOSSARY OF TERMS

a	Immediately soluble fraction of a feed
ADF	Acid detergent fibre
AEE	Acid ether extract
AIA	Acid insoluble ash
Ala	Alanine
AMEn	Apparent metabolisable energy, corrected to zero nitrogen retention
amyl	Amylase pretreatment
Arg	Arginine
ash	Ashed
Asp	Aspartic acid
Avail carbs	Available carbohydrates
b	Insoluble but potentially degradable fraction of a feed
c	Rate of degradation of 'b' fraction
C8:0	Caprylic acid (octanoic)
C10:0	Capric acid (decanoic)
C12:0	Lauric acid (dodecanoic)
C14:0	Myristic acid (tetradecanoic)
C16:0	Palmitic acid (hexadecanoic)
C16:1	Palmitoleic acid (hexadecenoic)
C18:0	Stearic acid (octadecanoic)
C18:1	Oleic acid (octadecenoic)
C18:2	Linoleic acid (octadecadienoic)
C18:3	Linolenic acid (octadecatrienoic)
C20:0	Arachidic acid (eicosanoic)
C20:4	Arachidonic acid (eicosatetraenoic)
C22:1	Erucic acid (docosenoic)
Ca	Calcium
CD	Pepsin-cellulase DOMD
Cell	Cellulose
CF	Crude fibre
CH_4E/GE	Methane energy as a proportion of GE
Cl	Chloride
Co	Cobalt
CP	Crude protein
Cu	Copper
Cys	Cystine
DE	Digestible energy
dg	Degradability
DM	Dry matter
DOMD	Digestible organic matter in the dry matter
EE	Ether extract
F	Fluorine
FE/GE	Faecal energy as a proportion of GE
Fe	Iron

g	gram
GE	Gross energy
Glu	Glutamic acid
Gly	Glycine
His	Histidine
HT	High temperature
i	iso-
I	Iodine
Ile	Isoleucine
inorg	Inorganic
IVD	*In vitro* DOMD using rumen fluid-pepsin
K	Potassium
kg	kilogram
kJ	kilojoule
Leu	Leucine
Lys	Lysine
MADF	Modified acid detergent fibre
Max	Maximum
ME	Metabolisable energy
Meth	Methionine
Mg	Magnesium
mg	milligram
Min	Minimum
MJ	Megajoule
Mn	Manganese
Mo	Molybdenum
n	Number of samples or normal -
Na	Sodium
NCD	Neutral detergent-cellulase DOMD
NDF	Neutral detergent fibre
NH_3N/TN	Ammonia nitrogen as g/kg of total nitrogen
NO_3N	Nitrate nitrogen
ODM	Oven dry matter
OM	Organic matter
P	Phosphorus
Phe	Phenylalanine
Pro	Proline
Pro.OH	Hydroxyproline
S	Sulphur
SD	Standard deviation
Se	Selenium
Ser	Serine
TA	Total ash
TDM	Toluene dry matter
Thr	Threonine
TMEn	True metabolisable energy corrected to zero nitrogen retention
Tryp	Tryptophan
Tyr	Tyrosine

UE/GE	Urinary energy as a proportion of GE
unash	Unashed
Val	Valine
VAR	Variety
var	Variety
VFA	Volatile fatty acid
WSC	Water soluble carbohydrates
Zn	Zinc

The following guide is intended to aid the reader in the use of this book by explaining for example how the data is arranged and details of its source.

1.   Source of data

The data used to complete these tables have been gathered from various laboratories in the UK. The source of the data is shown at the top of each page. The source codes are:

Source 1: ADAS Feed Evaluation Unit, Stratford on Avon.

Source 2: Rowett Research Institute, Feedstuffs Evaluation Unit, Aberdeen.

Source 3: ADAS Nutrition Chemistry Department, Leeds, in collaboration with the Institute for Grassland and Animal Production, (Poultry Division), Edinburgh.

Source 4: University of Nottingham, Sutton Bonington.

Source 5: ADAS Nutrition Chemistry Department, Cambridge.

Source 6: ADAS Nutrition Chemistry Department, Bristol.

2.   Layout

a. Overall
The book is divided into four sections, the Analytical, Ruminant, Pig and Poultry Databases. The Analytical Database contains all of the analytical data available whereas the analytical values given in the other three sections are restricted to determinations carried out in association with the animal experimentation. Digestibility and energy values quoted in the Ruminant, Pig and Poultry Databases have all been measured in vivo. No calculated or predicted digestibility or energy values are given in the book. The reader will note throughout the book that where there are gaps in the data, the appropriate headings are retained. This is deliberate to firstly highlight where information is required and secondly to allow readers to insert their own values when appropriate.

b. Feed classes
Within each database feeds are collected together according to feed class. The feed classes are based on the International Feed Classes. The first digit of the feed class number denotes the International Feed Class number. The feed classes used are:

    10.   Hays   - Sun-cured herbage, legumes, whole-crop cereals with or without supplementary ventilation. Residues from herbage seeds should be classified as straw.

    11.   HT Dried Green Crops - High temperature dried herbage, legumes or other forages.

12.	Straws	- Sun-cured residue arising from the combining or threshing of cereals, legumes or grass, with or without supplementary ventilation.
20.	Fresh herbages and forages fed fresh	- Fresh herbage, legumes (including whole-crop peas and beans), aerial parts of root crops, whole-crop cereals and forage brassicae. Material cut and prepared but sampled immediately prior to ensiling, sun-curing or HT drying should be included.
30.	Silages	- Only ensiled forages such as herbage, legumes, whole-crop cereals and aerial parts of root crops should be included. Ensiled wastes, by-products and root crops are classed as if they were not ensiled.
40.	Energy Feeds	- Products with less than 200g/kg crude protein and 180g/kg crude fibre in the DM (or less than 350g/kg cell wall in the DM). This class includes cereals, roots, tubers, compound feeds, complete diets, sugar beet pulp and molasses.
50.	Protein supplements	- Products containing 200g/kg or more crude protein in the DM. This includes protein concentrates such as soya bean meal and fish meal, and by-products such as brewers grains.

Within each feed class, feeds are arranged in alphabetical order according to their common name. Common names are used throughout the book although these are linked with their respective International Feed Names and Numbers in a separate section. This will allow readers unfamiliar with UK common names to establish the identity of most feeds without ambiguity.

3.   Expression of data

a. Dry matter base.
Where appropriate all values are expressed on a dry matter basis. The dry matter base refers with one or two exceptions to oven dry matter. The exceptions relate to the energy and DOMD contents of fermented feeds in the Ruminant Database. These values are expressed on a toluene dry matter basis.

b. Digestibility and energy values
The digestibility values for ruminants and pigs all refer to apparent digestibility measured by total faecal collections. Metabolisable energy values for ruminant feeds have been measured using sheep and are also apparent but additionally involved the measurement of the proportional loss of energy in urine and an assessment of methane energy loss. Methane losses were measured values in the data from Source 2 but most values from Source 1 were predicted from the relationship of Blaxter and Clapperton (1965).

Metabolisable energy values for poultry are quoted both as true and apparent values. All poultry metabolisable energy values were measured using the techniques described by McNab and Blair (1988). All poultry metabolisable energy contents have been corrected to zero nitrogen retention on the assumption that nitrogen retained or lost from the body contains 34.39 kJ/g.

2

c. Amino acids and fatty acids

Amino and fatty acids are all expressed as g/kg DM. They can be converted to g/16gN and g/kg fat respectively by use of the following formulae:

Amino acid g/16gN = (amino acid,g/kg DM / crude protein,g/kg DM) * 100

Fatty acid g/kg fat = (fatty acid,g/kg DM / fat,g/kg DM) * 1000

d. Degradability values

Degradability values for dry matter and nitrogen in ruminant feedstuffs in these tables have all been obtained using the polyester (Dacron) bag technique. In this procedure feedstuffs were incubated in the rumen for periods ranging from 0 to 72 hours depending on feed type and the proportional disappearance of dry matter and nitrogen measured.

The proportional disappearance of dry matter and nitrogen were then fitted to the exponential model of Ørskov and McDonald (1979):

$$P = a + b\,(1-e^{-ct}) \text{ where}$$

P = the rumen degradability at time t
a = the immediately soluble fraction of the feed
b = the insoluble but potentially degradable fraction
c = the rate of degradation of the 'b' fraction

Since the effective degradability of a feedstuff depends on the fractional rumen outflow rate, ARC (1984) recommended that effective degradability values should be calculated at fractional outflow rates of 0.02, 0.05 and $0.08h^{-1}$ corresponding approximately to a very low plane of nutrition, moderately productive animals and highly productive animals respectively. The calculated effective degradability values are also given.

ANALYTICAL METHODS

A variety of laboratory methods have been employed in the course of producing the analytical data presented in these tables. Methods for the same determinations may also vary between laboratories. The following is intended to give the reader an indication of some of the details and source reference to the main analytical methods.

The following determinations were undertaken using essentially the methods of MAFF (1984): AIA, Ca, CF, Cl, CP, Cu, EE, MADF, Mg, Mn, Na, NH_3N/TN, ODM, total P, TA, S, Fe, I, VFAs, lactic acid, WSC and Zn. AEE was measured using the method of Anon (1985) and inorganic P by the method of Pons and Guthrie (1946).

NDF, ADF, cellulose and lignin were in the case of Sources 1 and 3 determined by an ADAS internal method involving a sequential procedure with lignin determined using the potassium permanganate reagent. These determinations were carried out according to the methods of Goering and Van Soest (1970) by the laboratory of Source 2 using sulphuric acid for lignin assay. In all cases starch rich feedstuffs were treated with amylase to remove starch which can interfere with the determination of these fractions.

Amino acids were determined by ion-exchange chromatography based on Moore, Spackman and Stein (1958) and Moore (1963) except for tryptophan which was determined by the procedure of Nielson (1985) but using lithium hydroxide instead of sodium hydroxide.

CD and NCD were determined by the methods of Jones and Hayward (1975) and Alderman (1985) respectively. For the determination of NCD in forages the amylase pre-treatment step was omitted. IVD was determined by the laboratories of Sources 1 and 3 by a method based on Alexander and McGowan (1966) whilst the method of Tilley and Terry (1963) was used by Source 2.

Long chain (C8-C22) fatty acids determined by Source 3 were extracted from the feedstuff by the method of AOAC (1984) and then separated by gas chromatography. TDM where measured was determined by the method of Dewar and McDonald (1961) but with additional corrections to the distillate volume for alcohols. GE was in all cases determined by adiabatic bomb calorimetry of fresh undried feedstuffs. In the case of feedstuffs of low dry matter content (eg grass silage), polyethylene was used as a primer to aid combustion.

Co and Se were determined by the methods of Simmons (1975) and Hall and Gupta (1969) respectively.

INTERNATIONAL FEED NAMES AND NUMBERS

This section provides a cross reference between UK common names and the International Feed Names and Numbers. These are based on the feed description and names of the International Network of Feed Information Centres (INFIC, 1980). Where INFIC names do not exist or for further clarity some feed names have been embellished. This additional information is given in brackets.

COMMON NAME	INTERNATIONAL FEED NUMBER AND NAME

Feed class 10

Grass hay, barn cured	1-15-335 Grass, fan air dried
Grass hay, sun cured	1-02-250 Grass hay, sun cured
Lucerne hay	1-00-078 Alfalfa hay, sun cured

Feed class 11

HT dried grass	1-02-211 Grass meal dehydrated
HT dried grass, short cutting cycle	As above (cutting cycle <36 days)
HT dried grass, short cutting cycle, perennial	As above (based on Lolium perenne)
HT dried grass, short cutting cycle, tall fescue	As above (based on Festuca arundinacea)
HT dried lucerne	1-07-848 Alfalfa, dehydrated pelleted
HT dried red clover	1-22-726 Clover, red dehydrated

Feed class 12

Ammonia treated barley straw	1-12-457 Barley straw, ammoniated
Ammonia treated oats straw	1-06-272 Oats straw, ammoniated
Ammonia treated wheat straw	1-06-271 Ammonia treated wheat straw
Sodium hydroxide treated barley straw	1-00-568 Barley straw, treated with sodium hydroxide, wet
Sodium hydroxide treated oats straw	1-03-285 Oats straw, treated with sodium hydroxide
Sodium hydroxide treated wheat straw	1-27-550 Wheat straw, treated with sodium hydroxide
Untreated barley straw	1-00-498 Barley straw
Untreated oats straw	1-03-283 Oats straw
Untreated oilseed rape straw	1-03-863 Rape straw
Untreated triticale straw	(Triticale straw)
Untreated wheat straw	1-05-175 Wheat straw

Feed class 20

Cabbage, fresh	2-01-046 Cabbage, fresh
Forage sorghum/sudangrass hybrid	2-04-489 Sorghum, sudangrass, fresh
Fresh grass	2-02-260 Grass, fresh
Kale, Bittern	2-02-446 Kale, fresh (var Bittern)
Kale, Dwarf Thousand Head	2-23-733 Kale, Thousand Head (dwarf)
Kale, Maris Kestrel	2-02-446 Kale, fresh (var Maris Kestrel)

COMMON NAME	INTERNATIONAL FEED NUMBER AND NAME
Kale, Marrow Stem	2-02-456 Kale, marrow, fresh
Kale, Merlin	2-02-446 Kale, fresh (var.Merlin)
Kale, Thousand Head	2-23-733 Kale, Thousand Head, fresh
White clover	2-01-468 Clover, white, fresh

Feed class 30

Barley whole crop silage	3-00-512 Barley, silage
Bean whole crop silage	3-00-590 Bean, silage
Clover, silage	3-01-469 Clover, white, silage
Grass silage	3-02-222 Grass, silage
Grass silage, big bale	3-02-222 Grass, silage (baled and bagged or wrapped)
Grass silage, clamp	3-02-222 Grass, silage (ensiled in bunker)
Lucerne silage	3-00-212 Alfalfa, silage
Maize silage	3-02-822 Maize, silage
Pea whole crop silage	3-03-590 Pea, silage
Sugar beet top silage	3-22-125 Beet, sugar, aerial part, silage

Feed class 40

Apples, fresh	4-00-421 Apple, fruit, fresh
Apple pomace	4-00-424 Apple, pomace, wet
Barley grain, all seasons	4-00-549 Barley, grain
Barley grain, spring	4-25-097 Barley, Spring, grain
Barley grain, winter	4-00-569 Barley, Winter, grain
Cassava meal	4-09-598 Cassava, Common, tubers, dehydrated
Citrus pulp, dried	4-01-237 Citrus, pomace without fines, dehydrated
Coffee, residue, fresh	1-01-576 Coffee, grounds, wet
Coffee, residue, dried	4-06-651 Coffee, instant beverage residue dehydrated
Fodder beet, fresh	4-00-637 Beet, Mangel, roots, fresh
Grape juice concentrate	4-08-569 Grape, syrup
Maize fibre	4-07-113 Maize, starch process residue, wet
Maize gluten feed	4-25-384 Maize, starch process residue, dehydrated
Maize grain	4-02-879 Maize grain and
	4-02-859 Maize, grain, flaked
Molasses, sugar beet	4-30-289 Beet, Sugar, molasses
Molasses, sugar cane	4-11-204 Cane, molasses
Naked oats grain, all seasons	4-25-101 Oats, hull-less, grain
Naked oats grain, Spring	4-25-101 Oats, hull-less, grain (Spring)
Naked oats grain, Winter	4-25-101 Oats, hull-less, grain (Winter)
Oats grain, all seasons	4-03-309 Oats, grain
Oats grain, Spring	4-03-309 Oats, grain (Spring)
Oats grain, Winter	4-03-309 Oats grain (Winter)

COMMON NAME	INTERNATIONAL FEED NUMBER AND NAME
Olive pulp meal	4-03-413 Olive, fruit without pits meal mechanical extracted
Pectin extracted fruits	(Apple and citrus pulp, pectin extracted residue)
Potato, processing waste	4-03-775 Potato, process residue, dehydrated
Potatoes, fresh	4-03-787 Potato, tubers, fresh
Rice bran meal, expelled	4-13-293 Rice, bran with germs, meal mechanical extracted
Rice bran meal, extracted	4-03-930 Rice, bran with germs, meal solvent extracted
Rye grain	4-04-047 Rye, grain
Sainfoin, low temp dried	(Sainfoin dehydrated at low temperature)
Sorghum grain	4-04-383 Sorghum, grain
Sugar beet feed dried, molassed	4-00-672 Beet, Sugar, pulp with molasses, dehydrated
Sugar beet feed dried, unmolassed	4-00-669 Beet, Sugar, pulp, dehydrated
Sugar beet feed, ensiled	4-00-662 Beet, Sugar, pulp, silage
Sugar beet feed, molassed, ensiled	(Beet, Sugar, pulp with molasses, silage)
Sugar beet feed, pressed	4-08-582 Beet, Sugar, pulp, pressed
Sugar beet feed, pressed, molassed	4-06-938 Beet, Sugar, pulp with molasses pressed
Swedes	4-04-001 Ruta baga (Brassica napus), roots fresh
Triple nuts	(Beet, Sugar, pulp with urea and minerals, pelleted)
Triticale grain, Winter	4-20-362 Triticale, grain (winter)
Wheat bran	4-05-190 Wheat, bran
Wheat feed	4-06-749 Wheat, flour-by product, less than 12% fiber
Wheat grain, all seasons	4-05-211 Wheat, grain
Wheat grain, Spring	4-25-107 Wheat, Spring, grain
Wheat grain, Winter	4-28-312 Wheat, Winter, grain
Wheat middlings	4-05-205 Wheat, flour by-product, less than 9.5% fiber
Wheat offals	4-06-749 Wheat, flour by-product, less than 12% fiber

Feed class 50

Beans, field Spring	(Bean, Field, seeds spring; Vicia Faba)
Beans, field Winter	(Bean, Field, seeds, winter; Vicia Faba)
Blood meal	5-00-380 Animal, blood, meal
Brewers grains	5-00-517 Barley, brewers grains, wet
Copra, extracted	5-01-573 Coconut, kernels with coats, meal solvent extracted
Copra, expelled	5-01-572 Coconut, kernels with coats, meal mechanical extracted
Copra, full fat	4-08-190 Coconut, kernals with coats, dehydrated
Cottonseed meal	5-30-144 Cotton, seeds with some hulls, mechanical extracted (expeller), caked

COMMON NAME	INTERNATIONAL FEED NUMBER AND NAME
Distillers dark grains, barley based	5-12-185 Barley, distillers grains with solubles, dehydrated
Distillers dark grains, maize based	5-02-843 Maize, distillers grains with solubles, dehydrated
Distillers dark grains, wheat based	5-05-194 Wheat, distillers grains with solubles, dehydrated
Draff, barley based	5-00-519 Barley,distillers grains,wet
Dried skim milk	5-01-175 Cattle, skimmilk, dehydrated
Feather meal	5-03-795 Poultry, feathers meal hydrolysed
Fish, mixed, ensiled	5-24-002 Fish, silage
Fishmeal, Chilean	5-24-017 Fish, meal mechanical extracted more than 70% protein 3.1-8% fat (Chilean origin)
Fishmeal, herring	5-02-000 Fish, herring, meal mechanical extracted
Fishmeal, mixed meal	Fish, meal (various souces)
Fishmeal, offal meal white	Fish, meal (various from white fish)
Fishmeal, Peruvian	5-24-018 Fish, meal, mechanical extracted, more than 70% protein, more than 8% fat (Peruvian origin)
Fishmeal, white	Fish, meal (various from white fish)
Groundnut meal	5-03-648 Peanut, seeds without coats, mechanical extracted, caked
Linseed meal	5-02-043 Flax, common, seeds, mechanical extracted, caked
Maize germ meal	5-07-146 Maize, germs, meal mechanical extracted
Maize gluten meal	5-09-318 Maize, gluten, meal, 60% protein
Malt culms	5-00-545 Barley, malt sprouts, dehydrated
Meat and bone meal	5-00-388 Animal, meat with bone, meal rendered
Palm kernel meal	5-03-487 Palm (Elaeis spp), kernels with coats, meal mechanical extracted
Peas, field	5-03-600 Pea, seeds
Pot ale syrup	5-12-210 Barley, distillers solubles, condensed
Poultry offal meal	5-24-876 Poultry, by-product, dehydrated, viscera with feet, with heads
Rapeseed meal	5-03-871 Rape, seeds, meal solvent extracted
Sesame cake	5-11-533 Sesame, seeds, mechanical extracted, caked

COMMON NAME	INTERNATIONAL FEED NUMBER AND NAME
Soyabean meal, extracted	5-04-604 Soybean, seeds, meal solvent extracted
Soyabean meal, extracted, dehulled	5-04-612 Soybean, seeds without hulls, meal solvent extracted
Soyabean, full fat	5-04-597 Soybean, seeds, heat processed
Sunflower seed meal	5-25-634 Sunflower, seeds with some hulls, meal solvent extracted

ANALYTICAL   DATABASE

FEED CLASS 10

HAYS

ANALYTICAL DATABASE

FEED DESCRIPTION : **GRASS HAY, ALL CURING METHODS** (Sources 1, 2)

Determination	Mean	SD	Min	Max	n	Determination	Mean	SD	Min	Max	n
General (g/kg ODM)						**Volatile Fatty Acids (g/kg ODM)**					
ODM (fresh)	865.1	25.0	791.2	914.7	119	Lactic					
TDM (fresh)						Formic					
CP	107.4	34.6	52.0	199.0	128	Acetic					
CF	317.3	39.6	172.0	433.0	128	Propionic					
MADF	355.1	42.0	205.0	437.0	128	n butyric					
EE	16.8	5.1	5.0	38.0	125	i butyric					
AEE	16.2	1.9	14.0	19.0	5	n valeric					
TA	74.3	13.6	44.0	118.0	115	i valeric					
AIA	18.1	8.5	5.9	58.0	117	n caproic					
GE (MJ/kg ODM)	18.4	0.45	17.0	19.5	128	i caproic					
						NO$_3$N					
						NH$_3$N/TN					
Carbohydrates (g/kg ODM)						pH					
NDF ash	656.8	61.5	437.0	820.0	123	**Fatty Acids (g/kg ODM)**					
NDF unash											
ADF ash	366.6	46.2	207.0	554.0	123	C8:0					
ADF unash	379.4	37.7	303.0	459.0	84	C10:0					
Cellulose	304.8	29.3	238.0	368.0	89	C12:0					
Lignin	59.7	12.1	38.0	91.0	81	C14:0					
Starch	1.5	1.8	0.10	7.0	47	C16:0					
NCD	562.6	78.2	417.0	721.0	84	C16:1					
CD	511.2	77.3	359.0	655.0	59	C18:0					
IVD	583.5	67.2	278.0	801.0	118	C18:1					
WSC	107.6	53.5	8.0	247.0	85	C18:2					
Avail Carbs						C18:3					
Sugars						C20:0					
						C20:4					
Minerals (g/kg ODM)						C22:1					
Ca	5.2	2.5	1.9	25.0	128						
Mg	1.4	0.52	0.70	4.8	128	**Amino Acids (g/kg ODM)**					
Na	2.1	1.7	0.10	9.2	128						
K	20.7	5.3	8.1	35.0	128	Ala					
Cl						Arg					
P total	2.6	0.77	1.1	7.8	128	Asp					
P inorg						Cys					
P phytate						Glu					
Fe						Gly					
S						His					
						Ile					
						Leu					
Trace Elements (mg/kg ODM)						Lys avail					
						Lys total					
Co						Meth					
F						Phe					
I						Pro					
Mn	61.9	20.0	31.0	94.0	11	Pro.OH					
Mo						Ser					
Zn	20.8	2.7	15.0	25.0	11	Thr					
Cu	5.7	1.1	4.0	8.0	11	Tryp					
Se						Tyr					
						Val					

ANALYTICAL DATABASE

FEED DESCRIPTION : **GRASS HAY, BARN CURED** (Sources 1, 2)

Determination	Mean	SD	Min	Max	n	Determination	Mean	SD	Min	Max	n
General (g/kg ODM)						**Volatile Fatty Acids** (g/kg ODM)					
ODM (fresh)	866.9	22.9	816.4	906.7	47	Lactic					
TDM (fresh)						Formic					
CP	121.5	36.1	59.0	185.0	50	Acetic					
CF	297.0	38.0	172.0	353.0	50	Propionic					
MADF	334.4	42.8	205.0	422.0	50	n butyric					
EE	18.2	5.1	9.0	38.0	50	i butyric					
AEE						n valeric					
TA	77.2	15.3	56.0	117.0	37	i valeric					
AIA	16.1	6.3	9.4	36.0	45	n caproic					
GE (MJ/kg ODM)	18.4	0.51	17.0	19.4	50	i caproic					
						NO_3N					
Carbohydrates (g/kg ODM)						NH_3N/TN					
						pH					
NDF ash	627.3	60.2	437.0	725.0	50						
NDF unash						**Fatty Acids** (g/kg ODM)					
ADF ash	348.6	45.2	207.0	421.0	48						
ADF unash	363.8	33.7	303.0	448.0	41	C8:0					
Cellulose	293.2	27.4	238.0	336.0	42	C10:0					
Lignin	56.3	11.2	38.0	80.0	40	C12:0					
Starch	1.3	1.6	0.10	5.7	27	C14:0					
NCD	601.3	63.0	450.0	721.0	37	C16:0					
CD	542.5	71.4	359.0	655.0	32	C16:1					
IVD	612.1	64.3	391.0	776.0	46	C18:0					
WSC	118.8	60.6	13.0	244.0	35	C18:1					
Avail Carbs						C18:2					
Sugars						C18:3					
						C20:0					
						C20:4					
Minerals (g/kg ODM)						C22:1					
Ca	5.6	1.7	3.3	11.3	50						
Mg	1.4	0.34	1.0	2.1	50	**Amino Acids** (g/kg ODM)					
Na	2.5	1.8	0.20	8.7	50						
K	21.6	5.5	8.1	35.0	50	Ala					
Cl						Arg					
P total	2.7	0.63	1.7	4.0	50	Asp					
P inorg						Cys					
P phytate						Glu					
Fe						Gly					
S						His					
						Ile					
						Leu					
Trace Elements (mg/kg ODM)						Lys avail					
						Lys total					
Co						Meth					
F						Phe					
I						Pro					
Mn	68.2	12.3	54.0	84.0	5	Pro.OH					
Mo						Ser					
Zn	20.8	1.8	19.0	23.0	5	Thr					
Cu	5.6	1.5	4.0	8.0	5	Tryp					
Se						Tyr					
						Val					

ANALYTICAL DATABASE

FEED DESCRIPTION : **GRASS HAY, SUN CURED** (Sources 1, 2)

Determination	Mean	SD	Min	Max	n	Determination	Mean	SD	Min	Max	n
General (g/kg ODM)						**Volatile Fatty Acids (g/kg ODM)**					
ODM (fresh)	863.8	26.6	791.2	914.7	71	Lactic					
TDM (fresh)						Formic					
CP	98.5	30.7	52.0	199.0	77	Acetic					
CF	330.8	35.1	243.0	433.0	77	Propionic					
MADF	369.0	35.9	245.0	437.0	77	n butyric					
EE	16.0	4.9	5.0	30.0	74	i butyric					
AEE	16.2	1.9	14.0	19.0	5	n valeric					
TA	73.0	12.7	44.0	118.0	77	i valeric					
AIA	19.3	9.5	5.9	58.0	71	n caproic					
GE (MJ/kg ODM)	18.4	0.41	17.3	19.5	77	i caproic					
						NO_3N					
						NH_3N/TN					
Carbohydrates (g/kg ODM)						pH					
						Fatty Acids (g/kg ODM)					
NDF ash	678.0	53.9	491.0	820.0	72						
NDF unash											
ADF ash	378.8	43.2	244.0	554.0	74	C8:0					
ADF unash	395.0	35.7	305.0	459.0	42	C10:0					
Cellulose	315.7	27.2	244.0	368.0	46	C12:0					
Lignin	63.0	12.3	41.0	91.0	40	C14:0					
Starch	1.8	2.1	0.10	7.0	20	C16:0					
NCD	529.4	74.4	417.0	700.0	46	C16:1					
CD	472.0	68.5	365.0	638.0	26	C18:0					
IVD	564.2	62.7	278.0	801.0	71	C18:1					
WSC	98.3	46.5	8.0	247.0	49	C18:2					
Avail Carbs						C18:3					
Sugars						C20:0					
						C20:4					
						C22:1					
Minerals (g/kg ODM)											
Ca	5.0	2.9	1.9	25.0	77						
Mg	1.5	0.61	0.70	4.8	77	**Amino Acids (g/kg ODM)**					
Na	1.9	1.6	0.10	9.2	77						
K	20.1	5.2	11.0	32.0	77	Ala					
Cl						Arg					
P total	2.5	0.84	1.1	7.8	77	Asp					
P inorg						Cys					
P phytate						Glu					
Fe						Gly					
S						His					
						Ile					
						Leu					
Trace Elements (mg/kg ODM)						Lys avail					
						Lys total					
Co						Meth					
F						Phe					
I						Pro					
Mn	56.7	24.7	31.0	94.0	6	Pro.OH					
Mo						Ser					
Zn	20.8	3.5	15.0	25.0	6	Thr					
Cu	5.8	0.75	5.0	7.0	6	Tryp					
Se						Tyr					
						Val					

ANALYTICAL DATABASE

FEED DESCRIPTION : **LUCERNE HAY** (Source 1)

Determination	Mean	SD	Min	Max	n	Determination	Mean	SD	Min	Max	n
General (g/kg ODM)						**Volatile Fatty Acids** (g/kg ODM)					
ODM (fresh)	865.1	8.8	854.4	876.1	5	Lactic					
TDM (fresh)						Formic					
CP	183.0	4.2	180.0	186.0	2	Acetic					
CF	303.8	47.2	259.0	378.0	5	Propionic					
MADF	339.8	48.6	291.0	412.0	5	n butyric					
EE	12.8	3.4	10.0	17.0	5	i butyric					
AEE						n valeric					
TA	95.6	10.2	80.0	105.0	5	i valeric					
AIA	2.6	0.55	2.0	3.0	5	n caproic					
GE (MJ/kg ODM)	18.2	0.55	17.3	18.7	5	i caproic					
						NO_3N					
Carbohydrates (g/kg ODM)						NH_3N/TN					
						pH					
NDF ash	493.4	59.1	423.0	574.0	5						
NDF unash						**Fatty Acids** (g/kg ODM)					
ADF ash	374.8	50.4	320.0	448.0	5						
ADF unash	381.0	11.3	373.0	389.0	2	C8:0					
Cellulose	264.8	30.4	235.0	308.0	5	C10:0					
Lignin	107.0	27.9	88.0	139.0	3	C12:0					
Starch	4.6	2.0	2.1	7.0	5	C14:0					
NCD						C16:0					
CD	549.8	57.8	471.0	603.0	5	C16:1					
IVD	557.0	52.3	499.0	621.0	5	C18:0					
WSC						C18:1					
Avail Carbs						C18:2					
Sugars						C18:3					
						C20:0					
						C20:4					
Minerals (g/kg ODM)						C22:1					
Ca	15.6	1.8	13.8	18.0	5						
Mg	1.7	0.27	1.3	2.0	5	**Amino Acids** (g/kg ODM)					
Na	0.60	0.07	0.50	0.70	5						
K	27.3	5.0	22.2	34.2	5	Ala					
Cl						Arg					
P total	3.1	0.66	2.5	3.9	5	Asp					
P inorg						Cys					
P phytate						Glu					
Fe						Gly					
S						His					
						Ile					
						Leu					
Trace Elements (mg/kg ODM)						Lys avail					
						Lys total					
Co						Meth					
F						Phe					
I						Pro					
Mn						Pro.OH					
Mo						Ser					
Zn						Thr					
Cu						Tryp					
Se						Tyr					
						Val					

ANALYTICAL   DATABASE

FEED CLASS 11

HIGH TEMPERATURE DRIED GREEN CROPS

ANALYTICAL DATABASE

FEED DESCRIPTION : **HT DRIED GRASS, SHORT CUTTING CYCLE, ALL SPECIES** (Source 1)

Determination	Mean	SD	Min	Max	n	Determination	Mean	SD	Min	Max	n
General (g/kg ODM)						**Volatile Fatty Acids** (g/kg ODM)					
ODM (fresh)	917.2	19.6	890.3	979.4	20	Lactic					
TDM (fresh)						Formic					
CP	198.7	23.4	170.0	261.9	20	Acetic					
CF	227.6	20.9	179.0	257.8	20	Propionic					
MADF	276.7	35.6	220.0	347.0	20	n butyric					
EE	37.3	8.5	12.0	52.0	16	i butyric					
AEE	48.3	6.0	41.0	57.0	8	n valeric					
TA	108.3	22.7	75.0	173.0	20	i valeric					
AIA	26.0	17.8	3.7	86.2	20	n caproic					
GE (MJ/kg ODM)	18.5	0.54	17.6	19.4	20	i caproic					
						NO$_3$N					
						NH$_3$N/TN					
Carbohydrates (g/kg ODM)						pH					
NDF ash	541.1	66.1	303.0	640.0	20	**Fatty Acids** (g/kg ODM)					
NDF unash											
ADF ash	282.2	26.8	239.0	329.0	16	C8:0					
ADF unash	312.1	37.9	246.0	375.0	16	C10:0					
Cellulose	226.6	21.4	194.0	270.0	16	C12:0					
Lignin	60.1	16.1	29.0	92.0	16	C14:0					
Starch						C16:0					
NCD	733.4	58.6	627.0	815.0	20	C16:1					
CD						C18:0					
IVD	640.1	45.1	559.0	717.0	20	C18:1					
WSC	147.5	43.4	94.6	226.0	20	C18:2					
Avail Carbs						C18:3					
Sugars						C20:0					
						C20:4					
Minerals (g/kg ODM)						C22:1					
Ca	6.9	1.1	5.0	8.5	20						
Mg	1.9	0.52	1.1	2.9	20	**Amino Acids** (g/kg ODM)					
Na	3.1	0.95	0.90	5.5	20						
K	27.4	4.7	21.3	40.0	20	Ala					
Cl						Arg					
P total	3.8	0.44	3.1	4.9	20	Asp					
P inorg						Cys					
P phytate						Glu					
Fe						Gly					
S						His					
						Ile					
						Leu					
Trace Elements (mg/kg ODM)						Lys avail					
						Lys total					
Co						Meth					
F						Phe					
I						Pro					
Mn						Pro.OH					
Mo						Ser					
Zn						Thr					
Cu						Tryp					
Se						Tyr					
						Val					

ANALYTICAL DATABASE

FEED DESCRIPTION : **HT DRIED GRASS, SHORT CUTTING CYCLE, PERENNIAL** (Source 1)

Determination	Mean	SD	Min	Max	n	Determination	Mean	SD	Min	Max	n
General (g/kg ODM)						**Volatile Fatty Acids (g/kg ODM)**					
ODM (fresh)	915.6	20.9	890.3	979.4	17	Lactic					
TDM (fresh)						Formic					
CP	200.9	24.5	170.0	261.9	17	Acetic					
CF	225.8	22.1	179.0	257.8	17	Propionic					
MADF	267.6	29.8	220.0	317.0	17	n butyric					
EE	37.6	9.3	12.0	52.0	13	i butyric					
AEE	49.3	5.6	41.0	57.0	7	n valeric					
TA	102.0	15.6	75.0	130.0	17	i valeric					
AIA	20.6	9.1	3.7	38.1	17	n caproic					
GE (MJ/kg ODM)	18.6	0.49	17.8	19.4	17	i caproic					
						NO_3N					
						NH_3N/TN					
						pH					
Carbohydrates (g/kg ODM)											
						Fatty Acids (g/kg ODM)					
NDF ash	537.7	71.5	303.0	640.0	17						
NDF unash						C8:0					
ADF ash	278.9	26.1	239.0	319.0	13	C10:0					
ADF unash	303.2	35.0	246.0	346.0	13	C12:0					
Cellulose	224.8	23.1	194.0	270.0	13	C14:0					
Lignin	58.7	15.1	29.0	82.0	13	C16:0					
Starch						C16:1					
NCD	751.1	43.0	679.0	815.0	17	C18:0					
CD						C18:1					
IVD	652.2	36.9	575.0	717.0	17	C18:2					
WSC	154.9	42.6	102.0	226.0	17	C18:3					
Avail Carbs						C20:0					
Sugars						C20:4					
						C22:1					
Minerals (g/kg ODM)											
Ca	6.7	1.1	5.0	8.5	17						
Mg	1.8	0.50	1.1	2.9	17	**Amino Acids (g/kg ODM)**					
Na	3.2	1.0	0.90	5.5	17						
K	27.8	4.8	21.3	40.0	17	Ala					
Cl						Arg					
P total	3.8	0.45	3.1	4.9	17	Asp					
P inorg						Cys					
P phytate						Glu					
Fe						Gly					
S						His					
						Ile					
						Leu					
Trace Elements (mg/kg ODM)						Lys avail					
						Lys total					
Co						Meth					
F						Phe					
I						Pro					
Mn						Pro.OH					
Mo						Ser					
Zn						Thr					
Cu						Tryp					
Se						Tyr					
						Val					

19

ANALYTICAL DATABASE

FEED DESCRIPTION : **HT DRIED GRASS, SHORT CUTTING CYCLE, TALL FESCUE** (Source 1)

Determination	Mean	SD	Min	Max	n	Determination	Mean	SD	Min	Max	n
General (g/kg ODM)						**Volatile Fatty Acids (g/kg ODM)**					
ODM (fresh)	926.0	5.4	920.1	930.7	3	Lactic					
TDM (fresh)						Formic					
CP	186.1	10.6	175.7	196.8	3	Acetic					
CF	238.0	7.9	229.0	244.0	3	Propionic					
MADF	328.0	16.6	316.0	347.0	3	n butyric					
EE	36.0	4.0	32.0	40.0	3	i butyric					
AEE	41.0		41.0	41.0	1	n valeric					
TA	144.3	25.8	123.0	173.0	3	i valeric					
AIA	56.6	26.1	37.0	86.2	3	n caproic					
GE (MJ/kg ODM)	17.9	0.28	17.6	18.1	3	i caproic					
						NO_3N					
						NH_3N/TN					
Carbohydrates (g/kg ODM)						pH					
NDF ash	560.0	7.6	552.0	567.0	3	**Fatty Acids (g/kg ODM)**					
NDF unash											
ADF ash	296.7	30.3	269.0	329.0	3	C8:0					
ADF unash	351.0	25.1	325.0	375.0	3	C10:0					
Cellulose	234.3	11.6	222.0	245.0	3	C12:0					
Lignin	66.0	22.5	53.0	92.0	3	C14:0					
Starch						C16:0					
NCD	633.0	5.3	627.0	637.0	3	C16:1					
CD						C18:0					
IVD	571.5	13.3	559.0	585.5	3	C18:1					
WSC	105.4	16.7	94.6	124.7	3	C18:2					
Avail Carbs						C18:3					
Sugars						C20:0					
						C20:4					
Minerals (g/kg ODM)						C22:1					
Ca	7.6	0.38	7.2	7.9	3	**Amino Acids (g/kg ODM)**					
Mg	2.4	0.06	2.4	2.5	3						
Na	2.9	0.50	2.4	3.4	3	Ala					
K	25.4	4.3	21.4	30.0	3	Arg					
Cl						Asp					
P total	3.7	0.40	3.3	4.1	3	Cys					
P inorg						Glu					
P phytate						Gly					
Fe						His					
S						Ile					
						Leu					
Trace Elements (mg/kg ODM)						Lys avail					
						Lys total					
Co						Meth					
F						Phe					
I						Pro					
Mn						Pro.OH					
Mo						Ser					
Zn						Thr					
Cu						Tryp					
Se						Tyr					
						Val					

ANALYTICAL DATABASE

FEED DESCRIPTION : **HT DRIED GRASS, UNKNOWN CUTTING CYCLE, ALL SPECIES** (Sources 1, 2, 4)

Determination	Mean	SD	Min	Max	n
General (g/kg ODM)					
ODM (fresh)	894.1	27.3	841.0	961.9	80
TDM (fresh)					
CP	188.4	38.5	81.9	269.0	114
CF	232.3	33.8	168.0	308.0	114
MADF	280.3	36.4	193.0	369.0	113
EE	37.2	7.9	12.0	52.0	113
AEE	44.8	10.9	20.0	56.0	9
TA	93.8	28.1	53.0	280.0	111
AIA	21.4	16.1	4.9	129.0	71
GE (MJ/kg ODM)	18.6	0.59	15.0	19.7	114

Carbohydrates (g/kg ODM)	Mean	SD	Min	Max	n
NDF ash	537.7	49.1	403.0	692.0	105
NDF unash					
ADF ash	297.0	41.3	177.0	406.0	105
ADF unash	307.9	39.8	213.0	375.0	46
Cellulose	232.1	30.4	138.0	311.0	57
Lignin	49.2	29.8	18.0	149.0	62
Starch	12.2	27.0	0.10	106.0	31
NCD	762.7	63.1	616.0	849.5	47
CD	671.6	68.2	542.0	820.0	54
IVD	658.3	44.0	562.0	762.0	109
WSC	122.5	35.7	39.0	227.0	63
Avail Carbs					
Sugars	156.0		156.0	156.0	1

Minerals (g/kg ODM)	Mean	SD	Min	Max	n
Ca	7.4	4.9	3.8	49.8	114
Mg	1.8	0.47	1.0	4.6	112
Na	2.8	1.6	0.40	9.0	112
K	26.0	8.0	8.5	45.0	110
Cl					
P total	3.3	1.1	2.0	11.8	113
P inorg					
P phytate					
Fe					
S	3.5	0.31	3.0	3.8	8

Trace Elements (mg/kg ODM)	Mean	SD	Min	Max	n
Co					
F					
I					
Mn	52.9	19.0	29.0	125.0	42
Mo					
Zn	33.2	7.1	21.0	52.0	42
Cu	8.2	1.5	6.0	12.0	42
Se					

Determination	Mean	SD	Min	Max	n
Volatile Fatty Acids (g/kg ODM)					
Lactic					
Formic					
Acetic					
Propionic					
n butyric					
i butyric					
n valeric					
i valeric					
n caproic					
i caproic					
NO3N					
NH3N/TN					
pH					

Fatty Acids (g/kg ODM)	Mean	SD	Min	Max	n
C8:0					
C10:0					
C12:0					
C14:0					
C16:0					
C16:1					
C18:0					
C18:1					
C18:2					
C18:3					
C20:0					
C20:4					
C22:1					

Amino Acids (g/kg ODM)	Mean	SD	Min	Max	n
Ala	4.0		4.0	4.0	1
Arg	5.0		5.0	5.0	1
Asp	3.0		3.0	3.0	1
Cys					
Glu	11.0		11.0	11.0	1
Gly	3.0		3.0	3.0	1
His	1.0		1.0	1.0	1
Ile	5.0		5.0	5.0	1
Leu	9.0		9.0	9.0	1
Lys avail					
Lys total	4.0		4.0	4.0	1
Meth	1.0		1.0	1.0	1
Phe	6.0		6.0	6.0	1
Pro					
Pro.OH					
Ser	4.0		4.0	4.0	1
Thr	5.0		5.0	5.0	1
Tryp					
Tyr	4.0		4.0	4.0	1
Val	6.0		6.0	6.0	1

ANALYTICAL DATABASE

FEED DESCRIPTION : **HT DRIED LUCERNE** (Sources 1, 2)

Determination	Mean	SD	Min	Max	n	Determination	Mean	SD	Min	Max	n
General (g/kg ODM)						**Volatile Fatty Acids (g/kg ODM)**					
ODM (fresh)	895.0	24.6	824.7	924.5	22	Lactic					
TDM (fresh)						Formic					
CP	199.1	27.7	156.0	268.1	43	Acetic					
CF	260.1	42.4	166.0	348.0	50	Propionic					
MADF	316.1	46.3	211.0	415.0	50	n butyric					
EE	27.8	7.3	10.0	46.0	50	i butyric					
AEE						n valeric					
TA	102.2	9.6	83.0	114.0	24	i valeric					
AIA	7.0	6.5	1.0	29.0	44	n caproic					
GE (MJ/kg ODM)	18.7	0.39	18.1	20.5	50	i caproic					
						NO$_3$N					
						NH$_3$N/TN					
Carbohydrates (g/kg ODM)						pH					
NDF ash	465.4	46.1	332.0	548.0	50	**Fatty Acids (g/kg ODM)**					
NDF unash											
ADF ash	336.1	46.1	230.0	430.0	50	C8:0					
ADF unash	327.9	42.5	236.0	413.0	28	C10:0					
Cellulose	234.8	28.7	169.0	290.0	50	C12:0					
Lignin	91.5	23.5	50.0	146.0	49	C14:0					
Starch	14.3	13.1	0.30	45.0	14	C16:0					
NCD	618.6	48.8	540.0	772.0	43	C16:1					
CD	546.8	50.6	434.0	702.0	41	C18:0					
IVD	567.9	48.3	461.0	688.0	50	C18:1					
WSC	67.4	29.2	29.0	188.0	41	C18:2					
Avail Carbs						C18:3					
Sugars						C20:0					
						C20:4					
						C22:1					
Minerals (g/kg ODM)											
Ca	15.0	2.6	10.0	20.7	50						
Mg	2.3	0.65	1.3	4.2	50	**Amino Acids (g/kg ODM)**					
Na	1.3	0.77	0.20	3.3	50						
K	25.4	8.3	6.9	36.5	50	Ala					
Cl						Arg					
P total	3.0	0.80	1.8	6.6	50	Asp					
P inorg						Cys					
P phytate						Glu					
Fe						Gly					
S						His					
						Ile					
						Leu					
Trace Elements (mg/kg ODM)						Lys avail					
						Lys total					
Co						Meth					
F						Phe					
I						Pro					
Mn	41.2	15.5	29.0	62.0	6	Pro.OH					
Mo						Ser					
Zn	28.0	6.6	20.0	39.0	6	Thr					
Cu	7.7	0.52	7.0	8.0	6	Tryp					
Se						Tyr					
						Val					

ANALYTICAL DATABASE

FEED DESCRIPTION : **HT DRIED LUCERNE, VAR ENVER** (Source 1)

Determination	Mean	SD	Min	Max	n	Determination	Mean	SD	Min	Max	n
General (g/kg ODM)						**Volatile Fatty Acids (g/kg ODM)**					
ODM (fresh)	903.2	1.2	902.3	904.0	2	Lactic					
TDM (fresh)						Formic					
CP	197.5	1.6	196.4	198.6	2	Acetic					
CF	285.0	22.6	269.0	301.0	2	Propionic					
MADF	321.5	20.5	307.0	336.0	2	n butyric					
EE	26.0	5.7	22.0	30.0	2	i butyric					
AEE						n valeric					
TA	108.5	3.5	106.0	111.0	2	i valeric					
AIA	4.5	4.3	1.4	7.5	2	n caproic					
GE (MJ/kg ODM)	18.6	0.02	18.6	18.6	2	i caproic					
						NO_3N					
						NH_3N/TN					
Carbohydrates (g/kg ODM)						pH					
NDF ash	508.5	27.6	489.0	528.0	2	**Fatty Acids (g/kg ODM)**					
NDF unash											
ADF ash	326.5	24.7	309.0	344.0	2	C8:0					
ADF unash	349.0	4.2	346.0	352.0	2	C10:0					
Cellulose	227.5	47.4	194.0	261.0	2	C12:0					
Lignin	70.5	29.0	50.0	91.0	2	C14:0					
Starch						C16:0					
NCD	613.5	23.3	597.0	630.0	2	C16:1					
CD						C18:0					
IVD	543.0	32.5	520.0	566.0	2	C18:1					
WSC	83.8	15.8	72.6	95.0	2	C18:2					
Avail Carbs						C18:3					
Sugars						C20:0					
						C20:4					
Minerals (g/kg ODM)						C22:1					
Ca	15.2	0.92	14.5	15.8	2						
Mg	2.6	0.0	2.6	2.6	2	**Amino Acids (g/kg ODM)**					
Na	1.4	0.07	1.3	1.4	2						
K	28.7	1.6	27.5	29.8	2	Ala					
Cl						Arg					
P total	3.3	0.21	3.1	3.4	2	Asp					
P inorg						Cys					
P phytate						Glu					
Fe						Gly					
S						His					
						Ile					
						Leu					
Trace Elements (mg/kg ODM)						Lys avail					
						Lys total					
Co						Meth					
F						Phe					
I						Pro					
Mn						Pro.OH					
Mo						Ser					
Zn						Thr					
Cu						Tryp					
Se						Tyr					
						Val					

ANALYTICAL DATABASE

FEED DESCRIPTION : **HT DRIED LUCERNE, VAR EUROPE** (Source 1)

Determination	Mean	SD	Min	Max	n	Determination	Mean	SD	Min	Max	n
General (g/kg ODM)						**Volatile Fatty Acids (g/kg ODM)**					
ODM (fresh)	895.8		895.8	895.8	1	Lactic					
TDM (fresh)						Formic					
CP	189.7	29.5	156.0	251.0	9	Acetic					
CF	269.3	35.2	224.0	347.0	9	Propionic					
MADF	326.2	33.1	275.0	376.0	9	n butyric					
EE	28.4	4.5	23.0	36.0	9	i butyric					
AEE						n valeric					
TA	108.0		108.0	108.0	1	i valeric					
AIA	3.9	3.7	1.0	11.0	9	n caproic					
GE (MJ/kg ODM)	18.6	0.23	18.3	19.0	9	i caproic					
						NO_3N					
						NH_3N/TN					
Carbohydrates (g/kg ODM)						pH					
NDF ash	474.0	34.1	411.0	526.0	9	**Fatty Acids (g/kg ODM)**					
NDF unash											
ADF ash	340.9	29.2	292.0	401.0	9	C8:0					
ADF unash						C10:0					
Cellulose	240.4	16.5	217.0	272.0	9	C12:0					
Lignin	93.4	8.4	81.0	105.0	9	C14:0					
Starch	45.0		45.0	45.0	1	C16:0					
NCD	621.4	30.4	579.0	662.0	9	C16:1					
CD	534.3	30.3	496.0	577.0	9	C18:0					
IVD	550.3	27.0	522.0	590.0	9	C18:1					
WSC	61.2	20.0	33.0	92.0	9	C18:2					
Avail Carbs						C18:3					
Sugars						C20:0					
						C20:4					
						C22:1					
Minerals (g/kg ODM)											
Ca	13.3	2.2	10.3	17.7	9	**Amino Acids (g/kg ODM)**					
Mg	2.3	0.44	1.6	3.1	9						
Na	1.4	0.78	0.50	3.3	9	Ala					
K	27.1	6.4	14.6	33.2	9	Arg					
Cl						Asp					
P total	2.6	0.55	1.8	3.3	9	Cys					
P inorg						Glu					
P phytate						Gly					
Fe						His					
S						Ile					
						Leu					
						Lys avail					
Trace Elements (mg/kg ODM)						Lys total					
						Meth					
Co						Phe					
F						Pro					
I						Pro.OH					
Mn						Ser					
Mo						Thr					
Zn						Tryp					
Cu						Tyr					
Se						Val					

ANALYTICAL DATABASE

FEED DESCRIPTION : **HT DRIED LUCERNE, VAR VIRTUS** (Source 1)

Determination	Mean	SD	Min	Max	n	Determination	Mean	SD	Min	Max	n
General (g/kg ODM)						**Volatile Fatty Acids (g/kg ODM)**					
ODM (fresh)	918.7	5.0	910.6	924.5	6	Lactic					
TDM (fresh)						Formic					
CP	198.9	21.5	164.0	232.0	13	Acetic					
CF	264.6	27.3	222.0	304.0	16	Propionic					
MADF	325.9	31.7	269.0	387.0	16	n butyric					
EE	28.2	5.6	19.0	40.0	16	i butyric					
AEE						n valeric					
TA	102.4	11.5	86.0	114.0	7	i valeric					
AIA	7.6	7.3	1.0	29.0	16	n caproic					
GE (MJ/kg ODM)	18.7	0.31	18.2	19.2	16	i caproic					
						NO_3N					
						NH_3N/TN					
Carbohydrates (g/kg ODM)						pH					
NDF ash	474.9	27.2	426.0	510.0	16	**Fatty Acids (g/kg ODM)**					
NDF unash											
ADF ash	345.8	32.4	288.0	416.0	16	C8:0					
ADF unash	331.2	27.8	271.0	370.0	13	C10:0					
Cellulose	236.1	16.8	198.0	265.0	16	C12:0					
Lignin	96.4	14.9	66.0	117.0	16	C14:0					
Starch	17.4	8.7	3.6	28.7	6	C16:0					
NCD	607.2	30.3	559.0	682.0	16	C16:1					
CD	545.9	26.5	496.0	604.0	16	C18:0					
IVD	558.5	26.2	498.0	597.0	16	C18:1					
WSC	58.4	17.7	29.0	92.0	13	C18:2					
Avail Carbs						C18:3					
Sugars						C20:0					
						C20:4					
						C22:1					
Minerals (g/kg ODM)											
Ca	14.4	2.0	12.3	18.0	16						
Mg	2.2	0.37	1.7	2.9	16	**Amino Acids (g/kg ODM)**					
Na	1.1	0.74	0.40	2.6	16						
K	28.6	7.6	14.4	36.5	16	Ala					
Cl						Arg					
P total	3.0	0.59	2.2	4.8	16	Asp					
P inorg						Cys					
P phytate						Glu					
Fe						Gly					
S						His					
						Ile					
						Leu					
Trace Elements (mg/kg ODM)						Lys avail					
						Lys total					
Co						Meth					
F						Phe					
I						Pro					
Mn						Pro.OH					
Mo						Ser					
Zn						Thr					
Cu						Tryp					
Se						Tyr					
						Val					

ANALYTICAL DATABASE

FEED DESCRIPTION : **HT DRIED RED CLOVER** (Source 1)

Determination	Mean	SD	Min	Max	n	Determination	Mean	SD	Min	Max	n
General (g/kg ODM)						**Volatile Fatty Acids (g/kg ODM)**					
ODM (fresh)	879.1		879.1	879.1	1	Lactic					
TDM (fresh)						Formic					
CP	177.0		177.0	177.0	1	Acetic					
CF	242.0		242.0	242.0	1	Propionic					
MADF	295.0		295.0	295.0	1	n butyric					
EE	23.0		23.0	23.0	1	i butyric					
AEE						n valeric					
TA	91.0		91.0	91.0	1	i valeric					
AIA	5.0		5.0	5.0	1	n caproic					
GE (MJ/kg ODM)	18.7		18.7	18.7	1	i caproic					
						NO_3N					
Carbohydrates (g/kg ODM)						NH_3N/TN					
						pH					
NDF ash	483.0		483.0	483.0	1						
NDF unash						**Fatty Acids (g/kg ODM)**					
ADF ash	330.0		330.0	330.0	1						
ADF unash						C8:0					
Cellulose	235.0		235.0	235.0	1	C10:0					
Lignin	93.0		93.0	93.0	1	C12:0					
Starch	27.7		27.7	27.7	1	C14:0					
NCD						C16:0					
CD	558.0		558.0	558.0	1	C16:1					
IVD	594.0		594.0	594.0	1	C18:0					
WSC						C18:1					
Avail Carbs						C18:2					
Sugars						C18:3					
						C20:0					
						C20:4					
Minerals (g/kg ODM)						C22:1					
Ca	15.0		15.0	15.0	1						
Mg	2.1		2.1	2.1	1	**Amino Acids (g/kg ODM)**					
Na	0.40		0.40	0.40	1						
K	25.5		25.5	25.5	1	Ala					
Cl						Arg					
P total	2.7		2.7	2.7	1	Asp					
P inorg						Cys					
P phytate						Glu					
Fe						Gly					
S						His					
						Ile					
						Leu					
Trace Elements (mg/kg ODM)						Lys avail					
						Lys total					
Co						Meth					
F						Phe					
I						Pro					
Mn						Pro.OH					
Mo						Ser					
Zn						Thr					
Cu						Tryp					
Se						Tyr					
						Val					

ANALYTICAL   DATABASE

FEED CLASS 12

STRAWS

ANALYTICAL DATABASE

FEED DESCRIPTION : **AMMONIA TREATED BARLEY STRAW, ALL SEASONS** (Sources 1, 2)

Determination	Mean	SD	Min	Max	n	Determination	Mean	SD	Min	Max	n
General (g/kg ODM)						**Volatile Fatty Acids** (g/kg ODM)					
ODM (fresh)	870.6	19.8	843.2	908.0	23	Lactic					
TDM (fresh)						Formic					
CP	70.0	17.7	46.0	125.0	20	Acetic					
CF	450.0	93.9	73.0	523.0	21	Propionic					
MADF	520.5	39.6	415.0	565.0	21	n butyric					
EE	15.4	5.5	7.0	31.0	21	i butyric					
AEE						n valeric					
TA	45.8	11.4	28.0	73.0	21	i valeric					
AIA	12.4	5.9	4.0	26.0	20	n caproic					
GE (MJ/kg ODM)	18.7	0.51	18.0	19.7	21	i caproic					
						NO_3N					
Carbohydrates (g/kg ODM)						NH_3N/TN					
						pH					
NDF ash	778.0	56.8	598.0	889.0	21						
NDF unash						**Fatty Acids** (g/kg ODM)					
ADF ash	541.5	41.9	438.0	601.0	21						
ADF unash	562.0	47.3	508.0	596.0	3	C8:0					
Cellulose	439.5	35.7	387.0	464.0	4	C10:0					
Lignin	86.0	20.8	62.0	99.0	3	C12:0					
Starch	5.4	7.5	0.10	14.0	3	C14:0					
NCD	520.9	62.2	401.0	622.0	14	C16:0					
CD	312.0	37.5	249.0	384.0	9	C16:1					
IVD	515.3	53.5	388.0	641.0	21	C18:0					
WSC	14.3	2.8	10.0	20.0	13	C18:1					
Avail Carbs						C18:2					
Sugars						C18:3					
						C20:0					
						C20:4					
Minerals (g/kg ODM)						C22:1					
Ca	4.6	1.8	1.9	9.6	21						
Mg	0.58	0.24	0.29	1.2	21	**Amino Acids** (g/kg ODM)					
Na	1.1	0.87	0.20	3.1	21						
K	12.1	5.5	5.5	25.6	21	Ala					
Cl						Arg					
P total	1.1	1.5	0.40	7.4	21	Asp					
P inorg						Cys					
P phytate						Glu					
Fe						Gly					
S	0.63	0.06	0.60	0.70	3	His					
						Ile					
						Leu					
Trace Elements (mg/kg ODM)						Lys avail					
						Lys total					
Co						Meth					
F						Phe					
I						Pro					
Mn	29.0		29.0	29.0	1	Pro.OH					
Mo						Ser					
Zn	14.0		14.0	14.0	1	Thr					
Cu	2.0		2.0	2.0	1	Tryp					
Se						Tyr					
						Val					

ANALYTICAL DATABASE

FEED DESCRIPTION : **AMMONIA TREATED SPRING BARLEY STRAW** (Sources 1, 2)

Determination	Mean	SD	Min	Max	n
General (g/kg ODM)					
ODM (fresh)	876.5	20.5	844.0	908.0	13
TDM (fresh)					
CP	77.6	21.3	54.0	125.0	10
CF	454.7	42.7	364.0	502.0	11
MADF	506.9	46.4	415.0	559.0	11
EE	16.7	4.1	11.0	25.0	11
AEE					
TA	46.7	8.6	34.0	59.0	11
AIA	16.0	5.7	6.0	26.0	10
GE (MJ/kg ODM)	18.7	0.50	18.0	19.7	11
Carbohydrates (g/kg ODM)					
NDF ash	743.9	54.2	598.0	799.0	11
NDF unash					
ADF ash	525.7	42.6	438.0	560.0	11
ADF unash	562.0	47.3	508.0	596.0	3
Cellulose	439.5	35.7	387.0	464.0	4
Lignin	86.0	20.8	62.0	99.0	3
Starch	14.0		14.0	14.0	1
NCD	545.4	57.6	453.0	622.0	8
CD	341.8	29.2	317.0	384.0	4
IVD	540.9	51.0	470.0	641.0	11
WSC	16.0	2.8	13.0	20.0	6
Avail Carbs					
Sugars					
Minerals (g/kg ODM)					
Ca	4.7	1.9	3.2	9.6	11
Mg	0.57	0.24	0.30	1.0	11
Na	1.3	1.0	0.20	3.1	11
K	10.3	3.3	6.1	16.0	11
Cl					
P total	1.4	2.0	0.40	7.4	11
P inorg					
P phytate					
Fe					
S	0.65	0.07	0.60	0.70	2
Trace Elements (mg/kg ODM)					
Co					
F					
I					
Mn	29.0		29.0	29.0	1
Mo					
Zn	14.0		14.0	14.0	1
Cu	2.0		2.0	2.0	1
Se					

Determination	Mean	SD	Min	Max	n
Volatile Fatty Acids (g/kg ODM)					
Lactic					
Formic					
Acetic					
Propionic					
n butyric					
i butyric					
n valeric					
i valeric					
n caproic					
i caproic					
NO_3N					
NH_3N/TN					
pH					
Fatty Acids (g/kg ODM)					
C8:0					
C10:0					
C12:0					
C14:0					
C16:0					
C16:1					
C18:0					
C18:1					
C18:2					
C18:3					
C20:0					
C20:4					
C22:1					
Amino Acids (g/kg ODM)					
Ala					
Arg					
Asp					
Cys					
Glu					
Gly					
His					
Ile					
Leu					
Lys avail					
Lys total					
Meth					
Phe					
Pro					
Pro.OH					
Ser					
Thr					
Tryp					
Tyr					
Val					

ANALYTICAL DATABASE

FEED DESCRIPTION : **AMMONIA TREATED WINTER BARLEY STRAW** (Source 1)

Determination	Mean	SD	Min	Max	n	Determination	Mean	SD	Min	Max	n
General (g/kg ODM)						**Volatile Fatty Acids (g/kg ODM)**					
ODM (fresh)	866.3	18.1	847.4	890.7	7	Lactic					
TDM (fresh)						Formic					
CP	63.0	7.4	51.0	73.0	7	Acetic					
CF	493.7	18.8	465.0	523.0	7	Propionic					
MADF	546.7	18.8	523.0	565.0	7	n butyric					
EE	15.9	7.0	10.0	31.0	7	i butyric					
AEE						n valeric					
TA	42.9	15.2	28.0	73.0	7	i valeric					
AIA	7.7	2.6	4.0	11.0	7	n caproic					
GE (MJ/kg ODM)	18.7	0.37	18.2	19.4	7	i caproic					
						NO_3N					
						NH_3N/TN					
Carbohydrates (g/kg ODM)						pH					
NDF ash	810.0	17.9	785.0	829.0	7						
NDF unash						**Fatty Acids (g/kg ODM)**					
ADF ash	571.6	22.6	538.0	601.0	7						
ADF unash						C8:0					
Cellulose						C10:0					
Lignin						C12:0					
Starch						C14:0					
NCD	505.8	41.2	456.0	556.0	5	C16:0					
CD	288.2	23.9	249.0	312.0	5	C16:1					
IVD	496.9	28.8	450.0	538.0	7	C18:0					
WSC	13.6	1.7	12.0	16.0	5	C18:1					
Avail Carbs						C18:2					
Sugars						C18:3					
						C20:0					
						C20:4					
Minerals (g/kg ODM)						C22:1					
Ca	4.5	2.0	1.9	7.7	7						
Mg	0.67	0.26	0.50	1.2	7	**Amino Acids (g/kg ODM)**					
Na	0.94	0.75	0.20	2.5	7						
K	13.0	6.7	5.5	25.6	7	Ala					
Cl						Arg					
P total	0.61	0.18	0.40	0.90	7	Asp					
P inorg						Cys					
P phytate						Glu					
Fe						Gly					
S						His					
						Ile					
						Leu					
Trace Elements (mg/kg ODM)						Lys avail					
						Lys total					
Co						Meth					
F						Phe					
I						Pro					
Mn						Pro.OH					
Mo						Ser					
Zn						Thr					
Cu						Tryp					
Se						Tyr					
						Val					

ANALYTICAL DATABASE

FEED DESCRIPTION : **AMMONIA TREATED SPRING OATS STRAW** (Source 1)

Determination	Mean	SD	Min	Max	n	Determination	Mean	SD	Min	Max	n
General (g/kg ODM)						**Volatile Fatty Acids** (g/kg ODM)					
ODM (fresh)	875.1		875.1	875.1	1	Lactic					
TDM (fresh)						Formic					
CP	67.0		67.0	67.0	1	Acetic					
CF	474.0		474.0	474.0	1	Propionic					
MADF	530.0		530.0	530.0	1	n butyric					
EE	29.0		29.0	29.0	1	i butyric					
AEE						n valeric					
TA	66.0		66.0	66.0	1	i valeric					
AIA	14.0		14.0	14.0	1	n caproic					
GE (MJ/kg ODM)	18.5		18.5	18.5	1	i caproic					
						NO$_3$N					
						NH$_3$N/TN					
Carbohydrates (g/kg ODM)						pH					
NDF ash	743.0		743.0	743.0	1	**Fatty Acids** (g/kg ODM)					
NDF unash											
ADF ash	584.0		584.0	584.0	1	C8:0					
ADF unash						C10:0					
Cellulose						C12:0					
Lignin						C14:0					
Starch						C16:0					
NCD	649.0		649.0	649.0	1	C16:1					
CD	348.0		348.0	348.0	1	C18:0					
IVD	528.0		528.0	528.0	1	C18:1					
WSC	17.0		17.0	17.0	1	C18:2					
Avail Carbs						C18:3					
Sugars						C20:0					
						C20:4					
Minerals (g/kg ODM)						C22:1					
Ca	5.3		5.3	5.3	1						
Mg	1.2		1.2	1.2	1	**Amino Acids** (g/kg ODM)					
Na	5.8		5.8	5.8	1						
K	19.0		19.0	19.0	1	Ala					
Cl						Arg					
P total	0.70		0.70	0.70	1	Asp					
P inorg						Cys					
P phytate						Glu					
Fe						Gly					
S						His					
						Ile					
						Leu					
Trace Elements (mg/kg ODM)						Lys avail					
						Lys total					
Co						Meth					
F						Phe					
I						Pro					
Mn						Pro.OH					
Mo						Ser					
Zn						Thr					
Cu						Tryp					
Se						Tyr					
						Val					

ANALYTICAL DATABASE

FEED DESCRIPTION : **AMMONIA TREATED OATS STRAW, ALL SEASONS** (Source 1)

Determination	Mean	SD	Min	Max	n	Determination	Mean	SD	Min	Max	n
General (g/kg ODM)						**Volatile Fatty Acids (g/kg ODM)**					
ODM (fresh)	843.0	47.5	774.3	875.1	4	Lactic					
TDM (fresh)						Formic					
CP	75.3	22.8	59.0	109.0	4	Acetic					
CF	431.3	85.6	303.0	479.0	4	Propionic					
MADF	493.8	87.3	363.0	543.0	4	n butyric					
EE	17.8	8.7	10.0	29.0	4	i butyric					
AEE						n valeric					
TA	66.3	6.2	61.0	75.0	4	i valeric					
AIA	14.3	2.9	11.0	18.0	4	n caproic					
GE (MJ/kg ODM)	18.3	0.33	17.8	18.5	4	i caproic					
						NO_3N					
						NH_3N/TN					
Carbohydrates (g/kg ODM)						pH					
NDF ash	735.3	45.4	670.0	774.0	4	**Fatty Acids (g/kg ODM)**					
NDF unash											
ADF ash	522.0	106.1	364.0	584.0	4	C8:0					
ADF unash						C10:0					
Cellulose						C12:0					
Lignin						C14:0					
Starch						C16:0					
NCD	604.3	38.9	578.0	649.0	3	C16:1					
CD	331.0	24.4	303.0	348.0	3	C18:0					
IVD	551.5	33.9	517.0	584.0	4	C18:1					
WSC	15.7	2.3	13.0	17.0	3	C18:2					
Avail Carbs						C18:3					
Sugars						C20:0					
						C20:4					
Minerals (g/kg ODM)						C22:1					
Ca	4.6	1.5	2.5	6.0	4						
Mg	1.1	0.31	0.70	1.4	4	**Amino Acids (g/kg ODM)**					
Na	3.8	1.7	1.6	5.8	4						
K	18.5	3.3	16.0	23.0	4	Ala					
Cl						Arg					
P total	1.4	1.0	0.70	2.9	4	Asp					
P inorg						Cys					
P phytate						Glu					
Fe						Gly					
S						His					
						Ile					
						Leu					
Trace Elements (mg/kg ODM)						Lys avail					
						Lys total					
Co						Meth					
F						Phe					
I						Pro					
Mn						Pro.OH					
Mo						Ser					
Zn						Thr					
Cu						Tryp					
Se						Tyr					
						Val					

ANALYTICAL DATABASE

FEED DESCRIPTION : **AMMONIA TREATED WINTER OATS STRAW** (Source 1)

Determination	Mean	SD	Min	Max	n	Determination	Mean	SD	Min	Max	n
General (g/kg ODM)						**Volatile Fatty Acids** (g/kg ODM)					
ODM (fresh)	832.3	52.0	774.3	874.6	3	Lactic					
TDM (fresh)						Formic					
CP	78.0	27.1	59.0	109.0	3	Acetic					
CF	417.0	98.9	303.0	479.0	3	Propionic					
MADF	481.7	102.8	363.0	543.0	3	n butyric					
EE	14.0	5.3	10.0	20.0	3	i butyric					
AEE						n valeric					
TA	66.3	7.6	61.0	75.0	3	i valeric					
AIA	14.3	3.5	11.0	18.0	3	n caproic					
GE (MJ/kg ODM)	18.2	0.37	17.8	18.5	3	i caproic					
						NO_3N					
						NH_3N/TN					
Carbohydrates (g/kg ODM)						pH					
NDF ash	732.7	55.2	670.0	774.0	3	**Fatty Acids** (g/kg ODM)					
NDF unash											
ADF ash	501.3	119.6	364.0	583.0	3	C8:0					
ADF unash						C10:0					
Cellulose						C12:0					
Lignin						C14:0					
Starch						C16:0					
NCD	582.0	5.7	578.0	586.0	2	C16:1					
CD	322.5	27.6	303.0	342.0	2	C18:0					
IVD	559.3	36.8	517.0	584.0	3	C18:1					
WSC	15.0	2.8	13.0	17.0	2	C18:2					
Avail Carbs						C18:3					
Sugars						C20:0					
						C20:4					
Minerals (g/kg ODM)						C22:1					
Ca	4.3	1.8	2.5	6.0	3						
Mg	1.0	0.36	0.70	1.4	3	**Amino Acids** (g/kg ODM)					
Na	3.1	1.3	1.6	4.0	3						
K	18.3	4.0	16.0	23.0	3	Ala					
Cl						Arg					
P total	1.6	1.1	0.90	2.9	3	Asp					
P inorg						Cys					
P phytate						Glu					
Fe						Gly					
S						His					
						Ile					
						Leu					
Trace Elements (mg/kg ODM)						Lys avail					
						Lys total					
Co						Meth					
F						Phe					
I						Pro					
Mn						Pro.OH					
Mo						Ser					
Zn						Thr					
Cu						Tryp					
Se						Tyr					
						Val					

ANALYTICAL DATABASE

FEED DESCRIPTION : **AMMONIA TREATED WHEAT STRAW, ALL SEASONS** (Source 1)

Determination	Mean	SD	Min	Max	n	Determination	Mean	SD	Min	Max	n
General (g/kg ODM)						**Volatile Fatty Acids (g/kg ODM)**					
ODM (fresh)	868.5	25.7	789.0	899.0	17	Lactic					
TDM (fresh)						Formic					
CP	68.4	12.2	44.0	90.0	17	Acetic					
CF	433.8	97.3	62.0	486.0	17	Propionic					
MADF	532.5	20.2	500.0	569.0	17	n butyric					
EE	13.3	3.3	8.0	23.0	17	i butyric					
AEE						n valeric					
TA	55.5	13.6	37.0	84.0	17	i valeric					
AIA	23.3	9.6	11.0	47.0	17	n caproic					
GE (MJ/kg ODM)	18.6	0.47	17.9	19.4	17	i caproic					
						NO3N					
						NH3N/TN					
Carbohydrates (g/kg ODM)						pH					
NDF ash	773.2	81.0	567.0	869.0	17						
NDF unash						**Fatty Acids (g/kg ODM)**					
ADF ash	544.2	26.2	498.0	597.0	17						
ADF unash						C8:0					
Cellulose	418.0		418.0	418.0	1	C10:0					
Lignin	116.0		116.0	116.0	1	C12:0					
Starch	1.2	1.5	0.10	2.2	2	C14:0					
NCD	476.7	44.4	399.0	542.0	10	C16:0					
CD	280.8	25.1	239.0	331.0	9	C16:1					
IVD	490.3	58.4	370.0	563.0	17	C18:0					
WSC	12.0	2.7	8.4	19.0	12	C18:1					
Avail Carbs						C18:2					
Sugars						C18:3					
						C20:0					
						C20:4					
Minerals (g/kg ODM)						C22:1					
Ca	4.9	3.0	3.1	16.2	17						
Mg	0.75	0.17	0.50	1.1	17	**Amino Acids (g/kg ODM)**					
Na	0.14	0.09	0.10	0.40	16						
K	11.2	5.2	4.6	20.0	17	Ala					
Cl						Arg					
P total	0.75	0.27	0.30	1.3	17	Asp					
P inorg						Cys					
P phytate						Glu					
Fe						Gly					
S						His					
						Ile					
						Leu					
Trace Elements (mg/kg ODM)						Lys avail					
						Lys total					
Co						Meth					
F						Phe					
I						Pro					
Mn						Pro.OH					
Mo						Ser					
Zn						Thr					
Cu						Tryp					
Se						Tyr					
						Val					

ANALYTICAL DATABASE

FEED DESCRIPTION : **AMMONIA TREATED SPRING WHEAT STRAW** (Source 1)

Determination	Mean	SD	Min	Max	n	Determination	Mean	SD	Min	Max	n
General (g/kg ODM)						**Volatile Fatty Acids** (g/kg ODM)					
ODM (fresh)	877.9	9.4	864.1	885.3	4	Lactic					
TDM (fresh)						Formic					
CP	74.8	9.6	63.0	84.0	4	Acetic					
CF	455.8	9.9	447.0	470.0	4	Propionic					
MADF	530.8	11.2	514.0	538.0	4	n butyric					
EE	12.3	0.50	12.0	13.0	4	i butyric					
AEE						n valeric					
TA	63.5	9.7	58.0	78.0	4	i valeric					
AIA	22.5	11.1	12.0	34.0	4	n caproic					
GE (MJ/kg ODM)	18.2	0.36	17.9	18.6	4	i caproic					
						NO$_3$N					
						NH$_3$N/TN					
Carbohydrates (g/kg ODM)						pH					
NDF ash	782.3	22.8	760.0	807.0	4	**Fatty Acids** (g/kg ODM)					
NDF unash											
ADF ash	548.5	27.1	528.0	587.0	4	C8:0					
ADF unash						C10:0					
Cellulose						C12:0					
Lignin						C14:0					
Starch						C16:0					
NCD	470.8	50.5	423.0	542.0	4	C16:1					
CD	273.5	24.1	239.0	294.0	4	C18:0					
IVD	522.8	28.5	493.0	551.0	4	C18:1					
WSC	11.3	1.9	10.0	14.0	4	C18:2					
Avail Carbs						C18:3					
Sugars						C20:0					
						C20:4					
Minerals (g/kg ODM)						C22:1					
Ca	4.8	1.3	3.3	6.3	4						
Mg	0.68	0.24	0.50	1.0	4	**Amino Acids** (g/kg ODM)					
Na	0.18	0.15	0.10	0.40	4						
K	16.8	4.6	10.0	20.0	4	Ala					
Cl						Arg					
P total	0.68	0.22	0.50	1.0	4	Asp					
P inorg						Cys					
P phytate						Glu					
Fe						Gly					
S						His					
						Ile					
						Leu					
Trace Elements (mg/kg ODM)						Lys avail					
						Lys total					
Co						Meth					
F						Phe					
I						Pro					
Mn						Pro.OH					
Mo						Ser					
Zn						Thr					
Cu						Tryp					
Se						Tyr					
						Val					

ANALYTICAL DATABASE

FEED DESCRIPTION : **AMMONIA TREATED WINTER WHEAT STRAW** (Source 1)

Determination	Mean	SD	Min	Max	n	Determination	Mean	SD	Min	Max	n
General (g/kg ODM)						**Volatile Fatty Acids** (g/kg ODM)					
ODM (fresh)	873.3	18.0	836.9	899.0	11	Lactic					
TDM (fresh)						Formic					
CP	66.7	13.6	44.0	90.0	11	Acetic					
CF	425.8	121.8	62.0	486.0	11	Propionic					
MADF	535.4	22.3	505.0	569.0	11	n butyric					
EE	14.2	3.6	11.0	23.0	11	i butyric					
AEE						n valeric					
TA	52.6	15.2	37.0	84.0	11	i valeric					
AIA	23.6	10.5	11.0	47.0	11	n caproic					
GE (MJ/kg ODM)	18.6	0.41	18.0	19.2	11	i caproic					
						NO$_3$N					
Carbohydrates (g/kg ODM)						NH$_3$N/TN					
						pH					
NDF ash	778.6	75.8	567.0	851.0	11						
NDF unash						**Fatty Acids** (g/kg ODM)					
ADF ash	544.7	28.9	498.0	597.0	11						
ADF unash						C8:0					
Cellulose						C10:0					
Lignin						C12:0					
Starch	1.2	1.5	0.10	2.2	2	C14:0					
NCD	480.7	44.5	399.0	526.0	6	C16:0					
CD	286.6	26.9	260.0	331.0	5	C16:1					
IVD	492.4	56.9	403.0	563.0	11	C18:0					
WSC	11.3	1.6	8.4	13.0	7	C18:1					
Avail Carbs						C18:2					
Sugars						C18:3					
						C20:0					
						C20:4					
Minerals (g/kg ODM)						C22:1					
Ca	5.1	3.7	3.1	16.2	11						
Mg	0.78	0.17	0.50	1.1	11	**Amino Acids** (g/kg ODM)					
Na	0.13	0.07	0.10	0.30	10						
K	9.1	4.2	4.6	17.0	11	Ala					
Cl						Arg					
P total	0.75	0.31	0.30	1.3	11	Asp					
P inorg						Cys					
P phytate						Glu					
Fe						Gly					
S						His					
						Ile					
						Leu					
Trace Elements (mg/kg ODM)						Lys avail					
						Lys total					
Co						Meth					
F						Phe					
I						Pro					
Mn						Pro.OH					
Mo						Ser					
Zn						Thr					
Cu						Tryp					
Se						Tyr					
						Val					

ANALYTICAL DATABASE

FEED DESCRIPTION : **SODIUM HYDROXIDE TREATED BARLEY STRAW, ALL SEASONS** (Source 1)

Determination	Mean	SD	Min	Max	n	Determination	Mean	SD	Min	Max	n
General (g/kg ODM)						**Volatile Fatty Acids** (g/kg ODM)					
ODM (fresh)	805.7	40.6	757.7	875.3	7	Lactic					
TDM (fresh)						Formic					
CP	44.6	11.2	33.0	70.0	9	Acetic					
CF	430.2	37.2	373.0	491.0	10	Propionic					
MADF	487.0	33.4	439.0	536.0	10	n butyric					
EE	12.2	4.6	5.0	22.0	10	i butyric					
AEE						n valeric					
TA	114.8	18.1	92.0	152.0	10	i valeric					
AIA	21.4	7.4	10.0	30.0	10	n caproic					
GE (MJ/kg ODM)	17.4	0.36	16.8	17.8	10	i caproic					
						NO_3N					
						NH_3N/TN					
Carbohydrates (g/kg ODM)						pH					
						Fatty Acids (g/kg ODM)					
NDF ash	675.9	33.0	627.0	731.0	9						
NDF unash						C8:0					
ADF ash	495.7	34.5	443.0	535.0	9	C10:0					
ADF unash	506.0	30.4	461.0	549.0	9	C12:0					
Cellulose	404.5	18.4	378.0	436.0	10	C14:0					
Lignin	90.0	16.4	70.0	112.0	10	C16:0					
Starch	6.3	5.2	0.70	14.3	6	C16:1					
NCD	597.3	32.1	547.0	651.0	10	C18:0					
CD	424.2	38.6	381.0	492.0	9	C18:1					
IVD	618.3	50.7	501.0	690.0	10	C18:2					
WSC	14.8	4.5	11.0	20.0	4	C18:3					
Avail Carbs						C20:0					
Sugars						C20:4					
						C22:1					
Minerals (g/kg ODM)											
Ca	3.9	0.93	2.3	5.7	10						
Mg	0.69	0.30	0.30	1.1	10	**Amino Acids** (g/kg ODM)					
Na	32.0	10.5	8.1	47.5	10						
K	11.6	5.3	5.6	21.0	10	Ala					
Cl						Arg					
P total	0.97	0.37	0.40	1.5	10	Asp					
P inorg						Cys					
P phytate						Glu					
Fe						Gly					
S	1.3	0.50	0.90	2.1	5	His					
						Ile					
						Leu					
Trace Elements (mg/kg ODM)						Lys avail					
						Lys total					
Co						Meth					
F						Phe					
I						Pro					
Mn						Pro.OH					
Mo						Ser					
Zn						Thr					
Cu						Tryp					
Se						Tyr					
						Val					

ANALYTICAL DATABASE

FEED DESCRIPTION : **SODIUM HYDROXIDE TREATED SPRING BARLEY STRAW** (Source 1)

Determination	Mean	SD	Min	Max	n	Determination	Mean	SD	Min	Max	n
General (g/kg ODM)						**Volatile Fatty Acids** (g/kg ODM)					
ODM (fresh)	796.3	31.9	757.7	844.8	5	Lactic					
TDM (fresh)						Formic					
CP	43.8	11.7	33.0	70.0	8	Acetic					
CF	419.8	32.4	373.0	452.0	8	Propionic					
MADF	478.4	31.6	439.0	536.0	8	n butyric					
EE	12.6	4.2	8.0	22.0	8	i butyric					
AEE						n valeric					
TA	116.8	19.9	92.0	152.0	8	i valeric					
AIA	19.4	6.9	10.0	28.0	8	n caproic					
GE (MJ/kg ODM)	17.4	0.39	16.8	17.8	8	i caproic					
						NO_3N					
						NH_3N/TN					
Carbohydrates (g/kg ODM)						pH					
NDF ash	668.7	34.4	627.0	731.0	7	**Fatty Acids** (g/kg ODM)					
NDF unash											
ADF ash	486.7	33.8	443.0	529.0	7	C8:0					
ADF unash	502.1	30.0	461.0	549.0	8	C10:0					
Cellulose	399.1	15.6	378.0	414.0	8	C12:0					
Lignin	89.9	17.3	70.0	112.0	8	C14:0					
Starch	7.3	5.1	0.70	14.3	5	C16:0					
NCD	603.5	31.3	547.0	651.0	8	C16:1					
CD	425.0	41.2	381.0	492.0	8	C18:0					
IVD	633.4	32.7	575.0	690.0	8	C18:1					
WSC	16.0	4.6	11.0	20.0	3	C18:2					
Avail Carbs						C18:3					
Sugars						C20:0					
						C20:4					
						C22:1					
Minerals (g/kg ODM)											
Ca	4.1	0.84	2.9	5.7	8						
Mg	0.68	0.27	0.30	1.1	8	**Amino Acids** (g/kg ODM)					
Na	32.6	11.7	8.1	47.5	8						
K	12.5	5.6	5.6	21.0	8	Ala					
Cl						Arg					
P total	0.94	0.41	0.40	1.5	8	Asp					
P inorg						Cys					
P phytate						Glu					
Fe						Gly					
S	1.4	0.52	0.90	2.1	4	His					
						Ile					
						Leu					
Trace Elements (mg/kg ODM)						Lys avail					
						Lys total					
Co						Meth					
F						Phe					
I						Pro					
Mn						Pro.OH					
Mo						Ser					
Zn						Thr					
Cu						Tryp					
Se						Tyr					
						Val					

ANALYTICAL DATABASE

FEED DESCRIPTION : **SODIUM HYDROXIDE TREATED WINTER BARLEY STRAW** (Source 1)

Determination	Mean	SD	Min	Max	n	Determination	Mean	SD	Min	Max	n
General (g/kg ODM)						**Volatile Fatty Acids (g/kg ODM)**					
ODM (fresh)	829.3	65.1	783.2	875.3	2	Lactic					
TDM (fresh)						Formic					
CP	51.3		51.3	51.3	1	Acetic					
CF	472.0	26.9	453.0	491.0	2	Propionic					
MADF	521.5	7.8	516.0	527.0	2	n butyric					
EE	10.5	7.8	5.0	16.0	2	i butyric					
AEE						n valeric					
TA	107.0	5.7	103.0	111.0	2	i valeric					
AIA	29.5	0.71	29.0	30.0	2	n caproic					
GE (MJ/kg ODM)	17.6	0.28	17.4	17.8	2	i caproic					
						NO_3N					
						NH_3N/TN					
Carbohydrates (g/kg ODM)						pH					
						Fatty Acids (g/kg ODM)					
NDF ash	701.0	0.0	701.0	701.0	2						
NDF unash											
ADF ash	527.0	11.3	519.0	535.0	2	C8:0					
ADF unash	537.0		537.0	537.0	1	C10:0					
Cellulose	426.0	14.1	416.0	436.0	2	C12:0					
Lignin	90.5	17.7	78.0	103.0	2	C14:0					
Starch	1.2		1.2	1.2	1	C16:0					
NCD	572.5	29.0	552.0	593.0	2	C16:1					
CD	418.0		418.0	418.0	1	C18:0					
IVD	558.0	80.6	501.0	615.0	2	C18:1					
WSC	11.0		11.0	11.0	1	C18:2					
Avail Carbs						C18:3					
Sugars						C20:0					
						C20:4					
Minerals (g/kg ODM)						C22:1					
Ca	3.2	1.3	2.3	4.1	2						
Mg	0.73	0.52	0.36	1.1	2	**Amino Acids (g/kg ODM)**					
Na	29.5	4.2	26.5	32.5	2						
K	7.9	1.7	6.7	9.1	2	Ala					
Cl						Arg					
P total	1.1	0.0	1.1	1.1	2	Asp					
P inorg						Cys					
P phytate						Glu					
Fe						Gly					
S	0.90		0.90	0.90	1	His					
						Ile					
						Leu					
Trace Elements (mg/kg ODM)						Lys avail					
						Lys total					
Co						Meth					
F						Phe					
I						Pro					
Mn						Pro.OH					
Mo						Ser					
Zn						Thr					
Cu						Tryp					
Se						Tyr					
						Val					

ANALYTICAL DATABASE

FEED DESCRIPTION : **SODIUM HYDROXIDE TREATED OATS STRAW, ALL SEASONS** (Source 1)

Determination	Mean	SD	Min	Max	n	Determination	Mean	SD	Min	Max	n
General (g/kg ODM)						**Volatile Fatty Acids (g/kg ODM)**					
ODM (fresh)	786.5	6.8	778.8	791.4	3	Lactic					
TDM (fresh)						Formic					
CP	32.0	10.4	20.0	38.0	3	Acetic					
CF	398.3	30.9	379.0	434.0	3	Propionic					
MADF	468.0	51.1	438.0	527.0	3	n butyric					
EE	9.0	1.0	8.0	10.0	3	i butyric					
AEE						n valeric					
TA	150.0	25.5	122.0	172.0	3	i valeric					
AIA	32.3	5.0	27.0	37.0	3	n caproic					
GE (MJ/kg ODM)	16.8	0.36	16.5	17.2	3	i caproic					
						NO_3N					
						NH_3N/TN					
Carbohydrates (g/kg ODM)						pH					
NDF ash	625.3	59.8	569.0	688.0	3	**Fatty Acids (g/kg ODM)**					
NDF unash											
ADF ash	484.3	33.6	462.0	523.0	3	C8:0					
ADF unash						C10:0					
Cellulose	383.3	33.5	362.0	422.0	3	C12:0					
Lignin	85.7	4.9	80.0	89.0	3	C14:0					
Starch	1.7	1.3	0.70	2.6	2	C16:0					
NCD	563.0	36.6	528.0	601.0	3	C16:1					
CD	421.0	70.4	344.0	482.0	3	C18:0					
IVD	640.7	26.6	610.0	658.0	3	C18:1					
WSC						C18:2					
Avail Carbs						C18:3					
Sugars						C20:0					
						C20:4					
						C22:1					
Minerals (g/kg ODM)											
Ca	2.3	1.3	0.80	3.2	3						
Mg	4.0	5.0	1.1	9.8	3	**Amino Acids (g/kg ODM)**					
Na	40.7	20.6	17.0	55.0	3						
K	13.1	8.0	4.0	18.8	3	Ala					
Cl						Arg					
P total	0.63	0.15	0.50	0.80	3	Asp					
P inorg						Cys					
P phytate						Glu					
Fe						Gly					
S	1.6	0.64	0.90	2.0	3	His					
						Ile					
						Leu					
Trace Elements (mg/kg ODM)						Lys avail					
						Lys total					
Co						Meth					
F						Phe					
I						Pro					
Mn						Pro.OH					
Mo						Ser					
Zn						Thr					
Cu						Tryp					
Se						Tyr					
						Val					

ANALYTICAL DATABASE

FEED DESCRIPTION : **SODIUM HYDROXIDE TREATED SPRING OATS STRAW** (Source 1)

Determination	Mean	SD	Min	Max	n	Determination	Mean	SD	Min	Max	n
General (g/kg ODM)						**Volatile Fatty Acids** (g/kg ODM)					
ODM (fresh)	791.4		791.4	791.4	1	Lactic					
TDM (fresh)						Formic					
CP	20.0		20.0	20.0	1	Acetic					
CF	434.0		434.0	434.0	1	Propionic					
MADF	527.0		527.0	527.0	1	n butyric					
EE	8.0		8.0	8.0	1	i butyric					
AEE						n valeric					
TA	122.0		122.0	122.0	1	i valeric					
AIA	37.0		37.0	37.0	1	n caproic					
GE (MJ/kg ODM)	17.2		17.2	17.2	1	i caproic					
						NO_3N					
						NH_3N/TN					
						pH					
Carbohydrates (g/kg ODM)											
						Fatty Acids (g/kg ODM)					
NDF ash	688.0		688.0	688.0	1						
NDF unash						C8:0					
ADF ash	523.0		523.0	523.0	1	C10:0					
ADF unash						C12:0					
Cellulose	422.0		422.0	422.0	1	C14:0					
Lignin	88.0		88.0	88.0	1	C16:0					
Starch						C16:1					
NCD	528.0		528.0	528.0	1	C18:0					
CD	344.0		344.0	344.0	1	C18:1					
IVD	610.0		610.0	610.0	1	C18:2					
WSC						C18:3					
Avail Carbs						C20:0					
Sugars						C20:4					
						C22:1					
Minerals (g/kg ODM)											
						Amino Acids (g/kg ODM)					
Ca	0.80		0.80	0.80	1						
Mg	9.8		9.8	9.8	1	Ala					
Na	17.0		17.0	17.0	1	Arg					
K	4.0		4.0	4.0	1	Asp					
Cl						Cys					
P total	0.80		0.80	0.80	1	Glu					
P inorg						Gly					
P phytate						His					
Fe						Ile					
S	0.90		0.90	0.90	1	Leu					
						Lys avail					
						Lys total					
Trace Elements (mg/kg ODM)						Meth					
						Phe					
Co						Pro					
F						Pro.OH					
I						Ser					
Mn						Thr					
Mo						Tryp					
Zn						Tyr					
Cu						Val					
Se											

41

ANALYTICAL DATABASE

FEED DESCRIPTION : **SODIUM HYDROXIDE TREATED WINTER OATS STRAW** (Source 1)

Determination	Mean	SD	Min	Max	n	Determination	Mean	SD	Min	Max	n
General (g/kg ODM)						**Volatile Fatty Acids** (g/kg ODM)					
ODM (fresh)	784.1	7.5	778.8	789.4	2	Lactic					
TDM (fresh)						Formic					
CP	38.0	0.0	38.0	38.0	2	Acetic					
CF	380.5	2.1	379.0	382.0	2	Propionic					
MADF	438.5	0.71	438.0	439.0	2	n butyric					
EE	9.5	0.71	9.0	10.0	2	i butyric					
AEE						n valeric					
TA	164.0	11.3	156.0	172.0	2	i valeric					
AIA	30.0	4.2	27.0	33.0	2	n caproic					
GE (MJ/kg ODM)	16.6	0.14	16.5	16.7	2	i caproic					
						NO_3N					
Carbohydrates (g/kg ODM)						NH_3N/TN					
						pH					
NDF ash	594.0	35.4	569.0	619.0	2						
NDF unash						**Fatty Acids** (g/kg ODM)					
ADF ash	465.0	4.2	462.0	468.0	2						
ADF unash						C8:0					
Cellulose	364.0	2.8	362.0	366.0	2	C10:0					
Lignin	84.5	6.4	80.0	89.0	2	C12:0					
Starch	1.7	1.3	0.70	2.6	2	C14:0					
NCD	580.5	29.0	560.0	601.0	2	C16:0					
CD	459.5	31.8	437.0	482.0	2	C16:1					
IVD	656.0	2.8	654.0	658.0	2	C18:0					
WSC						C18:1					
Avail Carbs						C18:2					
Sugars						C18:3					
						C20:0					
						C20:4					
Minerals (g/kg ODM)						C22:1					
Ca	3.0	0.28	2.8	3.2	2						
Mg	1.1	0.0	1.1	1.1	2	**Amino Acids** (g/kg ODM)					
Na	52.5	3.5	50.0	55.0	2						
K	17.7	1.6	16.6	18.8	2	Ala					
Cl						Arg					
P total	0.55	0.07	0.50	0.60	2	Asp					
P inorg						Cys					
P phytate						Glu					
Fe						Gly					
S	2.0	0.0	2.0	2.0	2	His					
						Ile					
						Leu					
Trace Elements (mg/kg ODM)						Lys avail					
						Lys total					
Co						Meth					
F						Phe					
I						Pro					
Mn						Pro.OH					
Mo						Ser					
Zn						Thr					
Cu						Tryp					
Se						Tyr					
						Val					

FEED CLASS 12

ANALYTICAL DATABASE

FEED DESCRIPTION : **SODIUM HYDROXIDE TREATED WINTER WHEAT STRAW** (Source 1)

Determination	Mean	SD	Min	Max	n	Determination	Mean	SD	Min	Max	n
General (g/kg ODM)						**Volatile Fatty Acids (g/kg ODM)**					
ODM (fresh)	842.4	78.4	517.4	922.8	26	Lactic					
TDM (fresh)						Formic					
CP	36.1	6.6	23.0	63.0	27	Acetic					
CF	438.8	32.2	371.0	514.0	28	Propionic					
MADF	505.1	18.8	460.0	538.0	28	n butyric					
EE	8.7	3.5	6.0	24.0	28	i butyric					
AEE	11.5	1.6	9.0	16.0	20	n valeric					
TA	126.5	26.4	93.0	169.0	28	i valeric					
AIA	32.8	15.0	13.9	62.1	28	n caproic					
GE (MJ/kg ODM)	17.2	0.45	16.3	17.9	28	i caproic					
						NO_3N					
						NH_3N/TN					
						pH					
Carbohydrates (g/kg ODM)											
						Fatty Acids (g/kg ODM)					
NDF ash	688.9	41.7	629.0	760.0	25						
NDF unash						C8:0					
ADF ash	493.8	40.9	321.0	536.0	24	C10:0					
ADF unash	516.3	39.7	334.0	554.0	27	C12:0					
Cellulose	394.3	43.8	184.0	429.0	28	C14:0					
Lignin	91.5	16.1	44.0	128.0	28	C16:0					
Starch	8.7	7.7	2.0	17.1	3	C16:1					
NCD	530.5	44.9	457.9	611.7	27	C18:0					
CD	356.6	47.1	308.0	423.0	8	C18:1					
IVD	534.0	45.3	483.0	665.0	28	C18:2					
WSC	15.0		15.0	15.0	1	C18:3					
Avail Carbs						C20:0					
Sugars						C20:4					
						C22:1					
Minerals (g/kg ODM)											
Ca	4.8	1.1	2.5	6.6	28	**Amino Acids (g/kg ODM)**					
Mg	0.65	0.12	0.50	1.0	28						
Na	33.5	9.8	13.0	57.5	28	Ala					
K	7.4	2.8	5.0	17.4	28	Arg					
Cl						Asp					
P total	0.63	0.20	0.40	1.1	28	Cys					
P inorg						Glu					
P phytate						Gly					
Fe						His					
S	1.1	0.40	0.70	2.2	23	Ile					
						Leu					
Trace Elements (mg/kg ODM)						Lys avail					
						Lys total					
Co						Meth					
F						Phe					
I						Pro					
Mn						Pro.OH					
Mo						Ser					
Zn						Thr					
Cu						Tryp					
Se						Tyr					
						Val					

43

ANALYTICAL DATABASE

FEED DESCRIPTION : **UNTREATED BARLEY STRAW, ALL SEASONS** (Sources 1, 2)

Determination	Mean	SD	Min	Max	n	Determination	Mean	SD	Min	Max	n
General (g/kg ODM)						**Volatile Fatty Acids (g/kg ODM)**					
ODM (fresh)	867.0	26.0	779.7	911.7	53	Lactic					
TDM (fresh)						Formic					
CP	41.5	12.6	20.0	71.0	51	Acetic					
CF	434.0	33.8	353.0	517.0	53	Propionic					
MADF	496.6	37.2	393.0	564.0	52	n butyric					
EE	14.0	5.9	5.0	48.0	53	i butyric					
AEE						n valeric					
TA	56.7	16.8	27.0	97.0	53	i valeric					
AIA	19.2	11.7	1.0	47.0	52	n caproic					
GE (MJ/kg ODM)	18.4	0.59	16.9	19.7	53	i caproic					
						NO$_3$N					
						NH$_3$N/TN					
Carbohydrates (g/kg ODM)						pH					
						Fatty Acids (g/kg ODM)					
NDF ash	810.9	52.0	614.0	878.0	51						
NDF unash											
ADF ash	508.6	47.0	393.0	595.0	51	C8:0					
ADF unash	521.0	34.2	469.0	571.0	10	C10:0					
Cellulose	415.4	20.3	381.0	448.0	14	C12:0					
Lignin	91.2	16.5	65.0	119.0	13	C14:0					
Starch	10.9	13.6	0.10	46.6	16	C16:0					
NCD	380.2	50.4	288.0	487.0	38	C16:1					
CD	196.5	54.8	132.0	436.0	46	C18:0					
IVD	429.4	54.4	305.0	540.0	51	C18:1					
WSC	20.7	13.3	10.0	60.0	18	C18:2					
Avail Carbs						C18:3					
Sugars						C20:0					
						C20:4					
						C22:1					
Minerals (g/kg ODM)											
Ca	4.2	1.4	2.3	10.0	53						
Mg	0.68	0.31	0.30	1.9	53	**Amino Acids (g/kg ODM)**					
Na	1.3	1.4	0.20	6.7	53						
K	14.8	5.9	5.5	28.9	53	Ala					
Cl						Arg					
P total	1.1	1.1	0.10	8.2	53	Asp					
P inorg						Cys					
P phytate						Glu					
Fe						Gly					
S	1.8	0.70	0.60	3.1	17	His					
						Ile					
						Leu					
Trace Elements (mg/kg ODM)						Lys avail					
						Lys total					
Co						Meth					
F						Phe					
I						Pro					
Mn	38.0		38.0	38.0	1	Pro.OH					
Mo						Ser					
Zn	16.0		16.0	16.0	1	Thr					
Cu	2.0		2.0	2.0	1	Tryp					
Se						Tyr					
						Val					

ANALYTICAL DATABASE

FEED DESCRIPTION : **UNTREATED SPRING BARLEY STRAW** (Sources 1, 2)

Determination	Mean	SD	Min	Max	n	Determination	Mean	SD	Min	Max	n
General (g/kg ODM)						**Volatile Fatty Acids (g/kg ODM)**					
ODM (fresh)	861.9	23.8	779.7	902.8	32	Lactic					
TDM (fresh)						Formic					
CP	42.6	12.9	20.0	71.0	31	Acetic					
CF	429.7	37.2	353.0	517.0	32	Propionic					
MADF	494.2	39.3	393.0	554.0	31	n butyric					
EE	15.4	6.8	9.0	48.0	32	i butyric					
AEE						n valeric					
TA	56.3	16.8	27.0	97.0	32	i valeric					
AIA	20.7	11.5	5.0	47.0	31	n caproic					
GE (MJ/kg ODM)	18.5	0.61	16.9	19.7	32	i caproic					
						NO_3N					
						NH_3N/TN					
Carbohydrates (g/kg ODM)						pH					
						Fatty Acids (g/kg ODM)					
NDF ash	810.6	50.0	614.0	874.0	30						
NDF unash						C8:0					
ADF ash	504.8	47.3	393.0	558.0	30	C10:0					
ADF unash	519.0	35.6	469.0	571.0	9	C12:0					
Cellulose	417.3	21.3	381.0	448.0	12	C14:0					
Lignin	90.6	17.7	65.0	119.0	11	C16:0					
Starch	17.8	14.7	0.10	46.6	9	C16:1					
NCD	389.1	49.5	314.0	483.0	22	C18:0					
CD	205.9	66.8	132.0	436.0	27	C18:1					
IVD	432.6	53.9	320.0	540.0	32	C18:2					
WSC	14.1	5.0	10.0	26.0	10	C18:3					
Avail Carbs						C20:0					
Sugars						C20:4					
						C22:1					
Minerals (g/kg ODM)											
Ca	4.4	1.2	3.0	8.1	32	**Amino Acids (g/kg ODM)**					
Mg	0.66	0.31	0.30	1.9	32						
Na	1.1	0.89	0.20	3.8	32	Ala					
K	13.9	5.4	5.5	28.9	32	Arg					
Cl						Asp					
P total	1.3	1.4	0.30	8.2	32	Cys					
P inorg						Glu					
P phytate						Gly					
Fe						His					
S	1.9	0.72	1.1	3.1	12	Ile					
						Leu					
Trace Elements (mg/kg ODM)						Lys avail					
						Lys total					
Co						Meth					
F						Phe					
I						Pro					
Mn	38.0		38.0	38.0	1	Pro.OH					
Mo						Ser					
Zn	16.0		16.0	16.0	1	Thr					
Cu	2.0		2.0	2.0	1	Tryp					
Se						Tyr					
						Val					

FEED CLASS 12

ANALYTICAL DATABASE

FEED DESCRIPTION : **UNTREATED WINTER BARLEY STRAW** (Source 1)

Determination	Mean	SD	Min	Max	n	Determination	Mean	SD	Min	Max	n
General (g/kg ODM)						**Volatile Fatty Acids (g/kg ODM)**					
ODM (fresh)	874.4	31.1	804.4	911.7	17	Lactic					
TDM (fresh)						Formic					
CP	37.6	11.4	26.0	59.0	16	Acetic					
CF	441.8	30.0	384.0	490.0	17	Propionic					
MADF	501.9	38.2	419.0	564.0	17	n butyric					
EE	12.1	3.4	5.0	19.0	17	i butyric					
AEE						n valeric					
TA	56.9	17.4	28.0	84.0	17	i valeric					
AIA	17.1	12.4	1.0	46.0	17	n caproic					
GE (MJ/kg ODM)	18.3	0.58	17.4	19.4	17	i caproic					
						NO3N					
						NH3N/TN					
Carbohydrates (g/kg ODM)						pH					
NDF ash	809.4	61.0	620.0	878.0	17						
NDF unash						**Fatty Acids (g/kg ODM)**					
ADF ash	514.7	52.4	425.0	595.0	17						
ADF unash	539.0		539.0	539.0	1	C8:0					
Cellulose	403.5	2.1	402.0	405.0	2	C10:0					
Lignin	94.5	10.6	87.0	102.0	2	C12:0					
Starch	2.2	3.2	0.10	7.9	5	C14:0					
NCD	362.3	45.5	288.0	419.0	12	C16:0					
CD	183.9	30.0	139.0	248.0	15	C16:1					
IVD	429.7	58.1	305.0	521.0	16	C18:0					
WSC	30.9	16.3	15.0	60.0	7	C18:1					
Avail Carbs						C18:2					
Sugars						C18:3					
						C20:0					
						C20:4					
Minerals (g/kg ODM)						C22:1					
Ca	3.8	1.8	2.3	10.0	17						
Mg	0.73	0.31	0.35	1.4	17	**Amino Acids (g/kg ODM)**					
Na	1.8	2.1	0.20	6.7	17						
K	16.0	6.5	6.2	27.3	17	Ala					
Cl						Arg					
P total	0.75	0.35	0.10	1.4	17	Asp					
P inorg						Cys					
P phytate						Glu					
Fe						Gly					
S	2.0	0.41	1.4	2.4	4	His					
						Ile					
						Leu					
Trace Elements (mg/kg ODM)						Lys avail					
						Lys total					
Co						Meth					
F						Phe					
I						Pro					
Mn						Pro.OH					
Mo						Ser					
Zn						Thr					
Cu						Tryp					
Se						Tyr					
						Val					

ANALYTICAL DATABASE

FEED DESCRIPTION : **UNTREATED OATS STRAW, ALL SEASONS** (Source 1)

Determination	Mean	SD	Min	Max	n	Determination	Mean	SD	Min	Max	n
General (g/kg ODM)						**Volatile Fatty Acids** (g/kg ODM)					
ODM (fresh)	846.3	31.1	787.7	869.6	6	Lactic					
TDM (fresh)						Formic					
CP	34.3	10.6	20.0	48.0	6	Acetic					
CF	444.3	14.4	433.0	470.0	6	Propionic					
MADF	513.2	23.2	487.0	544.0	6	n butyric					
EE	13.8	4.9	8.0	21.0	6	i butyric					
AEE						n valeric					
TA	66.2	4.4	63.0	74.0	6	i valeric					
AIA	17.7	4.0	12.0	22.0	6	n caproic					
GE (MJ/kg ODM)	18.2	0.25	17.8	18.5	6	i caproic					
						NO_3N					
						NH_3N/TN					
Carbohydrates (g/kg ODM)						pH					
NDF ash	749.2	92.9	587.0	804.0	5						
NDF unash						**Fatty Acids** (g/kg ODM)					
ADF ash	523.4	15.1	500.0	538.0	5						
ADF unash	533.5	12.0	525.0	542.0	2	C8:0					
Cellulose	425.5	7.8	420.0	431.0	2	C10:0					
Lignin	91.5	2.1	90.0	93.0	2	C12:0					
Starch	0.85	0.21	0.70	1.0	2	C14:0					
NCD	428.8	94.8	367.0	607.0	6	C16:0					
CD	233.8	52.4	196.0	326.0	5	C16:1					
IVD	484.7	58.2	416.0	585.0	6	C18:0					
WSC	19.0		19.0	19.0	1	C18:1					
Avail Carbs						C18:2					
Sugars						C18:3					
						C20:0					
						C20:4					
Minerals (g/kg ODM)						C22:1					
Ca	3.9	1.2	2.5	5.4	6						
Mg	0.92	0.31	0.40	1.3	6	**Amino Acids** (g/kg ODM)					
Na	4.8	0.63	4.2	5.9	6						
K	17.9	2.4	16.0	22.0	6	Ala					
Cl						Arg					
P total	0.92	0.24	0.70	1.2	6	Asp					
P inorg						Cys					
P phytate						Glu					
Fe						Gly					
S	1.3	0.35	1.0	1.5	2	His					
						Ile					
						Leu					
Trace Elements (mg/kg ODM)						Lys avail					
						Lys total					
Co						Meth					
F						Phe					
I						Pro					
Mn						Pro.OH					
Mo						Ser					
Zn						Thr					
Cu						Tryp					
Se						Tyr					
						Val					

47

ANALYTICAL DATABASE

FEED DESCRIPTION : **UNTREATED SPRING OATS STRAW** (Source 1)

Determination	Mean	SD	Min	Max	n	Determination	Mean	SD	Min	Max	n
General (g/kg ODM)						**Volatile Fatty Acids (g/kg ODM)**					
ODM (fresh)	812.4	34.9	787.7	837.1	2	Lactic					
TDM (fresh)						Formic					
CP	29.0	7.1	24.0	34.0	2	Acetic					
CF	442.5	13.4	433.0	452.0	2	Propionic					
MADF	520.5	24.7	503.0	538.0	2	n butyric					
EE	14.5	9.2	8.0	21.0	2	i butyric					
AEE						n valeric					
TA	68.5	7.8	63.0	74.0	2	i valeric					
AIA	17.0	7.1	12.0	22.0	2	n caproic					
GE (MJ/kg ODM)	18.3	0.21	18.1	18.4	2	i caproic					
						NO_3N					
						NH_3N/TN					
Carbohydrates (g/kg ODM)						pH					
NDF ash	804.0		804.0	804.0	1	**Fatty Acids (g/kg ODM)**					
NDF unash											
ADF ash	517.0		517.0	517.0	1	C8:0					
ADF unash	542.0		542.0	542.0	1	C10:0					
Cellulose	431.0		431.0	431.0	1	C12:0					
Lignin	90.0		90.0	90.0	1	C14:0					
Starch	1.0		1.0	1.0	1	C16:0					
NCD	419.0	66.5	372.0	466.0	2	C16:1					
CD	212.0		212.0	212.0	1	C18:0					
IVD	464.5	31.8	442.0	487.0	2	C18:1					
WSC						C18:2					
Avail Carbs						C18:3					
Sugars						C20:0					
						C20:4					
						C22:1					
Minerals (g/kg ODM)											
Ca	4.5	0.85	3.9	5.1	2						
Mg	1.1	0.28	0.90	1.3	2	**Amino Acids (g/kg ODM)**					
Na	4.8	0.35	4.5	5.0	2						
K	17.0	0.0	17.0	17.0	2	Ala					
Cl						Arg					
P total	0.90	0.28	0.70	1.1	2	Asp					
P inorg						Cys					
P phytate						Glu					
Fe						Gly					
S	1.0		1.0	1.0	1	His					
						Ile					
						Leu					
Trace Elements (mg/kg ODM)						Lys avail					
						Lys total					
Co						Meth					
F						Phe					
I						Pro					
Mn						Pro.OH					
Mo						Ser					
Zn						Thr					
Cu						Tryp					
Se						Tyr					
						Val					

ANALYTICAL DATABASE

FEED DESCRIPTION : **UNTREATED WINTER OATS STRAW** (Source 1)

Determination	Mean	SD	Min	Max	n	Determination	Mean	SD	Min	Max	n
General (g/kg ODM)						**Volatile Fatty Acids** (g/kg ODM)					
ODM (fresh)	863.2	8.0	853.1	869.6	4	Lactic					
TDM (fresh)						Formic					
CP	37.0	11.9	20.0	48.0	4	Acetic					
CF	445.3	16.8	434.0	470.0	4	Propionic					
MADF	509.5	25.3	487.0	544.0	4	n butyric					
EE	13.5	3.3	9.0	17.0	4	i butyric					
AEE						n valeric					
TA	65.0	2.7	63.0	69.0	4	i valeric					
AIA	18.0	3.2	15.0	22.0	4	n caproic					
GE (MJ/kg ODM)	18.1	0.28	17.8	18.5	4	i caproic					
						NO$_3$N					
						NH$_3$N/TN					
Carbohydrates (g/kg ODM)						pH					
NDF ash	735.5	101.3	587.0	804.0	4	**Fatty Acids** (g/kg ODM)					
NDF unash											
ADF ash	525.0	17.0	500.0	538.0	4	C8:0					
ADF unash	525.0		525.0	525.0	1	C10:0					
Cellulose	420.0		420.0	420.0	1	C12:0					
Lignin	93.0		93.0	93.0	1	C14:0					
Starch	0.70		0.70	0.70	1	C16:0					
NCD	433.8	115.8	367.0	607.0	4	C16:1					
CD	239.3	58.9	196.0	326.0	4	C18:0					
IVD	494.8	70.0	416.0	585.0	4	C18:1					
WSC	19.0		19.0	19.0	1	C18:2					
Avail Carbs						C18:3					
Sugars						C20:0					
						C20:4					
Minerals (g/kg ODM)						C22:1					
Ca	3.6	1.3	2.5	5.4	4						
Mg	0.83	0.31	0.40	1.1	4	**Amino Acids** (g/kg ODM)					
Na	4.8	0.79	4.2	5.9	4						
K	18.4	2.9	16.0	22.0	4	Ala					
Cl						Arg					
P total	0.93	0.26	0.70	1.2	4	Asp					
P inorg						Cys					
P phytate						Glu					
Fe						Gly					
S	1.5		1.5	1.5	1	His					
						Ile					
						Leu					
Trace Elements (mg/kg ODM)						Lys avail					
						Lys total					
Co						Meth					
F						Phe					
I						Pro					
Mn						Pro.OH					
Mo						Ser					
Zn						Thr					
Cu						Tryp					
Se						Tyr					
						Val					

FEED CLASS 12

ANALYTICAL DATABASE

FEED DESCRIPTION : **UNTREATED OILSEED RAPE STRAW** (Source 1)

Determination	Mean	SD	Min	Max	n	Determination	Mean	SD	Min	Max	n
General (g/kg ODM)						**Volatile Fatty Acids (g/kg ODM)**					
ODM (fresh)	864.5	14.0	854.6	874.4	2	Lactic					
TDM (fresh)						Formic					
CP	62.0	5.7	58.0	66.0	2	Acetic					
CF	441.0	65.1	395.0	487.0	2	Propionic					
MADF	524.0	36.8	498.0	550.0	2	n butyric					
EE	19.0	2.8	17.0	21.0	2	i butyric					
AEE						n valeric					
TA	87.5	23.3	71.0	104.0	2	i valeric					
AIA	3.0	2.8	1.0	5.0	2	n caproic					
GE (MJ/kg ODM)	18.5	0.99	17.8	19.2	2	i caproic					
						NO3N					
						NH3N/TN					
Carbohydrates (g/kg ODM)						pH					
NDF ash	802.5	106.8	727.0	878.0	2	**Fatty Acids (g/kg ODM)**					
NDF unash											
ADF ash	581.5	47.4	548.0	615.0	2	C8:0					
ADF unash						C10:0					
Cellulose						C12:0					
Lignin						C14:0					
Starch						C16:0					
NCD						C16:1					
CD						C18:0					
IVD	332.5	37.5	306.0	359.0	2	C18:1					
WSC						C18:2					
Avail Carbs						C18:3					
Sugars						C20:0					
						C20:4					
Minerals (g/kg ODM)						C22:1					
Ca	19.8	5.9	15.6	24.0	2						
Mg	1.1	0.21	0.90	1.2	2	**Amino Acids (g/kg ODM)**					
Na	0.65	0.35	0.40	0.90	2	Ala					
K	19.9	5.8	15.8	24.0	2	Arg					
Cl						Asp					
P total	1.2	0.78	0.60	1.7	2	Cys					
P inorg						Glu					
P phytate						Gly					
Fe						His					
S						Ile					
						Leu					
						Lys avail					
Trace Elements (mg/kg ODM)						Lys total					
Co						Meth					
F						Phe					
I						Pro					
Mn						Pro.OH					
Mo						Ser					
Zn						Thr					
Cu						Tryp					
Se						Tyr					
						Val					

ANALYTICAL DATABASE

FEED DESCRIPTION : **UNTREATED WINTER TRITICALE STRAW** (Source 1)

Determination	Mean	SD	Min	Max	n	Determination	Mean	SD	Min	Max	n
General (g/kg ODM)						**Volatile Fatty Acids (g/kg ODM)**					
ODM (fresh)	873.1		873.1	873.1	1	Lactic					
TDM (fresh)						Formic					
CP	41.0		41.0	41.0	1	Acetic					
CF	455.0		455.0	455.0	1	Propionic					
MADF	462.0		462.0	462.0	1	n butyric					
EE	15.0		15.0	15.0	1	i butyric					
AEE						n valeric					
TA	37.0		37.0	37.0	1	i valeric					
AIA	11.0		11.0	11.0	1	n caproic					
GE (MJ/kg ODM)	17.8		17.8	17.8	1	i caproic					
						NO_3N					
Carbohydrates (g/kg ODM)						NH_3N/TN					
						pH					
NDF ash	622.0		622.0	622.0	1						
NDF unash						**Fatty Acids (g/kg ODM)**					
ADF ash											
ADF unash						C8:0					
Cellulose						C10:0					
Lignin						C12:0					
Starch						C14:0					
NCD						C16:0					
CD						C16:1					
IVD	476.0		476.0	476.0	1	C18:0					
WSC	12.0		12.0	12.0	1	C18:1					
Avail Carbs						C18:2					
Sugars						C18:3					
						C20:0					
						C20:4					
Minerals (g/kg ODM)						C22:1					
Ca	6.2		6.2	6.2	1						
Mg	2.3		2.3	2.3	1	**Amino Acids (g/kg ODM)**					
Na	0.20		0.20	0.20	1						
K	9.0		9.0	9.0	1	Ala					
Cl						Arg					
P total	2.3		2.3	2.3	1	Asp					
P inorg						Cys					
P phytate						Glu					
Fe						Gly					
S						His					
						Ile					
						Leu					
Trace Elements (mg/kg ODM)						Lys avail					
						Lys total					
Co						Meth					
F						Phe					
I						Pro					
Mn						Pro.OH					
Mo						Ser					
Zn						Thr					
Cu						Tryp					
Se						Tyr					
						Val					

ANALYTICAL DATABASE

FEED DESCRIPTION : **UNTREATED WHEAT STRAW, ALL SEASONS** (Source 1)

Determination	Mean	SD	Min	Max	n	Determination	Mean	SD	Min	Max	n
General (g/kg ODM)						**Volatile Fatty Acids (g/kg ODM)**					
ODM (fresh)	872.3	30.6	700.5	929.6	69	Lactic					
TDM (fresh)						Formic					
CP	38.9	10.2	22.0	78.1	68	Acetic					
CF	423.9	32.7	344.0	551.0	69	Propionic					
MADF	514.9	29.2	436.0	566.0	70	n butyric					
EE	11.9	4.1	2.0	21.0	70	i butyric					
AEE	9.0	1.4	8.0	11.0	4	n valeric					
TA	69.2	20.5	25.0	120.0	69	i valeric					
AIA	40.1	20.2	6.0	92.0	70	n caproic					
GE (MJ/kg ODM)	18.2	0.49	17.3	19.4	70	i caproic					
						NO$_3$N					
						NH$_3$N/TN					
Carbohydrates (g/kg ODM)						pH					
NDF ash	809.3	39.3	674.0	925.0	66	**Fatty Acids (g/kg ODM)**					
NDF unash											
ADF ash	502.2	36.8	400.0	565.0	63	C8:0					
ADF unash	539.7	39.7	433.0	604.0	22	C10:0					
Cellulose	401.9	29.7	301.0	455.0	27	C12:0					
Lignin	102.0	8.2	85.0	119.0	25	C14:0					
Starch	11.6	15.2	0.10	51.8	30	C16:0					
NCD	358.2	42.0	277.2	445.0	45	C16:1					
CD	171.8	31.8	110.0	255.0	59	C18:0					
IVD	410.8	62.7	265.0	550.0	67	C18:1					
WSC	12.8	6.5	5.0	29.0	31	C18:2					
Avail Carbs						C18:3					
Sugars						C20:0					
						C20:4					
Minerals (g/kg ODM)						C22:1					
Ca	3.9	1.1	2.2	6.7	70						
Mg	0.88	0.99	0.30	8.8	70	**Amino Acids (g/kg ODM)**					
Na	0.59	0.98	0.10	5.0	70						
K	10.2	3.7	2.1	19.6	70	Ala					
Cl						Arg					
P total	0.77	0.35	0.30	2.1	70	Asp					
P inorg						Cys					
P phytate						Glu					
Fe						Gly					
S	1.6	0.68	0.80	4.1	35	His					
						Ile					
						Leu					
Trace Elements (mg/kg ODM)						Lys avail					
						Lys total					
Co						Meth					
F						Phe					
I						Pro					
Mn						Pro.OH					
Mo						Ser					
Zn						Thr					
Cu						Tryp					
Se						Tyr					
						Val					

ANALYTICAL DATABASE

FEED DESCRIPTION : **UNTREATED SPRING WHEAT STRAW** (Source 1)

Determination	Mean	SD	Min	Max	n	Determination	Mean	SD	Min	Max	n
General (g/kg ODM)						**Volatile Fatty Acids** (g/kg ODM)					
ODM (fresh)	882.6	13.3	866.0	894.1	4	Lactic					
TDM (fresh)						Formic					
CP	36.5	7.9	25.0	43.0	4	Acetic					
CF	434.3	19.1	416.0	461.0	4	Propionic					
MADF	513.3	23.4	485.0	533.0	4	n butyric					
EE	13.8	2.2	11.0	16.0	4	i butyric					
AEE						n valeric					
TA	63.5	9.3	53.0	75.0	4	i valeric					
AIA	18.0	10.4	10.0	33.0	4	n caproic					
GE (MJ/kg ODM)	17.8	0.32	17.5	18.3	4	i caproic					
						NO_3N					
						NH_3N/TN					
Carbohydrates (g/kg ODM)						pH					
NDF ash	818.3	24.3	792.0	844.0	4	**Fatty Acids** (g/kg ODM)					
NDF unash											
ADF ash	534.5	26.9	503.0	565.0	4	C8:0					
ADF unash						C10:0					
Cellulose						C12:0					
Lignin						C14:0					
Starch						C16:0					
NCD	349.5	13.2	332.0	363.0	4	C16:1					
CD	206.5	41.5	162.0	253.0	4	C18:0					
IVD	385.3	43.8	325.0	430.0	4	C18:1					
WSC						C18:2					
Avail Carbs						C18:3					
Sugars						C20:0					
						C20:4					
Minerals (g/kg ODM)						C22:1					
Ca	4.9	0.91	3.8	5.9	4						
Mg	0.78	0.25	0.50	1.1	4	**Amino Acids** (g/kg ODM)					
Na	0.23	0.12	0.10	0.40	4						
K	14.8	2.4	12.0	17.6	4	Ala					
Cl						Arg					
P total	0.60	0.36	0.30	1.0	4	Asp					
P inorg						Cys					
P phytate						Glu					
Fe						Gly					
S	2.4		2.4	2.4	1	His					
						Ile					
						Leu					
Trace Elements (mg/kg ODM)						Lys avail					
						Lys total					
Co						Meth					
F						Phe					
I						Pro					
Mn						Pro.OH					
Mo						Ser					
Zn						Thr					
Cu						Tryp					
Se						Tyr					
						Val					

ANALYTICAL DATABASE

FEED DESCRIPTION : **UNTREATED WINTER WHEAT STRAW** (Source 1)

Determination	Mean	SD	Min	Max	n	Determination	Mean	SD	Min	Max	n
General (g/kg ODM)						**Volatile Fatty Acids (g/kg ODM)**					
ODM (fresh)	871.7	32.3	700.5	929.6	61	Lactic					
TDM (fresh)						Formic					
CP	39.1	10.5	22.0	78.1	60	Acetic					
CF	422.6	33.9	344.0	551.0	61	Propionic					
MADF	514.9	29.9	436.0	566.0	62	n butyric					
EE	11.7	4.1	2.0	21.0	62	i butyric					
AEE	9.0	1.4	8.0	11.0	4	n valeric					
TA	70.7	20.3	29.0	120.0	61	i valeric					
AIA	42.5	19.3	7.0	92.0	62	n caproic					
GE (MJ/kg ODM)	18.2	0.48	17.3	19.1	62	i caproic					
						NO₃N					
						NH₃N/TN					
Carbohydrates (g/kg ODM)						pH					
						Fatty Acids (g/kg ODM)					
NDF ash	806.4	37.9	674.0	870.0	58						
NDF unash											
ADF ash	498.8	36.5	400.0	558.0	56	C8:0					
ADF unash	541.5	39.7	433.0	604.0	21	C10:0					
Cellulose	398.9	29.2	301.0	439.0	24	C12:0					
Lignin	101.5	8.4	85.0	119.0	23	C14:0					
Starch	11.6	15.2	0.10	51.8	30	C16:0					
NCD	361.5	43.5	277.2	445.0	39	C16:1					
CD	169.9	29.5	110.0	255.0	52	C18:0					
IVD	415.5	62.6	265.0	550.0	59	C18:1					
WSC	12.8	6.5	5.0	29.0	31	C18:2					
Avail Carbs						C18:3					
Sugars						C20:0					
						C20:4					
						C22:1					
Minerals (g/kg ODM)											
Ca	3.8	1.0	2.2	6.7	62						
Mg	0.91	1.0	0.30	8.8	62	**Amino Acids (g/kg ODM)**					
Na	0.62	1.0	0.10	5.0	62						
K	9.9	3.4	2.1	17.2	62	Ala					
Cl						Arg					
P total	0.78	0.35	0.30	2.1	62	Asp					
P inorg						Cys					
P phytate						Glu					
Fe						Gly					
S	1.6	0.68	0.80	4.1	33	His					
						Ile					
						Leu					
Trace Elements (mg/kg ODM)						Lys avail					
						Lys total					
Co						Meth					
F						Phe					
I						Pro					
Mn						Pro.OH					
Mo						Ser					
Zn						Thr					
Cu						Tryp					
Se						Tyr					
						Val					

ANALYTICAL   DATABASE

FEED CLASS 20

FRESH HERBAGES AND FORAGES FED FRESH

ANALYTICAL DATABASE

FEED DESCRIPTION : **CABBAGE, FRESH** (Sources 1, 2)

Determination	Mean	SD	Min	Max	n	Determination	Mean	SD	Min	Max	n
General (g/kg ODM)						**Volatile Fatty Acids** (g/kg ODM)					
ODM (fresh)	106.5	13.3	84.0	119.0	5	Lactic					
TDM (fresh)						Formic					
CP	206.6	12.3	192.0	221.0	5	Acetic					
CF	96.2	26.7	74.0	142.0	5	Propionic					
MADF	128.4	14.9	107.0	143.0	5	n butyric					
EE	17.2	7.7	9.0	28.0	5	i butyric					
AEE						n valeric					
TA	107.6	18.9	90.0	134.0	5	i valeric					
AIA	4.0		4.0	4.0	1	n caproic					
GE (MJ/kg ODM)	17.6	0.96	16.6	19.1	5	i caproic					
						NO_3N					
Carbohydrates (g/kg ODM)						NH_3N/TN					
						pH					
NDF ash	243.8	191.7	141.0	586.0	5						
NDF unash						**Fatty Acids** (g/kg ODM)					
ADF ash	136.0	14.6	119.0	158.0	5						
ADF unash						C8:0					
Cellulose						C10:0					
Lignin	10.6	4.5	7.0	17.0	4	C12:0					
Starch	4.3	1.5	3.0	6.0	4	C14:0					
NCD	855.0	22.1	833.0	875.0	4	C16:0					
CD						C16:1					
IVD	767.8	40.9	710.0	800.0	5	C18:0					
WSC	316.0	30.4	284.0	353.0	4	C18:1					
Avail Carbs						C18:2					
Sugars						C18:3					
						C20:0					
						C20:4					
Minerals (g/kg ODM)						C22:1					
Ca	8.3	3.1	4.3	11.8	5						
Mg	1.5	0.18	1.3	1.8	5	**Amino Acids** (g/kg ODM)					
Na	1.5	0.31	1.2	2.0	5						
K	35.5	3.5	31.2	40.4	5	Ala					
Cl						Arg					
P total	1.9	1.5	1.1	4.5	5	Asp					
P inorg						Cys					
P phytate						Glu					
Fe						Gly					
S						His					
						Ile					
						Leu					
Trace Elements (mg/kg ODM)						Lys avail					
						Lys total					
Co						Meth					
F						Phe					
I						Pro					
Mn	21.5	3.8	19.0	27.0	4	Pro.OH					
Mo						Ser					
Zn	37.0	13.3	27.0	55.0	4	Thr					
Cu	2.3	0.58	2.0	3.0	3	Tryp					
Se						Tyr					
						Val					

ANALYTICAL DATABASE

FEED DESCRIPTION : **FORAGE SORGHUM/SUDANGRASS HYBRID, VAR TOPGRASS** (Source 1)

Determination	Mean	SD	Min	Max	n	Determination	Mean	SD	Min	Max	n
General (g/kg ODM)						**Volatile Fatty Acids (g/kg ODM)**					
ODM (fresh)	174.0		174.0	174.0	1	Lactic					
TDM (fresh)						Formic					
CP	137.0		137.0	137.0	1	Acetic					
CF	306.0		306.0	306.0	1	Propionic					
MADF	345.0		345.0	345.0	1	n butyric					
EE	12.0		12.0	12.0	1	i butyric					
AEE						n valeric					
TA	75.0		75.0	75.0	1	i valeric					
AIA	18.0		18.0	18.0	1	n caproic					
GE (MJ/kg ODM)	19.4		19.4	19.4	1	i caproic					
						NO_3N					
Carbohydrates (g/kg ODM)						NH_3N/TN					
						pH					
NDF ash	627.0		627.0	627.0	1						
NDF unash						**Fatty Acids (g/kg ODM)**					
ADF ash	370.0		370.0	370.0	1						
ADF unash						C8:0					
Cellulose	290.0		290.0	290.0	1	C10:0					
Lignin						C12:0					
Starch	1.3		1.3	1.3	1	C14:0					
NCD						C16:0					
CD	484.0		484.0	484.0	1	C16:1					
IVD	581.0		581.0	581.0	1	C18:0					
WSC						C18:1					
Avail Carbs						C18:2					
Sugars						C18:3					
						C20:0					
						C20:4					
Minerals (g/kg ODM)						C22:1					
Ca	4.6		4.6	4.6	1						
Mg	1.6		1.6	1.6	1	**Amino Acids (g/kg ODM)**					
Na	0.20		0.20	0.20	1						
K	21.6		21.6	21.6	1	Ala					
Cl						Arg					
P total	2.4		2.4	2.4	1	Asp					
P inorg						Cys					
P phytate						Glu					
Fe						Gly					
S						His					
						Ile					
						Leu					
Trace Elements (mg/kg ODM)						Lys avail					
						Lys total					
Co						Meth					
F						Phe					
I						Pro					
Mn						Pro.OH					
Mo						Ser					
Zn						Thr					
Cu						Tryp					
Se						Tyr					
						Val					

FEED CLASS 20

ANALYTICAL DATABASE

FEED DESCRIPTION : **FRESH GRASS, ALL SPECIES** (Source 1)

Determination	Mean	SD	Min	Max	n
General (g/kg ODM)					
ODM (fresh)	196.6	46.8	112.7	424.0	244
TDM (fresh)					
CP	156.1	51.4	54.0	360.6	216
CF	240.9	44.0	123.0	341.0	244
MADF	272.5	46.1	181.0	380.0	243
EE	21.7	5.5	11.0	43.0	244
AEE					
TA	78.0	16.9	18.0	151.0	243
AIA	12.6	8.0	0.20	72.1	243
GE (MJ/kg ODM)	18.7	0.45	17.5	19.9	244
Carbohydrates (g/kg ODM)					
NDF ash	577.3	59.2	415.0	765.0	242
NDF unash					
ADF ash	295.9	47.7	184.0	483.0	242
ADF unash	305.2	39.8	200.0	410.0	162
Cellulose	243.8	34.6	163.0	318.0	193
Lignin	53.9	18.9	8.0	108.0	132
Starch	2.5	2.6	0.10	13.0	81
NCD	713.7	81.0	519.0	865.0	182
CD	594.3	89.3	353.0	775.0	154
IVD	676.8	52.9	532.0	820.0	244
WSC	159.8	58.3	16.0	285.0	186
Avail Carbs					
Sugars					
Minerals (g/kg ODM)					
Ca	5.4	1.7	2.3	15.6	242
Mg	1.6	0.56	0.50	3.6	242
Na	2.5	2.1	0.30	14.0	242
K	24.3	6.6	10.2	45.4	242
Cl					
P total	3.0	0.68	1.7	5.6	242
P inorg					
P phytate					
Fe					
S	2.2	0.56	1.2	4.0	137
Trace Elements (mg/kg ODM)					
Co	0.11	0.25	0.02	2.6	122
F					
I					
Mn	89.7	62.4	11.0	260.0	137
Mo	0.75	0.46	0.15	3.0	135
Zn					
Cu	6.7	2.6	3.0	20.2	137
Se	0.05	0.02	0.02	0.10	71

Determination	Mean	SD	Min	Max	n
Volatile Fatty Acids (g/kg ODM)					
Lactic					
Formic					
Acetic					
Propionic					
n butyric					
i butyric					
n valeric					
i valeric					
n caproic					
i caproic					
NO_3N					
NH_3N/TN					
pH					
Fatty Acids (g/kg ODM)					
C8:0					
C10:0					
C12:0					
C14:0					
C16:0					
C16:1					
C18:0					
C18:1					
C18:2					
C18:3					
C20:0					
C20:4					
C22:1					
Amino Acids (g/kg ODM)					
Ala					
Arg					
Asp					
Cys					
Glu					
Gly					
His					
Ile					
Leu					
Lys avail					
Lys total					
Meth					
Phe					
Pro					
Pro.OH					
Ser					
Thr					
Tryp					
Tyr					
Val					

ANALYTICAL DATABASE

FEED DESCRIPTION : **FRESH GRASS, HYBRID RYEGRASS, VAR AUGUSTA** (Source 1)

Determination	Mean	SD	Min	Max	n	Determination	Mean	SD	Min	Max	n
General (g/kg ODM)						**Volatile Fatty Acids (g/kg ODM)**					
ODM (fresh)	162.7	22.1	121.7	180.7	6	Lactic					
TDM (fresh)						Formic					
CP	180.6	57.9	126.7	274.4	6	Acetic					
CF	249.0	36.6	202.0	294.0	6	Propionic					
MADF	270.7	31.7	224.0	308.0	6	n butyric					
EE	18.0	3.3	14.0	22.0	6	i butyric					
AEE						n valeric					
TA	100.7	18.2	76.0	127.0	6	i valeric					
AIA	16.5	8.5	11.1	32.4	6	n caproic					
GE (MJ/kg ODM)	18.5	0.38	17.9	18.9	6	i caproic					
						NO_3N					
						NH_3N/TN					
Carbohydrates (g/kg ODM)						pH					
NDF ash	586.2	37.3	550.0	637.0	6	**Fatty Acids (g/kg ODM)**					
NDF unash											
ADF ash	316.3	26.8	280.0	349.0	6	C8:0					
ADF unash	322.5	25.9	287.0	353.0	6	C10:0					
Cellulose	248.0	24.6	208.0	278.0	6	C12:0					
Lignin	57.5	16.5	40.0	80.0	6	C14:0					
Starch						C16:0					
NCD	724.0	52.7	639.0	781.0	6	C16:1					
CD	563.3	69.8	457.0	642.0	6	C18:0					
IVD	648.7	23.6	607.0	678.0	6	C18:1					
WSC	144.8	42.8	83.8	198.4	6	C18:2					
Avail Carbs						C18:3					
Sugars						C20:0					
						C20:4					
Minerals (g/kg ODM)						C22:1					
Ca	5.2	1.2	3.5	6.9	6						
Mg	1.9	0.33	1.4	2.3	6	**Amino Acids (g/kg ODM)**					
Na	2.3	0.58	1.5	2.9	6						
K	33.3	5.4	26.0	39.8	6	Ala					
Cl						Arg					
P total	3.8	0.61	3.1	4.6	6	Asp					
P inorg						Cys					
P phytate						Glu					
Fe						Gly					
S						His					
						Ile					
						Leu					
Trace Elements (mg/kg ODM)						Lys avail					
						Lys total					
Co						Meth					
F						Phe					
I						Pro					
Mn						Pro.OH					
Mo						Ser					
Zn						Thr					
Cu						Tryp					
Se						Tyr					
						Val					

ANALYTICAL DATABASE

FEED DESCRIPTION : **FRESH GRASS, ITALIAN RYEGRASS, VAR RvP** (Source 1)

Determination	Mean	SD	Min	Max	n	Determination	Mean	SD	Min	Max	n
General (g/kg ODM)						**Volatile Fatty Acids (g/kg ODM)**					
ODM (fresh)	222.9	55.1	141.0	363.0	30	Lactic					
TDM (fresh)						Formic					
CP	127.8	44.4	54.0	248.0	24	Acetic					
CF	217.1	36.2	155.0	269.0	30	Propionic					
MADF	245.3	45.9	184.0	325.0	30	n butyric					
EE	22.2	6.2	13.0	43.0	30	i butyric					
AEE						n valeric					
TA	72.6	14.7	45.0	104.0	30	i valeric					
AIA	13.1	7.1	3.0	36.0	30	n caproic					
GE (MJ/kg ODM)	18.6	0.43	17.9	19.3	30	i caproic					
						NO_3N					
						NH_3N/TN					
Carbohydrates (g/kg ODM)						pH					
						Fatty Acids (g/kg ODM)					
NDF ash	508.4	56.5	415.0	592.0	29						
NDF unash						C8:0					
ADF ash	278.7	66.7	184.0	483.0	29	C10:0					
ADF unash	276.9	38.3	200.0	326.0	16	C12:0					
Cellulose	221.8	32.8	163.0	270.0	25	C14:0					
Lignin	45.6	9.0	35.0	65.0	8	C16:0					
Starch						C16:1					
NCD	757.6	66.9	646.0	844.0	17	C18:0					
CD	633.4	48.5	552.0	702.0	12	C18:1					
IVD	716.0	52.4	627.0	820.0	30	C18:2					
WSC	220.7	46.7	171.0	285.0	7	C18:3					
Avail Carbs						C20:0					
Sugars						C20:4					
						C22:1					
Minerals (g/kg ODM)											
Ca	4.2	0.69	2.8	6.0	29						
Mg	1.3	0.51	0.60	2.4	29	**Amino Acids (g/kg ODM)**					
Na	0.81	0.38	0.30	1.7	29						
K	25.5	6.8	14.4	43.0	29	Ala					
Cl						Arg					
P total	2.9	0.66	1.7	4.4	29	Asp					
P inorg						Cys					
P phytate						Glu					
Fe						Gly					
S	2.0	0.57	1.2	3.4	27	His					
						Ile					
						Leu					
Trace Elements (mg/kg ODM)						Lys avail					
						Lys total					
Co	0.07	0.05	0.02	0.26	24	Meth					
F						Phe					
I						Pro					
Mn	98.7	62.8	21.0	207.0	27	Pro.OH					
Mo	0.76	0.51	0.18	2.0	27	Ser					
Zn						Thr					
Cu	6.5	1.9	3.6	10.7	27	Tryp					
Se	0.04	0.01	0.02	0.08	17	Tyr					
						Val					

ANALYTICAL DATABASE

FEED DESCRIPTION : **FRESH GRASS, PERENNIAL RYEGRASS, VAR AJAX** (Source 1)

Determination	Mean	SD	Min	Max	n	Determination	Mean	SD	Min	Max	n
General (g/kg ODM)						**Volatile Fatty Acids** (g/kg ODM)					
ODM (fresh)	199.8	41.2	144.0	276.0	12	Lactic					
TDM (fresh)						Formic					
CP	125.4	39.8	72.0	195.0	12	Acetic					
CF	257.9	41.2	197.0	308.0	12	Propionic					
MADF	306.3	42.4	235.0	380.0	12	n butyric					
EE	22.9	3.7	17.0	29.0	12	i butyric					
AEE						n valeric					
TA	72.4	11.0	56.0	91.0	12	i valeric					
AIA	12.3	6.5	6.0	26.0	12	n caproic					
GE (MJ/kg ODM)	18.5	0.37	17.9	19.0	12	i caproic					
						NO$_3$N					
						NH$_3$N/TN					
Carbohydrates (g/kg ODM)						pH					
NDF ash	580.3	43.9	498.0	633.0	12	**Fatty Acids** (g/kg ODM)					
NDF unash											
ADF ash	297.5	42.4	231.0	354.0	12						
ADF unash	298.3	37.8	242.0	351.0	8	C8:0					
Cellulose	265.3	36.8	203.0	309.0	12	C10:0					
Lignin	38.7	15.3	23.0	69.0	11	C12:0					
Starch						C14:0					
NCD	726.2	102.2	593.0	840.0	6	C16:0					
CD	609.8	54.8	553.0	696.0	6	C16:1					
IVD	685.3	47.5	608.0	779.0	12	C18:0					
WSC	149.3	52.7	100.0	224.0	6	C18:1					
Avail Carbs						C18:2					
Sugars						C18:3					
						C20:0					
						C20:4					
Minerals (g/kg ODM)						C22:1					
Ca	5.9	0.83	4.1	7.1	12						
Mg	1.1	0.27	0.50	1.4	12	**Amino Acids** (g/kg ODM)					
Na	1.8	0.52	1.1	2.6	12						
K	22.5	2.8	18.0	28.3	12	Ala					
Cl						Arg					
P total	3.0	1.1	1.9	5.6	12	Asp					
P inorg						Cys					
P phytate						Glu					
Fe						Gly					
S	2.2	0.48	1.5	2.9	8	His					
						Ile					
						Leu					
Trace Elements (mg/kg ODM)						Lys avail					
						Lys total					
Co	0.16	0.04	0.11	0.23	8	Meth					
F						Phe					
I						Pro					
Mn	95.1	20.1	71.0	125.0	8	Pro.OH					
Mo	0.94	0.88	0.15	3.0	8	Ser					
Zn						Thr					
Cu	10.7	5.6	3.9	20.2	8	Tryp					
Se	0.05	0.02	0.03	0.08	6	Tyr					
						Val					

61

ANALYTICAL DATABASE

FEED DESCRIPTION : **FRESH GRASS, PERENNIAL RYEGRASS, VAR MELLE** (Source 1)

Determination	Mean	SD	Min	Max	n	Determination	Mean	SD	Min	Max	n

General (g/kg ODM)

	Mean	SD	Min	Max	n
ODM (fresh)	209.8	51.9	148.0	279.0	8
TDM (fresh)					
CP	224.8	66.7	163.0	360.6	8
CF	222.4	35.6	171.0	288.0	8
MADF	254.0	37.7	183.0	313.0	8
EE	21.0	2.7	18.0	25.0	8
AEE					
TA	92.9	9.8	81.0	110.0	8
AIA	15.5	5.2	9.0	23.0	8
GE (MJ/kg ODM)	18.8	0.31	18.5	19.5	8

Carbohydrates (g/kg ODM)

	Mean	SD	Min	Max	n
NDF ash	572.8	26.6	533.0	618.0	8
NDF unash					
ADF ash	293.5	28.7	234.0	325.0	8
ADF unash	314.6	33.2	243.0	352.0	8
Cellulose	231.5	26.0	180.0	268.0	8
Lignin	67.5	9.4	57.0	80.0	8
Starch					
NCD	733.6	38.3	678.0	800.0	8
CD	574.6	69.3	519.0	688.0	8
IVD	656.7	31.3	603.0	704.0	8
WSC	110.4	67.3	16.0	193.0	8
Avail Carbs					
Sugars					

Minerals (g/kg ODM)

	Mean	SD	Min	Max	n
Ca	7.0	1.3	5.2	8.6	8
Mg	1.8	0.33	1.5	2.4	8
Na	3.3	1.4	0.60	4.6	8
K	28.0	5.1	20.0	34.1	8
Cl					
P total	2.8	0.33	2.4	3.3	8
P inorg					
P phytate					
Fe					
S	3.2		3.2	3.2	1

Trace Elements (mg/kg ODM)

Co
F
I
Mn
Mo
Zn
Cu
Se

Volatile Fatty Acids (g/kg ODM)

Lactic
Formic
Acetic
Propionic
n butyric
i butyric
n valeric
i valeric
n caproic
i caproic

NO_3N
NH_3N/TN
pH

Fatty Acids (g/kg ODM)

C8:0
C10:0
C12:0
C14:0
C16:0
C16:1
C18:0
C18:1
C18:2
C18:3
C20:0
C20:4
C22:1

Amino Acids (g/kg ODM)

Ala
Arg
Asp
Cys
Glu
Gly
His
Ile
Leu
Lys avail
Lys total
Meth
Phe
Pro
Pro.OH
Ser
Thr
Tryp
Tyr
Val

ANALYTICAL DATABASE

FEED DESCRIPTION : **FRESH GRASS, PERENNIAL RYEGRASS, VAR S23** (Source 1)

Determination	Mean	SD	Min	Max	n	Determination	Mean	SD	Min	Max	n
General (g/kg ODM)						**Volatile Fatty Acids** (g/kg ODM)					
ODM (fresh)	197.0	32.6	146.0	236.0	12	Lactic					
TDM (fresh)						Formic					
CP	101.8	25.8	68.0	138.0	6	Acetic					
CF	228.8	49.6	123.0	301.0	12	Propionic					
MADF	265.1	48.0	205.0	331.0	12	n butyric					
EE	27.3	6.2	19.0	39.0	12	i butyric					
AEE						n valeric					
TA	81.5	10.4	66.0	102.0	12	i valeric					
AIA	11.8	2.5	8.0	17.0	12	n caproic					
GE (MJ/kg ODM)	18.4	0.28	17.9	18.9	12	i caproic					
						NO_3N					
						NH_3N/TN					
Carbohydrates (g/kg ODM)						pH					
						Fatty Acids (g/kg ODM)					
NDF ash	572.0	54.8	510.0	664.4	12						
NDF unash											
ADF ash	289.3	48.4	226.0	373.0	12	C8:0					
ADF unash	270.8	45.8	208.0	341.0	8	C10:0					
Cellulose	241.3	43.5	178.0	310.0	12	C12:0					
Lignin	36.4	14.6	8.0	54.0	8	C14:0					
Starch	3.3	1.9	1.9	6.9	6	C16:0					
NCD						C16:1					
CD	691.7	74.9	547.0	774.0	12	C18:0					
IVD	706.0	36.1	636.0	753.0	12	C18:1					
WSC	196.9	40.6	143.0	244.0	8	C18:2					
Avail Carbs						C18:3					
Sugars						C20:0					
						C20:4					
Minerals (g/kg ODM)						C22:1					
Ca	4.4	1.0	3.3	6.6	12						
Mg	1.2	0.40	0.70	1.7	12	**Amino Acids** (g/kg ODM)					
Na	0.82	0.28	0.50	1.4	12						
K	30.0	5.4	20.0	40.0	12	Ala					
Cl						Arg					
P total	3.4	0.26	3.0	3.9	12	Asp					
P inorg						Cys					
P phytate						Glu					
Fe						Gly					
S	2.1	0.40	1.6	2.6	7	His					
						Ile					
						Leu					
Trace Elements (mg/kg ODM)						Lys avail					
						Lys total					
Co	0.03	0.01	0.02	0.04	6	Meth					
F						Phe					
I						Pro					
Mn	180.9	62.9	41.0	220.0	7	Pro.OH					
Mo	0.55	0.22	0.35	1.0	7	Ser					
Zn						Thr					
Cu	8.1	3.0	5.6	13.7	7	Tryp					
Se	0.06	0.01	0.05	0.07	6	Tyr					
						Val					

ANALYTICAL DATABASE

FEED DESCRIPTION : **FRESH GRASS, PERENNIAL RYEGRASS, VAR S24** (Source 1)

Determination	Mean	SD	Min	Max	n	Determination	Mean	SD	Min	Max	n
General (g/kg ODM)						**Volatile Fatty Acids (g/kg ODM)**					
ODM (fresh)	206.0	62.5	133.0	424.0	24	Lactic					
TDM (fresh)						Formic					
CP	126.5	39.5	77.0	212.0	17	Acetic					
CF	261.4	40.5	192.0	326.0	24	Propionic					
MADF	289.5	48.8	195.0	359.0	23	n butyric					
EE	20.0	5.1	13.0	33.0	24	i butyric					
AEE						n valeric					
TA	69.1	13.1	47.0	96.0	24	i valeric					
AIA	9.8	5.1	1.0	19.0	24	n caproic					
GE (MJ/kg ODM)	18.7	0.37	17.9	19.3	24	i caproic					
						NO_3N					
						NH_3N/TN					
Carbohydrates (g/kg ODM)						pH					
NDF ash	615.6	62.3	502.0	765.0	24	**Fatty Acids (g/kg ODM)**					
NDF unash											
ADF ash	333.2	36.0	270.0	389.0	24	C8:0					
ADF unash	322.8	39.1	273.0	384.0	12	C10:0					
Cellulose	267.4	32.5	213.0	318.0	23	C12:0					
Lignin	66.0	23.7	28.0	108.0	12	C14:0					
Starch						C16:0					
NCD	706.3	83.2	580.0	840.0	16	C16:1					
CD	599.8	83.6	487.0	722.0	12	C18:0					
IVD	695.8	58.1	591.0	769.0	24	C18:1					
WSC	160.2	59.2	100.0	224.0	5	C18:2					
Avail Carbs						C18:3					
Sugars						C20:0					
						C20:4					
Minerals (g/kg ODM)						C22:1					
Ca	3.6	0.48	2.6	4.3	23						
Mg	1.3	0.36	0.80	1.9	23	**Amino Acids (g/kg ODM)**					
Na	1.6	0.69	0.70	2.7	23						
K	23.2	5.8	12.3	33.0	23	Ala					
Cl						Arg					
P total	3.1	0.48	2.4	4.1	23	Asp					
P inorg						Cys					
P phytate						Glu					
Fe						Gly					
S	2.2	0.56	1.3	3.7	22	His					
						Ile					
						Leu					
Trace Elements (mg/kg ODM)						Lys avail					
						Lys total					
Co	0.07	0.03	0.02	0.15	19	Meth					
F						Phe					
I						Pro					
Mn	113.7	78.9	29.0	260.0	23	Pro.OH					
Mo	0.69	0.41	0.27	2.0	22	Ser					
Zn						Thr					
Cu	6.1	1.7	3.0	9.9	23	Tryp					
Se	0.04	0.01	0.02	0.06	16	Tyr					
						Val					

ANALYTICAL DATABASE

FEED DESCRIPTION : **FRESH GRASS, TALL FESCUE, VAR DOVEY** (Source 1)

Determination	Mean	SD	Min	Max	n	Determination	Mean	SD	Min	Max	n
General (g/kg ODM)						**Volatile Fatty Acids (g/kg ODM)**					
ODM (fresh)	187.7	33.2	155.0	241.0	6	Lactic					
TDM (fresh)						Formic					
CP	142.7	42.1	97.0	208.0	6	Acetic					
CF	259.2	15.0	238.0	276.0	6	Propionic					
MADF	302.8	22.6	267.0	323.0	6	n butyric					
EE	20.2	2.5	17.0	22.0	6	i butyric					
AEE						n valeric					
TA	76.7	10.4	62.0	90.0	6	i valeric					
AIA	20.2	6.8	13.0	33.0	6	n caproic					
GE (MJ/kg ODM)	18.4	0.36	17.8	18.8	6	i caproic					
						NO$_3$N					
						NH$_3$N/TN					
Carbohydrates (g/kg ODM)						pH					
NDF ash	647.0	22.5	605.0	672.0	6	**Fatty Acids (g/kg ODM)**					
NDF unash											
ADF ash	311.7	29.0	263.0	345.0	6	C8:0					
ADF unash	317.3	14.4	298.0	331.0	6	C10:0					
Cellulose	261.5	12.9	245.0	274.0	6	C12:0					
Lignin	40.3	4.0	36.0	46.0	6	C14:0					
Starch						C16:0					
NCD						C16:1					
CD	517.7	31.6	489.0	556.0	6	C18:0					
IVD	646.0	34.6	592.0	677.0	6	C18:1					
WSC	115.0	23.4	76.0	138.0	6	C18:2					
Avail Carbs						C18:3					
Sugars						C20:0					
						C20:4					
Minerals (g/kg ODM)						C22:1					
Ca	4.6	0.33	4.3	5.2	6	**Amino Acids (g/kg ODM)**					
Mg	1.3	0.17	1.1	1.5	6						
Na	1.7	0.21	1.5	2.0	6	Ala					
K	22.5	3.0	18.8	26.2	6	Arg					
Cl						Asp					
P total	2.8	0.21	2.4	3.0	6	Cys					
P inorg						Glu					
P phytate						Gly					
Fe						His					
S	2.2	0.56	1.6	3.1	6	Ile					
						Leu					
Trace Elements (mg/kg ODM)						Lys avail					
						Lys total					
Co	0.17	0.05	0.09	0.22	6	Meth					
F						Phe					
I						Pro					
Mn	82.0	9.1	68.0	92.0	6	Pro.OH					
Mo	0.69	0.13	0.55	0.90	6	Ser					
Zn						Thr					
Cu	6.1	0.70	5.3	6.9	6	Tryp					
Se	0.06	0.02	0.04	0.09	6	Tyr					
						Val					

ANALYTICAL DATABASE

FEED DESCRIPTION : **FRESH GRASS, TALL FESCUE, VAR S170** (Source 1)

Determination	Mean	SD	Min	Max	n	Determination	Mean	SD	Min	Max	n
General (g/kg ODM)						**Volatile Fatty Acids** (g/kg ODM)					
ODM (fresh)	207.0	40.9	153.0	267.0	12	Lactic					
TDM (fresh)						Formic					
CP	151.8	44.5	98.0	229.0	12	Acetic					
CF	249.3	27.9	202.0	293.0	12	Propionic					
MADF	284.9	30.9	231.0	336.0	12	n butyric					
EE	20.3	3.6	17.0	29.0	12	i butyric					
AEE						n valeric					
TA	81.6	8.6	70.0	95.0	12	i valeric					
AIA	14.9	4.7	7.0	22.0	12	n caproic					
GE (MJ/kg ODM)	18.6	0.38	18.0	19.1	12	i caproic					
						NO_3N					
						NH_3N/TN					
Carbohydrates (g/kg ODM)						pH					
						Fatty Acids (g/kg ODM)					
NDF ash	613.0	27.8	543.0	656.0	12						
NDF unash											
ADF ash	303.0	24.8	263.0	335.0	12	C8:0					
ADF unash	298.6	25.0	255.0	332.0	11	C10:0					
Cellulose	251.8	26.2	207.0	297.0	12	C12:0					
Lignin	41.4	6.6	34.0	55.0	7	C14:0					
Starch						C16:0					
NCD	683.0	67.3	550.0	763.0	9	C16:1					
CD	553.2	54.3	494.0	629.0	6	C18:0					
IVD	648.3	50.4	532.0	723.0	12	C18:1					
WSC	109.0	29.9	62.0	161.0	7	C18:2					
Avail Carbs						C18:3					
Sugars						C20:0					
						C20:4					
Minerals (g/kg ODM)						C22:1					
Ca	5.1	0.51	4.5	6.2	12						
Mg	1.5	0.15	1.3	1.7	12	**Amino Acids** (g/kg ODM)					
Na	0.93	0.29	0.50	1.5	12						
K	25.8	3.3	20.0	31.5	12	Ala					
Cl						Arg					
P total	2.7	0.64	2.1	4.4	12	Asp					
P inorg						Cys					
P phytate						Glu					
Fe						Gly					
S	2.9	0.43	2.3	3.4	9	His					
						Ile					
						Leu					
Trace Elements (mg/kg ODM)						Lys avail					
						Lys total					
Co	0.14	0.05	0.05	0.20	9	Meth					
F						Phe					
I						Pro					
Mn	121.3	11.4	99.0	134.0	9	Pro.OH					
Mo	0.65	0.26	0.40	1.0	9	Ser					
Zn						Thr					
Cu	7.3	1.9	4.5	9.8	9	Tryp					
Se	0.04	0.01	0.03	0.06	5	Tyr					
						Val					

ANALYTICAL DATABASE

FEED DESCRIPTION : **KALE, BITTERN** (Sources 1, 2)

Determination	Mean	SD	Min	Max	n	Determination	Mean	SD	Min	Max	n
General (g/kg ODM)						**Volatile Fatty Acids** (g/kg ODM)					
ODM (fresh)	133.2	26.1	114.7	151.6	2	Lactic					
TDM (fresh)						Formic					
CP	163.6	17.6	151.2	176.0	2	Acetic					
CF	152.6	21.8	137.2	168.0	2	Propionic					
MADF	195.2	37.9	168.4	222.0	2	n butyric					
EE	21.9	3.0	19.8	24.0	2	i butyric					
AEE						n valeric					
TA	114.5	16.3	103.0	126.0	2	i valeric					
AIA	3.0		3.0	3.0	1	n caproic					
GE (MJ/kg ODM)	17.2	0.24	17.0	17.3	2	i caproic					
						NO$_3$N					
Carbohydrates (g/kg ODM)						NH$_3$N/TN					
						pH					
NDF ash	257.6	51.5	221.2	294.0	2						
NDF unash						**Fatty Acids** (g/kg ODM)					
ADF ash	206.7	28.7	186.4	227.0	2						
ADF unash						C8:0					
Cellulose	205.0		205.0	205.0	1	C10:0					
Lignin	23.4		23.4	23.4	1	C12:0					
Starch	9.0		9.0	9.0	1	C14:0					
NCD	804.0		804.0	804.0	1	C16:0					
CD						C16:1					
IVD	691.0	15.6	680.0	702.0	2	C18:0					
WSC	233.4	78.3	178.0	288.8	2	C18:1					
Avail Carbs						C18:2					
Sugars						C18:3					
						C20:0					
						C20:4					
Minerals (g/kg ODM)						C22:1					
Ca	12.5	0.14	12.4	12.6	2						
Mg	1.5	0.07	1.4	1.5	2	**Amino Acids** (g/kg ODM)					
Na	1.3	0.14	1.2	1.4	2						
K	39.4	13.6	29.7	49.0	2	Ala					
Cl						Arg					
P total	3.9	0.50	3.5	4.2	2	Asp					
P inorg						Cys					
P phytate						Glu					
Fe						Gly					
S						His					
						Ile					
						Leu					
Trace Elements (mg/kg ODM)						Lys avail					
						Lys total					
Co						Meth					
F						Phe					
I						Pro					
Mn	21.0		21.0	21.0	1	Pro.OH					
Mo						Ser					
Zn	31.0		31.0	31.0	1	Thr					
Cu	4.0		4.0	4.0	1	Tryp					
Se						Tyr					
						Val					

67

ANALYTICAL DATABASE

FEED DESCRIPTION : **KALE, DWARF THOUSAND HEAD** (Source 2)

Determination	Mean	SD	Min	Max	n	Determination	Mean	SD	Min	Max	n
General (g/kg ODM)						**Volatile Fatty Acids (g/kg ODM)**					
ODM (fresh)	157.7		157.7	157.7	1	Lactic					
TDM (fresh)						Formic					
CP	158.3		158.3	158.3	1	Acetic					
CF	147.3		147.3	147.3	1	Propionic					
MADF	194.3		194.3	194.3	1	n butyric					
EE	20.4		20.4	20.4	1	i butyric					
AEE						n valeric					
TA	105.0		105.0	105.0	1	i valeric					
AIA						n caproic					
GE (MJ/kg ODM)	17.4		17.4	17.4	1	i caproic					
						NO_3N					
Carbohydrates (g/kg ODM)						NH_3N/TN					
						pH					
NDF ash	236.3		236.3	236.3	1						
NDF unash						**Fatty Acids (g/kg ODM)**					
ADF ash	200.7		200.7	200.7	1						
ADF unash						C8:0					
Cellulose						C10:0					
Lignin	23.0		23.0	23.0	1	C12:0					
Starch	5.0		5.0	5.0	1	C14:0					
NCD	788.0		788.0	788.0	1	C16:0					
CD						C16:1					
IVD	698.0		698.0	698.0	1	C18:0					
WSC	266.7		266.7	266.7	1	C18:1					
Avail Carbs						C18:2					
Sugars						C18:3					
						C20:0					
						C20:4					
Minerals (g/kg ODM)						C22:1					
Ca	12.2		12.2	12.2	1						
Mg	1.5		1.5	1.5	1	**Amino Acids (g/kg ODM)**					
Na	1.7		1.7	1.7	1						
K	28.5		28.5	28.5	1	Ala					
Cl						Arg					
P total	4.2		4.2	4.2	1	Asp					
P inorg						Cys					
P phytate						Glu					
Fe						Gly					
S						His					
						Ile					
						Leu					
Trace Elements (mg/kg ODM)						Lys avail					
						Lys total					
Co						Meth					
F						Phe					
I						Pro					
Mn	17.0		17.0	17.0	1	Pro.OH					
Mo						Ser					
Zn	37.0		37.0	37.0	1	Thr					
Cu	4.0		4.0	4.0	1	Tryp					
Se						Tyr					
						Val					

ANALYTICAL DATABASE

FEED DESCRIPTION : **KALE, MARIS KESTREL** (Sources 1, 2)

Determination	Mean	SD	Min	Max	n	Determination	Mean	SD	Min	Max	n
General (g/kg ODM)						**Volatile Fatty Acids** (g/kg ODM)					
ODM (fresh)	134.9	1.6	133.7	136.0	2	Lactic					
TDM (fresh)						Formic					
CP	166.4	33.4	142.7	190.0	2	Acetic					
CF	126.3	5.2	122.6	130.0	2	Propionic					
MADF	161.7	1.8	160.4	163.0	2	n butyric					
EE	18.4	0.56	18.0	18.8	2	i butyric					
AEE						n valeric					
TA	117.8	0.35	117.5	118.0	2	i valeric					
AIA	10.0		10.0	10.0	1	n caproic					
GE (MJ/kg ODM)	17.2	0.43	16.9	17.5	2	i caproic					
						NO$_3$N					
						NH$_3$N/TN					
Carbohydrates (g/kg ODM)						pH					
NDF ash	232.2	45.1	200.3	264.0	2	**Fatty Acids** (g/kg ODM)					
NDF unash											
ADF ash	182.2	12.4	173.4	191.0	2	C8:0					
ADF unash						C10:0					
Cellulose						C12:0					
Lignin	17.2		17.2	17.2	1	C14:0					
Starch	4.1		4.1	4.1	1	C16:0					
NCD	814.0		814.0	814.0	1	C16:1					
CD						C18:0					
IVD	719.5	0.71	719.0	720.0	2	C18:1					
WSC	301.6		301.6	301.6	1	C18:2					
Avail Carbs						C18:3					
Sugars						C20:0					
						C20:4					
						C22:1					
Minerals (g/kg ODM)											
Ca	12.5	0.50	12.1	12.8	2	**Amino Acids** (g/kg ODM)					
Mg	1.6	0.28	1.4	1.8	2						
Na	1.2	0.07	1.1	1.2	2	Ala					
K	29.8	5.4	26.0	33.6	2	Arg					
Cl						Asp					
P total	4.1	0.78	3.5	4.6	2	Cys					
P inorg						Glu					
P phytate						Gly					
Fe						His					
S						Ile					
						Leu					
						Lys avail					
Trace Elements (mg/kg ODM)						Lys total					
						Meth					
Co						Phe					
F						Pro					
I						Pro.OH					
Mn	11.0		11.0	11.0	1	Ser					
Mo						Thr					
Zn	25.0		25.0	25.0	1	Tryp					
Cu	4.0		4.0	4.0	1	Tyr					
Se						Val					

ANALYTICAL DATABASE

FEED DESCRIPTION : **KALE, MARROW STEM** (Sources 1, 2)

Determination	Mean	SD	Min	Max	n	Determination	Mean	SD	Min	Max	n
General (g/kg ODM)						**Volatile Fatty Acids** (g/kg ODM)					
ODM (fresh)	117.7	2.3	116.1	119.3	2	Lactic					
TDM (fresh)						Formic					
CP	152.2	8.2	146.4	158.0	2	Acetic					
CF	186.8	10.3	179.5	194.0	2	Propionic					
MADF	229.5	24.7	212.0	247.0	2	n butyric					
EE	19.1	2.7	17.2	21.0	2	i butyric					
AEE						n valeric					
TA	175.4	73.0	123.7	227.0	2	i valeric					
AIA	12.0		12.0	12.0	1	n caproic					
GE (MJ/kg ODM)	16.7	0.09	16.7	16.8	2	i caproic					
						NO3N					
Carbohydrates (g/kg ODM)						NH3N/TN					
						pH					
NDF ash	350.3	117.0	267.5	433.0	2						
NDF unash						**Fatty Acids** (g/kg ODM)					
ADF ash	243.0	21.2	228.0	258.0	2						
ADF unash						C8:0					
Cellulose	216.0		216.0	216.0	1	C10:0					
Lignin	33.8		33.8	33.8	1	C12:0					
Starch	5.0		5.0	5.0	1	C14:0					
NCD	736.0		736.0	736.0	1	C16:0					
CD						C16:1					
IVD	599.0	59.4	557.0	641.0	2	C18:0					
WSC	201.4	59.9	159.0	243.8	2	C18:1					
Avail Carbs						C18:2					
Sugars						C18:3					
						C20:0					
						C20:4					
Minerals (g/kg ODM)						C22:1					
Ca	14.5	2.3	12.8	16.1	2						
Mg	1.8	0.0	1.8	1.8	2	**Amino Acids** (g/kg ODM)					
Na	1.9	0.92	1.2	2.5	2						
K	41.0	11.4	32.9	49.0	2	Ala					
Cl						Arg					
P total	4.2	0.35	3.9	4.4	2	Asp					
P inorg						Cys					
P phytate						Glu					
Fe						Gly					
S						His					
						Ile					
						Leu					
Trace Elements (mg/kg ODM)						Lys avail					
						Lys total					
Co						Meth					
F						Phe					
I						Pro					
Mn	26.0		26.0	26.0	1	Pro.OH					
Mo						Ser					
Zn	38.0		38.0	38.0	1	Thr					
Cu	5.0		5.0	5.0	1	Tryp					
Se						Tyr					
						Val					

ANALYTICAL DATABASE

FEED DESCRIPTION : **KALE, MERLIN** (Source 2)

Determination	Mean	SD	Min	Max	n	Determination	Mean	SD	Min	Max	n
General (g/kg ODM)						**Volatile Fatty Acids** (g/kg ODM)					
ODM (fresh)	120.8		120.8	120.8	1	Lactic					
TDM (fresh)						Formic					
CP	147.0		147.0	147.0	1	Acetic					
CF	146.3		146.3	146.3	1	Propionic					
MADF	184.3		184.3	184.3	1	n butyric					
EE	18.3		18.3	18.3	1	i butyric					
AEE						n valeric					
TA	123.6		123.6	123.6	1	i valeric					
AIA						n caproic					
GE (MJ/kg ODM)	16.7		16.7	16.7	1	i caproic					
						NO3N					
Carbohydrates (g/kg ODM)						NH3N/TN					
						pH					
NDF ash	228.8		228.8	228.8	1						
NDF unash						**Fatty Acids** (g/kg ODM)					
ADF ash	198.5		198.5	198.5	1						
ADF unash						C8:0					
Cellulose						C10:0					
Lignin	22.3		22.3	22.3	1	C12:0					
Starch	7.0		7.0	7.0	1	C14:0					
NCD	787.0		787.0	787.0	1	C16:0					
CD						C16:1					
IVD	713.0		713.0	713.0	1	C18:0					
WSC	269.0		269.0	269.0	1	C18:1					
Avail Carbs						C18:2					
Sugars						C18:3					
						C20:0					
						C20:4					
Minerals (g/kg ODM)						C22:1					
Ca	15.5		15.5	15.5	1						
Mg	1.7		1.7	1.7	1	**Amino Acids** (g/kg ODM)					
Na	2.6		2.6	2.6	1						
K	35.2		35.2	35.2	1	Ala					
Cl						Arg					
P total	4.3		4.3	4.3	1	Asp					
P inorg						Cys					
P phytate						Glu					
Fe						Gly					
S						His					
						Ile					
						Leu					
Trace Elements (mg/kg ODM)						Lys avail					
						Lys total					
Co						Meth					
F						Phe					
I						Pro					
Mn	21.0		21.0	21.0	1	Pro.OH					
Mo						Ser					
Zn	38.0		38.0	38.0	1	Thr					
Cu	5.0		5.0	5.0	1	Tryp					
Se						Tyr					
						Val					

ANALYTICAL DATABASE

FEED DESCRIPTION : **KALE, THOUSAND HEAD** (Sources 1, 2)

Determination	Mean	SD	Min	Max	n	Determination	Mean	SD	Min	Max	n
General (g/kg ODM)						**Volatile Fatty Acids** (g/kg ODM)					
ODM (fresh)	143.2	8.6	137.1	149.2	2	Lactic					
TDM (fresh)						Formic					
CP	187.5	72.8	136.0	239.0	2	Acetic					
CF	134.7	20.3	120.3	149.0	2	Propionic					
MADF	174.3	23.6	157.7	191.0	2	n butyric					
EE	20.2	2.5	18.5	22.0	2	i butyric					
AEE						n valeric					
TA	117.0	12.7	108.0	126.0	2	i valeric					
AIA	6.0		6.0	6.0	1	n caproic					
GE (MJ/kg ODM)	17.3	0.38	17.1	17.6	2	i caproic					
						NO_3N					
Carbohydrates (g/kg ODM)						NH_3N/TN					
						pH					
NDF ash	259.3	87.2	197.7	321.0	2						
NDF unash						**Fatty Acids** (g/kg ODM)					
ADF ash	198.0	41.0	169.0	227.0	2						
ADF unash						C8:0					
Cellulose						C10:0					
Lignin	16.0		16.0	16.0	1	C12:0					
Starch	3.7		3.7	3.7	1	C14:0					
NCD	825.0		825.0	825.0	1	C16:0					
CD						C16:1					
IVD	703.5	33.2	680.0	727.0	2	C18:0					
WSC	321.3		321.3	321.3	1	C18:1					
Avail Carbs						C18:2					
Sugars						C18:3					
						C20:0					
						C20:4					
Minerals (g/kg ODM)						C22:1					
Ca	12.5	0.64	12.0	12.9	2						
Mg	1.6	0.21	1.4	1.7	2	**Amino Acids** (g/kg ODM)					
Na	1.2	0.57	0.80	1.6	2						
K	29.3	3.2	27.0	31.5	2	Ala					
Cl						Arg					
P total	4.2	0.71	3.7	4.7	2	Asp					
P inorg						Cys					
P phytate						Glu					
Fe						Gly					
S						His					
						Ile					
						Leu					
Trace Elements (mg/kg ODM)						Lys avail					
						Lys total					
Co						Meth					
F						Phe					
I						Pro					
Mn	12.0		12.0	12.0	1	Pro.OH					
Mo						Ser					
Zn	27.0		27.0	27.0	1	Thr					
Cu	5.0		5.0	5.0	1	Tryp					
Se						Tyr					
						Val					

ANALYTICAL DATABASE

FEED DESCRIPTION : **WHITE CLOVER, VAR BLANCA** (Source 1)

Determination	Mean	SD	Min	Max	n	Determination	Mean	SD	Min	Max	n
General (g/kg ODM)						**Volatile Fatty Acids (g/kg ODM)**					
ODM (fresh)	117.5	7.8	112.0	123.0	2	Lactic					
TDM (fresh)						Formic					
CP	297.5	5.0	294.0	301.0	2	Acetic					
CF	141.0	1.4	140.0	142.0	2	Propionic					
MADF	228.5	24.7	211.0	246.0	2	n butyric					
EE	25.5	5.0	22.0	29.0	2	i butyric					
AEE						n valeric					
TA	92.5	13.4	83.0	102.0	2	i valeric					
AIA	4.5	3.5	2.0	7.0	2	n caproic					
GE (MJ/kg ODM)	19.6	0.28	19.4	19.8	2	i caproic					
						NO_3N					
						NH_3N/TN					
Carbohydrates (g/kg ODM)						pH					
NDF ash	399.5	30.4	378.0	421.0	2	**Fatty Acids (g/kg ODM)**					
NDF unash											
ADF ash	252.5	20.5	238.0	267.0	2	C8:0					
ADF unash	255.5	21.9	240.0	271.0	2	C10:0					
Cellulose	183.0	14.1	173.0	193.0	2	C12:0					
Lignin	68.0	5.7	64.0	72.0	2	C14:0					
Starch						C16:0					
NCD						C16:1					
CD	723.0		723.0	723.0	1	C18:0					
IVD	682.0	19.8	668.0	696.0	2	C18:1					
WSC	83.5	46.0	51.0	116.0	2	C18:2					
Avail Carbs						C18:3					
Sugars						C20:0					
						C20:4					
						C22:1					
Minerals (g/kg ODM)											
Ca	16.2	1.3	15.3	17.1	2	**Amino Acids (g/kg ODM)**					
Mg	2.2	0.50	1.8	2.5	2						
Na	1.5	0.85	0.90	2.1	2	Ala					
K	25.7	7.6	20.3	31.1	2	Arg					
Cl						Asp					
P total	3.8	0.28	3.6	4.0	2	Cys					
P inorg						Glu					
P phytate						Gly					
Fe						His					
S						Ile					
						Leu					
Trace Elements (mg/kg ODM)						Lys avail					
						Lys total					
Co						Meth					
F						Phe					
I						Pro					
Mn						Pro.OH					
Mo						Ser					
Zn						Thr					
Cu						Tryp					
Se						Tyr					
						Val					

ANALYTICAL   DATABASE

FEED CLASS 30

SILAGES

ANALYTICAL DATABASE

FEED DESCRIPTION : **BARLEY WHOLE CROP SILAGE** (Source 1)

Determination	Mean	SD	Min	Max	n	Determination	Mean	SD	Min	Max	n
General (g/kg ODM)						**Volatile Fatty Acids (g/kg ODM)**					
ODM (fresh)	394.0	137.0	199.0	520.0	4	Lactic	21.1	25.0	4.2	58.2	4
TDM (fresh)	414.8	128.5	230.0	528.0	4	Formic	0.68	0.66	0.20	1.6	4
CP	90.3	12.0	80.0	106.0	4	Acetic	11.9	5.9	6.8	19.2	4
CF	216.0	36.8	194.0	271.0	4	Propionic	0.20		0.20	0.20	1
MADF	252.0	40.6	211.0	308.0	4	n butyric	2.0	0.98	0.90	2.6	3
EE	19.8	8.5	13.0	32.0	4	i butyric					
AEE						n valeric	0.30	0.14	0.20	0.40	2
TA	77.8	37.1	41.0	126.0	4	i valeric					
AIA	13.3	1.9	12.0	16.0	4	n caproic	0.77	0.64	0.30	1.5	3
GE (MJ/kg ODM)	19.1	1.5	17.7	20.5	4	i caproic					
						NO$_3$N					
						NH$_3$N/TN	110.0	72.6	40.0	210.0	4
Carbohydrates (g/kg ODM)						pH	5.9	2.4	3.6	8.9	4
NDF ash	575.0	82.9	485.0	669.0	4	**Fatty Acids (g/kg ODM)**					
NDF unash											
ADF ash	274.3	40.7	216.0	308.0	4	C8:0					
ADF unash						C10:0					
Cellulose	184.5	34.6	160.0	209.0	2	C12:0					
Lignin	106.0		106.0	106.0	1	C14:0					
Starch	234.2	47.2	171.0	285.0	4	C16:0					
NCD						C16:1					
CD	649.0	86.3	588.0	710.0	2	C18:0					
IVD	683.8	88.7	567.0	777.0	4	C18:1					
WSC	33.0		33.0	33.0	1	C18:2					
Avail Carbs						C18:3					
Sugars						C20:0					
						C20:4					
						C22:1					
Minerals (g/kg ODM)											
Ca	2.4	0.81	1.5	3.2	4						
Mg	0.85	0.10	0.70	0.90	4	**Amino Acids (g/kg ODM)**					
Na	13.5	15.7	0.20	31.0	4	Ala					
K	10.6	5.0	7.0	18.0	4	Arg					
Cl						Asp					
P total	2.3	0.32	2.0	2.7	4	Cys					
P inorg						Glu					
P phytate						Gly					
Fe						His					
S						Ile					
						Leu					
						Lys avail					
						Lys total					
Trace Elements (mg/kg ODM)						Meth					
						Phe					
Co						Pro					
F						Pro.OH					
I						Ser					
Mn						Thr					
Mo						Tryp					
Zn						Tyr					
Cu						Val					
Se											

ANALYTICAL DATABASE

FEED DESCRIPTION : **BEAN WHOLE CROP SILAGE** (Source 1)

Determination	Mean	SD	Min	Max	n	Determination	Mean	SD	Min	Max	n
General (g/kg ODM)						**Volatile Fatty Acids (g/kg ODM)**					
ODM (fresh)	228.5	17.7	216.0	241.0	2	Lactic	14.2	11.4	6.1	22.2	2
TDM (fresh)	237.0	19.8	223.0	251.0	2	Formic	10.5		10.5	10.5	1
CP	172.5	6.4	168.0	177.0	2	Acetic	27.5	23.2	11.1	43.9	2
CF	395.5	27.6	376.0	415.0	2	Propionic	4.5	5.6	0.50	8.4	2
MADF	470.5	16.3	459.0	482.0	2	n butyric	21.7	19.9	7.6	35.8	2
EE	12.5	0.71	12.0	13.0	2	i butyric	2.1	2.7	0.20	4.0	2
AEE						n valeric	0.80	0.85	0.20	1.4	2
TA	123.0	4.2	120.0	126.0	2	i valeric	0.70		0.70	0.70	1
AIA	45.0	7.1	40.0	50.0	2	n caproic	1.2	1.5	0.10	2.2	2
GE (MJ/kg ODM)	17.7	0.64	17.2	18.1	2	i caproic					
						NO3N					
Carbohydrates (g/kg ODM)						NH3N/TN	145.0	21.2	130.0	160.0	2
						pH	3.7	0.28	3.5	3.9	2
NDF ash	565.5	31.8	543.0	588.0	2						
NDF unash						**Fatty Acids (g/kg ODM)**					
ADF ash	500.0	32.5	477.0	523.0	2						
ADF unash						C8:0					
Cellulose						C10:0					
Lignin						C12:0					
Starch	1.8	0.28	1.6	2.0	2	C14:0					
NCD						C16:0					
CD						C16:1					
IVD	468.5	34.6	444.0	493.0	2	C18:0					
WSC	30.5	23.3	14.0	47.0	2	C18:1					
Avail Carbs						C18:2					
Sugars						C18:3					
						C20:0					
						C20:4					
Minerals (g/kg ODM)						C22:1					
Ca	6.5	0.21	6.3	6.6	2						
Mg	1.7	0.07	1.6	1.7	2	**Amino Acids (g/kg ODM)**					
Na	5.2	0.21	5.0	5.3	2						
K	26.0	0.0	26.0	26.0	2	Ala					
Cl						Arg					
P total	3.4	0.0	3.4	3.4	2	Asp					
P inorg						Cys					
P phytate						Glu					
Fe						Gly					
S						His					
						Ile					
						Leu					
Trace Elements (mg/kg ODM)						Lys avail					
						Lys total					
Co						Meth					
F						Phe					
I						Pro					
Mn						Pro.OH					
Mo						Ser					
Zn						Thr					
Cu						Tryp					
Se						Tyr					
						Val					

77

ANALYTICAL DATABASE

FEED DESCRIPTION : **GRASS SILAGE** (Sources 1, 2)

Determination	Mean	SD	Min	Max	n	Determination	Mean	SD	Min	Max	n
General (g/kg ODM)						**Volatile Fatty Acids (g/kg ODM)**					
ODM (fresh)	255.0	80.3	159.0	622.0	231	Lactic	76.4	51.7	3.3	317.6	213
TDM (fresh)	280.2	80.3	175.0	629.0	218	Formic	9.1	19.1	0.10	128.3	144
CP	168.4	39.0	82.0	303.0	231	Acetic	28.1	25.5	1.9	254.3	210
CF	306.2	40.5	202.0	439.0	231	Propionic	5.7	6.5	0.0	44.0	147
MADF	348.7	42.0	230.0	460.6	230	n butyric	8.8	11.0	0.20	60.4	191
EE	42.6	11.4	15.0	90.0	226	i butyric	2.1	2.8	0.01	18.5	90
AEE	43.3	12.1	28.0	68.0	14	n valeric	1.3	1.5	0.01	11.1	115
TA	92.7	17.4	54.0	183.0	231	i valeric	2.4	5.7	0.01	43.0	109
AIA	19.2	11.7	1.3	87.0	184	n caproic	2.3	3.2	0.01	17.8	112
GE (MJ/kg ODM)	20.9	1.2	17.5	25.7	231	i caproic	1.0	1.5	0.01	7.5	60
						NO3N					
						NH3N/TN	116.5	63.9	10.0	470.0	230
Carbohydrates (g/kg ODM)						pH	4.2	0.53	3.4	6.0	214
NDF ash	582.1	69.4	399.0	855.0	217						
NDF unash						**Fatty Acids (g/kg ODM)**					
ADF ash	362.6	46.8	226.0	513.0	204						
ADF unash	371.7	45.5	278.0	525.0	94	C8:0					
Cellulose	288.3	40.4	11.0	405.0	135	C10:0					
Lignin	53.8	17.9	25.0	127.0	137	C12:0					
Starch	10.1	38.8	0.10	301.8	66	C14:0					
NCD	642.2	71.0	407.0	801.0	134	C16:0					
CD	573.6	79.8	348.0	754.0	56	C16:1					
IVD	616.2	54.2	431.0	736.0	226	C18:0					
WSC	20.7	29.8	1.0	220.0	143	C18:1					
Avail Carbs						C18:2					
Sugars						C18:3					
						C20:0					
						C20:4					
Minerals (g/kg ODM)						C22:1					
Ca	6.4	1.9	1.9	16.9	231						
Mg	1.7	0.54	0.70	3.5	231	**Amino Acids (g/kg ODM)**					
Na	2.7	1.6	0.20	12.5	231						
K	25.8	6.8	5.7	63.8	230	Ala					
Cl						Arg					
P total	3.2	0.64	1.6	5.3	231	Asp					
P inorg						Cys					
P phytate						Glu					
Fe						Gly					
S	2.4		2.4	2.4	1	His					
						Ile					
						Leu					
Trace Elements (mg/kg ODM)						Lys avail					
						Lys total					
Co						Meth					
F						Phe					
I						Pro					
Mn	72.0	27.3	30.0	148.0	47	Pro.OH					
Mo						Ser					
Zn	34.2	10.1	19.0	69.0	47	Thr					
Cu	11.8	7.6	4.0	33.0	47	Tryp					
Se						Tyr					
						Val					

ANALYTICAL DATABASE

FEED DESCRIPTION : **GRASS SILAGE, BIG BALE** (Source 1)

Determination	Mean	SD	Min	Max	n	Determination	Mean	SD	Min	Max	n
General (g/kg ODM)						**Volatile Fatty Acids** (g/kg ODM)					
ODM (fresh)	349.6	113.1	172.7	622.0	32	Lactic	45.1	37.7	3.3	134.7	31
TDM (fresh)	368.4	110.4	195.0	629.0	31	Formic	2.8	6.1	0.10	26.9	18
CP	158.7	48.7	82.0	249.0	32	Acetic	12.4	10.6	1.9	43.2	32
CF	306.2	33.3	239.0	369.0	32	Propionic	4.4	5.2	0.30	15.9	13
MADF	344.9	35.4	271.0	424.0	32	n butyric	3.6	3.4	0.20	12.1	27
EE	31.0	9.2	15.0	47.0	32	i butyric	1.2	1.2	0.10	3.3	7
AEE	39.8	13.9	28.0	55.0	4	n valeric	0.36	0.32	0.10	1.0	10
TA	91.2	16.5	58.0	130.0	32	i valeric	0.44	0.63	0.03	2.0	9
AIA	17.7	10.7	1.3	40.0	32	n caproic	0.55	0.63	0.02	1.7	14
GE (MJ/kg ODM)	20.1	1.2	17.5	23.2	32	i caproic	0.21	0.22	0.02	0.60	7
						NO_3N					
Carbohydrates (g/kg ODM)						NH_3N/TN	107.8	47.8	30.0	230.0	32
						pH	4.9	0.58	3.9	6.0	32
NDF ash	605.3	57.0	485.0	723.0	32						
NDF unash						**Fatty Acids** (g/kg ODM)					
ADF ash	357.9	38.3	290.0	450.0	31						
ADF unash	376.3	40.4	294.0	453.0	31	C8:0					
Cellulose	290.1	30.2	223.0	346.0	31	C10:0					
Lignin	67.3	15.3	43.0	95.0	31	C12:0					
Starch	3.9	7.8	0.50	23.0	8	C14:0					
NCD	594.7	70.2	407.0	749.3	32	C16:0					
CD	348.0		348.0	348.0	1	C16:1					
IVD	586.9	47.5	431.0	679.0	31	C18:0					
WSC	42.5	52.6	3.0	220.0	21	C18:1					
Avail Carbs						C18:2					
Sugars						C18:3					
						C20:0					
						C20:4					
Minerals (g/kg ODM)						C22:1					
Ca	6.3	2.0	1.9	11.0	32						
Mg	1.9	0.68	0.90	3.4	32	**Amino Acids** (g/kg ODM)					
Na	3.4	1.9	0.20	7.4	32						
K	26.1	7.4	9.0	38.2	32	Ala					
Cl						Arg					
P total	3.1	0.72	1.7	4.5	32	Asp					
P inorg						Cys					
P phytate						Glu					
Fe						Gly					
S						His					
						Ile					
						Leu					
Trace Elements (mg/kg ODM)						Lys avail					
						Lys total					
Co						Meth					
F						Phe					
I						Pro					
Mn						Pro.OH					
Mo						Ser					
Zn						Thr					
Cu						Tryp					
Se						Tyr					
						Val					

ANALYTICAL DATABASE

FEED DESCRIPTION : **GRASS SILAGE, CLAMP** (Sources 1, 2)

Determination	Mean	SD	Min	Max	n
General (g/kg ODM)					
ODM (fresh)	241.6	63.1	159.0	515.0	185
TDM (fresh)	266.6	64.3	175.0	522.0	180
CP	170.1	37.5	87.0	303.0	185
CF	303.8	40.0	202.0	424.0	185
MADF	349.3	42.5	230.0	460.6	185
EE	44.5	10.7	22.0	90.0	185
AEE	38.7	9.3	31.0	49.0	3
TA	92.7	17.7	54.0	183.0	185
AIA	19.3	11.9	4.0	87.0	138
GE (MJ/kg ODM)	21.0	1.1	18.2	25.7	185
Carbohydrates (g/kg ODM)					
NDF ash	578.4	70.1	399.0	855.0	174
NDF unash					
ADF ash	362.7	46.5	226.0	474.5	165
ADF unash	364.1	41.2	278.0	445.0	58
Cellulose	285.7	41.5	11.0	356.0	97
Lignin	48.6	15.8	25.0	127.0	100
Starch	7.8	42.9	0.10	301.8	49
NCD	659.1	59.1	480.0	801.0	90
CD	577.8	74.3	356.0	754.0	55
IVD	621.3	52.8	466.0	736.0	184
WSC	18.3	23.0	1.0	132.0	109
Avail Carbs					
Sugars					
Minerals (g/kg ODM)					
Ca	6.4	2.0	4.0	16.9	185
Mg	1.7	0.51	0.70	3.5	185
Na	2.6	1.6	0.30	12.5	185
K	25.7	6.8	5.7	63.8	184
Cl					
P total	3.2	0.62	2.0	5.3	185
P inorg					
P phytate					
Fe					
S	2.4		2.4	2.4	1
Trace Elements (mg/kg ODM)					
Co					
F					
I					
Mn	72.0	27.3	30.0	148.0	47
Mo					
Zn	34.2	10.1	19.0	69.0	47
Cu	11.8	7.6	4.0	33.0	47
Se					

Determination	Mean	SD	Min	Max	n
Volatile Fatty Acids (g/kg ODM)					
Lactic	78.6	48.0	7.6	317.6	169
Formic	10.2	20.4	0.20	128.3	122
Acetic	31.6	27.2	2.0	254.3	164
Propionic	5.9	6.8	0.0	44.0	123
n butyric	9.4	10.7	0.20	60.4	153
i butyric	2.2	2.9	0.01	18.5	77
n valeric	1.4	1.6	0.01	11.1	99
i valeric	2.6	6.1	0.01	43.0	94
n caproic	2.4	2.9	0.01	16.4	94
i caproic	1.1	1.5	0.01	7.5	50
NO_3N					
NH_3N/TN	116.7	56.5	30.0	350.0	184
pH	4.1	0.41	3.4	5.3	168
Fatty Acids (g/kg ODM)					
C8:0					
C10:0					
C12:0					
C14:0					
C16:0					
C16:1					
C18:0					
C18:1					
C18:2					
C18:3					
C20:0					
C20:4					
C22:1					
Amino Acids (g/kg ODM)					
Ala					
Arg					
Asp					
Cys					
Glu					
Gly					
His					
Ile					
Leu					
Lys avail					
Lys total					
Meth					
Phe					
Pro					
Pro.OH					
Ser					
Thr					
Tryp					
Tyr					
Val					

ANALYTICAL DATABASE

FEED DESCRIPTION : **LUCERNE SILAGE** (Source 1)

Determination	Mean	SD	Min	Max	n	Determination	Mean	SD	Min	Max	n
General (g/kg ODM)						**Volatile Fatty Acids (g/kg ODM)**					
ODM (fresh)	338.1	101.3	238.0	512.0	8	Lactic	50.4	38.2	7.9	112.7	7
TDM (fresh)	359.9	94.2	267.0	523.0	8	Formic	21.7	41.8	1.2	123.7	8
CP	193.6	27.4	149.0	230.0	8	Acetic	18.3	10.2	7.5	35.9	7
CF	332.8	54.2	281.0	423.0	8	Propionic	4.7	5.9	0.80	13.5	4
MADF	375.9	60.0	322.0	490.0	8	n butyric	14.5	28.0	0.70	83.3	8
EE	24.5	4.4	18.0	33.0	8	i butyric	2.7	2.0	1.3	5.0	3
AEE						n valeric	0.98	0.74	0.10	2.0	6
TA	105.0	8.5	95.0	119.0	8	i valeric	3.5	2.9	0.40	8.3	5
AIA	13.6	8.2	4.0	24.0	8	n caproic	1.2	0.64	0.70	1.6	2
GE (MJ/kg ODM)	19.9	1.3	18.0	22.3	8	i caproic	2.6	0.78	2.0	3.1	2
						NO_3N					
Carbohydrates (g/kg ODM)						NH_3N/TN	97.5	32.8	70.0	170.0	8
						pH	4.3	0.40	3.9	5.2	8
NDF ash	495.2	81.9	403.0	606.0	6						
NDF unash						**Fatty Acids (g/kg ODM)**					
ADF ash	406.2	77.5	342.0	531.0	6						
ADF unash	346.5	5.0	343.0	350.0	2	C8:0					
Cellulose	288.8	29.2	263.0	323.0	4	C10:0					
Lignin	75.0	1.4	74.0	76.0	2	C12:0					
Starch	4.4	2.3	2.1	6.7	3	C14:0					
NCD						C16:0					
CD	515.3	25.8	494.0	544.0	3	C16:1					
IVD	546.8	66.0	415.0	603.0	8	C18:0					
WSC	12.0	11.3	4.0	20.0	2	C18:1					
Avail Carbs						C18:2					
Sugars						C18:3					
						C20:0					
						C20:4					
Minerals (g/kg ODM)						C22:1					
Ca	17.6	3.4	13.5	24.0	8						
Mg	1.8	0.23	1.4	2.1	8	**Amino Acids (g/kg ODM)**					
Na	1.3	0.95	0.30	3.4	8						
K	24.6	4.0	18.0	30.0	8	Ala					
Cl						Arg					
P total	3.0	0.35	2.3	3.4	7	Asp					
P inorg						Cys					
P phytate						Glu					
Fe						Gly					
S						His					
						Ile					
						Leu					
Trace Elements (mg/kg ODM)						Lys avail					
						Lys total					
Co						Meth					
F						Phe					
I						Pro					
Mn						Pro.OH					
Mo						Ser					
Zn						Thr					
Cu						Tryp					
Se						Tyr					
						Val					

ANALYTICAL DATABASE

FEED DESCRIPTION : **MAIZE SILAGE** (Sources 1, 2)

Determination	Mean	SD	Min	Max	n	Determination	Mean	SD	Min	Max	n
General (g/kg ODM)						**Volatile Fatty Acids (g/kg ODM)**					
ODM (fresh)	251.6	47.2	161.0	317.0	26	Lactic	68.7	27.5	31.3	158.3	26
TDM (fresh)	278.4	45.9	191.0	350.0	26	Formic	5.1	5.5	0.30	14.0	5
CP	100.8	15.9	81.9	154.0	26	Acetic	32.7	15.8	11.2	69.2	26
CF	220.3	55.3	165.0	348.0	26	Propionic	2.6	2.7	0.10	10.6	21
MADF	264.7	55.9	204.0	383.0	26	n butyric	2.3	2.0	0.30	8.1	20
EE	28.9	6.7	14.0	39.0	26	i butyric	1.5	1.7	0.39	5.0	8
AEE						n valeric	0.60	0.28	0.40	0.80	2
TA	53.9	13.0	39.0	91.5	26	i valeric					
AIA	18.4	10.3	6.9	43.7	10	n caproic	1.4	0.57	1.0	1.8	2
GE (MJ/kg ODM)	20.2	0.89	18.2	21.8	26	i caproic					
						NO$_3$N					
						NH$_3$N/TN	91.5	30.0	30.0	170.0	26
Carbohydrates (g/kg ODM)						pH	3.8	0.22	3.5	4.4	26
NDF ash	480.0	90.8	376.0	680.0	25	**Fatty Acids (g/kg ODM)**					
NDF unash											
ADF ash	277.1	51.3	217.0	386.0	25	C8:0					
ADF unash	377.2	33.0	324.0	408.0	6	C10:0					
Cellulose	270.7	52.7	185.0	329.0	9	C12:0					
Lignin	33.4	14.8	19.0	68.0	22	C14:0					
Starch	206.1	103.8	8.0	336.0	22	C16:0					
NCD	553.6	17.9	533.0	573.0	5	C16:1					
CD	594.0	57.0	538.0	652.0	3	C18:0					
IVD	667.0	55.7	491.5	725.0	26	C18:1					
WSC	4.8	1.4	3.2	7.0	6	C18:2					
Avail Carbs						C18:3					
Sugars						C20:0					
						C20:4					
Minerals (g/kg ODM)						C22:1					
Ca	4.3	2.0	1.7	11.9	26						
Mg	2.2	0.69	0.70	3.2	26	**Amino Acids (g/kg ODM)**					
Na	0.28	0.17	0.10	0.70	25						
K	12.3	4.1	6.0	21.1	26	Ala					
Cl						Arg					
P total	2.6	1.2	1.5	6.1	26	Asp					
P inorg						Cys					
P phytate						Glu					
Fe						Gly					
S						His					
						Ile					
						Leu					
Trace Elements (mg/kg ODM)						Lys avail					
						Lys total					
Co						Meth					
F						Phe					
I						Pro					
Mn	14.6	7.2	7.0	34.0	16	Pro.OH					
Mo						Ser					
Zn	45.3	13.9	27.0	79.0	16	Thr					
Cu	5.2	0.75	4.0	7.0	16	Tryp					
Se						Tyr					
						Val					

ANALYTICAL DATABASE

FEED DESCRIPTION : **MIXED CLOVER SILAGE** (Sources 1, 2)

Determination	Mean	SD	Min	Max	n
General (g/kg ODM)					
ODM (fresh)	217.2	43.2	156.0	301.0	10
TDM (fresh)	235.8	42.8	182.0	322.0	10
CP	233.5	64.3	165.0	395.0	10
CF	249.1	44.7	165.0	324.0	10
MADF	330.6	32.7	263.0	379.0	10
EE	36.2	11.7	15.0	54.0	10
AEE					
TA	116.1	19.0	93.0	156.0	10
AIA	21.0	19.8	4.0	61.0	9
GE (MJ/kg ODM)	19.6	1.2	18.6	22.8	10
Carbohydrates (g/kg ODM)					
NDF ash	439.9	75.2	294.0	564.0	10
NDF unash					
ADF ash	341.5	45.6	266.0	408.0	9
ADF unash	350.0	28.3	330.0	370.0	2
Cellulose	248.3	27.0	212.0	278.0	7
Lignin	71.8	24.4	54.6	89.0	2
Starch	2.2	2.4	0.50	3.9	2
NCD					
CD	634.7	85.0	575.0	732.0	3
IVD	588.1	69.0	522.0	704.0	10
WSC	20.3		20.3	20.3	1
Avail Carbs					
Sugars					
Minerals (g/kg ODM)					
Ca	16.7	5.5	8.9	25.5	10
Mg	2.3	0.75	1.4	3.7	10
Na	0.75	0.49	0.20	1.6	10
K	27.4	7.6	15.3	39.0	10
Cl					
P total	3.1	0.60	2.2	4.2	10
P inorg					
P phytate					
Fe					
S					
Trace Elements (mg/kg ODM)					
Co					
F					
I					
Mn	75.0		75.0	75.0	1
Mo					
Zn	47.0		47.0	47.0	1
Cu	11.0		11.0	11.0	1
Se					

Determination	Mean	SD	Min	Max	n
Volatile Fatty Acids (g/kg ODM)					
Lactic	80.2	39.4	32.9	183.7	10
Formic	24.6	27.0	3.2	81.4	8
Acetic	29.8	14.9	15.5	53.4	10
Propionic	3.7	2.1	2.4	6.1	3
n butyric	4.5	2.8	1.0	8.4	7
i butyric	1.1		1.1	1.1	1
n valeric	0.70	0.85	0.10	1.3	2
i valeric	1.2	0.78	0.60	1.7	2
n caproic	3.7	1.6	2.5	4.8	2
i caproic					
NO3N					
NH3N/TN	96.9	40.9	30.0	180.0	10
pH	4.2	0.40	3.8	5.0	10
Fatty Acids (g/kg ODM)					
C8:0					
C10:0					
C12:0					
C14:0					
C16:0					
C16:1					
C18:0					
C18:1					
C18:2					
C18:3					
C20:0					
C20:4					
C22:1					
Amino Acids (g/kg ODM)					
Ala					
Arg					
Asp					
Cys					
Glu					
Gly					
His					
Ile					
Leu					
Lys avail					
Lys total					
Meth					
Phe					
Pro					
Pro.OH					
Ser					
Thr					
Tryp					
Tyr					
Val					

ANALYTICAL DATABASE

FEED DESCRIPTION : **PEA WHOLE CROP SILAGE** (Source 1)

Determination	Mean	SD	Min	Max	n	Determination	Mean	SD	Min	Max	n
General (g/kg ODM)						**Volatile Fatty Acids (g/kg ODM)**					
ODM (fresh)	253.4	48.0	174.0	303.0	5	Lactic	48.9	21.4	13.2	69.5	5
TDM (fresh)	275.6	50.3	193.0	320.0	5	Formic	8.2	3.5	5.7	12.2	3
CP	178.9	47.1	123.8	222.0	5	Acetic	32.8	20.4	10.1	60.3	5
CF	277.8	56.0	180.0	318.0	5	Propionic	14.2	11.5	2.6	26.0	4
MADF	377.0	48.3	298.0	429.0	5	n butyric	15.4	18.5	2.8	47.5	5
EE	35.4	11.7	19.0	49.0	5	i butyric	2.6	2.7	0.90	5.8	3
AEE						n valeric	2.1	1.5	0.50	3.8	4
TA	142.8	64.1	72.0	218.0	5	i valeric	2.4	2.3	0.50	5.7	4
AIA	58.8	58.6	10.0	129.0	5	n caproic	2.6	1.9	1.2	3.9	2
GE (MJ/kg ODM)	19.3	1.8	17.3	21.3	5	i caproic	1.6		1.6	1.6	1
						NO$_3$N					
Carbohydrates (g/kg ODM)						NH$_3$N/TN	126.0	45.1	80.0	170.0	5
						pH	4.2	0.46	3.7	4.7	4
NDF ash	280.0		280.0	280.0	1						
NDF unash						**Fatty Acids (g/kg ODM)**					
ADF ash	239.0		239.0	239.0	1						
ADF unash	408.6	49.6	353.0	484.0	5	C8:0					
Cellulose	263.2	52.6	174.0	303.0	5	C10:0					
Lignin	89.3	16.4	77.0	108.0	3	C12:0					
Starch	6.4	6.6	0.10	13.3	3	C14:0					
NCD	698.0		698.0	698.0	1	C16:0					
CD	481.2	43.5	429.0	542.0	5	C16:1					
IVD	523.0	47.3	449.0	575.0	5	C18:0					
WSC	72.2	140.2	2.0	322.0	5	C18:1					
Avail Carbs						C18:2					
Sugars						C18:3					
						C20:0					
						C20:4					
Minerals (g/kg ODM)						C22:1					
Ca	12.6	3.8	7.8	18.5	5						
Mg	2.2	0.73	1.5	3.2	5	**Amino Acids (g/kg ODM)**					
Na	1.1	1.4	0.20	3.5	5						
K	22.0	7.5	11.9	30.8	5	Ala					
Cl						Arg					
P total	3.0	0.68	2.3	3.8	5	Asp					
P inorg						Cys					
P phytate						Glu					
Fe						Gly					
S						His					
						Ile					
						Leu					
Trace Elements (mg/kg ODM)						Lys avail					
						Lys total					
Co						Meth					
F						Phe					
I						Pro					
Mn						Pro.OH					
Mo						Ser					
Zn						Thr					
Cu						Tryp					
Se						Tyr					
						Val					

84

ANALYTICAL DATABASE

FEED DESCRIPTION : **SUGAR BEET TOP SILAGE** (Source 1)

Determination	Mean	SD	Min	Max	ń	Determination	Mean	SD	Min	Max	n
General (g/kg ODM)						**Volatile Fatty Acids** (g/kg ODM)					
ODM (fresh)						Lactic					
TDM (fresh)	208.0		208.0	208.0	1	Formic					
CP	174.0		174.0	174.0	1	Acetic					
CF	128.0		128.0	128.0	1	Propionic					
MADF	328.0		328.0	328.0	1	n butyric					
EE	38.0		38.0	38.0	1	i butyric					
AEE						n valeric					
TA	342.0		342.0	342.0	1	i valeric					
AIA	214.0		214.0	214.0	1	n caproic					
GE (MJ/kg ODM)	15.0		15.0	15.0	1	i caproic					
						NO_3N					
Carbohydrates (g/kg ODM)						NH_3N/TN	160.0		160.0	160.0	1
						pH	4.8		4.8	4.8	1
NDF ash											
NDF unash						**Fatty Acids** (g/kg ODM)					
ADF ash											
ADF unash	369.0		369.0	369.0	1	C8:0					
Cellulose	148.0		148.0	148.0	1	C10:0					
Lignin	67.0		67.0	67.0	1	C12:0					
Starch						C14:0					
NCD						C16:0					
CD						C16:1					
IVD	427.0		427.0	427.0	1	C18:0					
WSC						C18:1					
Avail Carbs						C18:2					
Sugars						C18:3					
						C20:0					
						C20:4					
Minerals (g/kg ODM)						C22:1					
Ca	15.7		15.7	15.7	1						
Mg	6.7		6.7	6.7	1	**Amino Acids** (g/kg ODM)					
Na	0.70		0.70	0.70	1						
K	22.8		22.8	22.8	1	Ala					
Cl						Arg					
P total	2.0		2.0	2.0	1	Asp					
P inorg						Cys					
P phytate						Glu					
Fe						Gly					
S						His					
						Ile					
						Leu					
Trace Elements (mg/kg ODM)						Lys avail					
						Lys total					
Co						Meth					
F						Phe					
I						Pro					
Mn						Pro.OH					
Mo						Ser					
Zn						Thr					
Cu						Tryp					
Se						Tyr					
						Val					

ANALYTICAL   DATABASE

FEED CLASS 40

ENERGY FEEDS

ANALYTICAL DATABASE

FEED DESCRIPTION : **APPLES, FRESH** (Source 1)

Determination	Mean	SD	Min	Max	n	Determination	Mean	SD	Min	Max	n
General (g/kg ODM)						**Volatile Fatty Acids** (g/kg ODM)					
ODM (fresh)	135.6	13.5	126.0	145.1	2	Lactic					
TDM (fresh)						Formic					
CP	38.3	8.1	32.6	44.0	2	Acetic					
CF	62.5	3.5	60.0	65.0	2	Propionic					
MADF	101.0	29.7	80.0	122.0	2	n butyric					
EE	12.0	2.8	10.0	14.0	2	i butyric					
AEE						n valeric					
TA	20.0	2.8	18.0	22.0	2	i valeric					
AIA	0.25	0.07	0.20	0.30	2	n caproic					
GE (MJ/kg ODM)	16.8	0.0	16.8	16.8	2	i caproic					
						NO_3N					
						NH_3N/TN					
						pH					
Carbohydrates (g/kg ODM)						**Fatty Acids** (g/kg ODM)					
NDF ash	126.0	12.7	117.0	135.0	2						
NDF unash						C8:0					
ADF ash	117.0	17.0	105.0	129.0	2	C10:0					
ADF unash	108.5	23.3	92.0	125.0	2	C12:0					
Cellulose	66.5	0.71	66.0	67.0	2	C14:0					
Lignin	23.0		23.0	23.0	1	C16:0					
Starch	2.1	0.78	1.5	2.6	2	C16:1					
NCD						C18:0					
CD	914.5	14.8	904.0	925.0	2	C18:1					
IVD	893.0	7.1	888.0	898.0	2	C18:2					
WSC	725.5	9.2	719.0	732.0	2	C18:3					
Avail Carbs						C20:0					
Sugars						C20:4					
						C22:1					
Minerals (g/kg ODM)											
Ca	0.50	0.28	0.30	0.70	2						
Mg	0.25	0.07	0.20	0.30	2	**Amino Acids** (g/kg ODM)					
Na	0.10	0.0	0.10	0.10	2						
K	9.0	1.5	7.9	10.0	2	Ala					
Cl						Arg					
P total	0.90	0.14	0.80	1.0	2	Asp					
P inorg						Cys					
P phytate						Glu					
Fe						Gly					
S						His					
						Ile					
						Leu					
Trace Elements (mg/kg ODM)						Lys avail					
						Lys total					
Co						Meth					
F						Phe					
I						Pro					
Mn						Pro.OH					
Mo						Ser					
Zn						Thr					
Cu						Tryp					
Se						Tyr					
						Val					

ANALYTICAL DATABASE

FEED DESCRIPTION : **APPLE POMACE** (Source 1)

Determination	Mean	SD	Min	Max	n	Determination	Mean	SD	Min	Max	n
General (g/kg ODM)						**Volatile Fatty Acids (g/kg ODM)**					
ODM (fresh)	242.0	32.8	204.0	282.0	5	Lactic	9.2		9.2	9.2	1
TDM (fresh)	243.5	23.3	227.0	260.0	2	Formic	4.6		4.6	4.6	1
CP	69.0	8.7	64.0	79.0	3	Acetic	8.0		8.0	8.0	1
CF	204.6	28.1	181.0	249.0	5	Propionic					
MADF	375.2	34.3	346.0	430.0	5	n butyric					
EE	27.4	3.8	23.0	32.0	5	i butyric					
AEE	28.5	5.8	20.0	33.0	4	n valeric					
TA	18.2	3.1	15.0	22.0	5	i valeric					
AIA	1.8	0.84	1.0	3.0	5	n caproic					
GE (MJ/kg ODM)	19.8	1.2	19.0	21.8	5	i caproic					
						NO_3N					
Carbohydrates (g/kg ODM)						NH_3N/TN	20.0		20.0	20.0	1
						pH	3.4		3.4	3.4	1
NDF ash	488.6	53.4	425.0	540.0	5						
NDF unash						**Fatty Acids (g/kg ODM)**					
ADF ash	414.6	72.4	355.0	522.0	5						
ADF unash	389.3	53.9	344.0	449.0	3	C8:0					
Cellulose	232.0	30.5	204.0	270.0	4	C10:0					
Lignin	172.0	8.5	166.0	178.0	2	C12:0					
Starch	30.0	35.2	1.9	78.0	5	C14:0					
NCD	768.5	16.4	751.0	783.0	4	C16:0					
CD	671.0	19.8	657.0	685.0	2	C16:1					
IVD	649.2	38.3	587.0	688.0	5	C18:0					
WSC	160.5	95.5	93.0	228.0	2	C18:1					
Avail Carbs						C18:2					
Sugars						C18:3					
						C20:0					
						C20:4					
Minerals (g/kg ODM)						C22:1					
Ca	1.6	0.61	0.90	2.4	5						
Mg	0.60	0.12	0.40	0.70	5	**Amino Acids (g/kg ODM)**					
Na	0.20	0.12	0.10	0.40	5						
K	6.8	0.52	6.0	7.4	5	Ala					
Cl						Arg					
P total	1.4	0.13	1.3	1.6	5	Asp					
P inorg						Cys					
P phytate						Glu					
Fe						Gly					
S						His					
						Ile					
						Leu					
Trace Elements (mg/kg ODM)						Lys avail					
						Lys total					
Co						Meth					
F						Phe					
I						Pro					
Mn						Pro.OH					
Mo						Ser					
Zn						Thr					
Cu						Tryp					
Se						Tyr					
						Val					

ANALYTICAL DATABASE

FEED DESCRIPTION : **BARLEY GRAIN, ALL SEASONS** (Sources 1, 2, 3, 4)

Determination	Mean	SD	Min	Max	n	Determination	Mean	SD	Min	Max	n
General (g/kg ODM)						**Volatile Fatty Acids (g/kg ODM)**					
ODM (fresh)	864.1	19.4	792.0	909.5	65	Lactic					
TDM (fresh)						Formic					
CP	128.5	14.6	100.0	170.6	65	Acetic					
CF	45.5	5.6	36.0	58.2	65	Propionic					
MADF	60.9	9.3	35.0	89.0	55	n butyric					
EE	16.2	5.5	5.0	40.0	65	i butyric					
AEE	25.7	6.6	13.8	32.6	50	n valeric					
TA	26.4	6.3	20.1	52.0	65	i valeric					
AIA	4.9	1.7	0.90	9.9	39	n caproic					
GE (MJ/kg ODM)	18.5	0.19	18.0	18.9	65	i caproic					
						NO_3N					
						NH_3N/TN					
Carbohydrates (g/kg ODM)						pH					
						Fatty Acids (g/kg ODM)					
NDF ash	200.9	47.8	133.4	366.0	63						
NDF unash											
ADF ash	63.7	10.7	43.0	91.0	55	C8:0					
ADF unash	69.1	11.0	51.0	98.0	26	C10:0					
Cellulose	46.6	7.4	34.0	67.0	36	C12:0					
Lignin	17.0	5.4	6.5	31.0	52	C14:0					
Starch	561.7	65.3	256.5	636.0	56	C16:0	3.6	0.39	2.8	4.1	10
NCD	886.6	13.5	851.0	913.0	40	C16:1					
CD						C18:0	0.17	0.07	0.09	0.30	10
IVD	802.1	26.2	732.5	875.0	38	C18:1	2.2	0.25	1.8	2.6	10
WSC	37.0	9.9	30.0	44.0	2	C18:2	9.8	0.78	8.2	10.6	10
Avail Carbs						C18:3	1.6	0.27	1.2	2.0	10
Sugars	16.5	7.0	7.6	30.0	12	C20:0					
						C20:4					
Minerals (g/kg ODM)						C22:1					
Ca	0.85	0.58	0.09	3.3	56	**Amino Acids (g/kg ODM)**					
Mg	1.2	0.20	0.80	2.1	54						
Na	0.29	0.36	0.10	1.8	40	Ala	4.9	1.0	3.0	6.0	20
K	5.0	0.70	3.6	7.0	55	Arg	6.1	0.78	4.9	8.0	20
Cl	1.0	0.42	0.40	1.6	10	Asp	6.9	2.0	2.0	11.0	20
P total	4.0	0.46	3.0	5.5	57	Cys	2.8	0.22	2.4	3.1	10
P inorg	0.30	0.11	0.20	0.50	10	Glu	31.6	6.4	22.0	45.0	20
P phytate						Gly	4.9	0.86	3.0	6.0	20
Fe	0.10	0.0	0.10	0.10	8	His	3.1	0.58	2.0	4.0	20
S	1.5	0.30	1.1	2.0	10	Ile	4.9	0.71	3.9	7.0	20
						Leu	9.2	1.3	7.7	13.0	20
Trace Elements (mg/kg ODM)						Lys avail					
						Lys total	4.9	0.77	4.0	7.0	20
Co						Meth	2.8	1.3	1.0	5.0	20
F						Phe	7.2	1.5	5.4	10.0	20
I	0.10	0.0	0.10	0.10	9	Pro	12.3	2.7	8.0	17.1	18
Mn	18.5	3.6	13.3	24.2	26	Pro.OH					
Mo	0.30	0.13	0.10	0.60	10	Ser	5.6	0.89	4.0	8.0	20
Zn	32.5	8.5	22.2	58.6	26	Thr	5.0	1.2	3.0	8.0	20
Cu	4.2	1.5	1.0	8.0	26	Tryp	1.9	0.38	1.0	2.0	7
Se	0.10	0.0	0.10	0.10	3	Tyr	4.5	0.79	3.6	7.0	20
						Val	6.3	0.85	5.0	8.0	20

ANALYTICAL DATABASE

FEED DESCRIPTION : **BARLEY GRAIN, SPRING** (Sources 1, 2, 4)

Determination	Mean	SD	Min	Max	n	Determination	Mean	SD	Min	Max	n
General (g/kg ODM)						**Volatile Fatty Acids (g/kg ODM)**					
ODM (fresh)	869.3	11.2	825.4	888.0	40	Lactic					
TDM (fresh)						Formic					
CP	128.0	14.8	100.0	170.6	40	Acetic					
CF	45.5	5.6	36.0	58.0	40	Propionic					
MADF	60.3	8.6	35.0	78.0	40	n butyric					
EE	14.5	5.1	5.0	25.0	40	i butyric					
AEE	25.0	7.0	14.1	32.0	24	n valeric					
TA	26.7	6.1	20.1	50.0	40	i valeric					
AIA	4.4	1.8	1.4	9.9	16	n caproic					
GE (MJ/kg ODM)	18.5	0.20	18.0	18.8	40	i caproic					
						NO_3N					
						NH_3N/TN					
Carbohydrates (g/kg ODM)						pH					
NDF ash	206.9	40.1	133.4	274.8	38	**Fatty Acids (g/kg ODM)**					
NDF unash											
ADF ash	65.1	9.7	50.0	86.0	32	C8:0					
ADF unash	66.6	10.1	51.0	88.0	16	C10:0					
Cellulose	45.1	6.3	34.0	57.0	16	C12:0					
Lignin	17.1	4.3	10.0	26.0	32	C14:0					
Starch	571.9	30.2	516.0	636.0	34	C16:0					
NCD	889.4	13.3	868.0	913.0	16	C16:1					
CD						C18:0					
IVD	800.1	19.0	768.0	834.5	16	C18:1					
WSC						C18:2					
Avail Carbs						C18:3					
Sugars	28.5	2.1	27.0	30.0	2	C20:0					
						C20:4					
Minerals (g/kg ODM)						C22:1					
Ca	0.69	0.25	0.09	1.4	34						
Mg	1.1	0.14	0.80	1.3	31	**Amino Acids (g/kg ODM)**					
Na	0.23	0.13	0.10	0.50	23						
K	5.1	0.73	3.8	7.0	32	Ala	4.4	1.4	3.0	6.0	8
Cl						Arg	6.4	0.92	5.0	8.0	8
P total	4.0	0.40	3.0	5.0	34	Asp	6.8	3.1	2.0	11.0	8
P inorg						Cys					
P phytate						Glu	33.0	8.2	23.0	45.0	8
Fe						Gly	4.8	1.0	3.0	6.0	8
S						His	2.9	0.64	2.0	4.0	8
						Ile	5.1	0.99	4.0	7.0	8
						Leu	9.8	1.8	8.0	13.0	8
						Lys avail					
Trace Elements (mg/kg ODM)						Lys total	5.1	0.99	4.0	7.0	8
						Meth	3.5	1.4	1.0	5.0	8
Co						Phe	7.9	1.8	6.0	10.0	8
F						Pro	10.2	1.9	8.0	13.0	6
I						Pro.OH					
Mn	17.9	3.4	14.0	24.0	16	Ser	5.8	1.2	4.0	8.0	8
Mo						Thr	5.5	1.6	3.0	8.0	8
Zn	31.3	4.3	24.0	38.0	16	Tryp	1.8	0.45	1.0	2.0	5
Cu	4.0	1.5	1.0	8.0	16	Tyr	4.8	1.0	4.0	7.0	8
Se						Val	6.4	1.2	5.0	8.0	8

91

ANALYTICAL DATABASE

FEED DESCRIPTION : **BARLEY GRAIN, WINTER** (Sources 1, 3, 4)

Determination	Mean	SD	Min	Max	n	Determination	Mean	SD	Min	Max	n
General (g/kg ODM)						**Volatile Fatty Acids (g/kg ODM)**					
ODM (fresh)	857.3	26.2	792.0	909.5	20	Lactic					
TDM (fresh)						Formic					
CP	130.2	15.6	100.6	160.0	20	Acetic					
CF	44.7	6.1	36.3	58.2	20	Propionic					
MADF	65.0	11.2	50.3	89.0	10	n butyric					
EE	18.2	2.6	13.6	22.7	20	i butyric					
AEE	28.3	5.1	13.8	32.6	20	n valeric					
TA	24.1	2.8	20.5	32.0	20	i valeric					
AIA	5.1	1.8	0.90	7.8	18	n caproic					
GE (MJ/kg ODM)	18.5	0.16	18.2	18.9	20	i caproic					
						NO_3N					
						NH_3N/TN					
						pH					
Carbohydrates (g/kg ODM)						**Fatty Acids (g/kg ODM)**					
NDF ash	178.4	31.9	140.0	241.5	20						
NDF unash											
ADF ash	60.7	12.3	43.0	91.0	18	C8:0					
ADF unash	73.3	11.8	61.0	98.0	8	C10:0					
Cellulose	47.4	8.0	36.0	67.0	18	C12:0					
Lignin	16.3	7.0	6.5	31.0	18	C14:0					
Starch	585.2	33.8	504.0	625.3	18	C16:0	3.6	0.39	2.8	4.1	10
NCD	885.5	14.2	851.0	904.3	18	C16:1					
CD						C18:0	0.17	0.07	0.09	0.30	10
IVD	798.7	28.9	732.5	851.0	17	C18:1	2.2	0.25	1.8	2.6	10
WSC						C18:2	9.8	0.78	8.2	10.6	10
Avail Carbs						C18:3	1.6	0.27	1.2	2.0	10
Sugars	14.1	4.6	7.6	21.0	10	C20:0					
						C20:4					
						C22:1					
Minerals (g/kg ODM)											
Ca	0.82	0.36	0.40	2.1	18						
Mg	1.2	0.15	1.0	1.6	18	**Amino Acids (g/kg ODM)**					
Na	0.17	0.09	0.10	0.30	12						
K	4.7	0.49	3.6	5.4	18	Ala	5.2	0.53	4.0	5.9	12
Cl	1.0	0.42	0.40	1.6	10	Arg	5.9	0.63	4.9	7.0	12
P total	3.9	0.37	3.1	4.6	18	Asp	7.0	0.81	6.0	9.0	12
P inorg	0.30	0.11	0.20	0.50	10	Cys	2.8	0.22	2.4	3.1	10
P phytate						Glu	30.6	5.0	22.0	40.0	12
Fe	0.10	0.0	0.10	0.10	8	Gly	5.1	0.75	3.0	6.0	12
S	1.5	0.30	1.1	2.0	10	His	3.2	0.51	2.0	4.0	12
						Ile	4.7	0.39	3.9	5.2	12
						Leu	8.9	0.76	7.7	10.0	12
Trace Elements (mg/kg ODM)						Lys avail					
						Lys total	4.7	0.56	4.0	6.0	12
Co						Meth	2.4	1.0	1.5	5.0	12
F						Phe	6.7	1.0	5.4	9.0	12
I	0.10	0.0	0.10	0.10	9	Pro	13.4	2.4	8.0	17.1	12
Mn	19.5	4.0	13.3	24.2	10	Pro.OH					
Mo	0.30	0.13	0.10	0.60	10	Ser	5.5	0.70	4.5	7.0	12
Zn	34.5	12.7	22.2	58.6	10	Thr	4.6	0.61	3.7	6.0	12
Cu	4.4	1.5	2.5	7.5	10	Tryp	2.0	0.0	2.0	2.0	2
Se	0.10	0.0	0.10	0.10	3	Tyr	4.3	0.55	3.6	5.2	12
						Val	6.2	0.58	5.2	7.3	12

ANALYTICAL DATABASE

FEED DESCRIPTION : **CASSAVA MEAL** (Sources 1, 2)

Determination	Mean	SD	Min	Max	n	Determination	Mean	SD	Min	Max	n
General (g/kg ODM)						**Volatile Fatty Acids (g/kg ODM)**					
ODM (fresh)	885.4	2.4	883.7	887.1	2	Lactic					
TDM (fresh)						Formic					
CP	27.6	1.5	26.0	29.0	5	Acetic					
CF	40.6	7.9	28.0	47.0	5	Propionic					
MADF	73.0	25.1	32.0	92.0	5	n butyric					
EE	4.4	1.8	2.0	7.0	5	i butyric					
AEE	6.0	1.4	5.0	7.0	2	n valeric					
TA	50.4	16.1	22.0	62.0	5	i valeric					
AIA	29.0	0.0	29.0	29.0	2	n caproic					
GE (MJ/kg ODM)	16.8	0.19	16.6	17.1	5	i caproic					
						NO$_3$N					
Carbohydrates (g/kg ODM)						NH$_3$N/TN					
						pH					
NDF ash	113.6	91.5	48.0	275.0	5						
NDF unash						**Fatty Acids (g/kg ODM)**					
ADF ash	63.0	22.5	37.0	76.0	3						
ADF unash	98.0		98.0	98.0	1	C8:0					
Cellulose	21.8	30.0	0.60	43.0	2	C10:0					
Lignin	13.3	7.6	5.0	20.0	3	C12:0					
Starch	645.0	94.8	527.0	755.0	5	C14:0					
NCD	899.5	9.2	893.0	906.0	2	C16:0					
CD						C16:1					
IVD	888.0	34.3	859.0	947.0	5	C18:0					
WSC	47.3	19.9	33.0	70.0	3	C18:1					
Avail Carbs						C18:2					
Sugars						C18:3					
						C20:0					
						C20:4					
Minerals (g/kg ODM)						C22:1					
Ca	2.2	0.63	1.8	3.3	5						
Mg	1.4	0.57	1.1	2.4	5	**Amino Acids (g/kg ODM)**					
Na	0.58	0.25	0.20	0.70	4						
K	8.1	1.5	5.7	9.8	5	Ala					
Cl						Arg					
P total	0.86	0.14	0.70	1.0	5	Asp					
P inorg						Cys					
P phytate						Glu					
Fe						Gly					
S						His					
						Ile					
						Leu					
Trace Elements (mg/kg ODM)						Lys avail					
						Lys total					
Co						Meth					
F						Phe					
I						Pro					
Mn	22.3	1.5	21.0	24.0	3	Pro.OH					
Mo						Ser					
Zn	12.0	5.0	7.0	17.0	3	Thr					
Cu	4.7	0.58	4.0	5.0	3	Tryp					
Se						Tyr					
						Val					

ANALYTICAL DATABASE

FEED DESCRIPTION : **CITRUS PULP, DRIED** (Sources 1, 2, 3)

Determination	Mean	SD	Min	Max	n	Determination	Mean	SD	Min	Max	n
General (g/kg ODM)						**Volatile Fatty Acids** (g/kg ODM)					
ODM (fresh)	889.5	9.5	875.0	912.5	13	Lactic					
TDM (fresh)						Formic					
CP	67.8	6.4	52.6	78.5	13	Acetic					
CF	131.4	11.1	111.6	153.0	13	Propionic					
MADF	221.3	11.0	203.0	239.0	8	n butyric					
EE	22.4	6.2	16.0	40.0	13	i butyric					
AEE	21.6	6.1	14.0	32.6	10	n valeric					
TA	63.3	4.3	59.0	73.0	13	i valeric					
AIA	3.6	2.6	1.8	10.7	11	n caproic					
GE (MJ/kg ODM)	17.5	0.15	17.3	17.9	13	i caproic					
						NO_3N					
						NH_3N/TN					
						pH					
Carbohydrates (g/kg ODM)											
						Fatty Acids (g/kg ODM)					
NDF ash	227.8	36.8	184.5	290.0	13						
NDF unash						C8:0					
ADF ash	202.2	54.2	129.5	266.0	13	C10:0					
ADF unash	245.5	19.7	217.0	262.0	4	C12:0					
Cellulose	154.1	60.2	91.0	299.0	11	C14:0	0.07	0.03	0.04	0.12	5
Lignin	39.4	38.6	7.0	116.0	13	C16:0	3.5	0.63	2.8	4.4	5
Starch	2.0	2.1	0.10	5.0	6	C16:1	0.13	0.08	0.07	0.25	4
NCD	904.0	12.1	870.0	916.0	13	C18:0	0.63	0.13	0.47	0.78	5
CD						C18:1	3.8	0.99	2.8	5.1	5
IVD	828.0	33.2	765.0	867.5	13	C18:2	5.0	0.66	4.2	6.0	5
WSC	247.5	33.7	182.0	290.8	7	C18:3	0.91	0.12	0.76	1.1	5
Avail Carbs						C20:0					
Sugars	250.3	14.9	240.5	276.5	5	C20:4					
						C22:1					
Minerals (g/kg ODM)											
Ca	14.6	2.4	10.7	18.8	13						
Mg	1.7	0.50	1.0	2.6	13	**Amino Acids** (g/kg ODM)					
Na	0.44	0.33	0.10	1.2	13						
K	10.7	1.5	8.4	13.9	13	Ala	2.8	0.22	2.5	3.1	5
Cl	0.18	0.04	0.10	0.20	5	Arg	3.2	0.20	2.9	3.4	5
P total	1.1	0.09	1.0	1.2	13	Asp	6.7	0.65	5.8	7.5	5
P inorg	0.48	0.04	0.40	0.50	5	Cys	0.60	0.07	0.52	0.69	5
P phytate						Glu	5.1	0.21	4.9	5.4	5
Fe	0.10	0.0	0.10	0.10	5	Gly	2.7	0.17	2.5	2.9	5
S	2.6	0.32	2.1	2.9	5	His	1.5	0.11	1.4	1.7	5
						Ile	2.2	0.10	2.1	2.4	5
						Leu	3.6	0.14	3.4	3.8	5
Trace Elements (mg/kg ODM)						Lys avail					
						Lys total	2.2	0.34	1.7	2.5	5
Co	0.12	0.05	0.10	0.20	5	Meth	0.71	0.06	0.61	0.78	5
F						Phe	2.8	0.07	2.7	2.9	5
I	0.10	0.0	0.10	0.10	3	Pro					
Mn	13.0	2.8	7.4	16.0	7	Pro.OH					
Mo	0.36	0.32	0.10	0.90	5	Ser	2.7	0.19	2.4	2.9	5
Zn	11.5	8.6	6.3	30.0	7	Thr	2.1	0.16	1.8	2.2	5
Cu	4.8	1.7	3.1	8.0	7	Tryp					
Se						Tyr	1.9	0.11	1.7	2.0	5
						Val	2.9	0.19	2.6	3.0	5

ANALYTICAL DATABASE

FEED DESCRIPTION : **COFFEE RESIDUE, DRIED** (Source 3)

Determination	Mean	SD	Min	Max	n	Determination	Mean	SD	Min	Max	n
General (g/kg ODM)						**Volatile Fatty Acids** (g/kg ODM)					
ODM (fresh)	901.3	31.3	856.0	941.5	5	Lactic					
TDM (fresh)						Formic					
CP	115.8	5.3	109.8	123.5	5	Acetic					
CF	403.0	8.3	389.1	410.9	5	Propionic					
MADF						n butyric					
EE	254.5	20.5	219.3	272.9	5	i butyric					
AEE	265.6	16.3	237.3	279.0	5	n valeric					
TA	18.7	31.0	3.7	74.1	5	i valeric					
AIA	7.9	16.5	0.20	37.4	5	n caproic					
GE (MJ/kg ODM)	25.2	0.60	24.3	25.9	5	i caproic					
						NO$_3$N					
						NH$_3$N/TN					
Carbohydrates (g/kg ODM)						pH					
NDF ash						**Fatty Acids** (g/kg ODM)					
NDF unash											
ADF ash						C8:0					
ADF unash						C10:0					
Cellulose						C12:0					
Lignin						C14:0					
Starch	3.2	3.9	0.20	7.9	5	C16:0	75.8	5.7	67.7	82.0	5
NCD	559.0	36.5	506.0	607.3	5	C16:1					
CD						C18:0	16.8	1.0	15.3	17.7	5
IVD	308.4	73.6	188.5	388.0	5	C18:1	21.2	1.5	19.0	22.8	5
WSC						C18:2	98.9	14.1	74.2	109.3	5
Avail Carbs						C18:3	2.6	0.36	2.4	3.2	5
Sugars	3.5	1.7	1.0	5.0	4	C20:0	3.6	0.38	2.9	3.8	5
						C20:4					
						C22:1					
Minerals (g/kg ODM)											
Ca	2.3	2.3	1.0	6.4	5						
Mg	0.26	0.20	0.10	0.60	5	**Amino Acids** (g/kg ODM)					
Na	0.34	0.09	0.30	0.50	5						
K	0.50	0.30	0.20	1.0	5	Ala	4.7	0.10	4.6	4.8	5
Cl	0.10	0.0	0.10	0.10	2	Arg	0.37	0.13	0.23	0.53	5
P total	0.36	0.36	0.20	1.0	5	Asp	3.6	0.20	3.3	3.8	5
P inorg	0.70		0.70	0.70	1	Cys	0.39	0.05	0.35	0.45	5
P phytate						Glu	14.6	2.0	11.3	16.1	5
Fe	2.0	3.9	0.20	9.0	5	Gly	5.4	0.28	4.9	5.6	5
S	1.3	0.06	1.2	1.3	4	His	2.8	1.9	1.7	6.2	5
						Ile	4.9	0.13	4.7	5.1	5
						Leu	9.9	0.34	9.3	10.2	5
Trace Elements (mg/kg ODM)						Lys avail	1.6	0.14	1.5	1.8	5
						Lys total					
Co	0.40	0.56	0.10	1.4	5	Meth	1.4	0.06	1.3	1.5	5
F						Phe	6.1	0.21	5.8	6.4	5
I	0.16	0.14	0.10	0.40	5	Pro	7.1		7.1	7.1	1
Mn	55.0	46.7	32.2	138.5	5	Pro.OH					
Mo	0.70	0.20	0.40	0.90	5	Ser	1.7	0.06	1.7	1.8	5
Zn	19.1	19.8	9.4	54.5	5	Thr	2.8	0.31	2.4	3.1	5
Cu	38.5	9.7	32.2	55.6	5	Tryp	4.0		4.0	4.0	1
Se	0.10	0.0	0.10	0.10	5	Tyr	3.7	0.30	3.2	4.0	4
						Val	6.7	0.22	6.3	6.9	5

ANALYTICAL DATABASE

FEED DESCRIPTION : **COFFEE RESIDUE, FRESH** (Source 1)

Determination	Mean	SD	Min	Max	n	Determination	Mean	SD	Min	Max	n
General (g/kg ODM)						**Volatile Fatty Acids** (g/kg ODM)					
ODM (fresh)	315.4		315.4	315.4	1	Lactic					
TDM (fresh)						Formic					
CP	107.0		107.0	107.0	1	Acetic					
CF	446.0		446.0	446.0	1	Propionic					
MADF	691.0		691.0	691.0	1	n butyric					
EE	211.0		211.0	211.0	1	i butyric					
AEE	199.0		199.0	199.0	1	n valeric					
TA	6.0		6.0	6.0	1	i valeric					
AIA	0.20		0.20	0.20	1	n caproic					
GE (MJ/kg ODM)	25.2		25.2	25.2	1	i caproic					
						NO_3N					
						NH_3N/TN					
						pH					
Carbohydrates (g/kg ODM)											
						Fatty Acids (g/kg ODM)					
NDF ash	740.0		740.0	740.0	1						
NDF unash						C8:0					
ADF ash	696.0		696.0	696.0	1	C10:0					
ADF unash						C12:0					
Cellulose	585.0		585.0	585.0	1	C14:0					
Lignin	30.0		30.0	30.0	1	C16:0					
Starch	11.0		11.0	11.0	1	C16:1					
NCD	452.0		452.0	452.0	1	C18:0					
CD						C18:1					
IVD	97.0		97.0	97.0	1	C18:2					
WSC						C18:3					
Avail Carbs						C20:0					
Sugars						C20:4					
						C22:1					
Minerals (g/kg ODM)											
Ca	1.0		1.0	1.0	1	**Amino Acids** (g/kg ODM)					
Mg	0.20		0.20	0.20	1						
Na	0.50		0.50	0.50	1	Ala					
K	0.50		0.50	0.50	1	Arg					
Cl						Asp					
P total	0.10		0.10	0.10	1	Cys					
P inorg						Glu					
P phytate						Gly					
Fe						His					
S						Ile					
						Leu					
						Lys avail					
Trace Elements (mg/kg ODM)						Lys total					
						Meth					
Co						Phe					
F						Pro					
I						Pro.OH					
Mn						Ser					
Mo						Thr					
Zn						Tryp					
Cu						Tyr					
Se						Val					

ANALYTICAL DATABASE

FEED DESCRIPTION : **FODDER BEET, FRESH** (Source 1)

Determination	Mean	SD	Min	Max	n	Determination	Mean	SD	Min	Max	n
General (g/kg ODM)						**Volatile Fatty Acids (g/kg ODM)**					
ODM (fresh)	182.8	18.6	158.7	214.1	10	Lactic					
TDM (fresh)						Formic					
CP	62.9	9.5	51.0	80.3	10	Acetic					
CF	56.0	7.2	43.0	65.0	10	Propionic					
MADF	91.1	18.1	62.0	120.0	10	n butyric					
EE	2.6	1.2	1.0	4.0	10	i butyric					
AEE	3.7	1.1	2.6	5.0	4	n valeric					
TA	81.3	19.9	50.0	105.0	10	i valeric					
AIA	28.5	15.4	13.0	62.0	10	n caproic					
GE (MJ/kg ODM)	16.0	0.37	15.6	16.6	10	i caproic					
						NO_3N					
						NH_3N/TN					
Carbohydrates (g/kg ODM)						pH					
NDF ash	135.9	22.6	105.0	172.0	10	**Fatty Acids (g/kg ODM)**					
NDF unash											
ADF ash	71.6	10.1	54.0	84.0	10	C8:0					
ADF unash	113.5	16.3	97.0	128.0	4	C10:0					
Cellulose	63.0	4.2	58.0	67.0	4	C12:0					
Lignin	21.0	7.5	12.0	29.0	4	C14:0					
Starch	0.80	1.9	0.10	5.0	7	C16:0					
NCD	874.3	23.6	848.0	905.0	4	C16:1					
CD						C18:0					
IVD	850.1	51.7	766.0	929.0	10	C18:1					
WSC	659.9	75.5	547.0	819.0	10	C18:2					
Avail Carbs						C18:3					
Sugars						C20:0					
						C20:4					
						C22:1					
Minerals (g/kg ODM)											
Ca	2.8	2.4	0.80	9.1	10						
Mg	1.6	0.30	1.1	2.1	10	**Amino Acids (g/kg ODM)**					
Na	3.0	1.6	0.80	6.0	10						
K	17.5	4.8	10.5	25.0	10	Ala					
Cl						Arg					
P total	1.8	0.27	1.5	2.4	10	Asp					
P inorg						Cys					
P phytate						Glu					
Fe						Gly					
S						His					
						Ile					
						Leu					
Trace Elements (mg/kg ODM)						Lys avail					
						Lys total					
Co						Meth					
F						Phe					
I						Pro					
Mn						Pro.OH					
Mo						Ser					
Zn						Thr					
Cu						Tryp					
Se						Tyr					
						Val					

ANALYTICAL DATABASE

FEED DESCRIPTION : **GRAPE JUICE CONCENTRATE** (Source 1)

Determination	Mean	SD	Min	Max	n	Determination	Mean	SD	Min	Max	n
General (g/kg ODM)						**Volatile Fatty Acids** (g/kg ODM)					
ODM (fresh)	599.0		599.0	599.0	1	Lactic					
TDM (fresh)						Formic					
CP						Acetic					
CF						Propionic					
MADF						n butyric					
EE	2.3		2.3	2.3	1	i butyric					
AEE						n valeric					
TA	15.0		15.0	15.0	1	i valeric					
AIA	5.0		5.0	5.0	1	n caproic					
GE (MJ/kg ODM)	16.0		16.0	16.0	1	i caproic					
						NO_3N					
						NH_3N/TN					
Carbohydrates (g/kg ODM)						pH					
NDF ash											
NDF unash						**Fatty Acids** (g/kg ODM)					
ADF ash											
ADF unash						C8:0					
Cellulose						C10:0					
Lignin						C12:0					
Starch						C14:0					
NCD						C16:0					
CD						C16:1					
IVD						C18:0					
WSC						C18:1					
Avail Carbs						C18:2					
Sugars						C18:3					
						C20:0					
						C20:4					
Minerals (g/kg ODM)						C22:1					
Ca											
Mg						**Amino Acids** (g/kg ODM)					
Na											
K						Ala					
Cl						Arg					
P total						Asp					
P inorg						Cys					
P phytate						Glu					
Fe						Gly					
S						His					
						Ile					
						Leu					
Trace Elements (mg/kg ODM)						Lys avail					
						Lys total					
Co						Meth					
F						Phe					
I						Pro					
Mn						Pro.OH					
Mo						Ser					
Zn						Thr					
Cu						Tryp					
Se						Tyr					
						Val					

ANALYTICAL DATABASE

FEED DESCRIPTION : **MAIZE FIBRE** (Source 1)

Determination	Mean	SD	Min	Max	n	Determination	Mean	SD	Min	Max	n
General (g/kg ODM)						**Volatile Fatty Acids (g/kg ODM)**					
ODM (fresh)	378.0	28.3	344.0	415.8	5	Lactic	16.6	16.2	3.4	43.1	5
TDM (fresh)	377.7	31.5	334.6	410.0	5	Formic	2.5	1.7	1.5	4.4	3
CP	147.2	38.5	110.7	211.8	5	Acetic	1.5	1.5	0.30	3.8	5
CF	132.4	22.5	98.0	156.0	5	Propionic	0.23	0.10	0.10	0.30	4
MADF	145.8	25.0	106.0	175.0	5	n butyric	0.88	0.54	0.20	1.5	4
EE	31.2	8.0	24.0	44.0	5	i butyric	0.20		0.20	0.20	1
AEE	42.0	5.9	35.0	49.0	4	n valeric	0.24	0.24	0.02	0.50	3
TA	21.8	28.1	9.0	72.0	5	i valeric	0.23	0.15	0.10	0.40	3
AIA	1.8	1.3	0.60	3.4	4	n caproic	0.38	0.26	0.10	0.60	4
GE (MJ/kg ODM)	19.9	0.85	18.5	20.7	5	i caproic	0.50		0.50	0.50	1
						NO_3N					
Carbohydrates (g/kg ODM)						NH_3N/TN	42.0	34.2	10.0	90.0	5
						pH	3.9	0.18	3.8	4.2	5
NDF ash	538.0	100.7	362.0	597.0	5						
NDF unash						**Fatty Acids (g/kg ODM)**					
ADF ash	154.2	21.3	120.0	176.0	5						
ADF unash	153.6	26.1	111.0	178.0	5	C8:0					
Cellulose	129.8	22.7	95.0	157.0	5	C10:0					
Lignin	27.4	8.9	18.0	40.0	5	C12:0					
Starch	181.2	55.8	101.0	255.0	5	C14:0					
NCD	615.8	47.1	565.5	671.2	4	C16:0					
CD						C16:1					
IVD	786.6	17.4	761.0	805.0	5	C18:0					
WSC	15.3	7.7	7.0	25.0	4	C18:1					
Avail Carbs						C18:2					
Sugars						C18:3					
						C20:0					
						C20:4					
Minerals (g/kg ODM)						C22:1					
Ca	0.26	0.17	0.10	0.50	5						
Mg	1.4	1.8	0.50	4.7	5						
Na	1.3	2.5	0.10	5.7	5	**Amino Acids (g/kg ODM)**					
K	4.4	7.5	0.70	17.8	5						
Cl						Ala					
P total	3.3	4.3	1.0	11.0	5	Arg					
P inorg						Asp					
P phytate						Cys					
Fe						Glu					
S						Gly					
						His					
						Ile					
						Leu					
Trace Elements (mg/kg ODM)						Lys avail					
						Lys total					
Co						Meth					
F						Phe					
I						Pro					
Mn						Pro.OH					
Mo						Ser					
Zn						Thr					
Cu						Tryp					
Se						Tyr					
						Val					

99

ANALYTICAL DATABASE

FEED DESCRIPTION : **MAIZE GLUTEN FEED** (Sources 1, 2, 3)

Determination	Mean	SD	Min	Max	n	Determination	Mean	SD	Min	Max	n
General (g/kg ODM)						Volatile Fatty Acids (g/kg ODM)					
ODM (fresh)	885.1	13.0	856.0	907.9	28	Lactic					
TDM (fresh)						Formic					
CP	219.5	12.1	201.0	252.4	28	Acetic					
CF	81.9	9.6	64.3	99.0	28	Propionic					
MADF	110.2	17.3	72.0	141.0	23	n butyric					
EE	44.1	17.3	17.0	80.0	28	i butyric					
AEE	51.4	16.1	29.0	81.0	28	n valeric					
TA	72.2	15.3	34.0	95.0	28	i valeric					
AIA	12.6	8.5	0.40	36.0	24	n caproic					
GE (MJ/kg ODM)	19.1	0.46	18.5	20.2	28	i caproic					
						NO_3N					
Carbohydrates (g/kg ODM)						NH_3N/TN					
						pH					
NDF ash	383.0	36.7	327.0	451.0	28						
NDF unash						Fatty Acids (g/kg ODM)					
ADF ash	114.2	17.4	81.0	147.0	28						
ADF unash	131.6	18.8	99.0	162.0	17	C8:0					
Cellulose	95.2	14.8	79.5	131.0	23	C10:0					
Lignin	20.8	10.0	9.0	41.0	25	C12:0					
Starch	185.8	53.7	91.0	283.0	26	C14:0					
NCD	723.6	25.0	687.0	800.0	28	C16:0	4.6	0.64	3.8	5.3	5
CD						C16:1					
IVD	728.9	56.6	577.0	795.0	27	C18:0	0.62	0.11	0.50	0.73	5
WSC	24.3	9.3	18.0	38.0	4	C18:1	6.2	1.0	5.3	7.4	5
Avail Carbs						C18:2	16.5	2.8	13.8	19.6	5
Sugars	20.7	7.4	11.1	31.3	5	C18:3	1.1	0.17	0.87	1.3	5
						C20:0					
						C20:4					
Minerals (g/kg ODM)						C22:1					
Ca	2.3	3.6	0.10	10.8	27						
Mg	4.1	0.70	2.4	5.3	28	Amino Acids (g/kg ODM)					
Na	2.6	1.4	0.20	4.8	28						
K	12.5	2.7	5.1	18.7	28	Ala	14.3	0.98	13.2	15.7	5
Cl	2.2	0.66	1.7	3.3	5	Arg	9.5	1.3	8.3	11.3	5
P total	9.3	1.2	6.4	11.6	28	Asp	12.5	0.82	11.4	13.3	5
P inorg	3.3	0.82	2.1	4.1	5	Cys	4.1	0.57	3.4	5.0	5
P phytate						Glu	31.3	1.4	29.9	33.0	5
Fe	0.48	0.26	0.10	0.80	5	Gly	9.6	0.53	9.0	10.4	5
S	4.7	0.70	3.9	5.8	5	His	6.5	0.47	6.1	7.1	5
						Ile	7.6	0.26	7.2	7.9	5
						Leu	19.3	1.1	18.0	20.5	5
Trace Elements (mg/kg ODM)						Lys avail					
						Lys total	6.1	0.27	5.9	6.4	5
Co	0.10	0.0	0.10	0.10	5	Meth	3.4	0.30	3.1	3.9	5
F						Phe	8.1	0.21	7.9	8.4	5
I						Pro					
Mn	27.8	6.5	20.8	39.0	9	Pro.OH					
Mo	0.82	0.08	0.70	0.90	5	Ser	8.7	0.56	8.2	9.7	5
Zn	80.1	10.3	67.4	100.0	9	Thr	7.5	0.34	7.0	7.8	5
Cu	6.7	5.0	2.0	17.9	9	Tryp					
Se	0.24	0.09	0.10	0.30	5	Tyr	6.8	0.71	5.7	7.6	5
						Val	10.7	0.46	10.0	11.2	5

ANALYTICAL DATABASE

FEED DESCRIPTION : **MAIZE GRAIN** (Sources 2, 3, 4)

Determination	Mean	SD	Min	Max	n	Determination	Mean	SD	Min	Max	n
General (g/kg ODM)						**Volatile Fatty Acids (g/kg ODM)**					
ODM (fresh)	873.1	12.7	855.0	890.0	12	Lactic					
TDM (fresh)						Formic					
CP	101.6	6.6	82.5	118.0	28	Acetic					
CF	19.9	2.3	17.0	26.0	28	Propionic					
MADF	29.1	3.2	24.0	35.0	23	n butyric					
EE	39.1	6.5	21.8	51.0	28	i butyric					
AEE	42.0	6.5	31.3	52.2	11	n valeric					
TA	14.9	2.2	11.3	20.7	28	i valeric					
AIA	0.16	0.06	0.10	0.20	5	n caproic					
GE (MJ/kg ODM)	18.9	0.10	18.6	19.1	28	i caproic					
						NO3N					
						NH3N/TN					
Carbohydrates (g/kg ODM)						pH					
						Fatty Acids (g/kg ODM)					
NDF ash	116.9	22.9	91.0	175.7	25						
NDF unash						C8:0					
ADF ash	27.9	5.5	18.5	38.0	21	C10:0					
ADF unash						C12:0					
Cellulose	23.1	0.65	22.5	24.0	5	C14:0					
Lignin	6.3	2.9	1.5	12.0	21	C16:0	4.4	0.48	4.1	5.2	5
Starch	699.6	26.1	661.0	755.0	24	C16:1					
NCD	927.2	2.9	924.0	931.0	5	C18:0	0.67	0.13	0.48	0.85	5
CD						C18:1	11.2	1.3	10.3	13.4	5
IVD	847.3	31.0	775.0	880.0	21	C18:2	22.1	1.5	20.8	24.6	5
WSC						C18:3	0.48	0.08	0.36	0.54	5
Avail Carbs						C20:0					
Sugars	17.7	6.5	10.4	27.0	8	C20:4					
						C22:1					
Minerals (g/kg ODM)											
						Amino Acids (g/kg ODM)					
Ca	0.14	0.11	0.10	0.50	17						
Mg	1.3	0.13	1.0	1.6	21	Ala	6.5	1.1	5.0	8.2	12
Na						Arg	3.7	0.96	1.0	5.0	12
K	3.5	0.22	3.2	4.2	21	Asp	5.1	1.2	3.0	6.6	12
Cl	0.74	0.09	0.60	0.80	5	Cys	2.4	0.11	2.3	2.5	5
P total	3.0	0.32	2.5	3.9	24	Glu	19.3	1.4	17.0	21.0	12
P inorg	0.36	0.14	0.30	0.60	5	Gly	2.9	0.81	2.0	3.8	12
P phytate						His	3.0	0.65	2.0	3.8	12
Fe	0.10	0.0	0.10	0.10	2	Ile	3.6	0.43	3.0	4.0	12
S	1.6	0.0	1.6	1.6	5	Leu	13.5	1.0	12.2	15.0	12
						Lys avail					
						Lys total	2.7	0.37	2.0	3.0	12
Trace Elements (mg/kg ODM)						Meth	2.3	0.62	1.0	3.0	12
						Phe	5.1	0.62	4.0	6.0	12
Co						Pro	8.5	0.69	7.0	9.1	9
F						Pro.OH					
I						Ser	4.8	0.39	4.0	5.1	12
Mn	5.9	3.0	4.0	17.0	21	Thr	3.7	0.37	3.0	4.0	12
Mo	0.30	0.07	0.20	0.40	5	Tryp	1.0	0.0	1.0	1.0	4
Zn	19.3	2.6	16.0	25.5	21	Tyr	4.6	0.89	3.8	6.0	12
Cu	2.2	0.42	1.8	3.0	21	Val	4.5	0.46	4.0	5.0	12
Se											

ANALYTICAL DATABASE

FEED DESCRIPTION : **MOLASSES, SUGAR BEET** (Source 1)

Determination	Mean	SD	Min	Max	n	Determination	Mean	SD	Min	Max	n
General (g/kg ODM)						**Volatile Fatty Acids** (g/kg ODM)					
ODM (fresh)	763.2	7.7	752.6	772.8	6	Lactic					
TDM (fresh)						Formic					
CP	136.1	8.6	126.5	147.0	6	Acetic					
CF						Propionic					
MADF						n butyric					
EE						i butyric					
AEE						n valeric					
TA	110.6	12.9	89.0	124.1	6	i valeric					
AIA	14.0	12.0	4.5	35.1	6	n caproic					
GE (MJ/kg ODM)	15.3	0.24	15.0	15.7	6	i caproic					
						NO₃N					
						NH₃N/TN					
						pH					
Carbohydrates (g/kg ODM)											
						Fatty Acids (g/kg ODM)					
NDF ash											
NDF unash						C8:0					
ADF ash						C10:0					
ADF unash						C12:0					
Cellulose						C14:0					
Lignin						C16:0					
Starch						C16:1					
NCD						C18:0					
CD						C18:1					
IVD						C18:2					
WSC						C18:3					
Avail Carbs						C20:0					
Sugars	631.7	16.6	603.0	653.0	6	C20:4					
						C22:1					
Minerals (g/kg ODM)											
Ca	1.2	0.72	0.65	2.4	5						
Mg	0.14	0.07	0.06	0.27	6	**Amino Acids** (g/kg ODM)					
Na	25.0	8.2	15.5	33.8	6						
K	49.1	5.4	41.7	56.8	5	Ala					
Cl						Arg					
P total	0.43	0.25	0.26	0.78	4	Asp					
P inorg						Cys					
P phytate						Glu					
Fe						Gly					
S						His					
						Ile					
						Leu					
						Lys avail					
Trace Elements (mg/kg ODM)						Lys total					
						Meth					
Co						Phe					
F						Pro					
I						Pro.OH					
Mn						Ser					
Mo						Thr					
Zn						Tryp					
Cu						Tyr					
Se						Val					

ANALYTICAL DATABASE

FEED DESCRIPTION : **MOLASSES, SUGAR CANE** (Source 1)

Determination	Mean	SD	Min	Max	n	Determination	Mean	SD	Min	Max	n
General (g/kg ODM)						**Volatile Fatty Acids (g/kg ODM)**					
ODM (fresh)	737.2	13.0	700.0	753.0	16	Lactic					
TDM (fresh)						Formic					
CP	55.3	40.6	27.0	181.9	12	Acetic					
CF						Propionic					
MADF						n butyric					
EE	4.3	2.1	1.9	6.0	3	i butyric					
AEE						n valeric					
TA	99.9	19.2	68.5	126.8	16	i valeric					
AIA	2.9	3.1	1.0	11.0	11	n caproic					
GE (MJ/kg ODM)	15.2	0.47	14.1	15.9	16	i caproic					
						NO_3N					
						NH_3N/TN					
Carbohydrates (g/kg ODM)						pH					
NDF ash						**Fatty Acids (g/kg ODM)**					
NDF unash											
ADF ash						C8:0					
ADF unash						C10:0					
Cellulose						C12:0					
Lignin						C14:0					
Starch						C16:0					
NCD						C16:1					
CD						C18:0					
IVD						C18:1					
WSC	656.9	33.5	625.0	713.5	5	C18:2					
Avail Carbs						C18:3					
Sugars						C20:0					
						C20:4					
Minerals (g/kg ODM)						C22:1					
Ca	9.6	1.5	7.2	12.0	8						
Mg	4.4	1.4	2.0	5.9	8	**Amino Acids (g/kg ODM)**					
Na	1.2	0.85	0.50	2.9	8						
K	38.6	15.7	21.0	70.0	8	Ala					
Cl						Arg					
P total	1.2	2.0	0.30	6.7	10	Asp					
P inorg						Cys					
P phytate						Glu					
Fe						Gly					
S						His					
						Ile					
						Leu					
Trace Elements (mg/kg ODM)						Lys avail					
						Lys total					
Co						Meth					
F						Phe					
I						Pro					
Mn						Pro.OH					
Mo						Ser					
Zn						Thr					
Cu						Tryp					
Se						Tyr					
						Val					

ANALYTICAL DATABASE

FEED DESCRIPTION : **NAKED OATS GRAIN, ALL SEASONS** (Sources 1, 3)

Determination	Mean	SD	Min	Max	n	Determination	Mean	SD	Min	Max	n
General (g/kg ODM)						**Volatile Fatty Acids** (g/kg ODM)					
ODM (fresh)	865.1	27.1	801.0	888.9	15	Lactic					
TDM (fresh)						Formic					
CP	128.0	17.1	103.0	164.0	15	Acetic					
CF	34.9	13.1	18.0	61.0	15	Propionic					
MADF	36.2	18.3	15.0	70.0	10	n butyric					
EE	90.2	8.2	71.0	100.0	15	i butyric					
AEE	101.2	11.8	65.0	113.0	14	n valeric					
TA	21.9	2.8	18.0	27.0	15	i valeric					
AIA	2.4	1.3	0.10	4.1	15	n caproic					
GE (MJ/kg ODM)	20.0	0.26	19.5	20.4	15	i caproic					
						NO_3N					
						NH_3N/TN					
Carbohydrates (g/kg ODM)						pH					
NDF ash	113.7	32.8	59.0	164.0	15	**Fatty Acids** (g/kg ODM)					
NDF unash											
ADF ash	42.0	17.9	20.0	75.5	15	C8:0					
ADF unash	41.4	19.3	19.0	71.0	10	C10:0					
Cellulose	29.2	15.1	7.0	50.0	14	C12:0					
Lignin	16.4	5.9	9.0	32.0	14	C14:0					
Starch	589.5	36.9	537.0	653.0	15	C16:0	12.3	0.93	11.5	13.8	5
NCD	932.0	26.9	871.8	959.0	14	C16:1					
CD						C18:0	0.43	0.14	0.32	0.65	5
IVD	761.8	81.6	509.0	856.5	15	C18:1	33.9	2.9	29.6	36.6	5
WSC	22.6	7.0	14.0	33.0	5	C18:2	36.3	2.1	34.0	39.4	5
Avail Carbs						C18:3	0.98	0.24	0.64	1.2	5
Sugars	7.5	0.81	6.6	8.8	5	C20:0					
						C20:4					
						C22:1					
Minerals (g/kg ODM)											
Ca	0.67	0.16	0.40	0.90	15						
Mg	1.3	0.12	1.1	1.5	15	**Amino Acids** (g/kg ODM)					
Na	0.16	0.07	0.10	0.30	11						
K	4.0	0.56	2.8	4.8	15	Ala	5.6	0.30	5.1	5.8	5
Cl	0.94	0.15	0.70	1.1	5	Arg	7.7	0.91	6.4	8.6	5
P total	4.2	0.52	3.1	4.9	15	Asp	9.4	0.68	8.3	10.0	5
P inorg	0.46	0.27	0.20	0.90	5	Cys	3.8	0.30	3.5	4.2	5
P phytate						Glu	21.1	1.4	18.9	22.3	5
Fe	0.15	0.06	0.10	0.20	4	Gly	5.9	0.45	5.3	6.4	5
S	1.6	0.16	1.4	1.8	5	His	3.2	0.17	2.9	3.4	5
						Ile	4.5	0.37	3.9	4.8	5
						Leu	9.2	0.68	8.1	9.8	5
Trace Elements (mg/kg ODM)						Lys avail					
						Lys total	5.0	0.45	4.4	5.4	5
Co						Meth	2.0	0.11	1.8	2.1	5
F						Phe	5.9	0.40	5.2	6.2	5
I						Pro	5.5	0.64	4.7	6.1	5
Mn	55.7	19.9	32.0	85.4	5	Pro.OH					
Mo	0.40	0.29	0.20	0.90	5	Ser	5.7	0.32	5.2	6.0	5
Zn	28.6	3.2	26.3	34.3	5	Thr	4.4	0.39	3.7	4.8	5
Cu	3.8	0.36	3.3	4.2	5	Tryp					
Se	0.10	0.0	0.10	0.10	3	Tyr	4.4	0.25	4.1	4.6	5
						Val	5.7	0.61	5.0	6.5	5

ANALYTICAL DATABASE

FEED DESCRIPTION : **NAKED OATS GRAIN, SPRING** (Sources 1, 3)

Determination	Mean	SD	Min	Max	n	Determination	Mean	SD	Min	Max	n
General (g/kg ODM)						**Volatile Fatty Acids** (g/kg ODM)					
ODM (fresh)	860.0	28.0	801.0	882.5	12	Lactic					
TDM (fresh)						Formic					
CP	123.2	15.7	103.0	164.0	12	Acetic					
CF	37.2	13.5	18.0	61.0	12	Propionic					
MADF	43.0	17.7	15.0	70.0	7	n butyric					
EE	91.7	8.4	71.0	100.0	12	i butyric					
AEE	101.4	13.2	65.0	113.0	11	n valeric					
TA	22.0	3.1	18.0	27.0	12	i valeric					
AIA	2.8	1.1	1.0	4.1	12	n caproic					
GE (MJ/kg ODM)	20.1	0.26	19.5	20.4	12	i caproic					
						NO_3N					
						NH_3N/TN					
Carbohydrates (g/kg ODM)						pH					
NDF ash	123.0	27.6	90.5	164.0	12	**Fatty Acids** (g/kg ODM)					
NDF unash											
ADF ash	44.4	18.5	20.0	75.5	12	C8:0					
ADF unash	43.3	20.9	19.0	71.0	7	C10:0					
Cellulose	34.0	12.9	9.8	50.0	11	C12:0					
Lignin	15.5	4.2	9.0	26.0	11	C14:0					
Starch	580.6	34.4	537.0	637.0	12	C16:0	12.3	0.93	11.5	13.8	5
NCD	924.8	26.0	871.8	958.0	11	C16:1					
CD						C18:0	0.43	0.14	0.32	0.65	5
IVD	749.4	85.6	509.0	829.0	12	C18:1	33.9	2.9	29.6	36.6	5
WSC	22.6	7.0	14.0	33.0	5	C18:2	36.3	2.1	34.0	39.4	5
Avail Carbs						C18:3	0.98	0.24	0.64	1.2	5
Sugars	7.5	0.81	6.6	8.8	5	C20:0					
						C20:4					
Minerals (g/kg ODM)						C22:1					
Ca	0.70	0.14	0.40	0.90	12						
Mg	1.3	0.13	1.1	1.5	12	**Amino Acids** (g/kg ODM)					
Na	0.16	0.07	0.10	0.30	11						
K	4.0	0.61	2.8	4.8	12	Ala	5.6	0.30	5.1	5.8	5
Cl	0.94	0.15	0.70	1.1	5	Arg	7.7	0.91	6.4	8.6	5
P total	4.1	0.52	3.1	4.8	12	Asp	9.4	0.68	8.3	10.0	5
P inorg	0.46	0.27	0.20	0.90	5	Cys	3.8	0.30	3.5	4.2	5
P phytate						Glu	21.1	1.4	18.9	22.3	5
Fe	0.15	0.06	0.10	0.20	4	Gly	5.9	0.45	5.3	6.4	5
S	1.6	0.16	1.4	1.8	5	His	3.2	0.17	2.9	3.4	5
						Ile	4.5	0.37	3.9	4.8	5
						Leu	9.2	0.68	8.1	9.8	5
Trace Elements (mg/kg ODM)						Lys avail					
						Lys total	5.0	0.45	4.4	5.4	5
Co						Meth	2.0	0.11	1.8	2.1	5
F						Phe	5.9	0.40	5.2	6.2	5
I						Pro	5.5	0.64	4.7	6.1	5
Mn	55.7	19.9	32.0	85.4	5	Pro.OH					
Mo	0.40	0.29	0.20	0.90	5	Ser	5.7	0.32	5.2	6.0	5
Zn	28.6	3.2	26.3	34.3	5	Thr	4.4	0.39	3.7	4.8	5
Cu	3.8	0.36	3.3	4.2	5	Tryp					
Se	0.10	0.0	0.10	0.10	3	Tyr	4.4	0.25	4.1	4.6	5
						Val	5.7	0.61	5.0	6.5	5

ANALYTICAL DATABASE

FEED DESCRIPTION : **NAKED OATS GRAIN, WINTER** (Source 1)

Determination	Mean	SD	Min	Max	n	Determination	Mean	SD	Min	Max	n
General (g/kg ODM)						**Volatile Fatty Acids** (g/kg ODM)					
ODM (fresh)	885.6	5.5	879.3	888.9	3	Lactic					
TDM (fresh)						Formic					
CP	147.3	2.1	145.4	149.5	3	Acetic					
CF	25.7	6.4	21.0	33.0	3	Propionic					
MADF	20.3	4.2	17.0	25.0	3	n butyric					
EE	84.0	3.0	81.0	87.0	3	i butyric					
AEE	100.3	6.4	93.0	105.0	3	n valeric					
TA	21.3	1.2	20.0	22.0	3	i valeric					
AIA	0.67	0.60	0.10	1.3	3	n caproic					
GE (MJ/kg ODM)	19.9	0.20	19.7	20.1	3	i caproic					
						NO_3N					
Carbohydrates (g/kg ODM)						NH_3N/TN					
						pH					
NDF ash	76.3	26.6	59.0	107.0	3						
NDF unash						**Fatty Acids** (g/kg ODM)					
ADF ash	32.3	13.7	23.0	48.0	3						
ADF unash	37.0	17.8	23.0	57.0	3	C8:0					
Cellulose	11.3	5.9	7.0	18.0	3	C10:0					
Lignin	19.7	10.8	12.0	32.0	3	C12:0					
Starch	625.2	25.3	603.5	653.0	3	C14:0					
NCD	958.2	1.1	957.0	959.0	3	C16:0					
CD						C16:1					
IVD	811.5	40.9	776.5	856.5	3	C18:0					
WSC						C18:1					
Avail Carbs						C18:2					
Sugars						C18:3					
						C20:0					
						C20:4					
Minerals (g/kg ODM)						C22:1					
Ca	0.57	0.21	0.40	0.80	3						
Mg	1.2	0.12	1.1	1.3	3	**Amino Acids** (g/kg ODM)					
Na											
K	3.9	0.36	3.5	4.2	3	Ala					
Cl						Arg					
P total	4.6	0.36	4.2	4.9	3	Asp					
P inorg						Cys					
P phytate						Glu					
Fe						Gly					
S						His					
						Ile					
						Leu					
Trace Elements (mg/kg ODM)						Lys avail					
						Lys total					
Co						Meth					
F						Phe					
I						Pro					
Mn						Pro.OH					
Mo						Ser					
Zn						Thr					
Cu						Tryp					
Se						Tyr					
						Val					

ANALYTICAL DATABASE

FEED DESCRIPTION : **OATS GRAIN, ALL SEASONS** (Sources 1, 2, 3, 4)

Determination	Mean	SD	Min	Max	n	Determination	Mean	SD	Min	Max	n
General (g/kg ODM)						**Volatile Fatty Acids** (g/kg ODM)					
ODM (fresh)	858.4	18.9	820.0	894.2	29	Lactic					
TDM (fresh)						Formic					
CP	107.6	14.5	79.4	148.8	29	Acetic					
CF	104.1	8.9	91.0	132.5	29	Propionic					
MADF	133.3	14.4	117.0	154.6	8	n butyric					
EE	41.1	16.0	16.0	71.8	29	i butyric					
AEE	58.0	17.5	29.0	79.7	13	n valeric					
TA	26.6	3.4	22.0	37.5	29	i valeric					
AIA	9.0	4.0	5.3	19.1	10	n caproic					
GE (MJ/kg ODM)	19.6	0.22	19.1	20.2	29	i caproic					
						NO3N					
						NH3N/TN					
Carbohydrates (g/kg ODM)						pH					
NDF ash	309.8	27.8	254.5	363.5	28	**Fatty Acids** (g/kg ODM)					
NDF unash											
ADF ash	149.2	13.1	129.0	177.0	26	C8:0					
ADF unash	146.2	7.3	136.0	155.0	5	C10:0					
Cellulose	104.7	9.9	94.0	127.0	10	C12:0					
Lignin	37.2	7.7	27.0	55.0	26	C14:0					
Starch	470.8	26.9	419.7	530.0	27	C16:0	7.6	1.6	6.5	10.4	5
NCD	763.1	31.5	713.0	819.0	10	C16:1					
CD						C18:0	0.46	0.14	0.25	0.62	5
IVD	664.7	19.0	633.0	702.0	26	C18:1	18.3	5.6	14.8	28.2	5
WSC						C18:2	19.8	3.5	15.1	24.8	5
Avail Carbs						C18:3	0.77	0.27	0.36	1.1	5
Sugars	10.7	5.1	8.1	21.0	6	C20:0					
						C20:4					
						C22:1					
Minerals (g/kg ODM)											
Ca	0.86	0.18	0.50	1.2	27	**Amino Acids** (g/kg ODM)					
Mg	3.0	4.2	0.80	13.3	26						
Na	0.15	0.07	0.10	0.30	21	Ala	5.8	0.92	4.0	7.0	8
K	5.0	0.88	3.0	6.0	26	Arg	7.9	1.7	6.0	11.0	8
Cl	0.84	0.18	0.60	1.1	5	Asp	9.9	1.4	8.6	13.0	8
P total	3.4	0.46	2.4	4.0	27	Cys	4.1	0.48	3.4	4.6	5
P inorg	0.32	0.05	0.30	0.40	5	Glu	23.4	3.3	19.5	30.0	8
P phytate						Gly	5.9	1.1	4.0	8.0	8
Fe	0.12	0.05	0.10	0.20	5	His	3.1	0.55	2.0	3.9	8
S	1.9	0.13	1.7	2.0	5	Ile	4.6	0.71	3.8	6.0	8
						Leu	9.0	1.1	7.6	11.0	8
						Lys avail					
Trace Elements (mg/kg ODM)						Lys total	4.9	0.62	4.0	6.0	8
						Meth	2.7	1.2	1.6	5.0	8
Co						Phe	6.3	0.88	5.2	8.0	8
F						Pro	6.1	0.95	5.0	7.5	7
I	0.10	0.0	0.10	0.10	2	Pro.OH					
Mn	45.2	15.4	27.0	92.0	21	Ser	6.1	0.68	5.0	7.0	8
Mo	0.70	0.61	0.30	1.6	4	Thr	4.2	0.43	3.7	5.0	8
Zn	26.1	3.7	20.0	34.1	21	Tryp	2.0	0.0	2.0	2.0	2
Cu	3.3	0.99	1.0	5.4	21	Tyr	4.6	0.70	3.8	6.0	8
Se						Val	6.4	1.0	5.0	8.0	8

ANALYTICAL DATABASE

FEED DESCRIPTION : **OATS GRAIN, SPRING** (Sources 2, 3, 4)

Determination	Mean	SD	Min	Max	n	Determination	Mean	SD	Min	Max	n
General (g/kg ODM)						**Volatile Fatty Acids (g/kg ODM)**					
ODM (fresh)	854.4	18.3	820.0	894.2	23	Lactic					
TDM (fresh)						Formic					
CP	107.5	15.8	79.4	148.8	23	Acetic					
CF	104.4	8.7	91.0	132.5	23	Propionic					
MADF	132.0	8.2	124.9	141.0	3	n butyric					
EE	37.2	14.7	16.0	71.8	23	i butyric					
AEE	50.6	18.5	29.0	79.7	8	n valeric					
TA	26.8	3.6	22.0	37.5	23	i valeric					
AIA	10.4	5.2	5.5	19.1	5	n caproic					
GE (MJ/kg ODM)	19.6	0.23	19.1	20.2	23	i caproic					
						NO_3N					
						NH_3N/TN					
						pH					
Carbohydrates (g/kg ODM)											
						Fatty Acids (g/kg ODM)					
NDF ash	314.5	27.6	254.5	363.5	22						
NDF unash						C8:0					
ADF ash	151.6	13.4	129.0	177.0	20	C10:0					
ADF unash						C12:0					
Cellulose	111.1	10.0	101.5	127.0	5	C14:0					
Lignin	36.6	7.5	27.0	55.0	20	C16:0	7.6	1.6	6.5	10.4	5
Starch	468.7	26.8	419.7	530.0	21	C16:1					
NCD	754.8	20.2	730.0	784.0	5	C18:0	0.46	0.14	0.25	0.62	5
CD						C18:1	18.3	5.6	14.8	28.2	5
IVD	662.8	19.1	633.0	702.0	20	C18:2	19.8	3.5	15.1	24.8	5
WSC						C18:3	0.77	0.27	0.36	1.1	5
Avail Carbs						C20:0					
Sugars	10.7	5.1	8.1	21.0	6	C20:4					
						C22:1					
Minerals (g/kg ODM)											
						Amino Acids (g/kg ODM)					
Ca	0.88	0.19	0.50	1.2	21						
Mg	3.6	4.7	0.80	13.3	20	Ala	5.8	0.92	4.0	7.0	8
Na	0.16	0.07	0.10	0.30	20	Arg	7.9	1.7	6.0	11.0	8
K	5.2	0.73	3.8	6.0	20	Asp	9.9	1.4	8.6	13.0	8
Cl	0.84	0.18	0.60	1.1	5	Cys	4.1	0.48	3.4	4.6	5
P total	3.4	0.45	3.0	4.0	21	Glu	23.4	3.3	19.5	30.0	8
P inorg	0.32	0.05	0.30	0.40	5	Gly	5.9	1.1	4.0	8.0	8
P phytate						His	3.1	0.55	2.0	3.9	8
Fe	0.12	0.05	0.10	0.20	5	Ile	4.6	0.71	3.8	6.0	8
S	1.9	0.13	1.7	2.0	5	Leu	9.0	1.1	7.6	11.0	8
						Lys avail					
						Lys total	4.9	0.62	4.0	6.0	8
Trace Elements (mg/kg ODM)						Meth	2.7	1.2	1.6	5.0	8
						Phe	6.3	0.88	5.2	8.0	8
Co						Pro	6.1	0.95	5.0	7.5	7
F						Pro.OH					
I	0.10	0.0	0.10	0.10	2	Ser	6.1	0.68	5.0	7.0	8
Mn	46.0	15.4	27.0	92.0	20	Thr	4.2	0.43	3.7	5.0	8
Mo	0.70	0.61	0.30	1.6	4	Tryp	2.0	0.0	2.0	2.0	2
Zn	26.0	3.8	20.0	34.1	20	Tyr	4.6	0.70	3.8	6.0	8
Cu	3.3	1.0	1.0	5.4	20	Val	6.4	1.0	5.0	8.0	8
Se											

ANALYTICAL DATABASE

FEED DESCRIPTION : **OATS GRAIN, WINTER** (Sources 1, 2)

Determination	Mean	SD	Min	Max	n	Determination	Mean	SD	Min	Max	n
General (g/kg ODM)						**Volatile Fatty Acids (g/kg ODM)**					
ODM (fresh)	873.7	12.6	851.0	889.4	6	Lactic					
TDM (fresh)						Formic					
CP	108.0	8.2	98.5	120.6	6	Acetic					
CF	102.7	10.4	93.0	117.0	6	Propionic					
MADF	134.0	18.1	117.0	154.6	5	n butyric					
EE	56.0	12.4	33.0	67.0	6	i butyric					
AEE	69.8	5.4	63.0	75.0	5	n valeric					
TA	25.8	2.5	23.0	30.0	6	i valeric					
AIA	7.6	2.1	5.3	10.7	5	n caproic					
GE (MJ/kg ODM)	19.5	0.18	19.3	19.7	6	i caproic					
						NO$_3$N					
						NH$_3$N/TN					
Carbohydrates (g/kg ODM)						pH					
NDF ash	292.3	22.7	256.0	312.0	6	**Fatty Acids (g/kg ODM)**					
NDF unash											
ADF ash	141.5	8.8	131.0	153.0	6	C8:0					
ADF unash	146.2	7.3	136.0	155.0	5	C10:0					
Cellulose	98.2	4.2	94.0	104.0	5	C12:0					
Lignin	39.2	8.8	29.0	54.0	6	C14:0					
Starch	478.2	28.1	436.0	517.0	6	C16:0					
NCD	771.4	40.7	713.0	819.0	5	C16:1					
CD						C18:0					
IVD	671.3	18.9	653.0	701.0	6	C18:1					
WSC						C18:2					
Avail Carbs						C18:3					
Sugars						C20:0					
						C20:4					
Minerals (g/kg ODM)						C22:1					
Ca	0.77	0.15	0.60	0.90	6						
Mg	1.0	0.06	0.90	1.1	6	**Amino Acids (g/kg ODM)**					
Na	0.10		0.10	0.10	1						
K	4.3	1.0	3.0	6.0	6	Ala					
Cl						Arg					
P total	3.3	0.54	2.4	4.0	6	Asp					
P inorg						Cys					
P phytate						Glu					
Fe						Gly					
S						His					
						Ile					
						Leu					
Trace Elements (mg/kg ODM)						Lys avail					
						Lys total					
Co						Meth					
F						Phe					
I						Pro					
Mn	30.0		30.0	30.0	1	Pro.OH					
Mo						Ser					
Zn	27.0		27.0	27.0	1	Thr					
Cu	4.0		4.0	4.0	1	Tryp					
Se						Tyr					
						Val					

ANALYTICAL DATABASE

FEED DESCRIPTION : **OLIVE PULP MEAL** (Source 1)

Determination	Mean	SD	Min	Max	n	Determination	Mean	SD	Min	Max	n

General (g/kg ODM)   **Volatile Fatty Acids** (g/kg ODM)

Determination	Mean	SD	Min	Max	n
ODM (fresh)	881.1		881.1	881.1	1
TDM (fresh)					
CP	108.0		108.0	108.0	1
CF	374.0		374.0	374.0	1
MADF	523.0		523.0	523.0	1
EE	18.0		18.0	18.0	1
AEE	16.0		16.0	16.0	1
TA	76.0		76.0	76.0	1
AIA	27.0		27.0	27.0	1
GE (MJ/kg ODM)	20.0		20.0	20.0	1

Volatile Fatty Acids:
Lactic
Formic
Acetic
Propionic
n butyric
i butyric
n valeric
i valeric
n caproic
i caproic

NO3N
NH3N/TN
pH

Carbohydrates (g/kg ODM)

Determination	Mean	SD	Min	Max	n
NDF ash	684.0		684.0	684.0	1
NDF unash					
ADF ash	543.0		543.0	543.0	1
ADF unash	567.0		567.0	567.0	1
Cellulose	300.0		300.0	300.0	1
Lignin	240.0		240.0	240.0	1
Starch	3.1		3.1	3.1	1
NCD	337.0		337.0	337.0	1
CD					
IVD	177.0		177.0	177.0	1
WSC	16.0		16.0	16.0	1
Avail Carbs					
Sugars					

Fatty Acids (g/kg ODM)

C8:0
C10:0
C12:0
C14:0
C16:0
C16:1
C18:0
C18:1
C18:2
C18:3
C20:0
C20:4
C22:1

Minerals (g/kg ODM)

Determination	Mean	SD	Min	Max	n
Ca	15.1		15.1	15.1	1
Mg	1.2		1.2	1.2	1
Na	29.5		29.5	29.5	1
K	9.3		9.3	9.3	1
Cl					
P total	1.1		1.1	1.1	1
P inorg					
P phytate					
Fe					
S					

Amino Acids (g/kg ODM)

Ala
Arg
Asp
Cys
Glu
Gly
His
Ile
Leu
Lys avail
Lys total
Meth
Phe
Pro
Pro.OH
Ser
Thr
Tryp
Tyr
Val

Trace Elements (mg/kg ODM)

Co
F
I
Mn
Mo
Zn
Cu
Se

ANALYTICAL DATABASE

FEED DESCRIPTION : **PECTIN EXTRACTED FRUITS** (Source 1)

Determination	Mean	SD	Min	Max	n	Determination	Mean	SD	Min	Max	n
General (g/kg ODM)						**Volatile Fatty Acids (g/kg ODM)**					
ODM (fresh)	163.5	13.4	154.0	173.0	2	Lactic	19.4		19.4	19.4	1
TDM (fresh)	166.5	13.4	157.0	176.0	2	Formic					
CP	105.0	1.4	104.0	106.0	2	Acetic	4.0		4.0	4.0	1
CF	399.5	20.5	385.0	414.0	2	Propionic					
MADF	624.5	21.9	609.0	640.0	2	n butyric					
EE	35.5	0.71	35.0	36.0	2	i butyric					
AEE	41.5	2.1	40.0	43.0	2	n valeric					
TA	13.0	4.2	10.0	16.0	2	i valeric					
AIA	2.0	1.4	1.0	3.0	2	n caproic					
GE (MJ/kg ODM)	20.7	0.78	20.1	21.2	2	i caproic					
						NO3N					
Carbohydrates (g/kg ODM)						NH3N/TN	20.0	0.0	20.0	20.0	2
						pH	3.2	0.35	2.9	3.4	2
NDF ash	767.0	4.2	764.0	770.0	2						
NDF unash						**Fatty Acids (g/kg ODM)**					
ADF ash	708.0	4.2	705.0	711.0	2						
ADF unash	674.5	2.1	673.0	676.0	2	C8:0					
Cellulose	463.5	30.4	442.0	485.0	2	C10:0					
Lignin	196.5	30.4	175.0	218.0	2	C12:0					
Starch	7.9		7.9	7.9	1	C14:0					
NCD	703.5	21.9	688.0	719.0	2	C16:0					
CD	492.0		492.0	492.0	1	C16:1					
IVD	531.5	24.7	514.0	549.0	2	C18:0					
WSC	9.0	4.2	6.0	12.0	2	C18:1					
Avail Carbs						C18:2					
Sugars						C18:3					
						C20:0					
						C20:4					
Minerals (g/kg ODM)						C22:1					
Ca	2.7	1.6	1.5	3.8	2						
Mg	0.10	0.0	0.10	0.10	2	**Amino Acids (g/kg ODM)**					
Na	0.50	0.28	0.30	0.70	2						
K	0.20	0.0	0.20	0.20	2	Ala					
Cl						Arg					
P total	1.4	0.0	1.4	1.4	2	Asp					
P inorg						Cys					
P phytate						Glu					
Fe						Gly					
S						His					
						Ile					
						Leu					
Trace Elements (mg/kg ODM)						Lys avail					
						Lys total					
Co						Meth					
F						Phe					
I						Pro					
Mn						Pro.OH					
Mo						Ser					
Zn						Thr					
Cu						Tryp					
Se						Tyr					
						Val					

ANALYTICAL DATABASE

FEED DESCRIPTION : **POTATOES, FRESH** (Source 2)

Determination	Mean	SD	Min	Max	n	Determination	Mean	SD	Min	Max	n
General (g/kg ODM)						**Volatile Fatty Acids (g/kg ODM)**					
ODM (fresh)	203.9	7.2	198.8	209.0	2	Lactic					
TDM (fresh)						Formic					
CP	108.2	7.0	103.3	113.2	2	Acetic					
CF	26.3	1.4	25.3	27.3	2	Propionic					
MADF	39.2	0.65	38.8	39.7	2	n butyric					
EE	2.4	0.11	2.3	2.5	2	i butyric					
AEE						n valeric					
TA	52.8	2.2	51.3	54.3	2	i valeric					
AIA						n caproic					
GE (MJ/kg ODM)	17.2	0.09	17.2	17.3	2	i caproic					
						NO$_3$N					
						NH$_3$N/TN					
						pH					
Carbohydrates (g/kg ODM)											
						Fatty Acids (g/kg ODM)					
NDF ash	73.2	3.6	70.7	75.8	2						
NDF unash						C8:0					
ADF ash	43.6	1.2	42.8	44.5	2	C10:0					
ADF unash						C12:0					
Cellulose						C14:0					
Lignin	14.1	0.18	14.0	14.3	2	C16:0					
Starch	565.0	21.5	549.8	580.3	2	C16:1					
NCD						C18:0					
CD						C18:1					
IVD	917.5	0.71	917.0	918.0	2	C18:2					
WSC	73.3	19.4	59.5	87.0	2	C18:3					
Avail Carbs						C20:0					
Sugars						C20:4					
						C22:1					
Minerals (g/kg ODM)											
						Amino Acids (g/kg ODM)					
Ca	0.35	0.07	0.30	0.40	2						
Mg	1.0	0.0	1.0	1.0	2	Ala					
Na	0.20	0.0	0.20	0.20	2	Arg					
K	23.6	0.78	23.0	24.1	2	Asp					
Cl						Cys					
P total	2.0	0.07	1.9	2.0	2	Glu					
P inorg						Gly					
P phytate						His					
Fe						Ile					
S						Leu					
						Lys avail					
						Lys total					
Trace Elements (mg/kg ODM)						Meth					
						Phe					
Co						Pro					
F						Pro.OH					
I						Ser					
Mn	12.5	6.4	8.0	17.0	2	Thr					
Mo						Tryp					
Zn	23.5	3.5	21.0	26.0	2	Tyr					
Cu	7.0	1.4	6.0	8.0	2	Val					
Se											

ANALYTICAL DATABASE

FEED DESCRIPTION : **POTATO, PROCESSING WASTE** (Source 1)

Determination	Mean	SD	Min	Max	n	Determination	Mean	SD	Min	Max	n
General (g/kg ODM)						**Volatile Fatty Acids** (g/kg ODM)					
ODM (fresh)	982.5		982.5	982.5	1	Lactic					
TDM (fresh)						Formic					
CP	91.0		91.0	91.0	1	Acetic					
CF	25.0		25.0	25.0	1	Propionic					
MADF	28.0		28.0	28.0	1	n butyric					
EE	22.0		22.0	22.0	1	i butyric					
AEE						n valeric					
TA	92.0		92.0	92.0	1	i valeric					
AIA	1.0		1.0	1.0	1	n caproic					
GE (MJ/kg ODM)	16.5		16.5	16.5	1	i caproic					
						NO_3N					
						NH_3N/TN					
Carbohydrates (g/kg ODM)						pH					
NDF ash						**Fatty Acids** (g/kg ODM)					
NDF unash											
ADF ash						C8:0					
ADF unash	33.0		33.0	33.0	1	C10:0					
Cellulose	29.0		29.0	29.0	1	C12:0					
Lignin	5.0		5.0	5.0	1	C14:0					
Starch	452.0		452.0	452.0	1	C16:0					
NCD						C16:1					
CD						C18:0					
IVD	937.0		937.0	937.0	1	C18:1					
WSC	132.0		132.0	132.0	1	C18:2					
Avail Carbs						C18:3					
Sugars						C20:0					
						C20:4					
						C22:1					
Minerals (g/kg ODM)											
Ca	0.60		0.60	0.60	1						
Mg	0.50		0.50	0.50	1	**Amino Acids** (g/kg ODM)					
Na	1.0		1.0	1.0	1						
K	10.7		10.7	10.7	1	Ala					
Cl						Arg					
P total	1.8		1.8	1.8	1	Asp					
P inorg						Cys					
P phytate						Glu					
Fe						Gly					
S						His					
						Ile					
						Leu					
Trace Elements (mg/kg ODM)						Lys avail					
						Lys total					
Co						Meth					
F						Phe					
I						Pro					
Mn						Pro.OH					
Mo						Ser					
Zn						Thr					
Cu						Tryp					
Se						Tyr					
						Val					

ANALYTICAL DATABASE

FEED DESCRIPTION : **RICE BRAN MEAL, EXPELLED** (Source 2)

Determination	Mean	SD	Min	Max	n	Determination	Mean	SD	Min	Max	n
General (g/kg ODM)						**Volatile Fatty Acids** (g/kg ODM)					
ODM (fresh)	902.0		902.0	902.0	1	Lactic					
TDM (fresh)						Formic					
CP	128.0		128.0	128.0	1	Acetic					
CF	158.0		158.0	158.0	1	Propionic					
MADF	229.0		229.0	229.0	1	n butyric					
EE	90.0		90.0	90.0	1	i butyric					
AEE						n valeric					
TA	113.0		113.0	113.0	1	i valeric					
AIA						n caproic					
GE (MJ/kg ODM)	18.9		18.9	18.9	1	i caproic					
						NO_3N					
						NH_3N/TN					
Carbohydrates (g/kg ODM)						pH					
NDF ash	370.0		370.0	370.0	1	**Fatty Acids** (g/kg ODM)					
NDF unash											
ADF ash	242.0		242.0	242.0	1	C8:0					
ADF unash						C10:0					
Cellulose						C12:0					
Lignin	58.0		58.0	58.0	1	C14:0					
Starch	302.0		302.0	302.0	1	C16:0					
NCD	660.0		660.0	660.0	1	C16:1					
CD						C18:0					
IVD	498.0		498.0	498.0	1	C18:1					
WSC	24.0		24.0	24.0	1	C18:2					
Avail Carbs						C18:3					
Sugars						C20:0					
						C20:4					
						C22:1					
Minerals (g/kg ODM)											
Ca	0.90		0.90	0.90	1	**Amino Acids** (g/kg ODM)					
Mg	4.5		4.5	4.5	1						
Na	0.10		0.10	0.10	1	Ala					
K	10.0		10.0	10.0	1	Arg					
Cl						Asp					
P total	11.0		11.0	11.0	1	Cys					
P inorg						Glu					
P phytate						Gly					
Fe						His					
S						Ile					
						Leu					
						Lys avail					
Trace Elements (mg/kg ODM)						Lys total					
						Meth					
Co						Phe					
F						Pro					
I						Pro.OH					
Mn	102.0		102.0	102.0	1	Ser					
Mo						Thr					
Zn	37.0		37.0	37.0	1	Tryp					
Cu	5.0		5.0	5.0	1	Tyr					
Se						Val					

ANALYTICAL DATABASE

FEED DESCRIPTION : **RICE BRAN MEAL, EXTRACTED** (Sources 2, 3)

Determination	Mean	SD	Min	Max	n	Determination	Mean	SD	Min	Max	n
General (g/kg ODM)						**Volatile Fatty Acids (g/kg ODM)**					
ODM (fresh)	896.3	10.7	875.0	909.0	8	Lactic					
TDM (fresh)						Formic					
CP	153.8	11.0	139.3	171.0	8	Acetic					
CF	166.6	13.1	151.0	186.0	8	Propionic					
MADF	277.7	35.9	254.0	319.0	3	n butyric					
EE	7.3	1.6	5.0	9.9	8	i butyric					
AEE	17.8	2.4	15.0	21.4	5	n valeric					
TA	70.2	74.8	14.5	170.0	8	i valeric					
AIA	8.1	0.63	7.5	8.9	5	n caproic					
GE (MJ/kg ODM)	16.7	0.18	16.5	17.0	8	i caproic					
						NO_3N					
						NH_3N/TN					
Carbohydrates (g/kg ODM)						pH					
NDF ash	450.7	54.4	401.0	561.0	8	**Fatty Acids (g/kg ODM)**					
NDF unash											
ADF ash	275.1	32.2	241.5	340.0	8	C8:0					
ADF unash						C10:0					
Cellulose	145.3	12.1	135.0	166.0	5	C12:0					
Lignin	70.1	14.6	56.0	100.0	8	C14:0					
Starch	236.3	44.9	172.0	301.5	8	C16:0	1.1	0.26	0.86	1.6	5
NCD	542.8	41.9	459.0	589.2	8	C16:1					
CD						C18:0	0.14	0.03	0.11	0.18	5
IVD	497.4	45.7	417.0	550.0	8	C18:1	2.2	0.52	1.7	3.1	5
WSC	30.3	11.2	22.0	43.0	3	C18:2	1.6	0.28	1.2	1.9	5
Avail Carbs						C18:3	0.11	0.06	0.07	0.22	5
Sugars	19.2	4.4	12.0	24.0	5	C20:0					
						C20:4					
Minerals (g/kg ODM)						C22:1					
Ca	0.91	0.96	0.20	2.2	8						
Mg	3.8	4.1	0.70	8.9	8	**Amino Acids (g/kg ODM)**					
Na	0.24	0.13	0.10	0.40	5						
K	5.6	5.9	1.3	14.2	8	Ala	8.9	0.48	8.2	9.4	5
Cl	0.70	0.25	0.30	1.0	5	Arg	10.0	0.54	9.5	10.9	5
P total	17.4	1.7	14.9	19.9	8	Asp	13.5	1.2	12.1	15.0	5
P inorg	1.9	0.36	1.5	2.3	5	Cys	2.5	0.07	2.4	2.6	5
P phytate						Glu	17.9	0.68	17.1	18.6	5
Fe	2.6	1.0	1.6	3.8	5	Gly	7.8	0.57	7.1	8.6	5
S	2.0	0.13	1.8	2.1	5	His	4.0	0.27	3.6	4.2	5
						Ile	6.0	0.16	5.9	6.3	5
						Leu	11.1	0.52	10.2	11.5	5
Trace Elements (mg/kg ODM)						Lys avail					
						Lys total	5.8	0.40	5.4	6.3	5
Co	1.0	0.32	0.60	1.4	5	Meth	2.6	0.14	2.4	2.8	5
F						Phe	7.3	0.54	6.6	8.0	5
I	0.50		0.50	0.50	1	Pro					
Mn	137.0	31.3	97.0	182.0	8	Pro.OH					
Mo	1.1	0.14	1.0	1.3	5	Ser	7.1	0.61	6.1	7.7	5
Zn	77.2	17.0	55.1	105.7	8	Thr	6.0	0.49	5.4	6.7	5
Cu	10.1	2.1	6.0	12.6	8	Tryp					
Se	0.16	0.06	0.10	0.20	5	Tyr	4.9	0.37	4.6	5.5	5
						Val	8.2	0.69	7.5	9.2	5

ANALYTICAL DATABASE

FEED DESCRIPTION : **RYE GRAIN** (Source 4)

Determination	Mean	SD	Min	Max	n	Determination	Mean	SD	Min	Max	n
General (g/kg ODM)						**Volatile Fatty Acids** (g/kg ODM)					
ODM (fresh)	868.5	5.0	865.0	872.0	2	Lactic					
TDM (fresh)						Formic					
CP	119.1	19.0	105.6	132.5	2	Acetic					
CF	20.3	0.28	20.1	20.5	2	Propionic					
MADF	133.0	11.4	124.9	141.0	2	n butyric					
EE	11.6	1.4	10.6	12.6	2	i butyric					
AEE	29.1	0.14	29.0	29.2	2	n valeric					
TA	18.0	0.57	17.6	18.4	2	i valeric					
AIA						n caproic					
GE (MJ/kg ODM)	18.5	0.38	18.2	18.8	2	i caproic					

NO$_3$N
NH$_3$N/TN
pH

Determination	Mean	SD	Min	Max	n
Carbohydrates (g/kg ODM)					
NDF ash	357.1	9.1	350.6	363.5	2
NDF unash					
ADF ash					
ADF unash					
Cellulose					
Lignin					
Starch					
NCD					
CD					
IVD					
WSC					
Avail Carbs					
Sugars					

Fatty Acids (g/kg ODM)

C8:0
C10:0
C12:0
C14:0
C16:0
C16:1
C18:0
C18:1
C18:2
C18:3
C20:0
C20:4
C22:1

Minerals (g/kg ODM)

Ca
Mg
Na
K
Cl
P total
P inorg
P phytate
Fe
S

Amino Acids (g/kg ODM)

Determination	Mean	SD	Min	Max	n
Ala	5.0	0.0	5.0	5.0	2
Arg	6.5	0.71	6.0	7.0	2
Asp	8.0	0.0	8.0	8.0	2
Cys					
Glu	28.5	9.2	22.0	35.0	2
Gly	5.0	0.0	5.0	5.0	2
His	3.0	0.0	3.0	3.0	2
Ile	4.5	0.71	4.0	5.0	2
Leu	7.5	0.71	7.0	8.0	2
Lys avail					
Lys total	4.5	0.71	4.0	5.0	2
Meth	3.5	0.71	3.0	4.0	2
Phe	5.5	0.71	5.0	6.0	2
Pro	13.5	3.5	11.0	16.0	2
Pro.OH					
Ser	5.0	0.0	5.0	5.0	2
Thr	4.0	0.0	4.0	4.0	2
Tryp	2.0	0.0	2.0	2.0	2
Tyr	3.5	0.71	3.0	4.0	2
Val	5.5	0.71	5.0	6.0	2

Trace Elements (mg/kg ODM)

Co
F
I
Mn
Mo
Zn
Cu
Se

ANALYTICAL DATABASE

FEED DESCRIPTION : **SAINFOIN, LOW TEMP DRIED** (Source 1)

Determination	Mean	SD	Min	Max	n	Determination	Mean	SD	Min	Max	n
General (g/kg ODM)						**Volatile Fatty Acids** (g/kg ODM)					
ODM (fresh)	854.1		854.1	854.1	1	Lactic					
TDM (fresh)						Formic					
CP	189.0		189.0	189.0	1	Acetic					
CF	182.0		182.0	182.0	1	Propionic					
MADF	256.0		256.0	256.0	1	n butyric					
EE	19.0		19.0	19.0	1	i butyric					
AEE	17.0		17.0	17.0	1	n valeric					
TA	78.0		78.0	78.0	1	i valeric					
AIA	9.0		9.0	9.0	1	n caproic					
GE (MJ/kg ODM)	20.0		20.0	20.0	1	i caproic					
						NO_3N					
						NH_3N/TN					
Carbohydrates (g/kg ODM)						pH					
NDF ash	448.0		448.0	448.0	1	**Fatty Acids** (g/kg ODM)					
NDF unash											
ADF ash						C8:0					
ADF unash	306.0		306.0	306.0	1	C10:0					
Cellulose	189.0		189.0	189.0	1	C12:0					
Lignin						C14:0					
Starch	4.7		4.7	4.7	1	C16:0					
NCD	701.0		701.0	701.0	1	C16:1					
CD						C18:0					
IVD	633.0		633.0	633.0	1	C18:1					
WSC						C18:2					
Avail Carbs						C18:3					
Sugars						C20:0					
						C20:4					
						C22:1					
Minerals (g/kg ODM)											
Ca	13.7		13.7	13.7	1						
Mg	2.1		2.1	2.1	1	**Amino Acids** (g/kg ODM)					
Na	1.0		1.0	1.0	1						
K	16.3		16.3	16.3	1	Ala					
Cl						Arg					
P total	3.0		3.0	3.0	1	Asp					
P inorg						Cys					
P phytate						Glu					
Fe						Gly					
S						His					
						Ile					
						Leu					
Trace Elements (mg/kg ODM)						Lys avail					
						Lys total					
Co						Meth					
F						Phe					
I						Pro					
Mn						Pro.OH					
Mo						Ser					
Zn						Thr					
Cu						Tryp					
Se						Tyr					
						Val					

ANALYTICAL DATABASE

FEED DESCRIPTION : **SORGHUM GRAIN** (Sources 2, 4)

Determination	Mean	SD	Min	Max	n	Determination	Mean	SD	Min	Max	n
General (g/kg ODM)						**Volatile Fatty Acids** (g/kg ODM)					
ODM (fresh)	897.4		897.4	897.4	1	Lactic					
TDM (fresh)						Formic					
CP	113.3	9.3	106.0	128.7	5	Acetic					
CF	20.1	1.3	19.0	22.0	5	Propionic					
MADF	47.7	9.5	41.0	64.0	5	n butyric					
EE	30.2	5.2	21.8	35.0	5	i butyric					
AEE						n valeric					
TA	17.0	1.2	16.0	19.0	5	i valeric					
AIA						n caproic					
GE (MJ/kg ODM)	18.7	0.15	18.5	18.9	5	i caproic					
						NO_3N					
						NH_3N/TN					
Carbohydrates (g/kg ODM)						pH					
NDF ash	107.3	2.2	105.0	110.0	4	**Fatty Acids** (g/kg ODM)					
NDF unash											
ADF ash	57.0	10.2	49.0	71.0	4	C8:0					
ADF unash						C10:0					
Cellulose						C12:0					
Lignin	23.8	7.3	18.0	34.0	4	C14:0					
Starch	730.4	30.8	690.0	761.0	5	C16:0					
NCD						C16:1					
CD						C18:0					
IVD	851.8	29.6	812.0	878.0	4	C18:1					
WSC						C18:2					
Avail Carbs						C18:3					
Sugars	15.0		15.0	15.0	1	C20:0					
						C20:4					
						C22:1					
Minerals (g/kg ODM)											
Ca	0.32	0.27	0.20	0.80	5						
Mg	1.1	0.13	1.0	1.3	4	**Amino Acids** (g/kg ODM)					
Na	0.50	0.0	0.50	0.50	4						
K	3.7	0.14	3.6	3.9	4	Ala	8.0		8.0	8.0	1
Cl						Arg	4.0		4.0	4.0	1
P total	2.8	0.48	2.2	3.2	5	Asp	6.0		6.0	6.0	1
P inorg						Cys					
P phytate						Glu	29.0		29.0	29.0	1
Fe						Gly	1.0		1.0	1.0	1
S						His	2.0		2.0	2.0	1
						Ile	5.0		5.0	5.0	1
						Leu	17.0		17.0	17.0	1
						Lys avail					
Trace Elements (mg/kg ODM)						Lys total	3.0		3.0	3.0	1
						Meth	2.0		2.0	2.0	1
Co						Phe	6.0		6.0	6.0	1
F						Pro					
I						Pro.OH					
Mn	8.3	0.50	8.0	9.0	4	Ser	6.0		6.0	6.0	1
Mo						Thr	4.0		4.0	4.0	1
Zn	14.3	0.96	13.0	15.0	4	Tryp					
Cu	3.0	0.0	3.0	3.0	4	Tyr	6.0		6.0	6.0	1
Se						Val	6.0		6.0	6.0	1

ANALYTICAL DATABASE

FEED DESCRIPTION : **SUGAR BEET FEED, DRIED, MOLASSED** (Sources 2, 3, 5)

Determination	Mean	SD	Min	Max	n	Determination	Mean	SD	Min	Max	n
General (g/kg ODM)						**Volatile Fatty Acids (g/kg ODM)**					
ODM (fresh)	876.0	16.7	831.0	907.0	58	Lactic					
TDM (fresh)						Formic					
CP	110.3	8.7	97.2	139.0	66	Acetic					
CF	131.9	9.1	118.0	145.0	19	Propionic					
MADF	173.9	7.0	164.0	191.0	14	n butyric					
EE	4.4	1.3	3.0	8.0	19	i butyric					
AEE	4.4	1.2	3.0	6.4	11	n valeric					
TA	88.4	9.3	75.0	109.6	19	i valeric					
AIA	17.2	7.1	6.0	28.1	11	n caproic					
GE (MJ/kg ODM)	17.0	0.25	16.5	17.4	19	i caproic					
						NO_3N					
						NH_3N/TN					
						pH					
Carbohydrates (g/kg ODM)						**Fatty Acids (g/kg ODM)**					
NDF ash	321.3	29.2	271.0	376.5	19						
NDF unash						C8:0					
ADF ash	178.5	7.9	164.0	190.0	19	C10:0					
ADF unash	189.2	7.5	175.0	195.0	6	C12:0					
Cellulose	146.5	7.7	135.0	161.0	11	C14:0					
Lignin	23.0	5.7	15.0	36.0	19	C16:0	0.37	0.08	0.26	0.45	5
Starch	65.2	59.6	0.10	136.7	10	C16:1					
NCD	860.0	14.1	826.0	877.0	11	C18:0	0.03	0.01	0.02	0.04	5
CD						C18:1	0.16	0.05	0.10	0.24	5
IVD	811.9	27.9	750.0	837.0	19	C18:2	1.1	0.27	0.71	1.3	5
WSC	281.1	20.7	251.0	317.0	14	C18:3	0.19	0.05	0.14	0.26	5
Avail Carbs						C20:0					
Sugars	235.4	14.6	211.9	248.6	5	C20:4					
						C22:1					
Minerals (g/kg ODM)											
Ca	7.6	2.0	5.0	12.4	19						
Mg	1.1	0.19	0.80	1.6	19	**Amino Acids (g/kg ODM)**					
Na	4.4	1.3	2.1	7.0	19						
K	18.2	1.9	14.7	21.8	19	Ala	3.4	0.05	3.4	3.5	5
Cl	2.5	0.78	2.0	3.8	5	Arg	2.8	0.25	2.6	3.2	5
P total	0.77	0.15	0.60	1.1	19	Asp	6.7	0.24	6.4	7.0	5
P inorg	0.30	0.0	0.30	0.30	5	Cys	1.2	0.04	1.1	1.2	5
P phytate						Glu	19.6	1.2	18.3	21.4	5
Fe						Gly	3.7	0.20	3.4	4.0	5
S	6.1	1.2	4.1	7.5	5	His	3.1	0.24	2.7	3.3	5
						Ile	3.4	0.08	3.3	3.5	5
						Leu	5.1	0.17	4.9	5.4	5
Trace Elements (mg/kg ODM)						Lys avail					
						Lys total	4.2	0.11	4.1	4.4	5
Co	0.54	0.15	0.40	0.70	5	Meth	1.0	0.12	0.84	1.1	5
F						Phe	2.9	0.18	2.7	3.1	5
I	0.50	0.22	0.20	0.80	5	Pro	3.3	0.17	3.1	3.5	5
Mn	31.0	8.9	18.0	41.0	8	Pro.OH					
Mo						Ser	4.0	0.22	3.8	4.3	5
Zn	22.1	4.9	15.0	30.0	8	Thr	3.6	0.15	3.4	3.8	5
Cu	12.6	4.9	3.0	20.0	8	Tryp					
Se	0.14	0.05	0.10	0.20	5	Tyr	3.7	0.24	3.5	4.1	5
						Val	4.5	0.20	4.2	4.8	5

ANALYTICAL DATABASE

FEED DESCRIPTION : **SUGAR BEET FEED, DRIED, UNMOLASSED** (Source 1)

Determination	Mean	SD	Min	Max	n	Determination	Mean	SD	Min	Max	n
General (g/kg ODM)						**Volatile Fatty Acids (g/kg ODM)**					
ODM (fresh)	856.1	40.1	826.2	901.7	3	Lactic					
TDM (fresh)						Formic					
CP	77.2		77.2	77.2	1	Acetic					
CF	159.3	43.5	128.0	209.0	3	Propionic					
MADF	206.7	47.6	172.0	261.0	3	n butyric					
EE	6.7	2.9	5.0	10.0	3	i butyric					
AEE	5.0	1.4	4.0	6.0	2	n valeric					
TA	68.3	21.5	46.0	89.0	3	i valeric					
AIA	14.3	6.4	7.0	19.0	3	n caproic					
GE (MJ/kg ODM)	17.1	0.50	16.6	17.6	3	i caproic					
						NO_3N					
						NH_3N/TN					
Carbohydrates (g/kg ODM)						pH					
						Fatty Acids (g/kg ODM)					
NDF ash	372.3	111.5	304.0	501.0	3						
NDF unash											
ADF ash	212.7	60.6	170.0	282.0	3	C8:0					
ADF unash	224.3	57.5	179.0	289.0	3	C10:0					
Cellulose	174.3	52.2	137.0	234.0	3	C12:0					
Lignin	38.0	2.6	36.0	41.0	3	C14:0					
Starch	3.1		3.1	3.1	1	C16:0					
NCD	883.5	3.5	881.0	886.0	2	C16:1					
CD	862.5	9.2	856.0	869.0	2	C18:0					
IVD	808.0	44.6	776.0	859.0	3	C18:1					
WSC	79.0		79.0	79.0	1	C18:2					
Avail Carbs						C18:3					
Sugars						C20:0					
						C20:4					
Minerals (g/kg ODM)						C22:1					
Ca	7.6	0.65	6.9	8.2	3						
Mg	1.8	0.85	1.2	2.8	3	**Amino Acids (g/kg ODM)**					
Na	3.2	2.1	1.2	5.4	3						
K	11.7	7.6	2.9	16.7	3	Ala					
Cl						Arg					
P total	0.77	0.06	0.70	0.80	3	Asp					
P inorg						Cys					
P phytate						Glu					
Fe						Gly					
S						His					
						Ile					
						Leu					
Trace Elements (mg/kg ODM)						Lys avail					
						Lys total					
Co						Meth					
F						Phe					
I						Pro					
Mn						Pro.OH					
Mo						Ser					
Zn						Thr					
Cu						Tryp					
Se						Tyr					
						Val					

ANALYTICAL DATABASE

FEED DESCRIPTION : **SUGAR BEET FEED, ENSILED** (Source 1)

Determination	Mean	SD	Min	Max	n	Determination	Mean	SD	Min	Max	n
General (g/kg ODM)						**Volatile Fatty Acids (g/kg ODM)**					
ODM (fresh)	163.0	15.9	142.0	178.0	4	Lactic	73.0	24.5	48.1	106.8	4
TDM (fresh)	174.5	15.9	154.0	191.0	4	Formic	29.5	5.9	24.1	35.5	4
CP	111.3	6.3	104.0	119.0	4	Acetic	39.4	25.2	15.7	71.2	4
CF	205.3	8.4	193.0	212.0	4	Propionic	8.5	8.3	2.6	14.4	2
MADF	289.8	7.3	282.0	296.0	4	n butyric	8.2	4.5	4.2	13.0	3
EE	6.5	3.4	2.0	10.0	4	i butyric	0.60		0.60	0.60	1
AEE	10.3	3.1	7.0	13.0	3	n valeric	4.1		4.1	4.1	1
TA	92.5	24.1	72.0	127.0	4	i valeric	1.3		1.3	1.3	1
AIA	47.5	14.8	35.0	67.0	4	n caproic	5.4		5.4	5.4	1
GE (MJ/kg ODM)	17.0	0.78	16.0	17.7	4	i caproic	7.6		7.6	7.6	1
						NO3N					
Carbohydrates (g/kg ODM)						NH3N/TN	60.0	18.3	40.0	80.0	4
						pH	3.9	0.22	3.7	4.2	4
NDF ash	418.0	35.7	384.0	458.0	4						
NDF unash						**Fatty Acids (g/kg ODM)**					
ADF ash	272.5	11.7	257.0	285.0	4						
ADF unash	302.5	19.4	276.0	317.0	4	C8:0					
Cellulose	230.8	7.3	224.0	240.0	4	C10:0					
Lignin	29.5	5.2	23.0	35.0	4	C12:0					
Starch	1.7	1.1	0.30	3.1	4	C14:0					
NCD	855.3	14.6	845.0	872.0	3	C16:0					
CD	771.8	27.5	733.0	798.0	4	C16:1					
IVD	746.0	45.3	687.0	797.0	4	C18:0					
WSC	36.3	20.6	16.0	64.0	4	C18:1					
Avail Carbs						C18:2					
Sugars						C18:3					
						C20:0					
						C20:4					
Minerals (g/kg ODM)						C22:1					
Ca	10.2	4.0	7.4	16.0	4						
Mg	1.9	0.10	1.8	2.0	4	**Amino Acids (g/kg ODM)**					
Na	0.78	0.17	0.60	1.0	4						
K	7.2	1.7	4.8	8.8	4	Ala					
Cl						Arg					
P total	1.2	0.11	1.1	1.3	4	Asp					
P inorg						Cys					
P phytate						Glu					
Fe						Gly					
S						His					
						Ile					
						Leu					
Trace Elements (mg/kg ODM)						Lys avail					
						Lys total					
Co						Meth					
F						Phe					
I						Pro					
Mn						Pro.OH					
Mo						Ser					
Zn						Thr					
Cu						Tryp					
Se						Tyr					
						Val					

ANALYTICAL DATABASE

FEED DESCRIPTION : **SUGAR BEET FEED, MOLASSED, ENSILED** (Source 1)

Determination	Mean	SD	Min	Max	n	Determination	Mean	SD	Min	Max	n
General (g/kg ODM)						**Volatile Fatty Acids (g/kg ODM)**					
ODM (fresh)	213.3	3.8	209.0	216.0	3	Lactic	59.0	4.4	55.9	62.1	2
TDM (fresh)	228.0	0.0	228.0	228.0	3	Formic	5.5	1.5	4.4	6.5	2
CP	131.2	7.3	127.0	139.6	3	Acetic	38.1	0.64	37.6	38.5	2
CF	145.3	8.5	139.0	155.0	3	Propionic	1.7	0.78	1.1	2.2	2
MADF	187.3	15.5	176.0	205.0	3	n butyric	3.7		3.7	3.7	1
EE	6.0	1.0	5.0	7.0	3	i butyric					
AEE	10.0		10.0	10.0	1	n valeric					
TA	95.7	10.7	84.0	105.0	3	i valeric					
AIA	24.7	2.5	22.0	27.0	3	n caproic					
GE (MJ/kg ODM)	17.6	0.15	17.5	17.8	3	i caproic					
						NO_3N					
Carbohydrates (g/kg ODM)						NH_3N/TN	43.3	5.8	40.0	50.0	3
						pH	3.8	0.0	3.8	3.8	3
NDF ash	340.5	10.6	333.0	348.0	2						
NDF unash						**Fatty Acids (g/kg ODM)**					
ADF ash	202.0	4.2	199.0	205.0	2						
ADF unash	240.7	17.9	220.0	252.0	3	C8:0					
Cellulose	171.0	4.0	167.0	175.0	3	C10:0					
Lignin	50.0	13.9	34.0	59.0	3	C12:0					
Starch	0.10		0.10	0.10	1	C14:0					
NCD	846.0	28.4	824.0	878.0	3	C16:0					
CD	742.7	13.3	734.0	758.0	3	C16:1					
IVD	776.7	6.5	770.0	783.0	3	C18:0					
WSC	21.5	6.4	16.2	28.6	3	C18:1					
Avail Carbs						C18:2					
Sugars						C18:3					
						C20:0					
						C20:4					
Minerals (g/kg ODM)						C22:1					
Ca	7.7	0.76	6.9	8.4	3						
Mg	1.5	0.27	1.3	1.8	3	**Amino Acids (g/kg ODM)**					
Na	7.3	2.1	5.0	9.0	3						
K	21.3	1.5	19.6	22.2	3	Ala					
Cl						Arg					
P total	0.83	0.25	0.60	1.1	3	Asp					
P inorg						Cys					
P phytate						Glu					
Fe						Gly					
S						His					
						Ile					
						Leu					
Trace Elements (mg/kg ODM)						Lys avail					
						Lys total					
Co						Meth					
F						Phe					
I						Pro					
Mn						Pro.OH					
Mo						Ser					
Zn						Thr					
Cu						Tryp					
Se						Tyr					
						Val					

ANALYTICAL DATABASE

FEED DESCRIPTION : **SUGER BEET FEED, PRESSED** (Sources 1, 5)

Determination	Mean	SD	Min	Max	n	Determination	Mean	SD	Min	Max	n
General (g/kg ODM)						**Volatile Fatty Acids** (g/kg ODM)					
ODM (fresh)	256.1	21.5	165.0	333.0	363	Lactic					
TDM (fresh)	259.9	24.6	169.0	315.0	54	Formic					
CP	97.5	4.4	81.0	123.0	274	Acetic					
CF	197.2	5.1	192.0	203.0	5	Propionic					
MADF	271.8	15.2	252.0	294.0	5	n butyric					
EE	5.6	0.55	5.0	6.0	5	i butyric					
AEE	5.0	0.0	5.0	5.0	4	n valeric					
TA	82.2	17.1	65.0	110.0	5	i valeric					
AIA	44.4	12.8	33.0	66.0	5	n caproic					
GE (MJ/kg ODM)	17.0	0.28	16.6	17.3	5	i caproic					
						NO_3N					
						NH_3N/TN					
Carbohydrates (g/kg ODM)						pH	4.6		4.6	4.6	1
NDF ash	523.3	45.5	489.0	590.0	4	**Fatty Acids** (g/kg ODM)					
NDF unash											
ADF ash	251.0	6.3	243.0	258.0	4	C8:0					
ADF unash	288.0	16.7	263.0	309.0	5	C10:0					
Cellulose	218.2	3.8	214.0	224.0	5	C12:0					
Lignin	29.4	5.0	22.0	35.0	5	C14:0					
Starch	3.5	2.7	1.0	6.3	3	C16:0					
NCD	804.0	44.1	743.0	850.0	5	C16:1					
CD	767.0	33.3	714.0	795.0	5	C18:0					
IVD	784.4	45.3	735.0	845.0	5	C18:1					
WSC	44.8	12.7	29.0	64.0	5	C18:2					
Avail Carbs						C18:3					
Sugars						C20:0					
						C20:4					
						C22:1					
Minerals (g/kg ODM)											
Ca	10.3	1.8	7.6	12.5	5	**Amino Acids** (g/kg ODM)					
Mg	1.9	0.34	1.4	2.3	5						
Na	0.50	0.25	0.20	0.80	5	Ala					
K	8.4	8.1	3.7	22.8	5	Arg					
Cl						Asp					
P total	1.2	0.13	1.0	1.3	5	Cys					
P inorg						Glu					
P phytate						Gly					
Fe						His					
S						Ile					
						Leu					
						Lys avail					
Trace Elements (mg/kg ODM)						Lys total					
						Meth					
Co						Phe					
F						Pro					
I						Pro.OH					
Mn						Ser					
Mo						Thr					
Zn						Tryp					
Cu						Tyr					
Se						Val					

ANALYTICAL DATABASE

FEED DESCRIPTION : **SUGAR BEET FEED, PRESSED, MOLASSED** (Source 5)

Determination	Mean	SD	Min	Max	n	Determination	Mean	SD	Min	Max	n
General (g/kg ODM)						**Volatile Fatty Acids (g/kg ODM)**					
ODM (fresh)	322.4	15.9	275.8	352.0	51	Lactic					
TDM (fresh)						Formic					
CP	104.1	2.5	101.0	112.0	16	Acetic					
CF	129.0		129.0	129.0	1	Propionic					
MADF	163.0		163.0	163.0	1	n butyric					
EE	2.0		2.0	2.0	1	i butyric					
AEE	8.0		8.0	8.0	1	n valeric					
TA	69.0		69.0	69.0	1	i valeric					
AIA	17.0		17.0	17.0	1	n caproic					
GE (MJ/kg ODM)	17.1		17.1	17.1	1	i caproic					
						NO$_3$N					
Carbohydrates (g/kg ODM)						NH$_3$N/TN					
						pH					
NDF ash											
NDF unash						**Fatty Acids (g/kg ODM)**					
ADF ash											
ADF unash	172.0		172.0	172.0	1	C8:0					
Cellulose	146.0		146.0	146.0	1	C10:0					
Lignin	13.9		13.9	13.9	1	C12:0					
Starch	7.2		7.2	7.2	1	C14:0					
NCD	904.0		904.0	904.0	1	C16:0					
CD	853.0		853.0	853.0	1	C16:1					
IVD	805.0		805.0	805.0	1	C18:0					
WSC						C18:1					
Avail Carbs						C18:2					
Sugars						C18:3					
						C20:0					
						C20:4					
Minerals (g/kg ODM)						C22:1					
Ca	4.9		4.9	4.9	1						
Mg	1.6		1.6	1.6	1	**Amino Acids (g/kg ODM)**					
Na	7.0		7.0	7.0	1						
K	15.8		15.8	15.8	1	Ala					
Cl						Arg					
P total	0.80		0.80	0.80	1	Asp					
P inorg						Cys					
P phytate						Glu					
Fe						Gly					
S						His					
						Ile					
						Leu					
Trace Elements (mg/kg ODM)						Lys avail					
						Lys total					
Co						Meth					
F						Phe					
I						Pro					
Mn						Pro.OH					
Mo						Ser					
Zn						Thr					
Cu						Tryp					
Se						Tyr					
						Val					

ANALYTICAL DATABASE

FEED DESCRIPTION : **SWEDES** (Source 2)

Determination	Mean	SD	Min	Max	n	Determination	Mean	SD	Min	Max	n
General (g/kg ODM)						**Volatile Fatty Acids** (g/kg ODM)					
ODM (fresh)	104.5	13.1	95.3	113.8	2	Lactic					
TDM (fresh)						Formic					
CP	90.5	8.1	84.8	96.3	2	Acetic					
CF	82.2	1.5	81.2	83.3	2	Propionic					
MADF	114.3	7.0	109.4	119.3	2	n butyric					
EE	3.8	0.28	3.6	4.0	2	i butyric					
AEE						n valeric					
TA	60.1	8.0	54.4	65.8	2	i valeric					
AIA						n caproic					
GE (MJ/kg ODM)	17.3	0.07	17.3	17.4	2	i caproic					
						NO3N					
						NH3N/TN					
Carbohydrates (g/kg ODM)						pH					
NDF ash	140.4	1.6	139.2	141.5	2	**Fatty Acids** (g/kg ODM)					
NDF unash											
ADF ash	125.4	6.5	120.8	130.0	2	C8:0					
ADF unash						C10:0					
Cellulose						C12:0					
Lignin	13.8	0.35	13.5	14.0	2	C14:0					
Starch						C16:0					
NCD						C16:1					
CD						C18:0					
IVD	844.0	17.0	832.0	856.0	2	C18:1					
WSC	587.2	12.7	578.3	596.2	2	C18:2					
Avail Carbs						C18:3					
Sugars						C20:0					
						C20:4					
Minerals (g/kg ODM)						C22:1					
Ca	3.5	0.07	3.4	3.5	2						
Mg	1.1	0.07	1.0	1.1	2	**Amino Acids** (g/kg ODM)					
Na	1.5	0.21	1.3	1.6	2						
K	18.7	2.5	16.9	20.4	2	Ala					
Cl						Arg					
P total	2.6	0.28	2.4	2.8	2	Asp					
P inorg						Cys					
P phytate						Glu					
Fe						Gly					
S						His					
						Ile					
						Leu					
Trace Elements (mg/kg ODM)						Lys avail					
						Lys total					
Co						Meth					
F						Phe					
I						Pro					
Mn	16.5	0.71	16.0	17.0	2	Pro.OH					
Mo						Ser					
Zn	29.5	5.0	26.0	33.0	2	Thr					
Cu	11.0	5.7	7.0	15.0	2	Tryp					
Se						Tyr					
						Val					

125

ANALYTICAL DATABASE

FEED DESCRIPTION : **TRIPLE NUTS** (Source 2)

Determination	Mean	SD	Min	Max	n	Determination	Mean	SD	Min	Max	n
General (g/kg ODM)						**Volatile Fatty Acids (g/kg ODM)**					
ODM (fresh)						Lactic					
TDM (fresh)						Formic					
CP	204.0	1.4	202.0	205.0	4	Acetic					
CF	114.5	1.3	113.0	116.0	4	Propionic					
MADF	157.8	1.3	156.0	159.0	4	n butyric					
EE	4.8	1.7	3.0	7.0	4	i butyric					
AEE						n valeric					
TA	109.5	2.6	107.0	113.0	4	i valeric					
AIA						n caproic					
GE (MJ/kg ODM)	16.2	0.03	16.1	16.2	4	i caproic					
						NO3N					
						NH3N/TN					
Carbohydrates (g/kg ODM)						pH					
NDF ash	261.5	3.4	258.0	266.0	4	**Fatty Acids (g/kg ODM)**					
NDF unash											
ADF ash	167.5	4.7	164.0	174.0	4	C8:0					
ADF unash						C10:0					
Cellulose						C12:0					
Lignin	22.0	2.5	19.0	24.0	4	C14:0					
Starch						C16:0					
NCD						C16:1					
CD						C18:0					
IVD	815.0	2.9	812.0	819.0	4	C18:1					
WSC	258.8	3.8	254.0	263.0	4	C18:2					
Avail Carbs						C18:3					
Sugars						C20:0					
						C20:4					
						C22:1					
Minerals (g/kg ODM)											
Ca	15.2	1.1	14.1	16.8	4	**Amino Acids (g/kg ODM)**					
Mg	2.6	0.05	2.6	2.7	4						
Na	5.8	0.17	5.6	6.0	4	Ala					
K	13.1	0.39	12.7	13.5	4	Arg					
Cl						Asp					
P total	5.8	0.48	5.3	6.4	4	Cys					
P inorg						Glu					
P phytate						Gly					
Fe						His					
S						Ile					
						Leu					
						Lys avail					
Trace Elements (mg/kg ODM)						Lys total					
Co						Meth					
F						Phe					
I						Pro					
Mn	99.5	4.2	95.0	105.0	4	Pro.OH					
Mo						Ser					
Zn	67.3	2.9	65.0	71.0	4	Thr					
Cu	10.3	0.50	10.0	11.0	4	Tryp					
Se						Tyr					
						Val					

ANALYTICAL DATABASE

FEED DESCRIPTION : **TRITICALE GRAIN, WINTER** (Sources 1, 3)

Determination	Mean	SD	Min	Max	n	Determination	Mean	SD	Min	Max	n
General (g/kg ODM)						**Volatile Fatty Acids (g/kg ODM)**					
ODM (fresh)	863.6	15.1	845.4	891.0	14	Lactic					
TDM (fresh)						Formic					
CP	137.7	20.8	102.3	172.7	14	Acetic					
CF	23.6	3.5	19.6	30.0	14	Propionic					
MADF	32.0	4.7	26.0	41.0	9	n butyric					
EE	15.5	1.8	12.0	18.5	14	i butyric					
AEE	21.7	2.4	18.0	24.8	14	n valeric					
TA	20.7	1.7	18.0	25.0	14	i valeric					
AIA	0.94	0.78	0.10	2.9	14	n caproic					
GE (MJ/kg ODM)	18.3	0.26	17.7	18.6	14	i caproic					
						NO$_3$N					
						NH$_3$N/TN					
Carbohydrates (g/kg ODM)						pH					
NDF ash	118.5	18.0	83.0	147.0	14	**Fatty Acids (g/kg ODM)**					
NDF unash											
ADF ash	35.9	5.4	27.0	44.0	14	C8:0					
ADF unash	34.5	5.2	28.0	45.0	8	C10:0					
Cellulose	24.5	3.6	19.5	34.0	13	C12:0					
Lignin	11.4	2.1	7.7	14.0	13	C14:0					
Starch	516.5	97.2	378.9	688.3	14	C16:0	2.2	0.18	1.9	2.3	5
NCD	917.3	9.8	904.4	933.3	10	C16:1					
CD						C18:0	0.12	0.04	0.08	0.18	5
IVD	863.9	20.0	838.0	903.0	14	C18:1	1.8	0.23	1.6	2.2	5
WSC	51.4	10.9	44.0	70.0	5	C18:2	8.0	0.82	6.6	8.7	5
Avail Carbs						C18:3	1.0	0.09	0.97	1.1	5
Sugars	32.2	1.2	31.0	34.0	5	C20:0					
						C20:4					
Minerals (g/kg ODM)						C22:1					
Ca	0.51	0.16	0.30	0.70	14						
Mg	1.2	0.14	1.0	1.4	14	**Amino Acids (g/kg ODM)**					
Na	0.32	0.27	0.10	0.80	11						
K	5.5	0.86	4.1	6.8	14	Ala	6.0	0.75	4.8	6.6	5
Cl						Arg	7.8	0.93	6.3	8.8	5
P total	4.3	0.41	3.7	4.8	14	Asp	8.6	0.47	7.8	9.1	5
P inorg	0.26	0.09	0.20	0.40	5	Cys	3.2	0.42	2.5	3.6	5
P phytate						Glu	40.2	8.5	25.4	46.9	5
Fe	40.2	9.8	32.6	55.4	5	Gly	6.5	0.85	5.0	7.0	5
S	1.7	0.32	1.2	2.0	5	His	3.8	0.44	3.1	4.2	5
						Ile	5.6	0.84	4.3	6.2	5
						Leu	10.4	1.6	7.6	11.6	5
Trace Elements (mg/kg ODM)						Lys avail					
						Lys total	5.1	0.35	4.5	5.4	5
Co	0.10		0.10	0.10	1	Meth	2.3	0.35	1.7	2.7	5
F						Phe	7.8	1.3	5.6	9.0	5
I						Pro					
Mn	24.8	6.0	17.8	30.8	5	Pro.OH					
Mo	0.56	0.23	0.30	0.80	5	Ser	6.8	1.1	5.1	7.7	5
Zn	38.9	4.8	34.2	44.5	5	Thr	5.0	0.63	3.9	5.5	5
Cu	3.9	1.6	2.5	6.7	5	Tryp					
Se						Tyr	4.8	0.44	4.4	5.4	5
						Val	7.7	0.99	6.0	8.6	5

ANALYTICAL DATABASE

FEED DESCRIPTION : **WHEAT BRAN** (Sources 2, 3, 4)

Determination	Mean	SD	Min	Max	n	Determination	Mean	SD	Min	Max	n

General (g/kg ODM)

						Volatile Fatty Acids (g/kg ODM)					
ODM (fresh)	891.7	11.3	874.0	906.0	10	Lactic					
TDM (fresh)						Formic					
CP	174.0	15.0	140.9	197.0	10	Acetic					
CF	104.4	12.9	86.6	121.0	10	Propionic					
MADF	145.9	19.9	118.0	169.3	5	n butyric					
EE	39.4	6.8	32.7	53.0	10	i butyric					
AEE	52.1	3.2	46.7	54.5	5	n valeric					
TA	65.5	5.4	56.0	73.0	10	i valeric					
AIA	1.6	0.22	1.3	1.8	5	n caproic					
GE (MJ/kg ODM)	18.9	0.13	18.7	19.2	10	i caproic					

						NO3N					
						NH3N/TN					
						pH					

Carbohydrates (g/kg ODM)

						Fatty Acids (g/kg ODM)					
NDF ash	474.7	54.7	402.5	550.0	9						
NDF unash						C8:0					
ADF ash	137.4	20.5	110.5	173.0	9	C10:0					
ADF unash						C12:0					
Cellulose	86.4	13.0	74.0	106.0	5	C14:0					
Lignin	39.7	6.1	31.0	49.0	9	C16:0	5.0	0.47	4.1	5.3	5
Starch	195.8	49.2	116.0	269.0	10	C16:1					
NCD	685.2	38.7	634.0	728.0	5	C18:0	0.16	0.04	0.14	0.22	5
CD						C18:1	4.8	0.62	4.2	5.8	5
IVD	628.8	50.8	535.0	697.5	9	C18:2	18.1	1.6	15.6	19.3	5
WSC						C18:3	1.8	0.24	1.5	2.1	5
Avail Carbs						C20:0					
Sugars	63.6	7.5	51.0	71.6	6	C20:4					
						C22:1					

Minerals (g/kg ODM)

						Amino Acids (g/kg ODM)					
Ca	1.1	0.18	0.70	1.3	10						
Mg	6.2	2.7	4.3	12.0	9	Ala	7.5	1.8	4.0	9.0	6
Na	0.12	0.03	0.10	0.19	7	Arg	11.7	1.2	10.0	13.4	6
K	14.8	4.0	7.5	18.7	9	Asp	11.3	1.9	8.0	13.4	6
Cl	0.98	0.11	0.80	1.1	5	Cys	4.0	0.25	3.8	4.5	5
P total	12.6	3.0	7.3	15.2	10	Glu	33.8	4.5	26.0	38.4	6
P inorg	0.82	0.08	0.70	0.90	5	Gly	8.7	1.4	6.0	10.1	6
P phytate						His	4.7	0.91	3.0	5.6	6
Fe	0.14	0.05	0.10	0.20	5	Ile	5.4	0.74	4.0	6.0	6
S	2.8	0.12	2.6	2.9	5	Leu	10.3	1.3	8.0	11.4	6
						Lys avail					

Trace Elements (mg/kg ODM)

						Lys total	6.5	0.40	6.0	7.1	6
Co						Meth	2.6	0.18	2.4	2.8	5
F						Phe	6.7	0.96	5.0	7.6	6
I						Pro	11.0	0.80	9.9	12.1	5
Mn	78.8	25.5	41.0	121.5	9	Pro.OH					
Mo	1.0	0.18	0.80	1.2	5	Ser	7.4	0.81	6.0	8.2	6
Zn	78.1	10.9	64.0	98.0	9	Thr	5.4	0.76	4.0	6.2	6
Cu	13.0	2.0	10.0	16.0	9	Tryp					
Se						Tyr	4.6	0.86	3.0	5.6	6
						Val	7.7	0.91	6.0	8.5	6

ANALYTICAL DATABASE

FEED DESCRIPTION : **WHEAT FEED** (Sources 1, 2, 3)

Determination	Mean	SD	Min	Max	n	Determination	Mean	SD	Min	Max	n
General (g/kg ODM)						**Volatile Fatty Acids** (g/kg ODM)					
ODM (fresh)	889.7	18.0	861.3	918.0	13	Lactic					
TDM (fresh)						Formic					
CP	179.2	12.8	159.0	197.0	13	Acetic					
CF	81.0	14.3	40.0	96.0	13	Propionic					
MADF	108.5	25.3	54.0	141.0	8	n butyric					
EE	43.4	10.6	31.0	73.0	13	i butyric					
AEE	50.6	3.2	43.7	54.7	9	n valeric					
TA	51.3	6.0	34.0	58.0	13	i valeric					
AIA	2.9	1.4	1.2	5.1	9	n caproic					
GE (MJ/kg ODM)	19.1	0.19	18.7	19.3	13	i caproic					
						NO_3N					
						NH_3N/TN					
Carbohydrates (g/kg ODM)						pH					
						Fatty Acids (g/kg ODM)					
NDF ash	363.7	53.6	243.0	435.0	13						
NDF unash											
ADF ash	111.2	18.2	61.0	138.0	13	C8:0					
ADF unash	118.0	7.0	110.6	127.5	4	C10:0					
Cellulose	77.6	5.9	68.8	85.5	9	C12:0					
Lignin	34.5	8.6	23.0	49.0	13	C14:0					
Starch	276.7	75.2	148.0	449.0	13	C16:0	5.8	0.87	4.6	6.9	5
NCD	747.8	15.2	730.0	771.0	9	C16:1					
CD						C18:0	0.25	0.07	0.14	0.30	5
IVD	693.7	41.6	616.0	802.0	13	C18:1	5.6	1.3	4.1	7.1	5
WSC	84.3	7.0	74.0	89.1	4	C18:2	21.3	2.6	17.6	24.1	5
Avail Carbs						C18:3	2.3	0.21	2.1	2.6	5
Sugars	56.6	6.1	49.8	64.8	5	C20:0					
						C20:4					
						C22:1					
Minerals (g/kg ODM)											
Ca	1.1	0.14	0.90	1.4	13	**Amino Acids** (g/kg ODM)					
Mg	5.2	2.6	3.3	10.7	13						
Na	0.14	0.06	0.10	0.20	5	Ala	7.9	0.72	6.8	8.6	5
K	13.0	2.2	7.4	17.0	13	Arg	11.6	0.55	11.0	12.2	5
Cl	1.1	0.20	0.80	1.3	5	Asp	12.0	0.45	11.6	12.7	5
P total	10.5	2.0	6.8	15.3	13	Cys	4.2	0.09	4.1	4.3	5
P inorg	0.62	0.24	0.40	1.0	5	Glu	35.8	1.3	34.8	38.1	5
P phytate						Gly	8.9	0.47	8.5	9.5	5
Fe	0.22	0.05	0.20	0.30	5	His	5.1	0.29	4.8	5.4	5
S	1.8	0.23	1.5	2.1	5	Ile	5.7	0.12	5.6	5.9	5
						Leu	11.0	0.20	10.7	11.1	5
						Lys avail					
Trace Elements (mg/kg ODM)						Lys total	7.2	0.28	6.8	7.5	5
						Meth	2.7	0.17	2.5	3.0	5
Co						Phe	7.0	0.16	6.9	7.2	5
F						Pro	11.4	0.43	10.8	12.0	5
I						Pro.OH					
Mn	88.7	33.3	30.0	139.0	9	Ser	7.6	0.25	7.4	8.1	5
Mo	0.74	0.17	0.50	0.90	5	Thr	5.9	0.16	5.7	6.1	5
Zn	103.7	22.7	71.0	141.5	9	Tryp					
Cu	13.6	1.9	11.5	17.0	9	Tyr	4.9	0.06	4.9	5.0	5
Se						Val	8.0	0.16	7.8	8.2	5

ANALYTICAL DATABASE

FEED DESCRIPTION : **WHEAT GRAIN, ALL SEASONS** (Sources 1, 2, 3, 4)

Determination	Mean	SD	Min	Max	n	Determination	Mean	SD	Min	Max	n
General (g/kg ODM)						**Volatile Fatty Acids** (g/kg ODM)					
ODM (fresh)	856.9	21.2	788.5	888.0	45	Lactic					
TDM (fresh)						Formic					
CP	127.6	16.5	97.0	161.3	45	Acetic					
CF	21.2	4.1	10.0	32.0	45	Propionic					
MADF	29.4	4.1	20.0	38.0	35	n butyric					
EE	17.3	3.4	12.0	30.0	45	i butyric					
AEE	21.4	2.5	15.7	26.0	29	n valeric					
TA	16.8	2.2	11.7	22.0	45	i valeric					
AIA	2.6	2.4	0.40	8.1	17	n caproic					
GE (MJ/kg ODM)	18.4	0.23	17.9	19.0	45	i caproic					
						NO_3N					
						NH_3N/TN					
						pH					
Carbohydrates (g/kg ODM)						**Fatty Acids** (g/kg ODM)					
NDF ash	123.7	21.1	91.5	175.0	44						
NDF unash						C8:0					
ADF ash	30.1	4.3	23.0	40.0	36	C10:0					
ADF unash	37.4	8.3	27.0	57.0	10	C12:0					
Cellulose	21.4	2.7	16.0	26.0	20	C14:0					
Lignin	11.2	2.3	7.5	16.0	36	C16:0	2.4	0.15	2.2	2.6	10
Starch	674.1	33.1	615.0	768.0	37	C16:1					
NCD	927.8	6.3	913.0	936.0	20	C18:0	0.11	0.14	0.05	0.50	10
CD						C18:1	1.7	0.12	1.5	1.9	10
IVD	860.6	24.3	815.0	919.5	36	C18:2	8.8	0.38	8.0	9.3	10
WSC						C18:3	1.0	0.14	0.86	1.2	10
Avail Carbs						C20:0					
Sugars	26.6	9.5	4.9	38.0	11	C20:4					
						C22:1					
Minerals (g/kg ODM)											
Ca	0.55	0.21	0.20	1.1	37	**Amino Acids** (g/kg ODM)					
Mg	1.1	0.13	0.80	1.3	36						
Na	0.12	0.06	0.10	0.40	24	Ala	4.5	0.74	3.0	6.0	19
K	4.6	0.39	3.8	5.5	36	Arg	6.0	0.72	4.5	7.0	19
Cl	1.0	0.15	0.80	1.2	10	Asp	6.7	1.0	5.0	9.0	19
P total	3.3	0.42	2.6	4.4	37	Cys	2.9	0.20	2.5	3.1	10
P inorg	0.25	0.13	0.10	0.50	10	Glu	37.1	7.5	25.0	52.0	19
P phytate						Gly	5.2	0.85	4.0	7.0	19
Fe	0.14	0.05	0.10	0.20	8	His	3.6	0.70	2.0	4.6	19
S	1.6	0.08	1.5	1.8	10	Ile	5.0	0.93	3.8	7.0	19
						Leu	9.5	1.6	6.8	13.0	19
Trace Elements (mg/kg ODM)						Lys avail					
						Lys total	3.8	0.47	3.0	4.7	19
Co						Meth	2.9	1.5	1.0	5.0	19
F						Phe	6.7	1.4	4.5	9.0	19
I	0.10	0.0	0.10	0.10	4	Pro	10.9	2.4	6.0	15.2	19
Mn	35.6	15.2	14.0	69.0	26	Pro.OH					
Mo	0.29	0.12	0.10	0.50	10	Ser	6.5	1.2	4.7	9.0	19
Zn	25.8	7.0	9.0	46.0	26	Thr	4.6	1.1	3.1	7.0	19
Cu	4.5	1.2	2.9	7.0	26	Tryp	1.9	0.33	1.0	2.0	9
Se	0.40		0.40	0.40	1	Tyr	4.4	0.94	3.1	6.0	19
						Val	5.8	0.62	4.6	7.0	19

ANALYTICAL DATABASE

FEED DESCRIPTION : **WHEAT GRAIN, SPRING** (Sources 2, 4)

Determination	Mean	SD	Min	Max	n	Determination	Mean	SD	Min	Max	n
General (g/kg ODM)						**Volatile Fatty Acids (g/kg ODM)**					
ODM (fresh)	864.0	9.9	857.0	871.0	2	Lactic					
TDM (fresh)						Formic					
CP	146.0	12.7	137.0	155.0	2	Acetic					
CF	21.3	0.42	21.0	21.6	2	Propionic					
MADF	27.7	1.9	26.3	29.0	2	n butyric					
EE	24.1	8.4	18.1	30.0	2	i butyric					
AEE	20.7		20.7	20.7	1	n valeric					
TA	17.9	1.6	16.7	19.0	2	i valeric					
AIA						n caproic					
GE (MJ/kg ODM)	18.8	0.38	18.5	19.0	2	i caproic					
						NO$_3$N					
						NH$_3$N/TN					
Carbohydrates (g/kg ODM)						pH					
						Fatty Acids (g/kg ODM)					
NDF ash	145.0	15.5	134.0	155.9	2						
NDF unash											
ADF ash	36.0		36.0	36.0	1	C8:0					
ADF unash						C10:0					
Cellulose						C12:0					
Lignin	12.0		12.0	12.0	1	C14:0					
Starch	625.0		625.0	625.0	1	C16:0					
NCD						C16:1					
CD						C18:0					
IVD	856.0		856.0	856.0	1	C18:1					
WSC						C18:2					
Avail Carbs						C18:3					
Sugars						C20:0					
						C20:4					
Minerals (g/kg ODM)						C22:1					
Ca	0.48		0.48	0.48	1						
Mg	1.2		1.2	1.2	1	**Amino Acids (g/kg ODM)**					
Na	0.10		0.10	0.10	1						
K	4.5		4.5	4.5	1	Ala	5.0		5.0	5.0	1
Cl						Arg	7.0		7.0	7.0	1
P total	3.9		3.9	3.9	1	Asp	8.0		8.0	8.0	1
P inorg						Cys					
P phytate						Glu	50.0		50.0	50.0	1
Fe						Gly	7.0		7.0	7.0	1
S						His	4.0		4.0	4.0	1
						Ile	6.0		6.0	6.0	1
						Leu	11.0		11.0	11.0	1
Trace Elements (mg/kg ODM)						Lys avail					
						Lys total	4.0		4.0	4.0	1
Co						Meth	5.0		5.0	5.0	1
F						Phe	8.0		8.0	8.0	1
I						Pro	11.0		11.0	11.0	1
Mn	31.0		31.0	31.0	1	Pro.OH					
Mo						Ser	8.0		8.0	8.0	1
Zn	22.0		22.0	22.0	1	Thr	6.0		6.0	6.0	1
Cu	6.0		6.0	6.0	1	Tryp	2.0		2.0	2.0	1
Se						Tyr	6.0		6.0	6.0	1
						Val	6.0		6.0	6.0	1

ANALYTICAL DATABASE

FEED DESCRIPTION : **WHEAT GRAIN, WINTER** (Sources 1, 2, 3, 4)

Determination	Mean	SD	Min	Max	n	Determination	Mean	SD	Min	Max	n
General (g/kg ODM)						**Volatile Fatty Acids** (g/kg ODM)					
ODM (fresh)	856.6	21.6	788.5	888.0	43	Lactic					
TDM (fresh)						Formic					
CP	126.8	16.2	97.0	161.3	43	Acetic					
CF	21.2	4.2	10.0	32.0	43	Propionic					
MADF	29.5	4.2	20.0	38.0	33	n butyric					
EE	17.0	2.9	12.0	23.0	43	i butyric					
AEE	21.5	2.6	15.7	26.0	28	n valeric					
TA	16.7	2.2	11.7	22.0	43	i valeric					
AIA	2.6	2.4	0.40	8.1	17	n caproic					
GE (MJ/kg ODM)	18.4	0.21	17.9	19.0	43	i caproic					
						NO_3N					
Carbohydrates (g/kg ODM)						NH_3N/TN					
						pH					
NDF ash	122.7	21.0	91.5	175.0	42						
NDF unash						**Fatty Acids** (g/kg ODM)					
ADF ash	30.0	4.2	23.0	40.0	35						
ADF unash	37.4	8.3	27.0	57.0	10	C8:0					
Cellulose	21.4	2.7	16.0	26.0	20	C10:0					
Lignin	11.1	2.3	7.5	16.0	35	C12:0					
Starch	675.5	32.5	615.0	768.0	36	C14:0					
NCD	927.8	6.3	913.0	936.0	20	C16:0	2.4	0.15	2.2	2.6	10
CD						C16:1					
IVD	860.8	24.6	815.0	919.5	35	C18:0	0.11	0.14	0.05	0.50	10
WSC						C18:1	1.7	0.12	1.5	1.9	10
Avail Carbs						C18:2	8.8	0.38	8.0	9.3	10
Sugars	26.6	9.5	4.9	38.0	11	C18:3	1.0	0.14	0.86	1.2	10
						C20:0					
						C20:4					
Minerals (g/kg ODM)						C22:1					
Ca	0.55	0.21	0.20	1.1	36						
Mg	1.1	0.13	0.80	1.3	35	**Amino Acids** (g/kg ODM)					
Na	0.12	0.07	0.10	0.40	23						
K	4.6	0.40	3.8	5.5	35	Ala	4.5	0.75	3.0	6.0	18
Cl	1.0	0.15	0.80	1.2	10	Arg	6.0	0.69	4.5	7.0	18
P total	3.3	0.42	2.6	4.4	36	Asp	6.6	1.0	5.0	9.0	18
P inorg	0.25	0.13	0.10	0.50	10	Cys	2.9	0.20	2.5	3.1	10
P phytate						Glu	36.4	7.0	25.0	52.0	18
Fe	0.14	0.05	0.10	0.20	8	Gly	5.1	0.74	4.0	7.0	18
S	1.6	0.08	1.5	1.8	10	His	3.6	0.71	2.0	4.6	18
						Ile	4.9	0.92	3.8	7.0	18
						Leu	9.4	1.7	6.8	13.0	18
Trace Elements (mg/kg ODM)						Lys avail					
						Lys total	3.8	0.49	3.0	4.7	18
Co						Meth	2.8	1.5	1.0	5.0	18
F						Phe	6.6	1.4	4.5	9.0	18
I	0.10	0.0	0.10	0.10	4	Pro	10.9	2.5	6.0	15.2	18
Mn	35.8	15.5	14.0	69.0	25	Pro.OH					
Mo	0.29	0.12	0.10	0.50	10	Ser	6.4	1.2	4.7	9.0	18
Zn	25.9	7.1	9.0	46.0	25	Thr	4.5	1.1	3.1	7.0	18
Cu	4.4	1.1	2.9	7.0	25	Tryp	1.9	0.35	1.0	2.0	8
Se	0.40		0.40	0.40	1	Tyr	4.3	0.89	3.1	6.0	18
						Val	5.8	0.64	4.6	7.0	18

ANALYTICAL DATABASE

FEED DESCRIPTION : **WHEAT MIDDLINGS** (Source 4)

Determination	Mean	SD	Min	Max	n	Determination	Mean	SD	Min	Max	n
General (g/kg ODM)						**Volatile Fatty Acids** (g/kg ODM)					
ODM (fresh)	878.7		878.7	878.7	1	Lactic					
TDM (fresh)						Formic					
CP	174.5		174.5	174.5	1	Acetic					
CF	71.3		71.3	71.3	1	Propionic					
MADF	98.8		98.8	98.8	1	n butyric					
EE	39.3		39.3	39.3	1	i butyric					
AEE	37.4		37.4	37.4	1	n valeric					
TA	47.5		47.5	47.5	1	i valeric					
AIA						n caproic					
GE (MJ/kg ODM)	19.2		19.2	19.2	1	i caproic					
						NO_3N					
						NH_3N/TN					
						pH					
Carbohydrates (g/kg ODM)											
						Fatty Acids (g/kg ODM)					
NDF ash											
NDF unash						C8:0					
ADF ash						C10:0					
ADF unash						C12:0					
Cellulose						C14:0					
Lignin						C16:0					
Starch	306.0		306.0	306.0	1	C16:1					
NCD						C18:0					
CD						C18:1					
IVD						C18:2					
WSC						C18:3					
Avail Carbs						C20:0					
Sugars	65.0		65.0	65.0	1	C20:4					
						C22:1					
Minerals (g/kg ODM)											
						Amino Acids (g/kg ODM)					
Ca	1.4		1.4	1.4	1						
Mg						Ala	4.0		4.0	4.0	1
Na						Arg	10.0		10.0	10.0	1
K						Asp	4.0		4.0	4.0	1
Cl						Cys					
P total	10.6		10.6	10.6	1	Glu	36.0		36.0	36.0	1
P inorg						Gly	6.0		6.0	6.0	1
P phytate						His	3.0		3.0	3.0	1
Fe						Ile	5.0		5.0	5.0	1
S						Leu	11.0		11.0	11.0	1
						Lys avail					
						Lys total	6.0		6.0	6.0	1
Trace Elements (mg/kg ODM)						Meth	2.0		2.0	2.0	1
						Phe	7.0		7.0	7.0	1
Co						Pro					
F						Pro.OH					
I						Ser	4.0		4.0	4.0	1
Mn						Thr	6.0		6.0	6.0	1
Mo						Tryp					
Zn						Tyr	5.0		5.0	5.0	1
Cu						Val	9.0		9.0	9.0	1
Se											

ANALYTICAL DATABASE

FEED DESCRIPTION : **WHEAT OFFALS** (Source 2)

Determination	Mean	SD	Min	Max	n	Determination	Mean	SD	Min	Max	n
General (g/kg ODM)						**Volatile Fatty Acids** (g/kg ODM)					
ODM (fresh)	877.6	6.3	864.0	886.0	8	Lactic					
TDM (fresh)						Formic					
CP	184.6	17.4	163.0	211.0	8	Acetic					
CF	70.3	19.9	38.0	103.0	8	Propionic					
MADF	101.6	30.2	53.0	150.0	8	n butyric					
EE	46.9	5.9	41.0	59.0	8	i butyric					
AEE						n valeric					
TA	51.0	11.6	31.0	71.0	8	i valeric					
AIA						n caproic					
GE (MJ/kg ODM)	19.1	0.15	18.8	19.3	8	i caproic					
						NO$_3$N					
						NH$_3$N/TN					
Carbohydrates (g/kg ODM)						pH					
NDF ash	353.6	81.7	238.0	505.0	8	**Fatty Acids** (g/kg ODM)					
NDF unash											
ADF ash	103.5	26.9	58.0	147.0	8	C8:0					
ADF unash						C10:0					
Cellulose						C12:0					
Lignin	36.4	6.1	23.0	42.0	8	C14:0					
Starch	329.1	108.4	157.0	500.0	8	C16:0					
NCD						C16:1					
CD						C18:0					
IVD	693.4	63.5	595.0	797.0	8	C18:1					
WSC						C18:2					
Avail Carbs						C18:3					
Sugars						C20:0					
						C20:4					
						C22:1					
Minerals (g/kg ODM)											
Ca	1.0	0.11	0.80	1.2	8						
Mg	8.7	1.8	5.9	11.5	8	**Amino Acids** (g/kg ODM)					
Na	0.14		0.14	0.14	1	Ala					
K	12.9	1.1	11.5	14.5	8	Arg					
Cl						Asp					
P total	11.9	1.2	10.3	13.8	8	Cys					
P inorg						Glu					
P phytate						Gly					
Fe						His					
S						Ile					
						Leu					
						Lys avail					
Trace Elements (mg/kg ODM)						Lys total					
						Meth					
Co						Phe					
F						Pro					
I						Pro.OH					
Mn	77.6	20.0	50.0	108.0	8	Ser					
Mo						Thr					
Zn	85.8	9.0	72.0	100.0	8	Tryp					
Cu	14.9	1.5	12.0	16.0	8	Tyr					
Se						Val					

134

ANALYTICAL   DATABASE

FEED CLASS 50

PROTEIN SUPPLEMENTS

ANALYTICAL DATABASE

FEED DESCRIPTION : **BEANS, FIELD SPRING** (Sources 1, 2, 4)

Determination	Mean	SD	Min	Max	n	Determination	Mean	SD	Min	Max	n
General (g/kg ODM)						**Volatile Fatty Acids** (g/kg ODM)					
ODM (fresh)	861.4	5.7	857.4	865.4	2	Lactic					
TDM (fresh)						Formic					
CP	329.5	33.5	264.8	369.0	10	Acetic					
CF	74.5	7.5	66.0	84.0	10	Propionic					
MADF	111.2	7.8	101.0	120.7	10	n butyric					
EE	13.0	4.3	8.0	22.1	10	i butyric					
AEE	16.0		16.0	16.0	1	n valeric					
TA	36.9	3.1	32.0	42.0	10	i valeric					
AIA	0.20		0.20	0.20	1	n caproic					
GE (MJ/kg ODM)	18.6	0.17	18.2	18.8	10	i caproic					
						NO3N					
Carbohydrates (g/kg ODM)						NH3N/TN					
						pH					
NDF ash	186.4	27.8	118.2	210.0	9	**Fatty Acids** (g/kg ODM)					
NDF unash											
ADF ash	122.5	9.5	110.0	138.0	8	C8:0					
ADF unash						C10:0					
Cellulose						C12:0					
Lignin	14.8	2.7	11.0	19.0	8	C14:0					
Starch	365.1	27.7	335.0	424.0	10	C16:0					
NCD	940.0		940.0	940.0	1	C16:1					
CD						C18:0					
IVD	809.1	9.2	799.0	828.0	9	C18:1					
WSC						C18:2					
Avail Carbs						C18:3					
Sugars	47.0		47.0	47.0	1	C20:0					
						C20:4					
Minerals (g/kg ODM)						C22:1					
Ca	1.1	0.23	0.80	1.6	10						
Mg	1.8	0.29	1.2	2.2	9	**Amino Acids** (g/kg ODM)					
Na											
K	10.9	1.3	9.5	13.4	9	Ala	18.0		18.0	18.0	1
Cl						Arg	30.0		30.0	30.0	1
P total	5.2	0.67	3.8	6.1	10	Asp	23.0		23.0	23.0	1
P inorg						Cys					
P phytate						Glu	58.0		58.0	58.0	1
Fe						Gly	18.0		18.0	18.0	1
S						His	8.0		8.0	8.0	1
						Ile	12.0		12.0	12.0	1
						Leu	25.0		25.0	25.0	1
Trace Elements (mg/kg ODM)						Lys avail					
						Lys total	20.0		20.0	20.0	1
Co						Meth	5.0		5.0	5.0	1
F						Phe	15.0		15.0	15.0	1
I						Pro					
Mn	7.8	1.5	6.0	11.0	8	Pro.OH					
Mo						Ser	17.0		17.0	17.0	1
Zn	38.4	7.4	27.0	47.0	8	Thr	14.0		14.0	14.0	1
Cu	12.9	2.7	9.0	18.0	8	Tryp					
Se						Tyr	12.0		12.0	12.0	1
						Val	18.0		18.0	18.0	1

ANALYTICAL DATABASE

FEED DESCRIPTION : **BEANS, FIELD WINTER** (Sources 1, 2)

Determination	Mean	SD	Min	Max	n	Determination	Mean	SD	Min	Max	n
General (g/kg ODM)						**Volatile Fatty Acids** (g/kg ODM)					
ODM (fresh)	847.8	8.7	841.6	853.9	2	Lactic					
TDM (fresh)						Formic					
CP	267.4	11.7	253.0	283.0	6	Acetic					
CF	90.9	16.1	80.0	122.9	6	Propionic					
MADF	128.8	20.2	115.0	169.0	6	n butyric					
EE	13.4	2.2	10.0	16.0	5	i butyric					
AEE	18.0	0.0	18.0	18.0	2	n valeric					
TA	34.9	4.3	30.0	42.8	6	i valeric					
AIA	1.5	1.8	0.20	2.7	2	n caproic					
GE (MJ/kg ODM)	18.4	0.25	17.9	18.6	6	i caproic					
						NO_3N					
						NH_3N/TN					
Carbohydrates (g/kg ODM)						pH					
NDF ash	167.3	21.8	130.0	186.0	6	**Fatty Acids** (g/kg ODM)					
NDF unash											
ADF ash	123.8	4.3	118.0	127.0	4	C8:0					
ADF unash						C10:0					
Cellulose						C12:0					
Lignin	17.5	6.5	12.0	26.0	4	C14:0					
Starch	394.7	41.3	315.0	433.0	6	C16:0					
NCD	919.5	16.3	908.0	931.0	2	C16:1					
CD						C18:0					
IVD	808.1	23.6	767.0	828.0	6	C18:1					
WSC						C18:2					
Avail Carbs						C18:3					
Sugars						C20:0					
						C20:4					
						C22:1					
Minerals (g/kg ODM)											
Ca	1.3	0.33	1.0	1.9	6						
Mg	1.9	0.43	1.3	2.3	6	**Amino Acids** (g/kg ODM)					
Na	0.40		0.40	0.40	1	Ala					
K	11.9	0.74	11.0	13.1	6	Arg					
Cl						Asp					
P total	8.6	2.1	5.9	10.8	6	Cys					
P inorg						Glu					
P phytate						Gly					
Fe						His					
S						Ile					
						Leu					
						Lys avail					
						Lys total					
						Meth					
Trace Elements (mg/kg ODM)						Phe					
						Pro					
Co						Pro.OH					
F						Ser					
I						Thr					
Mn	8.0	0.0	8.0	8.0	4	Tryp					
Mo						Tyr					
Zn	33.3	3.5	29.0	37.0	4	Val					
Cu	15.3	1.7	13.0	17.0	4						
Se											

ANALYTICAL DATABASE

FEED DESCRIPTION : **BLOOD MEAL** (Source 3)

Determination	Mean	SD	Min	Max	n	Determination	Mean	SD	Min	Max	n
General (g/kg ODM)						**Volatile Fatty Acids** (g/kg ODM)					
ODM (fresh)	914.8	16.7	894.5	937.5	5	Lactic					
TDM (fresh)						Formic					
CP	904.8	3.2	901.3	908.3	5	Acetic					
CF	2.3	0.31	2.0	2.8	5	Propionic					
MADF						n butyric					
EE						i butyric					
AEE	12.0	2.2	9.4	14.4	5	n valeric					
TA	19.6	0.96	18.0	20.5	5	i valeric					
AIA	1.8	0.22	1.5	2.0	5	n caproic					
GE (MJ/kg ODM)	24.5	0.25	24.2	24.9	5	i caproic					
						NO_3N					
						NH_3N/TN					
						pH					
Carbohydrates (g/kg ODM)											
						Fatty Acids (g/kg ODM)					
NDF ash											
NDF unash						C8:0					
ADF ash						C10:0					
ADF unash						C12:0					
Cellulose						C14:0					
Lignin						C16:0					
Starch						C16:1	0.07	0.03	0.04	0.12	5
NCD						C18:0					
CD						C18:1	0.04	0.02	0.02	0.06	5
IVD	840.8	12.7	822.0	856.5	5	C18:2	0.06	0.06	0.02	0.17	5
WSC						C18:3					
Avail Carbs						C20:0					
Sugars						C20:4					
						C22:1					
Minerals (g/kg ODM)											
						Amino Acids (g/kg ODM)					
Ca	0.56	0.26	0.10	0.70	5						
Mg	0.20	0.0	0.20	0.20	5	Ala	67.7	3.0	64.8	71.1	5
Na	3.6	0.32	3.1	3.9	5	Arg	30.8	2.2	28.3	34.2	5
K	1.9	0.12	1.8	2.1	5	Asp	99.1	3.5	95.4	102.7	5
Cl	3.3	0.20	3.0	3.5	5	Cys	10.9	0.83	10.0	12.3	5
P total	1.5	0.19	1.3	1.7	5	Glu	78.8	3.3	75.0	83.6	5
P inorg	0.28	0.04	0.20	0.30	5	Gly	39.2	0.87	38.3	40.2	5
P phytate						His	71.0	5.0	66.1	76.6	5
Fe	2.3	0.14	2.2	2.5	5	Ile	13.7	0.71	13.0	14.6	5
S	8.4	0.25	8.0	8.6	5	Leu	112.1	3.9	107.7	117.1	5
						Lys avail					
						Lys total	85.5	2.5	83.6	88.9	5
Trace Elements (mg/kg ODM)						Meth	10.0	0.39	9.6	10.4	5
						Phe	66.2	2.0	63.1	68.8	5
Co						Pro	34.1	1.5	33.0	36.7	5
F						Pro.OH					
I	0.34	0.05	0.30	0.40	5	Ser	46.9	2.3	43.4	49.2	5
Mn	0.24	0.05	0.20	0.30	5	Thr	45.1	2.3	42.4	47.2	5
Mo	0.26	0.11	0.10	0.40	5	Tryp					
Zn	25.0	1.2	23.9	27.0	5	Tyr	24.4	3.6	20.6	30.2	5
Cu	5.9	0.56	5.0	6.3	5	Val	74.1	4.3	67.3	78.3	5
Se	0.62	0.08	0.50	0.70	5						

ANALYTICAL DATABASE

FEED DESCRIPTION : **BREWERS GRAINS** (Sources 1, 2, 5, 6)

Determination	Mean	SD	Min	Max	n	Determination	Mean	SD	Min	Max	n
General (g/kg ODM)						**Volatile Fatty Acids** (g/kg ODM)					
ODM (fresh)	249.9	31.3	120.0	338.0	92	Lactic	27.2	13.7	2.0	48.1	20
TDM (fresh)	261.3	34.4	204.0	366.0	82	Formic	3.1	0.78	2.5	3.6	2
CP	218.0	34.2	172.0	327.0	64	Acetic	12.5	13.9	0.13	55.9	26
CF	170.5	16.9	126.0	207.0	64	Propionic	3.6	3.8	0.32	12.9	13
MADF	236.2	23.4	190.0	287.0	19	n butyric	1.2	1.2	0.13	4.3	21
EE	61.5	16.7	32.0	99.0	64	i butyric					
AEE	55.3	13.7	46.0	71.0	3	n valeric	0.40	0.28	0.20	0.60	2
TA	38.3	6.0	3.7	56.0	64	i valeric	0.40		0.40	0.40	1
AIA	15.5	4.3	7.0	26.0	14	n caproic	0.60		0.60	0.60	1
GE (MJ/kg ODM)	21.3	0.35	20.7	21.9	20	i caproic	0.40		0.40	0.40	1
						NO3N					
Carbohydrates (g/kg ODM)						NH3N/TN	17.5	15.0	10.0	40.0	4
						pH	4.5	0.66	2.7	5.7	55
NDF ash	618.1	63.9	499.0	753.0	17						
NDF unash						**Fatty Acids** (g/kg ODM)					
ADF ash	263.7	26.6	216.0	315.0	17						
ADF unash	321.9	44.5	258.0	392.0	14	C8:0					
Cellulose	196.5	20.8	156.0	231.0	14	C10:0					
Lignin	86.4	36.5	47.0	172.0	19	C12:0					
Starch	38.4	24.4	7.3	96.0	15	C14:0					
NCD	591.1	35.8	492.0	647.0	19	C16:0					
CD	470.7	66.1	391.0	644.0	12	C16:1					
IVD	482.5	54.1	400.0	647.0	19	C18:0					
WSC	12.7	6.1	4.0	27.0	18	C18:1					
Avail Carbs						C18:2					
Sugars						C18:3					
						C20:0					
						C20:4					
Minerals (g/kg ODM)						C22:1					
Ca	3.5	1.4	1.1	6.2	20						
Mg	1.7	0.36	1.1	2.5	20	**Amino Acids** (g/kg ODM)					
Na	0.26	0.30	0.04	1.4	18						
K	0.56	0.95	0.07	4.5	20	Ala					
Cl						Arg					
P total	5.1	1.0	2.7	7.5	20	Asp					
P inorg						Cys					
P phytate						Glu					
Fe						Gly					
S						His					
						Ile					
						Leu					
						Lys avail					
						Lys total					
						Meth					
						Phe					
Trace Elements (mg/kg ODM)						Pro					
Co						Pro.OH					
F						Ser					
I						Thr					
Mn	31.0	4.1	25.0	37.0	6	Tryp					
Mo						Tyr					
Zn	72.8	12.5	60.0	94.0	6	Val					
Cu	18.7	9.2	12.0	31.0	6						
Se											

ANALYTICAL DATABASE

FEED DESCRIPTION : **COPRA, EXPELLED** (Sources 2, 4)

Determination	Mean	SD	Min	Max	n
General (g/kg ODM)					
ODM (fresh)	933.7	26.7	894.0	956.0	6
TDM (fresh)					
CP	198.2	29.6	154.0	233.0	6
CF	94.7	22.3	68.0	126.0	6
MADF	250.3	41.0	176.0	298.0	6
EE	168.0	96.4	72.0	333.0	6
AEE					
TA	51.7	8.9	43.0	63.0	6
AIA					
GE (MJ/kg ODM)	21.3	2.0	19.2	24.6	6

Determination	Mean	SD	Min	Max	n
Carbohydrates (g/kg ODM)					
NDF ash	517.0	21.2	502.0	532.0	2
NDF unash					
ADF ash	281.0	11.3	273.0	289.0	2
ADF unash					
Cellulose					
Lignin	65.0	8.5	59.0	71.0	2
Starch	2.0	0.0	2.0	2.0	2
NCD	695.5	16.3	684.0	707.0	2
CD					
IVD	642.5	82.7	584.0	701.0	2
WSC					
Avail Carbs					
Sugars	114.0	39.6	86.0	142.0	2

Determination	Mean	SD	Min	Max	n
Minerals (g/kg ODM)					
Ca	0.55	0.21	0.40	0.70	2
Mg	3.0	0.21	2.8	3.1	2
Na	0.85	0.50	0.50	1.2	2
K	23.6	0.42	23.3	23.9	2
Cl					
P total	5.4	0.07	5.3	5.4	2
P inorg					
P phytate					
Fe					
S					

Determination	Mean	SD	Min	Max	n
Trace Elements (mg/kg ODM)					
Co					
F					
I					
Mn	58.5	23.3	42.0	75.0	2
Mo					
Zn	76.0	12.7	67.0	85.0	2
Cu	26.0	12.7	17.0	35.0	2
Se					

Determination	Mean	SD	Min	Max	n
Volatile Fatty Acids (g/kg ODM)					
Lactic					
Formic					
Acetic					
Propionic					
n butyric					
i butyric					
n valeric					
i valeric					
n caproic					
i caproic					
NO_3N					
NH_3N/TN					
pH					

Determination	Mean	SD	Min	Max	n
Fatty Acids (g/kg ODM)					
C8:0					
C10:0					
C12:0					
C14:0					
C16:0					
C16:1					
C18:0					
C18:1					
C18:2					
C18:3					
C20:0					
C20:4					
C22:1					

Determination	Mean	SD	Min	Max	n
Amino Acids (g/kg ODM)					
Ala	8.9	0.29	8.7	9.1	2
Arg	25.0	2.1	21.3	27.0	6
Asp	15.6	0.63	15.2	16.1	2
Cys	8.0	0.24	7.8	8.2	2
Glu	26.2	1.1	25.4	26.9	2
Gly	8.4	0.05	8.4	8.5	2
His	3.6	0.70	3.0	4.4	6
Ile	6.2	0.43	5.8	7.0	6
Leu	13.0	0.89	11.9	14.0	6
Lys avail					
Lys total	5.4	0.71	5.0	6.8	6
Meth	3.9	1.5	2.0	6.0	6
Phe	8.7	0.28	8.5	8.9	2
Pro	7.2	0.59	6.8	7.6	2
Pro.OH	0.65		0.65	0.65	1
Ser	8.8	0.44	8.5	9.1	2
Thr	5.9	1.1	5.0	7.5	6
Tryp	2.0	0.0	2.0	2.0	4
Tyr	6.0	0.14	5.9	6.1	2
Val	10.0	0.85	9.1	11.0	6

ANALYTICAL DATABASE

FEED DESCRIPTION : **COPRA, EXTRACTED** (Source 4)

Determination	Mean	SD	Min	Max	n	Determination	Mean	SD	Min	Max	n
General (g/kg ODM)						**Volatile Fatty Acids (g/kg ODM)**					
ODM (fresh)	899.0		899.0	899.0	1	Lactic					
TDM (fresh)						Formic					
CP	246.0		246.0	246.0	1	Acetic					
CF	108.0		108.0	108.0	1	Propionic					
MADF	299.0		299.0	299.0	1	n butyric					
EE	4.0		4.0	4.0	1	i butyric					
AEE						n valeric					
TA	62.0		62.0	62.0	1	i valeric					
AIA						n caproic					
GE (MJ/kg ODM)	18.3		18.3	18.3	1	i caproic					
						NO_3N					
						NH_3N/TN					
Carbohydrates (g/kg ODM)						pH					
NDF ash											
NDF unash						**Fatty Acids (g/kg ODM)**					
ADF ash											
ADF unash						C8:0					
Cellulose						C10:0					
Lignin						C12:0					
Starch						C14:0					
NCD						C16:0					
CD						C16:1					
IVD						C18:0					
WSC						C18:1					
Avail Carbs						C18:2					
Sugars						C18:3					
						C20:0					
						C20:4					
Minerals (g/kg ODM)						C22:1					
Ca											
Mg						**Amino Acids (g/kg ODM)**					
Na											
K						Ala					
Cl						Arg	24.0		24.0	24.0	1
P total						Asp					
P inorg						Cys					
P phytate						Glu					
Fe						Gly					
S						His	4.0		4.0	4.0	1
						Ile	5.0		5.0	5.0	1
						Leu	12.0		12.0	12.0	1
Trace Elements (mg/kg ODM)						Lys avail					
						Lys total	5.0		5.0	5.0	1
Co						Meth	5.0		5.0	5.0	1
F						Phe					
I						Pro					
Mn						Pro.OH					
Mo						Ser					
Zn						Thr	5.0		5.0	5.0	1
Cu						Tryp	2.0		2.0	2.0	1
Se						Tyr					
						Val	9.0		9.0	9.0	1

ANALYTICAL DATABASE

FEED DESCRIPTION : **COPRA, FULL FAT** (Source 4)

Determination	Mean	SD	Min	Max	n	Determination	Mean	SD	Min	Max	n
General (g/kg ODM)						**Volatile Fatty Acids (g/kg ODM)**					
ODM (fresh)	959.0		959.0	959.0	1	Lactic					
TDM (fresh)						Formic					
CP	76.0		76.0	76.0	1	Acetic					
CF	35.0		35.0	35.0	1	Propionic					
MADF	103.0		103.0	103.0	1	n butyric					
EE	662.0		662.0	662.0	1	i butyric					
AEE						n valeric					
TA	12.0		12.0	12.0	1	i valeric					
AIA						n caproic					
GE (MJ/kg ODM)	34.4		34.4	34.4	1	i caproic					
						NO_3N					
						NH_3N/TN					
						pH					
Carbohydrates (g/kg ODM)											
NDF ash						**Fatty Acids (g/kg ODM)**					
NDF unash											
ADF ash						C8:0					
ADF unash						C10:0					
Cellulose						C12:0					
Lignin						C14:0					
Starch						C16:0					
NCD						C16:1					
CD						C18:0					
IVD						C18:1					
WSC						C18:2					
Avail Carbs						C18:3					
Sugars						C20:0					
						C20:4					
						C22:1					
Minerals (g/kg ODM)											
Ca						**Amino Acids (g/kg ODM)**					
Mg											
Na						Ala					
K						Arg	16.0		16.0	16.0	1
Cl						Asp					
P total						Cys					
P inorg						Glu					
P phytate						Gly					
Fe						His	1.0		1.0	1.0	1
S						Ile	3.0		3.0	3.0	1
						Leu	8.0		8.0	8.0	1
						Lys avail					
						Lys total	4.0		4.0	4.0	1
Trace Elements (mg/kg ODM)						Meth	3.0		3.0	3.0	1
						Phe					
Co						Pro					
F						Pro.OH					
I						Ser					
Mn						Thr	3.0		3.0	3.0	1
Mo						Tryp	1.0		1.0	1.0	1
Zn						Tyr					
Cu						Val	6.0		6.0	6.0	1
Se											

142

ANALYTICAL DATABASE

FEED DESCRIPTION : **COTTONSEED MEAL** (Sources 1, 3)

Determination	Mean	SD	Min	Max	n	Determination	Mean	SD	Min	Max	n
General (g/kg ODM)						**Volatile Fatty Acids** (g/kg ODM)					
ODM (fresh)	943.6	22.8	901.5	976.0	9	Lactic					
TDM (fresh)						Formic					
CP	378.8	17.3	355.9	400.9	9	Acetic					
CF	171.1	23.7	132.5	202.0	9	Propionic					
MADF	245.0	36.1	200.0	283.0	4	n butyric					
EE	63.7	5.8	56.0	72.0	9	i butyric					
AEE	67.0	3.9	59.6	74.0	9	n valeric					
TA	61.2	4.2	53.5	66.0	9	i valeric					
AIA	3.8	1.7	1.0	6.5	9	n caproic					
GE (MJ/kg ODM)	20.6	0.24	20.2	20.9	9	i caproic					
						NO_3N					
						NH_3N/TN					
Carbohydrates (g/kg ODM)						pH					
						Fatty Acids (g/kg ODM)					
NDF ash	384.8	49.6	330.0	467.0	9						
NDF unash						C8:0					
ADF ash	245.4	34.9	193.0	303.0	9	C10:0					
ADF unash	279.5	22.4	257.0	309.0	4	C12:0					
Cellulose	167.5	33.8	121.5	217.0	9	C14:0	0.38	0.04	0.30	0.40	5
Lignin	61.6	15.6	47.5	86.0	9	C16:0	13.9	1.2	12.3	15.6	5
Starch	16.5	7.7	7.7	32.1	8	C16:1	0.20	0.0	0.20	0.20	5
NCD	749.9	29.1	686.0	785.0	9	C18:0	1.2	0.04	1.1	1.2	5
CD						C18:1	9.9	0.95	8.6	11.1	5
IVD	570.8	65.6	500.0	655.0	4	C18:2	36.3	2.6	32.8	39.5	5
WSC	67.9	1.0	67.0	69.0	3	C18:3	0.20	0.0	0.20	0.20	5
Avail Carbs						C20:0					
Sugars	50.8	2.8	46.2	53.5	5	C20:4					
						C22:1					
Minerals (g/kg ODM)											
Ca	2.1	0.21	1.7	2.4	9	**Amino Acids** (g/kg ODM)					
Mg	5.8	0.43	5.1	6.4	9						
Na	0.19	0.06	0.10	0.30	9	Ala	16.7	0.64	15.9	17.4	5
K	15.8	0.84	14.7	16.9	9	Arg	47.8	2.4	45.0	51.3	5
Cl	1.1	0.08	1.0	1.2	5	Asp	9.8	0.49	9.1	10.2	5
P total	8.9	1.1	6.5	10.3	9	Cys	6.7	0.27	6.4	7.1	5
P inorg	1.1	0.12	1.0	1.3	5	Glu	75.8	3.4	72.3	80.6	5
P phytate						Gly	17.2	0.48	16.7	18.0	5
Fe						His	14.3	1.1	12.7	15.7	5
S	5.0	0.32	4.5	5.4	5	Ile	13.1	0.80	11.9	14.1	5
						Leu	24.1	0.87	23.0	25.4	5
						Lys avail					
Trace Elements (mg/kg ODM)						Lys total	17.9	1.0	16.8	19.2	5
						Meth	6.4	0.25	6.1	6.7	5
Co	0.10	0.0	0.10	0.10	5	Phe	21.8	0.91	21.0	22.8	5
F						Pro	14.4	0.75	13.9	15.7	5
I	0.14	0.06	0.10	0.20	5	Pro.OH					
Mn						Ser	18.0	0.86	17.1	19.1	5
Mo						Thr	14.0	0.99	13.2	15.7	5
Zn						Tryp					
Cu						Tyr	11.7	0.63	10.7	12.4	5
Se	0.10	0.0	0.10	0.10	5	Val	17.5	0.91	16.2	18.6	5

ANALYTICAL DATABASE

FEED DESCRIPTION : **DISTILLERS DARK GRAINS, BARLEY BASED** (Sources 2, 3)

Determination	Mean	SD	Min	Max	n	Determination	Mean	SD	Min	Max	n
General (g/kg ODM)						**Volatile Fatty Acids** (g/kg ODM)					
ODM (fresh)	907.1	20.9	880.0	930.0	7	Lactic					
TDM (fresh)						Formic					
CP	274.9	13.1	251.0	289.2	7	Acetic					
CF	121.3	12.8	99.7	137.0	7	Propionic					
MADF	166.5	14.8	156.0	177.0	2	n butyric					
EE	67.0	7.8	53.0	74.2	7	i butyric					
AEE	84.6	7.8	73.2	91.6	5	n valeric					
TA	60.3	4.2	56.0	68.5	7	i valeric					
AIA	11.0	1.8	8.9	13.7	5	n caproic					
GE (MJ/kg ODM)	21.3	0.26	20.9	21.7	7	i caproic					
						NO_3N					
						NH_3N/TN					
Carbohydrates (g/kg ODM)						pH					
NDF ash	419.5	21.9	404.0	435.0	2	**Fatty Acids** (g/kg ODM)					
NDF unash											
ADF ash	174.5	13.4	165.0	184.0	2	C8:0					
ADF unash						C10:0					
Cellulose						C12:0					
Lignin	32.0	2.8	30.0	34.0	2	C14:0					
Starch	26.0	8.4	14.0	34.3	7	C16:0	12.3	2.5	8.5	14.4	5
NCD	687.2	19.8	671.0	721.0	5	C16:1					
CD						C18:0	0.70	0.12	0.60	0.90	5
IVD	553.6	21.8	536.0	596.0	7	C18:1	6.3	0.79	5.4	7.5	5
WSC	18.0	1.4	17.0	19.0	2	C18:2	32.1	4.1	25.0	34.8	5
Avail Carbs						C18:3	4.0	1.1	2.3	4.9	5
Sugars	38.9	18.0	23.1	65.9	5	C20:0					
						C20:4					
Minerals (g/kg ODM)						C22:1					
Ca	1.7	0.32	1.4	2.2	7						
Mg	3.3	0.34	2.7	3.8	7	**Amino Acids** (g/kg ODM)					
Na	1.2	1.2	0.40	3.5	7	Ala	16.0	0.49	15.4	16.5	5
K	10.2	0.83	9.4	11.9	7	Arg	11.7	0.70	10.8	12.5	5
Cl	3.2	0.47	2.8	4.0	5	Asp	18.5	0.93	16.9	19.3	5
P total	9.6	0.80	8.3	10.6	7	Cys	4.9	0.43	4.2	5.3	5
P inorg	6.3	1.0	4.6	7.1	5	Glu	47.3	6.6	42.6	58.9	5
P phytate						Gly	12.0	0.89	10.6	12.9	5
Fe	0.24	0.05	0.20	0.30	5	His	7.7	0.57	7.2	8.6	5
S	3.7	0.17	3.5	3.9	5	Ile	10.6	0.62	9.7	11.2	5
						Leu	19.8	3.0	17.7	25.0	5
Trace Elements (mg/kg ODM)						Lys avail					
						Lys total	10.3	2.8	5.4	12.4	5
Co	0.10	0.0	0.10	0.10	3	Meth	4.0	0.51	3.7	4.9	5
F						Phe	12.7	1.3	11.9	15.0	5
I	0.24	0.06	0.20	0.30	5	Pro	25.9	1.1	24.3	27.0	5
Mn	35.1	0.75	34.0	36.5	7	Pro.OH					
Mo	1.5	0.65	1.2	2.7	5	Ser	11.3	0.40	11.0	12.0	5
Zn	55.4	4.7	48.0	59.5	7	Thr	10.4	0.21	10.1	10.6	5
Cu	40.5	16.8	7.0	54.2	7	Tryp					
Se	0.18	0.18	0.10	0.50	5	Tyr	8.2	0.91	7.3	9.7	5
						Val	14.4	0.53	13.7	15.1	5

ANALYTICAL DATABASE

FEED DESCRIPTION : **DISTILLERS DARK GRAINS, MAIZE BASED** (Sources 1, 2)

Determination	Mean	SD	Min	Max	n	Determination	Mean	SD	Min	Max	n
General (g/kg ODM)						**Volatile Fatty Acids** (g/kg ODM)					
ODM (fresh)	889.4	27.7	857.8	930.0	5	Lactic					
TDM (fresh)						Formic					
CP	317.4	70.1	261.0	437.0	5	Acetic					
CF	90.6	8.0	80.0	101.0	5	Propionic					
MADF	165.4	48.0	116.0	225.0	5	n butyric					
EE	109.6	18.6	90.0	130.0	5	i butyric					
AEE	108.5	0.71	108.0	109.0	2	n valeric					
TA	46.4	15.7	20.0	58.0	5	i valeric					
AIA	4.1	1.7	2.9	5.3	2	n caproic					
GE (MJ/kg ODM)	22.4	0.79	21.7	23.7	5	i caproic					
						NO_3N					
						NH_3N/TN					
Carbohydrates (g/kg ODM)						pH					
NDF ash	342.6	83.0	232.0	412.0	5	**Fatty Acids** (g/kg ODM)					
NDF unash											
ADF ash	215.6	55.7	151.0	261.0	5	C8:0					
ADF unash	272.5	6.4	268.0	277.0	2	C10:0					
Cellulose	138.5	3.5	136.0	141.0	2	C12:0					
Lignin	92.0	39.9	50.0	134.0	5	C14:0					
Starch	24.2	11.4	14.0	43.0	5	C16:0					
NCD	822.5	9.2	816.0	829.0	2	C16:1					
CD						C18:0					
IVD	621.0	28.8	595.0	668.0	5	C18:1					
WSC	50.2	44.5	6.0	107.6	5	C18:2					
Avail Carbs						C18:3					
Sugars						C20:0					
						C20:4					
						C22:1					
Minerals (g/kg ODM)											
Ca	1.4	0.65	0.40	2.1	5						
Mg	3.2	1.5	0.60	4.5	5	**Amino Acids** (g/kg ODM)					
Na	1.2	1.3	0.10	2.7	5						
K	9.5	4.8	1.0	12.8	5	Ala					
Cl						Arg					
P total	8.4	2.5	4.2	10.5	5	Asp					
P inorg						Cys					
P phytate						Glu					
Fe						Gly					
S						His					
						Ile					
						Leu					
Trace Elements (mg/kg ODM)						Lys avail					
						Lys total					
Co						Meth					
F						Phe					
I						Pro					
Mn	19.7	8.1	11.0	27.0	3	Pro.OH					
Mo						Ser					
Zn	49.3	25.7	20.0	68.0	3	Thr					
Cu	83.7	15.0	68.0	98.0	3	Tryp					
Se						Tyr					
						Val					

145

ANALYTICAL DATABASE

FEED DESCRIPTION : **DISTILLERS DARK GRAINS, WHEAT BASED** (Sources 1, 3)

Determination	Mean	SD	Min	Max	n	Determination	Mean	SD	Min	Max	n
General (g/kg ODM)						**Volatile Fatty Acids (g/kg ODM)**					
ODM (fresh)	889.7	32.8	845.2	932.5	10	Lactic					
TDM (fresh)						Formic					
CP	302.3	25.5	264.9	335.6	10	Acetic					
CF	88.8	12.8	68.0	104.0	10	Propionic					
MADF	230.6	36.5	187.0	276.0	5	n butyric					
EE	55.0	20.6	32.4	92.4	10	i butyric					
AEE	69.4	17.4	42.4	103.2	10	n valeric					
TA	52.4	10.3	41.5	73.2	10	i valeric					
AIA	2.4	1.5	0.60	5.1	10	n caproic					
GE (MJ/kg ODM)	21.5	0.65	20.7	22.6	10	i caproic					
						NO$_3$N					
						NH$_3$N/TN					
Carbohydrates (g/kg ODM)						pH					
NDF ash	334.6	91.2	230.0	462.0	10	**Fatty Acids (g/kg ODM)**					
NDF unash											
ADF ash	193.0	58.0	119.0	275.0	10	C8:0					
ADF unash	246.0	24.9	210.0	274.0	5	C10:0					
Cellulose	109.9	30.7	84.5	194.0	10	C12:0					
Lignin	84.5	50.2	31.5	157.0	10	C14:0					
Starch	44.9	19.8	26.0	68.5	5	C16:0	9.2	3.2	6.3	13.1	5
NCD	822.0	42.6	773.0	884.0	10	C16:1					
CD						C18:0	0.92	0.77	0.30	1.9	5
IVD	621.3	21.3	583.0	666.0	10	C18:1	11.0	9.9	3.4	23.6	5
WSC	85.9	33.3	55.0	132.4	5	C18:2	33.7	19.3	18.0	58.7	5
Avail Carbs						C18:3	2.1	0.56	1.5	2.7	5
Sugars	63.2	8.1	50.3	69.9	5	C20:0					
						C20:4					
Minerals (g/kg ODM)						C22:1					
Ca	1.8	0.62	1.0	2.8	10						
Mg	2.8	0.44	2.1	3.4	10	**Amino Acids (g/kg ODM)**					
Na	3.1	3.9	0.10	12.7	10						
K	12.2	1.8	8.9	15.4	10	Ala	16.5	4.4	12.8	22.2	5
Cl	3.2	0.36	2.8	3.7	5	Arg	10.0	2.8	6.6	13.6	5
P total	8.8	1.1	7.4	11.0	10	Asp	17.0	1.8	14.8	19.5	5
P inorg	4.9	1.7	3.6	7.2	5	Cys	4.8	1.1	3.2	5.7	5
P phytate						Glu	61.6	11.4	47.0	77.0	5
Fe						Gly	11.8	0.77	10.6	12.7	5
S	4.1	0.84	3.4	5.5	5	His	9.8	1.4	8.0	11.4	5
						Ile	11.5	0.82	10.4	12.4	5
						Leu	25.7	8.8	18.2	35.3	5
Trace Elements (mg/kg ODM)						Lys avail					
						Lys total	6.5	1.0	5.0	7.7	5
Co	0.23	0.12	0.10	0.30	3	Meth	4.2	0.52	3.6	4.9	5
F						Phe	14.1	0.80	13.1	15.0	5
I						Pro	24.8	2.2	22.7	28.5	5
Mn						Pro.OH					
Mo						Ser	12.7	0.65	11.8	13.5	5
Zn						Thr	10.0	0.74	9.0	11.1	5
Cu						Tryp					
Se	0.17	0.06	0.10	0.20	3	Tyr	10.0	1.8	8.2	12.0	5
						Val	14.6	1.0	13.4	16.1	5

ANALYTICAL DATABASE

FEED DESCRIPTION : **DRAFF, BARLEY BASED** (Source 2)

Determination	Mean	SD	Min	Max	n	Determination	Mean	SD	Min	Max	n
General (g/kg ODM)						**Volatile Fatty Acids** (g/kg ODM)					
ODM (fresh)	248.0	7.1	243.0	253.0	2	Lactic					
TDM (fresh)	255.0		255.0	255.0	1	Formic					
CP	210.5	5.0	207.0	214.0	2	Acetic					
CF	198.5	12.0	190.0	207.0	2	Propionic					
MADF	274.0		274.0	274.0	1	n butyric					
EE	86.0	2.8	84.0	88.0	2	i butyric					
AEE						n valeric					
TA	34.0	1.4	33.0	35.0	2	i valeric					
AIA						n caproic					
GE (MJ/kg ODM)	21.5	0.14	21.4	21.6	2	i caproic					
						NO_3N					
Carbohydrates (g/kg ODM)						NH_3N/TN					
						pH	4.9	0.99	4.2	5.6	2
NDF ash	672.5	23.3	656.0	689.0	2						
NDF unash						**Fatty Acids** (g/kg ODM)					
ADF ash	294.0	42.4	264.0	324.0	2						
ADF unash						C8:0					
Cellulose						C10:0					
Lignin	63.0	7.1	58.0	68.0	2	C12:0					
Starch	17.5	5.0	14.0	21.0	2	C14:0					
NCD						C16:0					
CD						C16:1					
IVD						C18:0					
WSC	5.0	1.4	4.0	6.0	2	C18:1					
Avail Carbs						C18:2					
Sugars						C18:3					
						C20:0					
						C20:4					
Minerals (g/kg ODM)						C22:1					
Ca	1.5		1.5	1.5	1						
Mg	1.8		1.8	1.8	1	**Amino Acids** (g/kg ODM)					
Na	0.10		0.10	0.10	1						
K						Ala					
Cl						Arg					
P total	3.8		3.8	3.8	1	Asp					
P inorg						Cys					
P phytate						Glu					
Fe						Gly					
S						His					
						Ile					
						Leu					
Trace Elements (mg/kg ODM)						Lys avail					
						Lys total					
Co						Meth					
F						Phe					
I						Pro					
Mn	39.0		39.0	39.0	1	Pro.OH					
Mo						Ser					
Zn	80.0		80.0	80.0	1	Thr					
Cu	17.5	0.71	17.0	18.0	2	Tryp					
Se						Tyr					
						Val					

ANALYTICAL DATABASE

FEED DESCRIPTION : **DRIED SKIM MILK** (Source 4)

Determination	Mean	SD	Min	Max	n	Determination	Mean	SD	Min	Max	n
General (g/kg ODM)						**Volatile Fatty Acids (g/kg ODM)**					
ODM (fresh)	911.8		911.8	911.8	1	Lactic					
TDM (fresh)						Formic					
CP	356.5		356.5	356.5	1	Acetic					
CF						Propionic					
MADF						n butyric					
EE	38.1		38.1	38.1	1	i butyric					
AEE						n valeric					
TA	81.1		81.1	81.1	1	i valeric					
AIA						n caproic					
GE (MJ/kg ODM)	18.9		18.9	18.9	1	i caproic					
						NO_3N					
						NH_3N/TN					
						pH					
Carbohydrates (g/kg ODM)											
						Fatty Acids (g/kg ODM)					
NDF ash											
NDF unash						C8:0					
ADF ash						C10:0					
ADF unash						C12:0					
Cellulose						C14:0					
Lignin						C16:0					
Starch						C16:1					
NCD						C18:0					
CD						C18:1					
IVD						C18:2					
WSC						C18:3					
Avail Carbs						C20:0					
Sugars	353.0		353.0	353.0	1	C20:4					
						C22:1					
Minerals (g/kg ODM)											
						Amino Acids (g/kg ODM)					
Ca	12.7		12.7	12.7	1						
Mg						Ala	12.0		12.0	12.0	1
Na						Arg	11.0		11.0	11.0	1
K						Asp	27.0		27.0	27.0	1
Cl						Cys					
P total	10.1		10.1	10.1	1	Glu	81.0		81.0	81.0	1
P inorg						Gly	8.0		8.0	8.0	1
P phytate						His	9.0		9.0	9.0	1
Fe						Ile	18.0		18.0	18.0	1
S						Leu	36.0		36.0	36.0	1
						Lys avail					
						Lys total	25.0		25.0	25.0	1
Trace Elements (mg/kg ODM)						Meth	5.0		5.0	5.0	1
						Phe	18.0		18.0	18.0	1
Co						Pro					
F						Pro.OH					
I						Ser	22.0		22.0	22.0	1
Mn						Thr	18.0		18.0	18.0	1
Mo						Tryp					
Zn						Tyr	19.0		19.0	19.0	1
Cu						Val	23.0		23.0	23.0	1
Se											

ANALYTICAL DATABASE

FEED DESCRIPTION : **FEATHER MEAL** (Source 3)

Determination	Mean	SD	Min	Max	n	Determination	Mean	SD	Min	Max	n
General (g/kg ODM)						**Volatile Fatty Acids** (g/kg ODM)					
ODM (fresh)	906.8	12.3	885.0	914.5	5	Lactic					
TDM (fresh)						Formic					
CP	891.7	2.1	889.3	894.7	5	Acetic					
CF	4.7	0.21	4.6	5.1	5	Propionic					
MADF						n butyric					
EE	64.0	0.73	62.7	64.4	5	i butyric					
AEE	79.9	0.63	79.1	80.5	5	n valeric					
TA	25.2	0.27	25.0	25.5	5	i valeric					
AIA	2.7	0.10	2.6	2.8	5	n caproic					
GE (MJ/kg ODM)	24.0	0.08	23.9	24.1	5	i caproic					
						NO3N					
						NH3N/TN					
Carbohydrates (g/kg ODM)						pH					
NDF ash											
NDF unash						**Fatty Acids** (g/kg ODM)					
ADF ash											
ADF unash						C8:0					
Cellulose						C10:0					
Lignin						C12:0					
Starch						C14:0	0.64	0.06	0.60	0.70	5
NCD						C16:0	11.1	0.24	10.9	11.5	5
CD						C16:1	2.0	0.07	1.9	2.1	5
IVD	626.6	20.1	597.0	653.5	5	C18:0	4.4	0.09	4.3	4.5	5
WSC						C18:1	12.8	0.30	12.5	13.2	5
Avail Carbs						C18:2	1.1	0.09	1.0	1.2	5
Sugars	1.8	0.93	1.0	2.8	3	C18:3					
						C20:0					
						C20:4					
Minerals (g/kg ODM)						C22:1					
Ca	5.6	0.07	5.5	5.7	5						
Mg	0.38	0.04	0.30	0.40	5	**Amino Acids** (g/kg ODM)					
Na	1.4	0.0	1.4	1.4	5						
K	1.5	0.0	1.5	1.5	5	Ala	47.4	4.8	44.3	55.8	5
Cl	2.3	0.06	2.3	2.4	5	Arg	59.4	3.6	53.5	62.4	5
P total	3.1	0.06	3.1	3.2	5	Asp	61.7	1.9	59.7	64.4	5
P inorg	2.6	0.07	2.5	2.7	5	Cys	41.5	2.5	39.0	45.0	5
P phytate						Glu	89.2	2.4	86.7	92.8	5
Fe	0.68	0.11	0.50	0.80	5	Gly	71.9	1.9	70.0	74.4	5
S	18.1	0.56	17.6	18.8	5	His	13.4	1.2	12.2	15.2	5
						Ile	44.8	2.4	41.3	47.9	5
						Leu	76.1	2.0	72.7	78.0	5
Trace Elements (mg/kg ODM)						Lys avail					
						Lys total	20.1	0.81	18.9	21.0	5
Co						Meth	6.1	0.42	5.6	6.7	5
F						Phe	45.9	1.7	44.2	48.7	5
I	0.58	0.04	0.50	0.60	5	Pro	80.6	18.8	47.1	92.1	5
Mn	19.8	0.58	19.2	20.6	5	Pro.OH					
Mo	0.40	0.14	0.30	0.60	5	Ser	108.1	5.3	103.4	116.6	5
Zn	152.2	3.0	149.5	156.5	5	Thr	45.7	1.8	43.0	47.9	5
Cu	10.3	0.84	9.4	11.5	5	Tryp					
Se	0.76	0.06	0.70	0.80	5	Tyr	20.2	1.7	18.3	21.9	5
						Val	69.2	2.4	66.5	72.7	5

ANALYTICAL DATABASE

FEED DESCRIPTION : **FISHMEAL, CHILEAN** (Sources 1, 2, 3, 4)

Determination	Mean	SD	Min	Max	n
General (g/kg ODM)					
ODM (fresh)	911.0	18.4	893.0	959.1	10
TDM (fresh)					
CP	708.9	29.9	631.1	736.0	10
CF					
MADF					
EE	87.8	13.6	64.0	104.2	10
AEE	102.6	8.7	91.0	118.0	7
TA	168.5	12.4	149.5	194.0	10
AIA	3.9	1.6	2.0	6.0	7
GE (MJ/kg ODM)	20.7	0.56	19.6	21.5	10

Determination	Mean	SD	Min	Max	n
Carbohydrates (g/kg ODM)					
NDF ash					
NDF unash					
ADF ash					
ADF unash					
Cellulose					
Lignin					
Starch					
NCD	824.6	14.9	808.0	837.0	3
CD					
IVD	556.3	40.2	509.0	611.0	7
WSC					
Avail Carbs					
Sugars					

Determination	Mean	SD	Min	Max	n
Minerals (g/kg ODM)					
Ca	42.8	8.4	33.3	55.3	8
Mg	2.5	0.19	2.1	2.7	8
Na	10.4	3.6	6.3	18.0	8
K	9.4	2.5	5.8	12.2	8
Cl	13.4	3.8	9.8	18.2	4
P total	27.4	3.5	23.4	33.8	8
P inorg	24.2	3.1	20.4	26.7	4
P phytate					
Fe	0.35	0.06	0.30	0.40	4
S	10.7	0.41	10.3	11.1	4

Determination	Mean	SD	Min	Max	n
Trace Elements (mg/kg ODM)					
Co	0.10	0.0	0.10	0.10	4
F					
I					
Mn	24.4	11.0	18.5	44.0	5
Mo	0.37	0.15	0.20	0.50	3
Zn	111.7	15.1	99.0	137.0	5
Cu	8.0	2.9	4.0	12.1	5
Se	0.43	0.05	0.40	0.50	4

Determination	Mean	SD	Min	Max	n
Volatile Fatty Acids (g/kg ODM)					
Lactic					
Formic					
Acetic					
Propionic					
n butyric					
i butyric					
n valeric					
i valeric					
n caproic					
i caproic					
NO_3N					
NH_3N/TN					
pH					

Determination	Mean	SD	Min	Max	n
Fatty Acids (g/kg ODM)					
C8:0					
C10:0					
C12:0					
C14:0	4.1	0.27	3.9	4.5	4
C16:0	12.8	0.55	12.4	13.6	4
C16:1	4.7	0.39	4.2	5.1	4
C18:0	2.8	0.15	2.7	3.0	4
C18:1	7.2	1.0	6.2	8.6	4
C18:2	2.0	0.90	1.4	3.3	4
C18:3					
C20:0					
C20:4					
C22:1					

Determination	Mean	SD	Min	Max	n
Amino Acids (g/kg ODM)					
Ala	45.2	2.9	40.7	48.6	5
Arg	39.1	3.4	35.0	42.4	5
Asp	61.7	4.4	56.7	65.6	5
Cys	7.3	1.2	5.2	8.1	5
Glu	81.1	6.0	73.6	87.6	5
Gly	42.8	2.8	39.3	45.5	5
His	26.6	3.4	21.3	29.1	5
Ile	30.0	4.3	23.6	33.4	5
Leu	51.8	5.2	44.9	56.7	5
Lys avail					
Lys total	55.6	6.8	46.4	60.8	5
Meth	18.3	1.1	17.0	19.6	5
Phe	27.4	1.9	24.3	29.6	5
Pro	27.1	1.4	25.0	28.6	5
Pro.OH					
Ser	26.6	1.2	24.6	27.9	5
Thr	30.5	1.6	27.8	31.6	5
Tryp					
Tyr	22.3	2.2	18.9	25.0	5
Val	36.4	3.7	30.8	38.4	4

ANALYTICAL DATABASE

FEED DESCRIPTION : **FISHMEAL, HERRING** (Sources 1, 2, 4)

Determination	Mean	SD	Min	Max	n	Determination	Mean	SD	Min	Max	n
General (g/kg ODM)						**Volatile Fatty Acids (g/kg ODM)**					
ODM (fresh)	913.1	16.5	889.0	939.2	10	Lactic					
TDM (fresh)						Formic					
CP	758.3	31.1	714.0	824.0	10	Acetic					
CF						Propionic					
MADF						n butyric					
EE	94.8	23.7	64.0	136.6	10	i butyric					
AEE	73.0		73.0	73.0	1	n valeric					
TA	138.7	24.5	111.9	178.2	10	i valeric					
AIA	3.1		3.1	3.1	1	n caproic					
GE (MJ/kg ODM)	22.0	0.78	20.7	23.1	10	i caproic					
						NO3N					
						NH3N/TN					
Carbohydrates (g/kg ODM)						pH					
NDF ash						**Fatty Acids (g/kg ODM)**					
NDF unash											
ADF ash						C8:0					
ADF unash						C10:0					
Cellulose						C12:0					
Lignin						C14:0					
Starch						C16:0					
NCD	869.2		869.2	869.2	1	C16:1					
CD						C18:0					
IVD	645.0		645.0	645.0	1	C18:1					
WSC	4.0		4.0	4.0	1	C18:2					
Avail Carbs						C18:3					
Sugars						C20:0					
						C20:4					
Minerals (g/kg ODM)						C22:1					
Ca	34.4	4.5	31.3	39.5	3						
Mg	2.1	0.06	2.1	2.2	2	**Amino Acids (g/kg ODM)**					
Na	6.7	0.42	6.4	7.0	2						
K	7.7	2.2	6.1	9.2	2	Ala	52.6	3.3	50.3	55.0	2
Cl						Arg	47.6	3.7	45.0	50.3	2
P total	23.6	2.1	22.3	26.0	3	Asp	77.4	2.3	75.8	79.0	2
P inorg						Cys	7.4		7.4	7.4	1
P phytate						Glu	103.9	7.2	98.9	109.0	2
Fe						Gly	49.6	11.9	41.2	58.0	2
S						His	16.5	3.5	14.0	19.0	2
						Ile	32.4	2.0	31.0	33.8	2
						Leu	59.2	0.23	59.0	59.3	2
						Lys avail					
Trace Elements (mg/kg ODM)						Lys total	63.3	6.1	59.0	67.6	2
Co						Meth	24.8	1.1	24.0	25.5	2
F						Phe	32.9	1.3	32.0	33.8	2
I						Pro	28.0		28.0	28.0	1
Mn	16.0		16.0	16.0	1	Pro.OH	4.9		4.9	4.9	1
Mo						Ser	33.4	0.55	33.0	33.8	2
Zn	137.0		137.0	137.0	1	Thr	35.0	4.2	32.0	37.9	2
Cu	2.0		2.0	2.0	1	Tryp					
Se						Tyr	27.8	2.6	26.0	29.7	2
						Val	37.0		37.0	37.0	1

151

FEED CLASS 50

ANALYTICAL DATABASE

FEED DESCRIPTION : **FISHMEAL, MIXED MEAL** (Source 1)

Determination	Mean	SD	Min	Max	n	Determination	Mean	SD	Min	Max	n

General (g/kg ODM)

Determination	Mean	SD	Min	Max	n
ODM (fresh)	931.5	0.92	930.4	932.0	3
TDM (fresh)					
CP	700.7	12.9	686.0	710.0	3
CF					
MADF					
EE	89.0	32.1	68.0	126.0	3
AEE	86.0	13.0	78.0	101.0	3
TA	213.7	10.4	202.0	222.0	3
AIA	5.0	1.0	4.0	6.0	3
GE (MJ/kg ODM)	19.7	0.30	19.4	20.0	3

Volatile Fatty Acids (g/kg ODM)

Lactic
Formic
Acetic
Propionic
n butyric
i butyric
n valeric
i valeric
n caproic
i caproic

NO3N
NH3N/TN
pH

Carbohydrates (g/kg ODM)

Determination	Mean	SD	Min	Max	n
NDF ash					
NDF unash					
ADF ash					
ADF unash					
Cellulose					
Lignin					
Starch					
NCD	776.7	18.1	760.0	796.0	3
CD					
IVD	701.0	7.0	693.0	706.0	3
WSC					
Avail Carbs					
Sugars					

Fatty Acids (g/kg ODM)

C8:0
C10:0
C12:0
C14:0
C16:0
C16:1
C18:0
C18:1
C18:2
C18:3
C20:0
C20:4
C22:1

Minerals (g/kg ODM)

Determination	Mean	SD	Min	Max	n
Ca	65.3	5.0	60.0	70.0	3
Mg	2.0	0.06	2.0	2.1	3
Na	7.2	1.4	6.3	8.8	3
K	8.7	1.1	7.9	9.9	3
Cl					
P total	37.3	1.2	36.0	38.0	3
P inorg					
P phytate					
Fe					
S					

Amino Acids (g/kg ODM)

Ala
Arg
Asp
Cys
Glu
Gly
His
Ile
Leu
Lys avail
Lys total
Meth
Phe
Pro
Pro.OH
Ser
Thr
Tryp
Tyr
Val

Trace Elements (mg/kg ODM)

Co
F
I
Mn
Mo
Zn
Cu
Se

ANALYTICAL DATABASE

FEED DESCRIPTION : **FISHMEAL, OFFAL MEAL WHITE** (Sources 1, 4)

Determination	Mean	SD	Min	Max	n	Determination	Mean	SD	Min	Max	n

General (g/kg ODM)

Determination	Mean	SD	Min	Max	n
ODM (fresh)	913.7	18.3	893.0	937.5	4
TDM (fresh)					
CP	715.7	9.3	706.0	728.0	4
CF					
MADF					
EE	79.6	10.8	71.0	95.4	4
AEE	90.0	5.3	84.0	94.0	3
TA	207.8	10.6	192.0	214.1	4
AIA	8.7	6.4	4.0	16.0	3
GE (MJ/kg ODM)	20.2	0.49	19.7	20.9	4

Carbohydrates (g/kg ODM)

Determination	Mean	SD	Min	Max	n
NDF ash					
NDF unash					
ADF ash					
ADF unash					
Cellulose					
Lignin					
Starch					
NCD	781.3	4.6	776.0	784.0	3
CD					
IVD	608.7	17.4	589.0	622.0	3
WSC					
Avail Carbs					
Sugars					

Minerals (g/kg ODM)

Determination	Mean	SD	Min	Max	n
Ca	57.2	9.0	46.9	63.4	3
Mg	2.0	0.11	1.9	2.1	3
Na	6.8	1.2	5.5	7.8	3
K	8.9	3.7	4.8	12.1	3
Cl					
P total	33.2	4.7	27.8	36.2	3
P inorg					
P phytate					
Fe					
S					

Trace Elements (mg/kg ODM)

Determination
Co
F
I
Mn
Mo
Zn
Cu
Se

Volatile Fatty Acids (g/kg ODM)

Determination
Lactic
Formic
Acetic
Propionic
n butyric
i butyric
n valeric
i valeric
n caproic
i caproic
NO$_3$N
NH$_3$N/TN
pH

Fatty Acids (g/kg ODM)

Determination
C8:0
C10:0
C12:0
C14:0
C16:0
C16:1
C18:0
C18:1
C18:2
C18:3
C20:0
C20:4
C22:1

Amino Acids (g/kg ODM)

Determination
Ala
Arg
Asp
Cys
Glu
Gly
His
Ile
Leu
Lys avail
Lys total
Meth
Phe
Pro
Pro.OH
Ser
Thr
Tryp
Tyr
Val

ANALYTICAL DATABASE

FEED DESCRIPTION : **FISHMEAL, PERUVIAN** (Source 4)

Determination	Mean	SD	Min	Max	n	Determination	Mean	SD	Min	Max	n
General (g/kg ODM)						Volatile Fatty Acids (g/kg ODM)					
ODM (fresh)	889.0		889.0	889.0	1	Lactic					
TDM (fresh)						Formic					
CP	709.0		709.0	709.0	1	Acetic					
CF						Propionic					
MADF						n butyric					
EE	121.6		121.6	121.6	1	i butyric					
AEE						n valeric					
TA	190.2		190.2	190.2	1	i valeric					
AIA						n caproic					
GE (MJ/kg ODM)	22.0		22.0	22.0	1	i caproic					

	NO_3N
	NH_3N/TN
Carbohydrates (g/kg ODM)	pH

Carbohydrates (g/kg ODM)

NDF ash
NDF unash
ADF ash
ADF unash
Cellulose
Lignin
Starch
NCD
CD
IVD
WSC
Avail Carbs
Sugars

Fatty Acids (g/kg ODM)

C8:0
C10:0
C12:0
C14:0
C16:0
C16:1
C18:0
C18:1
C18:2
C18:3
C20:0
C20:4
C22:1

Minerals (g/kg ODM)

Ca
Mg
Na
K
Cl
P total
P inorg
P phytate
Fe
S

Amino Acids (g/kg ODM)

Ala
Arg
Asp
Cys
Glu
Gly
His
Ile
Leu
Lys avail
Lys total
Meth
Phe
Pro
Pro.OH
Ser
Thr
Tryp
Tyr
Val

Trace Elements (mg/kg ODM)

Co
F
I
Mn
Mo
Zn
Cu
Se

ANALYTICAL DATABASE

FEED DESCRIPTION : **FISHMEAL, WHITE** (Sources 1, 2, 4)

Determination	Mean	SD	Min	Max	n	Determination	Mean	SD	Min	Max	n
General (g/kg ODM)						**Volatile Fatty Acids (g/kg ODM)**					
ODM (fresh)	911.0	21.5	887.5	955.0	8	Lactic					
TDM (fresh)						Formic					
CP	693.0	21.4	672.0	738.0	8	Acetic					
CF						Propionic					
MADF						n butyric					
EE	74.6	17.9	52.3	98.0	8	i butyric					
AEE	87.1	15.3	72.4	107.0	5	n valeric					
TA	213.4	28.9	169.0	265.7	8	i valeric					
AIA	3.4	1.8	1.0	6.0	5	n caproic					
GE (MJ/kg ODM)	19.7	0.79	18.5	21.0	8	i caproic					
						NO_3N					
						NH_3N/TN					
Carbohydrates (g/kg ODM)						pH					
NDF ash						**Fatty Acids (g/kg ODM)**					
NDF unash											
ADF ash						C8:0					
ADF unash						C10:0					
Cellulose						C12:0					
Lignin						C14:0					
Starch						C16:0					
NCD	795.8	26.4	770.0	830.0	4	C16:1					
CD						C18:0					
IVD	654.4	50.1	587.0	706.0	5	C18:1					
WSC	4.7	1.2	4.0	6.0	3	C18:2					
Avail Carbs						C18:3					
Sugars						C20:0					
						C20:4					
Minerals (g/kg ODM)						C22:1					
Ca	56.2	6.0	46.0	64.7	7						
Mg	2.3	0.31	1.7	2.5	6	**Amino Acids (g/kg ODM)**					
Na	11.2	1.5	8.7	13.0	6						
K	10.2	1.3	8.4	11.4	6	Ala	52.0	5.7	48.0	56.1	2
Cl						Arg	37.4	7.6	32.0	42.8	2
P total	38.1	14.5	28.6	70.1	7	Asp	62.5	0.71	62.0	63.0	2
P inorg						Cys	5.9		5.9	5.9	1
P phytate						Glu	89.4	2.2	87.8	91.0	2
Fe						Gly	63.6	3.4	61.3	66.0	2
S						His	13.1	4.4	10.0	16.2	2
						Ile	25.2	1.2	24.4	26.0	2
						Leu	46.4	0.88	45.8	47.0	2
						Lys avail					
Trace Elements (mg/kg ODM)						Lys total	39.3	1.8	38.0	40.6	2
Co						Meth	20.3	0.47	20.0	20.7	2
F						Phe	26.9	2.7	25.0	28.8	2
I						Pro	13.3		13.3	13.3	1
Mn	27.0		27.0	27.0	1	Pro.OH	30.2	7.4	25.0	35.4	2
Mo						Ser	32.7	0.37	32.5	33.0	2
Zn	81.0		81.0	81.0	1	Thr	30.4	1.9	29.0	31.7	2
Cu	2.0		2.0	2.0	1	Tryp					
Se						Tyr	22.7	2.4	21.0	24.4	2
						Val	37.0		37.0	37.0	1

ANALYTICAL DATABASE

FEED DESCRIPTION : **FISH, MIXED, ENSILED** (Source 4)

Determination	Mean	SD	Min	Max	n	Determination	Mean	SD	Min	Max	n
General (g/kg ODM)						**Volatile Fatty Acids** (g/kg ODM)					
ODM (fresh)	226.7	20.9	188.3	267.8	12	Lactic					
TDM (fresh)						Formic					
CP	603.8	72.3	514.4	727.8	12	Acetic					
CF						Propionic					
MADF						n butyric					
EE	128.9	76.0	12.5	245.1	12	i butyric					
AEE						n valeric					
TA	92.0	17.0	63.6	116.7	12	i valeric					
AIA						n caproic					
GE (MJ/kg ODM)	19.1	1.2	16.5	21.1	12	i caproic					

NO_3N
NH_3N/TN
pH

Carbohydrates (g/kg ODM)

NDF ash
NDF unash
ADF ash
ADF unash
Cellulose
Lignin
Starch
NCD
CD
IVD
WSC
Avail Carbs
Sugars

Fatty Acids (g/kg ODM)

C8:0
C10:0
C12:0
C14:0
C16:0
C16:1
C18:0
C18:1
C18:2
C18:3
C20:0
C20:4
C22:1

Minerals (g/kg ODM)

Ca
Mg
Na
K
Cl
P total
P inorg
P phytate
Fe
S

Amino Acids (g/kg ODM)

Ala
Arg
Asp
Cys
Glu
Gly
His
Ile
Leu
Lys avail
Lys total
Meth
Phe
Pro
Pro.OH
Ser
Thr
Tryp
Tyr
Val

Trace Elements (mg/kg ODM)

Co
F
I
Mn
Mo
Zn
Cu
Se

156

ANALYTICAL DATABASE

FEED DESCRIPTION : **GROUNDNUT MEAL** (Sources 2, 4)

Determination	Mean	SD	Min	Max	n	Determination	Mean	SD	Min	Max	n
General (g/kg ODM)						**Volatile Fatty Acids (g/kg ODM)**					
ODM (fresh)	924.5		924.5	924.5	1	Lactic					
TDM (fresh)						Formic					
CP	511.9	35.3	476.0	546.6	3	Acetic					
CF	81.3	13.9	65.9	93.0	3	Propionic					
MADF	125.9	7.9	120.7	135.0	3	n butyric					
EE	70.0	9.0	61.0	79.0	3	i butyric					
AEE						n valeric					
TA	68.8	14.3	58.0	85.0	3	i valeric					
AIA						n caproic					
GE (MJ/kg ODM)	20.6	0.34	20.2	20.9	3	i caproic					
						NO_3N					
Carbohydrates (g/kg ODM)						NH_3N/TN					
						pH					
NDF ash	180.1	45.2	148.1	212.0	2						
NDF unash						**Fatty Acids (g/kg ODM)**					
ADF ash	145.5	3.5	143.0	148.0	2						
ADF unash						C8:0					
Cellulose						C10:0					
Lignin	40.5	9.2	34.0	47.0	2	C12:0					
Starch	52.5	7.8	47.0	58.0	2	C14:0					
NCD						C16:0					
CD						C16:1					
IVD	716.0	14.1	706.0	726.0	2	C18:0					
WSC	94.5	3.5	92.0	97.0	2	C18:1					
Avail Carbs						C18:2					
Sugars	77.0		77.0	77.0	1	C18:3					
						C20:0					
						C20:4					
Minerals (g/kg ODM)						C22:1					
Ca	2.0	1.7	0.90	4.0	3						
Mg	3.5	0.21	3.3	3.6	2	**Amino Acids (g/kg ODM)**					
Na	0.20	0.14	0.10	0.30	2						
K	14.3	2.6	12.4	16.1	2	Ala	24.0		24.0	24.0	1
Cl						Arg	60.0		60.0	60.0	1
P total	6.2	0.20	6.0	6.4	3	Asp	61.0		61.0	61.0	1
P inorg						Cys					
P phytate						Glu	112.0		112.0	112.0	1
Fe						Gly	33.0		33.0	33.0	1
S						His	12.0		12.0	12.0	1
						Ile	19.0		19.0	19.0	1
						Leu	35.0		35.0	35.0	1
Trace Elements (mg/kg ODM)						Lys avail					
						Lys total	18.0		18.0	18.0	1
Co						Meth	5.0		5.0	5.0	1
F.						Phe	25.0		25.0	25.0	1
I						Pro					
Mn	49.5	37.5	23.0	76.0	2	Pro.OH					
Mo						Ser	26.0		26.0	26.0	1
Zn	51.0	9.9	44.0	58.0	2	Thr	14.0		14.0	14.0	1
Cu	17.5	6.4	13.0	22.0	2	Tryp					
Se						Tyr	19.0		19.0	19.0	1
						Val	22.0		22.0	22.0	1

ANALYTICAL DATABASE

FEED DESCRIPTION : **LINSEED MEAL** (Source 3)

Determination	Mean	SD	Min	Max	n	Determination	Mean	SD	Min	Max	n

General (g/kg ODM)

						Volatile Fatty Acids (g/kg ODM)					
ODM (fresh)	884.9	1.0	884.0	886.0	5	Lactic					
TDM (fresh)						Formic					
CP	391.0	3.4	387.0	395.0	5	Acetic					
CF	74.9	0.92	74.1	76.4	5	Propionic					
MADF						n butyric					
EE	87.3	2.0	84.8	90.0	5	i butyric					
AEE	96.0	2.0	93.7	98.7	5	n valeric					
TA	51.0	0.0	51.0	51.0	5	i valeric					
AIA	1.2	0.23	0.90	1.5	5	n caproic					
GE (MJ/kg ODM)	24.2	0.09	24.2	24.4	5	i caproic					

						NO3N					
						NH3N/TN					
						pH					

Carbohydrates (g/kg ODM)

						Fatty Acids (g/kg ODM)					
NDF ash	192.2	8.6	183.0	206.0	5						
NDF unash						C8:0					
ADF ash	130.9	6.0	124.0	140.0	5	C10:0					
ADF unash						C12:0					
Cellulose	57.0	9.0	45.5	68.0	5	C14:0					
Lignin	16.4	7.8	9.0	25.5	5	C16:0	4.9	0.28	4.6	5.3	5
Starch	52.3	1.3	50.4	53.6	5	C16:1					
NCD	856.1	3.1	852.3	860.8	5	C18:0	2.7	0.15	2.5	2.8	5
CD						C18:1	16.0	0.72	15.2	16.8	5
IVD	680.7	7.9	672.0	690.5	5	C18:2	10.6	5.2	1.2	13.2	5
WSC						C18:3	40.4	1.4	37.9	41.5	5
Avail Carbs						C20:0					
Sugars	42.4	0.73	41.3	43.2	5	C20:4					
						C22:1					

Minerals (g/kg ODM)

						Amino Acids (g/kg ODM)					
Ca	3.4	0.05	3.4	3.5	5						
Mg	5.4	0.09	5.3	5.5	5	Ala	18.6	0.10	18.4	18.7	5
Na	0.70	0.0	0.70	0.70	5	Arg	39.0	0.24	38.8	39.4	5
K	11.2	0.13	11.1	11.4	5	Asp	37.1	0.30	36.7	37.4	5
Cl	0.27	0.06	0.20	0.30	3	Cys	7.0	0.29	6.7	7.4	5
P total	8.7	0.08	8.6	8.8	5	Glu	78.8	0.93	77.8	80.2	5
P inorg	1.0	0.05	1.0	1.1	5	Gly	23.3	0.20	23.0	23.6	5
P phytate						His	10.6	0.52	10.1	11.5	5
Fe	0.14	0.06	0.10	0.20	5	Ile	17.8	0.18	17.6	18.0	5
S	4.1	0.18	4.0	4.4	5	Leu	24.2	0.16	24.0	24.4	5
						Lys avail					

Trace Elements (mg/kg ODM)

						Lys total	16.3	0.39	15.8	16.8	5
Co	0.30	0.0	0.30	0.30	5	Meth	7.2	0.24	6.8	7.4	5
F						Phe	19.4	0.17	19.1	19.5	5
I	0.38	0.13	0.30	0.60	5	Pro	16.0	0.34	15.6	16.4	4
Mn	38.7	0.72	37.9	39.7	5	Pro.OH					
Mo	1.4	0.11	1.2	1.5	5	Ser	18.3	0.22	18.0	18.6	5
Zn	66.2	0.81	65.1	67.2	5	Thr	15.3	0.15	15.2	15.5	5
Cu	17.7	0.18	17.5	17.9	5	Tryp					
Se	0.82	0.05	0.80	0.90	5	Tyr	10.2	0.17	10.0	10.4	5
						Val	20.9	0.40	20.4	21.3	5

ANALYTICAL DATABASE

FEED DESCRIPTION : **MAIZE GERM MEAL** (Sources 2, 3)

Determination	Mean	SD	Min	Max	n	Determination	Mean	SD	Min	Max	n
General (g/kg ODM)						**Volatile Fatty Acids (g/kg ODM)**					
ODM (fresh)	879.3	6.3	873.5	887.5	5	Lactic					
TDM (fresh)						Formic					
CP	107.6	8.0	98.0	119.0	9	Acetic					
CF	41.6	2.3	38.5	45.0	9	Propionic					
MADF	63.3	7.7	54.0	71.0	4	n butyric					
EE	82.3	30.4	53.8	129.0	9	i butyric					
AEE	63.9	2.9	60.3	68.3	5	n valeric					
TA	25.2	6.9	18.5	37.0	9	i valeric					
AIA	1.5	0.23	1.3	1.8	5	n caproic					
GE (MJ/kg ODM)	19.7	0.54	19.2	20.5	9	i caproic					
						NO_3N					
						NH_3N/TN					
Carbohydrates (g/kg ODM)						pH					
NDF ash	223.8	47.1	178.0	319.0	9	**Fatty Acids (g/kg ODM)**					
NDF unash											
ADF ash	59.7	11.5	48.5	80.0	9	C8:0					
ADF unash						C10:0					
Cellulose	35.3	3.3	32.0	38.5	5	C12:0					
Lignin	15.9	5.8	10.0	26.0	9	C14:0					
Starch	532.4	107.5	368.0	624.3	9	C16:0	5.9	0.57	5.4	6.8	5
NCD	851.5	8.3	838.1	858.9	5	C16:1					
CD						C18:0	0.92	0.11	0.80	1.1	5
IVD	732.1	88.2	613.0	823.5	9	C18:1	13.3	1.0	12.4	14.9	5
WSC	42.5	4.4	37.0	46.0	4	C18:2	33.8	1.9	31.4	36.8	5
Avail Carbs						C18:3	0.96	0.14	0.90	1.2	5
Sugars	15.9	2.5	12.3	19.2	5	C20:0					
						C20:4					
Minerals (g/kg ODM)						C22:1					
Ca	0.18	0.04	0.10	0.20	9						
Mg	2.1	0.69	1.5	3.3	9	**Amino Acids (g/kg ODM)**					
Na	0.10	0.0	0.10	0.10	9						
K	6.1	1.5	4.7	8.4	9	Ala	8.1	0.24	7.9	8.4	5
Cl	0.60	0.07	0.50	0.70	5	Arg	6.4	0.88	5.3	7.6	5
P total	5.2	1.6	3.7	8.3	9	Asp	8.1	0.30	7.8	8.5	5
P inorg	0.40	0.0	0.40	0.40	5	Cys	2.4	0.10	2.3	2.5	5
P phytate						Glu	20.9	1.1	19.9	22.2	5
Fe	0.10	0.0	0.10	0.10	5	Gly	4.8	0.19	4.6	5.1	5
S	1.1	0.06	1.0	1.1	5	His	3.9	0.18	3.7	4.1	5
						Ile	4.1	0.13	4.0	4.3	5
						Leu	12.5	0.31	12.2	13.0	5
Trace Elements (mg/kg ODM)						Lys avail					
						Lys total	4.4	0.26	4.0	4.7	5
Co	0.12	0.05	0.10	0.20	5	Meth	1.8	0.13	1.7	1.9	5
F						Phe	5.6	0.16	5.4	5.8	5
I	0.10	0.0	0.10	0.10	5	Pro	10.1	0.33	9.7	10.4	5
Mn	11.6	3.5	6.0	18.0	9	Pro.OH					
Mo	0.18	0.05	0.10	0.20	5	Ser	5.2	0.34	4.6	5.6	5
Zn	42.2	10.3	30.5	59.0	9	Thr	4.4	0.15	4.3	4.6	5
Cu	3.7	1.6	2.3	6.0	9	Tryp					
Se	0.10	0.0	0.10	0.10	5	Tyr	4.7	0.14	4.6	5.0	5
						Val	5.9	0.20	5.7	6.2	5

ANALYTICAL DATABASE

FEED DESCRIPTION : **MAIZE GLUTEN MEAL** (Sources 1, 3)

Determination	Mean	SD	Min	Max	n	Determination	Mean	SD	Min	Max	n
General (g/kg ODM)						**Volatile Fatty Acids (g/kg ODM)**					
ODM (fresh)	904.4	12.4	883.0	922.8	10	Lactic					
TDM (fresh)						Formic					
CP	668.9	33.9	616.1	729.3	10	Acetic					
CF	12.0	5.5	3.6	23.0	10	Propionic					
MADF	136.4	99.5	14.0	283.0	5	n butyric					
EE	29.4	12.2	14.9	53.0	10	i butyric					
AEE	69.2	17.8	48.0	99.5	7	n valeric					
TA	11.2	4.3	7.0	21.0	10	i valeric					
AIA	1.2	2.0	0.10	6.0	8	n caproic					
GE (MJ/kg ODM)	23.7	0.61	22.9	24.9	10	i caproic					
						NO$_3$N					
						NH$_3$N/TN					
						pH					
Carbohydrates (g/kg ODM)						**Fatty Acids (g/kg ODM)**					
NDF ash	83.9	93.4	12.0	246.0	8						
NDF unash						C8:0					
ADF ash	104.7	108.3	2.0	255.0	10	C10:0					
ADF unash	187.8	81.9	69.0	256.0	4	C12:0					
Cellulose	56.2	66.5	2.5	162.0	9	C14:0					
Lignin	28.0	37.3	0.35	108.0	9	C16:0	2.5	1.2	1.3	4.6	5
Starch	155.0	54.6	81.0	244.5	10	C16:1					
NCD	984.0	5.8	975.0	991.0	7	C18:0	0.38	0.19	0.20	0.70	5
CD						C18:1	5.1	2.8	2.8	9.9	5
IVD	822.5	29.4	764.0	854.5	10	C18:2	12.5	7.5	6.2	25.5	5
WSC	5.5	1.7	3.0	7.0	4	C18:3	0.48	0.26	0.20	0.90	5
Avail Carbs						C20:0					
Sugars	2.8	0.80	2.0	4.1	5	C20:4					
						C22:1					
Minerals (g/kg ODM)											
Ca	0.64	1.3	0.10	4.0	9	**Amino Acids (g/kg ODM)**					
Mg	0.52	0.25	0.28	0.90	10						
Na	1.4	0.94	0.10	2.8	10	Ala	56.8	3.4	51.8	61.2	5
K	1.1	0.67	0.20	2.4	10	Arg	17.2	1.9	15.5	20.3	5
Cl						Asp	37.7	1.9	35.8	40.4	5
P total	2.8	1.2	1.5	5.0	10	Cys	12.4	1.1	11.2	13.8	5
P inorg	0.30	0.18	0.20	0.60	5	Glu	125.9	7.2	119.6	136.4	5
P phytate						Gly	17.1	0.74	16.1	18.0	5
Fe	0.14	0.06	0.10	0.20	5	His	15.8	0.90	14.8	16.8	5
S	5.9	0.33	5.4	6.2	5	Ile	26.6	1.4	25.0	28.7	5
						Leu	102.8	5.4	97.4	111.0	5
Trace Elements (mg/kg ODM)						Lys avail					
						Lys total	10.9	0.64	10.1	11.9	5
Co						Meth	16.2	1.7	13.6	17.7	5
F						Phe	39.6	2.6	37.6	43.9	5
I						Pro	57.5	4.2	53.5	62.1	5
Mn	9.7	2.8	6.6	13.0	5	Pro.OH					
Mo	0.54	0.23	0.30	0.90	5	Ser	31.3	1.5	29.6	33.0	5
Zn	48.5	8.6	43.6	63.8	5	Thr	22.2	1.3	20.8	23.6	5
Cu	14.3	2.7	10.1	17.4	5	Tryp					
Se	0.24	0.13	0.10	0.40	5	Tyr	33.7	2.4	31.2	36.9	5
						Val	30.4	2.2	27.6	32.7	5

ANALYTICAL DATABASE

FEED DESCRIPTION : **MALT CULMS** (Source 3)

Determination	Mean	SD	Min	Max	n	Determination	Mean	SD	Min	Max	n
General (g/kg ODM)						**Volatile Fatty Acids (g/kg ODM)**					
ODM (fresh)	914.8	28.9	888.5	964.5	5	Lactic					
TDM (fresh)						Formic					
CP	282.8	26.4	246.7	319.7	5	Acetic					
CF	136.5	12.6	115.0	146.5	5	Propionic					
MADF						n butyric					
EE	14.3	3.2	9.9	17.4	5	i butyric					
AEE	25.9	4.2	21.3	32.3	5	n valeric					
TA	65.3	2.4	61.5	68.0	5	i valeric					
AIA	12.5	7.5	3.6	21.2	5	n caproic					
GE (MJ/kg ODM)	18.7	0.35	18.2	19.0	5	i caproic					
						NO_3N					
						NH_3N/TN					
Carbohydrates (g/kg ODM)						pH					
NDF ash	462.9	34.9	425.5	510.5	5	**Fatty Acids (g/kg ODM)**					
NDF unash											
ADF ash	162.5	23.3	125.5	188.0	5	C8:0					
ADF unash						C10:0					
Cellulose	147.8	21.5	113.0	170.0	5	C12:0					
Lignin	10.7	3.5	5.0	14.5	5	C14:0	0.05	0.03	0.02	0.08	5
Starch	63.3	36.0	26.3	121.7	5	C16:0	1.6	0.33	1.0	1.9	5
NCD	380.9	17.6	363.8	400.0	5	C16:1	0.04	0.02	0.02	0.07	5
CD						C18:0	0.06	0.02	0.03	0.08	5
IVD	687.4	39.8	646.5	740.0	5	C18:1	0.70	0.21	0.44	1.0	5
WSC						C18:2	2.9	0.64	2.3	3.8	5
Avail Carbs						C18:3	1.6	0.24	1.4	2.0	5
Sugars	107.2	47.9	65.2	184.4	5	C20:0					
						C20:4					
						C22:1					
Minerals (g/kg ODM)											
Ca	2.7	1.0	1.3	3.9	5						
Mg	2.0	0.34	1.6	2.5	5	**Amino Acids (g/kg ODM)**					
Na	0.42	0.08	0.30	0.50	5						
K	17.3	3.2	14.6	21.8	5	Ala	11.3	4.0	4.3	14.5	5
Cl	6.1	1.2	5.0	7.6	5	Arg	9.9	3.6	4.0	13.4	5
P total	7.4	0.90	6.4	8.8	5	Asp	25.7	9.5	9.4	33.2	5
P inorg	4.0	0.59	3.1	4.7	5	Cys	3.4	1.2	1.4	4.4	5
P phytate						Glu	23.6	8.9	9.1	33.3	5
Fe	0.60	0.20	0.40	0.80	5	Gly	9.1	3.2	3.7	12.2	5
S	5.1	0.97	4.1	6.2	5	His	4.8	1.8	1.9	6.7	5
						Ile	7.8	2.7	3.1	9.9	5
						Leu	12.9	4.5	5.2	16.9	5
Trace Elements (mg/kg ODM)						Lys avail					
						Lys total	11.3	4.2	4.5	15.8	5
Co						Meth	3.4	1.2	1.3	4.6	5
F						Phe	7.5	2.6	3.1	9.6	5
I						Pro	13.4	5.7	4.7	18.9	5
Mn	83.4	22.1	64.0	119.5	5	Pro.OH					
Mo	2.5	0.88	1.5	3.8	5	Ser	7.6	2.7	3.1	10.0	5
Zn	111.7	10.6	100.0	129.0	5	Thr	8.0	2.8	3.3	10.6	5
Cu	13.9	2.6	11.4	18.0	5	Tryp					
Se						Tyr	5.3	1.9	2.2	7.3	5
						Val	10.9	3.8	4.2	14.2	5

ANALYTICAL DATABASE

FEED DESCRIPTION : **MEAT AND BONE MEAL** (Sources 2, 3, 4)

Determination	Mean	SD	Min	Max	n	Determination	Mean	SD	Min	Max	n
General (g/kg ODM)						**Volatile Fatty Acids (g/kg ODM)**					
ODM (fresh)	960.2	22.6	911.7	973.0	13	Lactic					
TDM (fresh)						Formic					
CP	533.6	23.4	514.3	603.0	13	Acetic					
CF	20.6	4.9	16.0	34.0	12	Propionic					
MADF						n butyric					
EE	127.9	47.2	8.0	175.0	13	i butyric					
AEE	151.4	11.8	139.3	165.3	10	n valeric					
TA	283.5	22.8	250.0	332.0	13	i valeric					
AIA	15.7	1.8	13.2	18.0	10	n caproic					
GE (MJ/kg ODM)	18.3	1.3	15.2	19.9	13	i caproic					
						NO3N					
						NH3N/TN					
						pH					
Carbohydrates (g/kg ODM)											
						Fatty Acids (g/kg ODM)					
NDF ash											
NDF unash						C8:0					
ADF ash						C10:0					
ADF unash						C12:0					
Cellulose						C14:0	2.6	0.16	2.4	2.8	10
Lignin						C16:0	28.1	4.2	23.9	33.4	10
Starch						C16:1	3.6	0.74	2.6	4.4	10
NCD						C18:0	20.6	0.53	19.9	21.6	10
CD						C18:1	39.2	7.2	31.8	47.0	10
IVD	465.0	19.9	431.5	491.0	12	C18:2	3.3	1.9	1.0	5.5	10
WSC						C18:3					
Avail Carbs						C20:0					
Sugars	4.2	0.87	3.1	5.4	5	C20:4					
						C22:1					
Minerals (g/kg ODM)											
Ca	89.9	13.0	57.0	113.4	13	**Amino Acids (g/kg ODM)**					
Mg	2.2	0.18	1.6	2.3	12						
Na	8.0	1.0	5.3	9.8	12	Ala	40.3	5.8	34.1	55.5	13
K	5.2	0.61	3.9	5.7	12	Arg	36.6	3.9	32.7	44.0	13
Cl	6.7	1.4	5.2	8.1	10	Asp	36.1	4.6	22.0	39.4	13
P total	42.6	6.5	27.8	56.0	13	Cys	7.8	1.3	6.4	9.8	10
P inorg	41.6	3.1	36.9	46.1	10	Glu	58.4	2.5	51.3	61.3	13
P phytate						Gly	65.8	6.2	61.3	80.0	13
Fe	1.2	0.19	1.0	1.4	10	His	12.0	3.2	5.0	16.4	13
S	9.2	0.72	8.2	10.5	10	Ile	21.2	21.4	12.7	92.4	13
						Leu	31.5	2.2	26.5	34.0	13
						Lys avail					
Trace Elements (mg/kg ODM)						Lys total	26.8	2.0	23.0	29.3	13
						Meth	7.4	0.36	7.0	8.0	13
Co	1.4	0.17	1.2	1.6	5	Phe	17.8	1.5	15.3	19.8	13
F						Pro	40.3	3.1	36.4	46.4	12
I	1.2	0.30	0.90	1.7	10	Pro.OH	30.8	1.7	29.6	32.0	2
Mn	38.9	8.8	28.2	48.1	12	Ser	21.5	2.4	18.5	24.9	13
Mo	0.90	0.18	0.70	1.3	10	Thr	17.3	2.0	12.9	19.6	13
Zn	130.1	43.1	101.5	256.0	12	Tryp					
Cu	29.1	7.2	19.9	44.4	12	Tyr	12.4	1.0	10.6	14.1	13
Se	0.46	0.15	0.30	0.60	10	Val	22.9	1.8	19.6	25.1	13

ANALYTICAL DATABASE

FEED DESCRIPTION : **PALM KERNEL MEAL** (Source 1)

Determination	Mean	SD	Min	Max	n	Determination	Mean	SD	Min	Max	n
General (g/kg ODM)						**Volatile Fatty Acids (g/kg ODM)**					
ODM (fresh)	895.1	23.2	851.9	918.1	7	Lactic					
TDM (fresh)						Formic					
CP	169.6	22.4	140.3	192.8	7	Acetic					
CF	189.0	45.6	139.0	244.0	7	Propionic					
MADF	425.4	43.9	392.0	505.0	7	n butyric					
EE	82.7	8.2	69.0	96.0	7	i butyric					
AEE	76.0	10.3	58.0	87.0	6	n valeric					
TA	43.6	3.3	39.3	50.0	7	i valeric					
AIA	7.4	2.1	3.9	10.4	7	n caproic					
GE (MJ/kg ODM)	20.4	0.44	19.6	20.9	7	i caproic					
						NO_3N					
						NH_3N/TN					
Carbohydrates (g/kg ODM)						pH					
NDF ash	692.7	39.0	637.0	731.0	7	**Fatty Acids (g/kg ODM)**					
NDF unash											
ADF ash	469.7	38.1	428.0	518.0	7						
ADF unash	490.2	36.6	438.0	530.0	6	C8:0					
Cellulose	406.9	24.0	379.0	442.0	7	C10:0					
Lignin	68.4	11.6	54.0	84.0	7	C12:0					
Starch	12.4	11.7	0.10	26.0	6	C14:0					
NCD	446.6	41.8	388.0	496.0	7	C16:0					
CD						C16:1					
IVD	616.8	52.9	556.0	682.0	6	C18:0					
WSC	39.0		39.0	39.0	1	C18:1					
Avail Carbs						C18:2					
Sugars						C18:3					
						C20:0					
						C20:4					
Minerals (g/kg ODM)						C22:1					
Ca	2.4	0.27	2.1	2.9	7						
Mg	3.0	0.41	2.4	3.4	7	**Amino Acids (g/kg ODM)**					
Na	0.15	0.10	0.10	0.30	4						
K	6.9	1.2	5.7	9.2	7	Ala					
Cl						Arg					
P total	6.2	0.61	5.4	6.9	7	Asp					
P inorg						Cys					
P phytate						Glu					
Fe						Gly					
S	3.2	0.21	3.0	3.3	2	His					
						Ile					
						Leu					
Trace Elements (mg/kg ODM)						Lys avail					
						Lys total					
Co						Meth					
F						Phe					
I						Pro					
Mn						Pro.OH					
Mo						Ser					
Zn						Thr					
Cu						Tryp					
Se						Tyr					
						Val					

ANALYTICAL DATABASE

FEED DESCRIPTION : **PEAS, FIELD** (Sources 2, 3)

Determination	Mean	SD	Min	Max	n
General (g/kg ODM)					
ODM (fresh)	866.3	15.5	842.5	884.0	7
TDM (fresh)					
CP	254.3	15.7	226.3	284.0	11
CF	59.7	3.5	52.3	65.0	11
MADF	82.5	9.7	69.0	99.0	6
EE	14.1	2.6	11.0	20.0	11
AEE	24.5	2.1	22.0	26.3	5
TA	29.6	2.9	26.0	35.0	11
AIA	0.84	0.47	0.40	1.6	5
GE (MJ/kg ODM)	18.5	0.23	17.9	18.7	11
Carbohydrates (g/kg ODM)					
NDF ash	115.7	22.1	94.0	173.0	11
NDF unash					
ADF ash	75.6	13.1	61.0	105.0	11
ADF unash					
Cellulose	64.9	6.5	58.5	74.0	5
Lignin	7.7	6.0	1.0	20.0	11
Starch	440.4	44.4	374.0	519.0	11
NCD	956.6	6.3	944.0	961.5	7
CD					
IVD	885.3	30.6	814.0	910.5	11
WSC	75.0	2.8	73.0	77.0	2
Avail Carbs					
Sugars	56.9	7.3	45.8	65.4	5
Minerals (g/kg ODM)					
Ca	1.0	0.21	0.70	1.4	11
Mg	1.6	0.44	1.1	2.3	11
Na	0.13	0.05	0.10	0.20	7
K	11.0	0.68	9.9	12.2	11
Cl	0.74	0.12	0.60	0.90	5
P total	5.8	2.1	4.0	9.4	11
P inorg	0.44	0.06	0.40	0.50	5
P phytate					
Fe	0.12	0.05	0.10	0.20	5
S	2.3	0.08	2.2	2.4	5
Trace Elements (mg/kg ODM)					
Co	0.10	0.0	0.10	0.10	3
F					
I	0.30	0.19	0.10	0.60	5
Mn	9.0	2.1	6.0	12.1	11
Mo	2.3	1.6	0.80	4.3	5
Zn	36.2	7.4	27.3	48.3	11
Cu	8.3	1.3	6.0	10.0	11
Se					

Determination	Mean	SD	Min	Max	n
Volatile Fatty Acids (g/kg ODM)					
Lactic					
Formic					
Acetic					
Propionic					
n butyric					
i butyric					
n valeric					
i valeric					
n caproic					
i caproic					
NO3N					
NH3N/TN					
pH					
Fatty Acids (g/kg ODM)					
C8:0					
C10:0					
C12:0					
C14:0					
C16:0	1.2	0.21	0.87	1.4	5
C16:1					
C18:0	0.36	0.09	0.21	0.44	5
C18:1	2.8	0.88	1.4	3.7	5
C18:2	5.1	0.33	4.7	5.6	5
C18:3	1.7	0.19	1.5	1.9	5
C20:0					
C20:4					
C22:1					
Amino Acids (g/kg ODM)					
Ala	10.8	0.57	9.8	11.2	5
Arg	20.8	2.5	16.8	22.6	5
Asp	28.3	1.6	25.5	29.6	5
Cys	3.3	0.25	3.0	3.6	5
Glu	39.6	2.0	36.4	41.8	5
Gly	10.8	0.60	9.7	11.2	5
His	7.0	0.42	6.3	7.3	5
Ile	10.4	0.63	9.4	10.9	5
Leu	17.5	1.0	15.6	18.2	5
Lys avail					
Lys total	17.9	1.5	15.5	19.0	5
Meth	2.4	0.14	2.2	2.6	5
Phe	11.9	0.59	11.0	12.5	5
Pro	10.5	0.38	10.1	11.0	5
Pro.OH					
Ser	11.8	0.81	10.4	12.4	5
Thr	9.8	0.67	8.7	10.3	5
Tryp					
Tyr	7.8	0.54	7.0	8.4	5
Val	11.7	0.66	10.8	12.5	5

ANALYTICAL DATABASE

FEED DESCRIPTION : **POT ALE SYRUP** (Source 2)

Determination	Mean	SD	Min	Max	n	Determination	Mean	SD	Min	Max	n
General (g/kg ODM)						**Volatile Fatty Acids** (g/kg ODM)					
ODM (fresh)	483.0		483.0	483.0	1	Lactic					
TDM (fresh)	509.0		509.0	509.0	1	Formic					
CP	374.0		374.0	374.0	1	Acetic					
CF	2.0		2.0	2.0	1	Propionic					
MADF						n butyric					
EE	2.0		2.0	2.0	1	i butyric					
AEE						n valeric					
TA	95.0		95.0	95.0	1	i valeric					
AIA						n caproic					
GE (MJ/kg ODM)	20.0		20.0	20.0	1	i caproic					
						NO_3N					
						NH_3N/TN					
Carbohydrates (g/kg ODM)						pH	3.8		3.8	3.8	1
NDF ash	6.0		6.0	6.0	1	**Fatty Acids** (g/kg ODM)					
NDF unash											
ADF ash						C8:0					
ADF unash						C10:0					
Cellulose						C12:0					
Lignin	15.0		15.0	15.0	1	C14:0					
Starch	13.0		13.0	13.0	1	C16:0					
NCD						C16:1					
CD						C18:0					
IVD						C18:1					
WSC	23.0		23.0	23.0	1	C18:2					
Avail Carbs						C18:3					
Sugars						C20:0					
						C20:4					
Minerals (g/kg ODM)						C22:1					
Ca	1.9		1.9	1.9	1						
Mg	6.4		6.4	6.4	1	**Amino Acids** (g/kg ODM)					
Na	0.90		0.90	0.90	1						
K	22.3		22.3	22.3	1	Ala					
Cl						Arg					
P total	20.1		20.1	20.1	1	Asp					
P inorg						Cys					
P phytate						Glu					
Fe						Gly					
S						His					
						Ile					
						Leu					
Trace Elements (mg/kg ODM)						Lys avail					
						Lys total					
Co						Meth					
F						Phe					
I						Pro					
Mn	35.0		35.0	35.0	1	Pro.OH					
Mo						Ser					
Zn	22.0		22.0	22.0	1	Thr					
Cu	95.0		95.0	95.0	1	Tryp					
Se						Tyr					
						Val					

ANALYTICAL DATABASE

FEED DESCRIPTION : **POULTRY OFFAL MEAL** (Source 3)

Determination	Mean	SD	Min	Max	n	Determination	Mean	SD	Min	Max	n
General (g/kg ODM)						**Volatile Fatty Acids (g/kg ODM)**					
ODM (fresh)	904.5	10.4	896.0	922.0	5	Lactic					
TDM (fresh)						Formic					
CP	544.9	31.6	497.0	584.3	5	Acetic					
CF	3.8	0.61	3.3	4.7	5	Propionic					
MADF						n butyric					
EE	346.9	34.2	322.8	407.3	5	i butyric					
AEE	354.5	32.5	331.3	411.8	5	n valeric					
TA	73.2	17.9	49.1	89.9	5	i valeric					
AIA	3.1	2.9	0.10	6.4	5	n caproic					
GE (MJ/kg ODM)	26.8	0.86	25.8	27.8	5	i caproic					
						NO_3N					
						NH_3N/TN					
Carbohydrates (g/kg ODM)						pH					
NDF ash						**Fatty Acids (g/kg ODM)**					
NDF unash											
ADF ash						C8:0					
ADF unash						C10:0					
Cellulose						C12:0					
Lignin						C14:0	2.1	0.19	1.8	2.2	4
Starch						C16:0	53.3	2.6	50.7	56.6	4
NCD	558.2	35.3	498.5	587.8	5	C16:1	13.7	2.3	11.1	16.4	4
CD						C18:0	12.4	0.68	11.8	13.2	4
IVD	405.1	27.9	360.0	429.0	5	C18:1	78.3	9.8	68.6	88.9	4
WSC						C18:2	18.8	15.4	4.5	32.5	4
Avail Carbs						C18:3	3.8	2.2	1.8	5.9	4
Sugars	3.4	1.1	1.8	4.4	5	C20:0					
						C20:4					
Minerals (g/kg ODM)						C22:1					
Ca	19.0	5.4	12.9	23.5	5						
Mg	0.70	0.16	0.50	0.90	5	**Amino Acids (g/kg ODM)**					
Na	2.7	0.29	2.2	2.9	5						
K	3.3	0.31	2.8	3.5	5	Ala	29.4	1.7	26.8	30.9	5
Cl	3.0	0.35	2.4	3.3	5	Arg	36.4	3.3	33.4	41.1	5
P total	9.7	2.1	8.1	13.3	5	Asp	36.6	1.8	34.9	39.3	5
P inorg	8.5	2.3	6.7	12.5	5	Cys	18.0	2.5	14.6	21.1	5
P phytate						Glu	57.1	5.6	50.4	65.8	5
Fe	1.3	2.4	0.10	5.6	5	Gly	44.3	3.0	39.8	46.8	5
S	10.4	2.9	8.2	15.2	5	His	13.9	1.5	12.1	16.1	5
						Ile	23.8	1.9	21.6	25.9	5
						Leu	40.6	3.2	36.9	44.8	5
Trace Elements (mg/kg ODM)						Lys avail					
						Lys total	24.3	1.9	21.9	27.1	5
Co						Meth	6.0	0.37	5.7	6.5	5
F						Phe	25.2	2.0	22.9	27.9	5
I	0.30	0.07	0.20	0.40	5	Pro	47.8	4.9	41.1	52.4	5
Mn	16.3	6.7	11.1	26.6	5	Pro.OH					
Mo	0.46	0.21	0.20	0.70	5	Ser	34.8	2.8	31.1	37.2	5
Zn	89.1	22.5	66.5	126.5	5	Thr	23.7	1.7	21.8	25.4	5
Cu	8.6	2.2	5.2	11.0	5	Tryp					
Se	0.50	0.07	0.40	0.60	5	Tyr	15.1	1.4	14.0	17.5	5
						Val	35.3	4.0	30.0	38.9	5

ANALYTICAL DATABASE

FEED DESCRIPTION : **RAPESEED MEAL** (Sources 1, 2, 3)

Determination	Mean	SD	Min	Max	n	Determination	Mean	SD	Min	Max	n
General (g/kg ODM)						**Volatile Fatty Acids (g/kg ODM)**					
ODM (fresh)	898.8	13.3	881.5	929.0	17	Lactic					
TDM (fresh)						Formic					
CP	401.5	19.0	350.9	432.0	17	Acetic					
CF	110.9	20.0	70.9	141.0	17	Propionic					
MADF	198.9	17.4	179.0	241.0	12	n butyric					
EE	34.3	18.2	6.8	87.0	17	i butyric					
AEE	53.5	16.6	25.0	83.0	13	n valeric					
TA	76.1	9.7	67.0	97.0	17	i valeric					
AIA	23.4	25.8	0.70	62.0	14	n caproic					
GE (MJ/kg ODM)	19.7	0.35	19.1	20.5	17	i caproic					
						NO_3N					
						NH_3N/TN					
Carbohydrates (g/kg ODM)						pH					
NDF ash	294.5	55.8	247.0	459.0	17	**Fatty Acids (g/kg ODM)**					
NDF unash											
ADF ash	205.7	39.1	167.0	324.0	17	C8:0					
ADF unash	234.8	48.9	200.0	340.0	8	C10:0					
Cellulose	140.5	57.4	70.0	229.0	13	C12:0					
Lignin	53.0	29.1	25.5	124.0	14	C14:0					
Starch	39.8	25.1	4.0	86.0	14	C16:0	1.8	0.37	1.3	2.2	5
NCD	766.1	15.6	724.0	789.0	16	C16:1	0.41	0.06	0.33	0.47	5
CD						C18:0	0.41	0.12	0.25	0.56	5
IVD	644.3	73.3	377.0	695.5	17	C18:1	13.5	3.8	8.1	18.2	5
WSC	102.6	9.5	90.0	117.0	7	C18:2	7.0	1.7	4.5	8.9	5
Avail Carbs						C18:3	2.4	0.70	1.4	3.3	5
Sugars	106.8	1.7	105.3	109.5	5	C20:0					
						C20:4					
Minerals (g/kg ODM)						C22:1					
Ca	8.4	2.7	5.1	15.6	17						
Mg	4.4	0.53	3.5	5.4	17	**Amino Acids (g/kg ODM)**					
Na	0.41	0.32	0.10	0.90	9	Ala	16.4	0.45	15.6	16.8	8
K	14.3	2.2	9.2	16.6	17	Arg	21.5	2.0	19.0	24.2	8
Cl	0.10		0.10	0.10	1	Asp	25.4	1.6	23.5	27.4	8
P total	11.3	1.5	7.5	13.2	17	Cys	12.1	4.4	8.2	18.9	8
P inorg	0.72	0.11	0.60	0.80	5	Glu	60.9	3.0	56.1	64.8	8
P phytate						Gly	18.1	0.98	16.3	19.3	8
Fe	0.24	0.06	0.20	0.30	5	His	11.2	0.78	9.6	12.2	8
S	16.9	1.7	14.6	18.6	5	Ile	14.8	2.5	11.3	17.9	8
						Leu	25.1	1.5	22.6	27.5	8
						Lys avail					
Trace Elements (mg/kg ODM)						Lys total	21.9	0.97	20.5	23.3	8
Co	0.16	0.09	0.10	0.30	5	Meth	7.2	0.78	6.3	8.6	8
F						Phe	15.4	1.4	13.0	17.3	8
I	0.10	0.0	0.10	0.10	5	Pro	23.4	1.8	21.4	24.6	3
Mn	54.5	6.2	48.4	64.0	8	Pro.OH	5.0	1.4	3.8	6.5	3
Mo	1.0	0.06	1.0	1.1	5	Ser	15.7	0.62	14.8	16.6	8
Zn	81.5	9.1	71.0	100.0	8	Thr	16.5	0.98	14.9	17.8	8
Cu	6.1	2.3	3.0	8.2	8	Tryp					
Se	0.14	0.09	0.10	0.30	5	Tyr	11.6	0.89	10.3	13.0	8
						Val	18.7	2.2	15.9	22.0	8

ANALYTICAL DATABASE

FEED DESCRIPTION : **SESAME CAKE** (Source 3)

Determination	Mean	SD	Min	Max	n	Determination	Mean	SD	Min	Max	n
General (g/kg ODM)						**Volatile Fatty Acids** (g/kg ODM)					
ODM (fresh)	951.7	2.1	949.5	954.0	5	Lactic					
TDM (fresh)						Formic					
CP	487.8	7.9	476.4	498.6	5	Acetic					
CF	56.8	0.67	56.0	57.6	5	Propionic					
MADF						n butyric					
EE	113.8	5.3	107.4	120.6	5	i butyric					
AEE	116.2	3.9	113.0	122.2	5	n valeric					
TA	140.8	1.6	138.5	142.5	5	i valeric					
AIA	40.9	1.8	39.0	43.5	5	n caproic					
GE (MJ/kg ODM)	19.9	0.10	19.8	20.0	5	i caproic					
						NO_3N					
						NH_3N/TN					
Carbohydrates (g/kg ODM)						pH					
NDF ash											
NDF unash						**Fatty Acids** (g/kg ODM)					
ADF ash											
ADF unash						C8:0					
Cellulose						C10:0					
Lignin						C12:0					
Starch	14.8	2.3	12.2	17.4	5	C14:0					
NCD	832.0	2.7	829.0	836.0	5	C16:0	9.2	0.66	8.3	10.0	5
CD						C16:1					
IVD	617.2	5.2	612.5	625.0	5	C18:0	6.9	0.38	6.5	7.3	5
WSC						C18:1	40.4	2.8	36.4	44.0	5
Avail Carbs						C18:2	45.9	3.2	42.7	50.9	5
Sugars	38.3	1.3	36.8	39.8	5	C18:3	0.50	0.0	0.50	0.50	5
						C20:0					
						C20:4					
Minerals (g/kg ODM)						C22:1					
Ca	19.5	0.58	18.9	20.4	5						
Mg	5.9	0.08	5.8	6.0	5	**Amino Acids** (g/kg ODM)					
Na	0.10	0.0	0.10	0.10	3						
K	10.0	0.23	9.6	10.2	5	Ala	22.1	1.0	20.6	23.3	5
Cl	0.84	0.12	0.70	1.0	5	Arg	63.8	2.9	59.4	66.3	5
P total						Asp	39.6	1.2	37.5	40.7	5
P inorg						Cys	11.0	0.43	10.5	11.4	5
P phytate						Glu	88.8	3.4	84.3	92.7	5
Fe	1.9	0.23	1.5	2.1	5	Gly	23.5	0.69	22.3	24.1	5
S	7.6	0.40	7.3	8.3	5	His	14.6	0.74	13.5	15.4	5
						Ile	18.4	1.1	17.3	20.0	5
						Leu	32.1	1.2	30.5	33.3	5
Trace Elements (mg/kg ODM)						Lys avail					
						Lys total	11.1	0.66	10.2	11.7	5
Co	0.76	0.23	0.40	1.0	5	Meth	12.8	0.63	12.1	13.5	5
F						Phe	21.8	0.64	20.8	22.5	5
I	0.16	0.06	0.10	0.20	5	Pro	16.3	0.64	15.3	17.0	5
Mn	81.9	4.2	76.0	87.0	5	Pro.OH					
Mo	2.0	0.08	1.9	2.1	5	Ser	21.7	0.73	20.8	22.8	5
Zn	124.1	5.4	116.0	130.0	5	Thr	17.0	0.48	16.4	17.7	5
Cu	43.2	0.68	42.5	44.3	5	Tryp					
Se	0.22	0.05	0.20	0.30	5	Tyr	16.2	0.78	15.0	17.1	5
						Val	22.5	1.4	21.2	24.8	5

ANALYTICAL DATABASE

FEED DESCRIPTION : **SOYABEAN MEAL, EXTRACTED** (Sources 2, 3, 4)

Determination	Mean	SD	Min	Max	n	Determination	Mean	SD	Min	Max	n
General (g/kg ODM)						**Volatile Fatty Acids (g/kg ODM)**					
ODM (fresh)	885.8	10.3	874.5	902.0	9	Lactic					
TDM (fresh)						Formic					
CP	493.3	32.8	400.0	530.8	15	Acetic					
CF	70.3	12.1	48.0	91.0	12	Propionic					
MADF	102.2	16.8	83.5	126.0	7	n butyric					
EE	17.6	4.0	12.7	26.0	15	i butyric					
AEE	26.6	3.2	22.7	31.7	5	n valeric					
TA	68.5	3.8	64.0	79.0	12	i valeric					
AIA	1.4	0.75	0.80	2.3	5	n caproic					
GE (MJ/kg ODM)	19.5	0.25	19.1	19.9	15	i caproic					
						NO$_3$N					
						NH$_3$N/TN					
Carbohydrates (g/kg ODM)						pH					
NDF ash	124.8	43.3	64.5	185.0	11	**Fatty Acids (g/kg ODM)**					
NDF unash											
ADF ash	90.8	38.9	38.5	139.0	11	C8:0					
ADF unash						C10:0					
Cellulose	45.0	19.5	27.5	67.0	5	C12:0					
Lignin	13.6	5.7	6.0	22.0	11	C14:0					
Starch	23.9	18.0	8.0	54.0	11	C16:0	1.6	0.45	1.2	2.2	5
NCD	904.4	4.2	898.8	909.5	5	C16:1					
CD						C18:0	0.41	0.11	0.32	0.59	5
IVD	819.1	24.1	775.0	850.5	11	C18:1	2.0	0.47	1.5	2.7	5
WSC	107.0	15.2	82.0	126.0	6	C18:2	6.4	1.7	4.7	9.1	5
Avail Carbs						C18:3	1.2	0.35	0.93	1.8	5
Sugars	99.7	11.6	85.8	120.0	6	C20:0					
						C20:4					
						C22:1					
Minerals (g/kg ODM)											
Ca	3.9	1.6	2.8	8.7	12						
Mg	3.0	0.23	2.4	3.3	11	**Amino Acids (g/kg ODM)**					
Na	0.16	0.05	0.10	0.20	11	Ala	22.6	1.0	21.6	24.0	6
K	25.0	0.99	23.7	27.0	11	Arg	39.0	3.2	33.0	41.8	6
Cl	0.10	0.0	0.10	0.10	2	Asp	56.8	4.7	53.1	66.0	6
P total	7.4	0.44	6.8	8.5	12	Cys	6.9	0.45	6.5	7.5	5
P inorg	0.66	0.11	0.50	0.80	5	Glu	87.9	11.5	74.9	101.0	6
P phytate						Gly	21.7	1.2	20.9	24.0	6
Fe	0.18	0.11	0.10	0.30	5	His	15.7	2.4	11.0	17.2	6
S	4.6	0.25	4.4	5.0	5	Ile	25.2	1.5	23.0	27.4	6
						Leu	40.4	1.3	38.6	42.0	6
Trace Elements (mg/kg ODM)						Lys avail					
						Lys total	33.4	3.5	27.0	36.5	6
Co	0.24	0.15	0.10	0.50	5	Meth	6.9	0.26	6.5	7.3	6
F						Phe	26.9	0.72	26.1	28.0	6
I						Pro	28.4	0.01	28.4	28.4	2
Mn	37.6	10.7	23.0	57.9	11	Pro.OH					
Mo	4.0	2.5	1.8	8.2	5	Ser	27.0	1.9	24.5	29.1	6
Zn	49.0	9.9	28.0	61.0	11	Thr	20.5	1.1	18.5	21.6	6
Cu	15.8	2.6	11.8	21.0	11	Tryp					
Se	0.30	0.19	0.10	0.50	5	Tyr	19.1	1.3	17.1	21.0	6
						Val	28.8	1.4	27.1	31.0	6

ANALYTICAL DATABASE

FEED DESCRIPTION : **SOYABEAN MEAL, EXTRACTED, DEHULLED** (Source 3)

Determination	Mean	SD	Min	Max	n

General (g/kg ODM)

Determination	Mean	SD	Min	Max	n
ODM (fresh)	887.4	5.2	880.0	892.0	5
TDM (fresh)					
CP	547.1	5.6	538.0	552.0	5
CF	34.0	1.7	33.1	37.0	5
MADF					
EE	20.0	7.1	10.2	25.2	5
AEE	31.2	8.6	20.8	38.3	5
TA	70.1	1.7	67.0	71.0	5
AIA	0.88	0.42	0.60	1.6	5
GE (MJ/kg ODM)	19.9	0.06	19.8	19.9	5

Carbohydrates (g/kg ODM)

Determination	Mean	SD	Min	Max	n
NDF ash	109.2	34.1	69.5	143.5	5
NDF unash					
ADF ash	67.2	25.3	36.0	92.0	5
ADF unash					
Cellulose	58.6	20.3	37.0	78.5	5
Lignin	7.8	3.0	3.0	10.5	5
Starch	34.1	13.7	20.7	50.7	5
NCD	921.5	2.6	917.0	923.3	5
CD					
IVD	864.0	18.0	842.0	891.0	5
WSC					
Avail Carbs					
Sugars	105.2	5.0	99.4	111.0	5

Minerals (g/kg ODM)

Determination	Mean	SD	Min	Max	n
Ca	3.0	0.37	2.6	3.6	5
Mg	3.1	0.14	3.0	3.3	5
Na	0.17	0.12	0.10	0.30	3
K	26.7	0.40	26.2	27.3	5
Cl	0.20	0.10	0.10	0.30	3
P total	7.9	0.15	7.8	8.1	5
P inorg	0.70	0.07	0.60	0.80	5
P phytate					
Fe	0.12	0.05	0.10	0.20	5
S	4.9	0.10	4.8	5.0	5

Trace Elements (mg/kg ODM)

Determination	Mean	SD	Min	Max	n
Co	0.20	0.0	0.20	0.20	5
F					
I	0.10		0.10	0.10	1
Mn	48.0	14.7	39.9	74.2	5
Mo	3.6	0.05	3.6	3.7	5
Zn	55.5	6.0	46.2	60.2	5
Cu	17.2	0.56	16.5	18.0	5
Se	0.44	0.05	0.40	0.50	5

Volatile Fatty Acids (g/kg ODM)

Determination	Mean	SD	Min	Max	n
Lactic					
Formic					
Acetic					
Propionic					
n butyric					
i butyric					
n valeric					
i valeric					
n caproic					
i caproic					
NO$_3$N					
NH$_3$N/TN					
pH					

Fatty Acids (g/kg ODM)

Determination	Mean	SD	Min	Max	n
C8:0					
C10:0					
C12:0	0.04		0.04	0.04	1
C14:0					
C16:0	2.0	0.47	1.4	2.4	5
C16:1	0.07		0.07	0.07	1
C18:0	0.54	0.16	0.34	0.68	5
C18:1	2.9	0.85	1.7	3.6	5
C18:2	8.1	3.6	3.4	10.9	5
C18:3	1.6	0.74	0.68	2.2	5
C20:0					
C20:4					
C22:1					

Amino Acids (g/kg ODM)

Determination	Mean	SD	Min	Max	n
Ala	23.9	1.3	22.6	25.9	5
Arg	41.7	1.1	40.3	43.0	5
Asp	61.7	0.84	61.0	63.0	5
Cys	7.7	0.31	7.2	7.9	5
Glu	101.8	12.4	87.2	112.6	5
Gly	22.4	0.56	21.5	22.9	5
His	16.8	0.58	15.9	17.5	5
Ile	27.2	0.74	26.8	28.5	5
Leu	43.2	1.9	41.9	46.3	5
Lys avail					
Lys total	35.6	2.1	33.8	38.2	5
Meth	7.5	0.25	7.2	7.8	5
Phe	28.4	0.51	27.6	28.9	5
Pro	31.4	0.41	31.1	31.9	3
Pro.OH					
Ser	28.3	2.0	26.2	30.9	5
Thr	21.8	0.65	20.7	22.4	5
Tryp					
Tyr	19.6	1.6	17.1	20.9	5
Val	28.9	2.2	27.3	31.7	5

ANALYTICAL DATABASE

FEED DESCRIPTION : **SOYABEAN, FULL FAT** (Sources 2, 3)

Determination	Mean	SD	Min	Max	n	Determination	Mean	SD	Min	Max	n
General (g/kg ODM)						**Volatile Fatty Acids (g/kg ODM)**					
ODM (fresh)	898.1	10.7	890.0	924.0	9	Lactic					
TDM (fresh)						Formic					
CP	415.3	11.0	395.0	428.7	9	Acetic					
CF	47.8	4.4	42.0	55.2	9	Propionic					
MADF	94.3	25.1	70.0	125.0	4	n butyric					
EE	221.5	14.6	200.0	232.0	9	i butyric					
AEE	228.5	5.1	223.0	239.0	8	n valeric					
TA	54.4	1.4	51.0	55.5	9	i valeric					
AIA	0.90	0.16	0.70	1.1	5	n caproic					
GE (MJ/kg ODM)	23.8	0.18	23.6	24.1	9	i caproic					
						NO$_3$N					
						NH$_3$N/TN					
Carbohydrates (g/kg ODM)						pH					
NDF ash	122.1	12.3	105.0	144.0	9	**Fatty Acids (g/kg ODM)**					
NDF unash											
ADF ash	82.1	20.7	67.5	129.0	9	C8:0					
ADF unash						C10:0					
Cellulose	60.2	1.8	58.5	63.0	5	C12:0					
Lignin	7.9	2.0	6.0	11.0	9	C14:0					
Starch	14.7	3.1	8.0	18.4	9	C16:0	22.6	0.58	21.8	23.4	5
NCD	924.3	2.1	921.5	929.0	9	C16:1					
CD						C18:0	7.8	0.42	7.3	8.4	5
IVD	688.2	83.6	617.0	812.0	9	C18:1	47.4	1.6	45.0	49.1	5
WSC	83.5	3.9	80.0	89.0	4	C18:2	122.4	2.4	119.0	125.0	5
Avail Carbs						C18:3	19.7	0.77	18.5	20.4	5
Sugars	76.4	4.2	71.4	81.3	5	C20:0					
						C20:4					
Minerals (g/kg ODM)						C22:1					
Ca	2.7	0.28	2.1	3.0	9						
Mg	2.4	0.07	2.2	2.4	9	**Amino Acids (g/kg ODM)**					
Na	0.14	0.05	0.10	0.20	5	Ala	16.6	1.1	14.9	17.7	5
K	19.0	1.4	17.3	20.2	9	Arg	27.8	1.8	25.6	29.6	5
Cl	0.58	0.26	0.30	0.90	5	Asp	42.8	1.0	41.5	44.3	5
P total	5.9	0.14	5.6	6.1	9	Cys	5.8	0.20	5.5	5.9	5
P inorg	0.64	0.06	0.60	0.70	5	Glu	73.9	2.9	70.3	78.1	5
P phytate						Gly	16.4	0.50	15.7	17.0	5
Fe	0.10	0.0	0.10	0.10	5	His	12.8	0.51	12.0	13.4	5
S	3.5	0.05	3.5	3.6	5	Ile	18.2	0.27	17.7	18.4	5
						Leu	29.6	0.59	28.8	30.2	5
Trace Elements (mg/kg ODM)						Lys avail					
						Lys total	24.2	0.99	23.0	25.5	5
Co	0.10	0.0	0.10	0.10	5	Meth	5.5	0.23	5.1	5.7	5
F						Phe	20.4	0.74	19.3	21.0	5
I						Pro	21.5	0.53	21.0	22.3	5
Mn	30.9	3.1	24.0	33.7	9	Pro.OH					
Mo	2.4	0.08	2.3	2.5	5	Ser	18.6	0.81	17.6	19.6	5
Zn	52.0	3.8	48.2	58.0	9	Thr	15.7	0.50	15.1	16.4	5
Cu	13.4	1.2	11.0	15.0	9	Tryp					
Se	0.30	0.0	0.30	0.30	5	Tyr	14.7	0.30	14.2	15.0	5
						Val	19.5	0.52	18.8	20.2	5

ANALYTICAL DATABASE

FEED DESCRIPTION : **SUNFLOWER SEED MEAL** (Source 1)

Determination	Mean	SD	Min	Max	n	Determination	Mean	SD	Min	Max	n
General (g/kg ODM)						**Volatile Fatty Acids (g/kg ODM)**					
ODM (fresh)	897.6	7.7	886.6	905.1	6	Lactic					
TDM (fresh)						Formic					
CP	335.5	31.4	301.8	390.1	6	Acetic					
CF	265.2	19.3	234.0	285.0	6	Propionic					
MADF	292.7	26.5	252.0	331.0	6	n butyric					
EE	23.0	10.7	9.0	35.0	6	i butyric					
AEE	26.8	6.2	20.0	35.0	4	n valeric					
TA	71.2	7.8	59.0	80.0	6	i valeric					
AIA	2.4	2.3	1.0	7.0	6	n caproic					
GE (MJ/kg ODM)	19.5	0.29	19.0	19.8	6	i caproic					
						NO3N					
						NH3N/TN					
Carbohydrates (g/kg ODM)						pH					
NDF ash	473.3	29.7	445.0	525.0	6	**Fatty Acids (g/kg ODM)**					
NDF unash											
ADF ash	328.2	28.2	294.0	372.0	6	C8:0					
ADF unash	330.3	27.5	293.0	373.0	6	C10:0					
Cellulose	249.8	27.4	214.0	287.0	6	C12:0					
Lignin	74.8	9.8	63.0	86.0	6	C14:0					
Starch	2.8	1.8	1.5	4.1	2	C16:0					
NCD	632.5	35.9	587.0	671.0	4	C16:1					
CD						C18:0					
IVD	610.0	92.2	528.0	780.0	6	C18:1					
WSC	66.3	6.5	61.0	79.0	6	C18:2					
Avail Carbs						C18:3					
Sugars						C20:0					
						C20:4					
Minerals (g/kg ODM)						C22:1					
Ca	4.8	1.4	3.3	6.5	6						
Mg	5.8	0.49	5.2	6.4	6	**Amino Acids (g/kg ODM)**					
Na	1.0	1.2	0.10	2.9	6						
K	17.1	1.8	14.4	19.2	6	Ala					
Cl						Arg					
P total	10.8	1.9	8.7	14.2	6	Asp					
P inorg						Cys					
P phytate						Glu					
Fe						Gly					
S						His					
						Ile					
						Leu					
Trace Elements (mg/kg ODM)						Lys avail					
						Lys total					
Co						Meth					
F						Phe					
I						Pro					
Mn						Pro.OH					
Mo						Ser					
Zn						Thr					
Cu						Tryp					
Se						Tyr					
						Val					

RUMINANT DATABASE

FEED CLASS 10

HAYS

RUMINANT DATABASE

FEED DESCRIPTION : **GRASS HAY, ALL CURING METHODS** (Sources 1, 2)

Determination	Mean	SD	Min	Max	n	Determination	Mean	SD	Min	Max	n
General (g/kg ODM)						**Degradability**					
ODM (fresh)	865.1	25.0	791.2	914.7	119	Dry matter					
TDM (fresh)						a (%)	16.3	5.6	11.1	22.2	3
CP	107.4	34.6	52.0	199.0	128	b (%)	54.1	4.1	49.4	57.2	3
MADF	355.1	42.0	205.0	437.0	128	c (h^{-1})	0.05	0.0	0.05	0.05	3
EE	16.8	5.1	5.0	38.0	125						
AEE	16.2	1.9	14.0	19.0	5	dg (%) @ outflow rate					
TA	74.3	13.6	44.0	118.0	115	$0.02h^{-1}$	55.0	8.5	46.0	63.0	3
GE (MJ/kg ODM)	18.4	0.45	17.0	19.5	128	$0.05h^{-1}$	43.0	8.0	35.0	51.0	3
						$0.08h^{-1}$	37.3	7.5	30.0	45.0	3
NDF ash	656.8	61.5	437.0	820.0	123						
NDF unash						Nitrogen					
ADF ash	366.6	46.2	207.0	554.0	123	a (%)	11.8		11.8	11.8	1
ADF unash	379.4	37.7	303.0	459.0	84	b (%)	72.2		72.2	72.2	1
						c (h^{-1})	0.09		0.09	0.09	1
Energy Values											
						dg (%) @ outflow rate					
DE (MJ/kg ODM)	11.2	1.4	7.7	15.8	112	$0.02h^{-1}$	71.0		71.0	71.0	1
ME (MJ/kg ODM)	8.8	1.0	5.9	13.0	90	$0.05h^{-1}$	58.0		58.0	58.0	1
FE/GE	0.39	0.07	0.19	0.57	123	$0.08h^{-1}$	50.0		50.0	50.0	1
UE/GE	0.04	0.02	0.01	0.09	90						
CH_4E/GE	0.08	0.01	0.06	0.10	123						
ME/DE	0.81	0.02	0.74	0.83	79						
ME/GE	0.48	0.06	0.33	0.67	90						
Digestibility Coefficients											
DM	0.62	0.08	0.34	0.79	114						
OM	0.64	0.07	0.40	0.84	124						
CP	0.55	0.11	0.29	0.75	111						
CF	0.68	0.09	0.44	0.97	112						
EE	0.48	0.14	0.08	0.84	107						
NDF	0.63	0.06	0.54	0.70	18						
ADF	0.63	0.05	0.54	0.69	15						
Cell	0.68	0.05	0.61	0.75	15						
GE	0.61	0.07	0.43	0.81	123						
DOMD(g/kg ODM)	596.2	57.4	362.0	777.7	124						

RUMINANT DATABASE

FEED DESCRIPTION : **GRASS HAY, BARN CURED** (Sources 1, 2)

Determination	Mean	SD	Min	Max	n	Determination	Mean	SD	Min	Max	n
General (g/kg ODM)						**Degradability**					
ODM (fresh)	866.9	22.9	816.4	906.7	47	Dry matter					
TDM (fresh)						a (%)	13.3	3.1	11.1	15.5	2
CP	121.5	36.1	59.0	185.0	50	b (%)	53.3	5.5	49.4	57.2	2
MADF	334.4	42.8	205.0	422.0	50	c (h^{-1})	0.05	0.0	0.05	0.05	2
EE	18.2	5.1	9.0	38.0	50						
AEE						dg (%) @ outflow rate					
TA	77.2	15.3	56.0	117.0	37	0.02h^{-1}	51.0	7.1	46.0	56.0	2
GE (MJ/kg ODM)	18.4	0.51	17.0	19.4	50	0.05h^{-1}	39.0	5.7	35.0	43.0	2
						0.08h^{-1}	33.5	5.0	30.0	37.0	2
NDF ash	627.3	60.2	437.0	725.0	50						
NDF unash						Nitrogen					
ADF ash	348.6	45.2	207.0	421.0	48	a (%)	11.8		11.8	11.8	1
ADF unash	363.8	33.7	303.0	448.0	41	b (%)	72.2		72.2	72.2	1
						c (h^{-1})	0.09		0.09	0.09	1
Energy Values											
						dg (%) @ outflow rate					
DE (MJ/kg ODM)	11.9	1.5	7.9	15.8	45	0.02h^{-1}	71.0		71.0	71.0	1
ME (MJ/kg ODM)	9.2	1.4	6.1	13.0	22	0.05h^{-1}	58.0		58.0	58.0	1
FE/GE	0.36	0.07	0.19	0.57	50	0.08h^{-1}	50.0		50.0	50.0	1
UE/GE	0.04	0.01	0.03	0.06	22						
CH$_4$E/GE	0.08	0.01	0.06	0.09	50						
ME/DE	0.81	0.02	0.77	0.83	17						
ME/GE	0.50	0.06	0.33	0.67	22						

Digestibility Coefficients

DM	0.65	0.07	0.42	0.79	47
OM	0.67	0.06	0.47	0.84	51
CP	0.61	0.11	0.33	0.75	45
CF	0.71	0.09	0.53	0.97	45
EE	0.52	0.15	0.09	0.84	45
NDF	0.59	0.05	0.54	0.66	6
ADF	0.61	0.02	0.60	0.64	3
Cell	0.65	0.04	0.61	0.69	3
GE	0.64	0.07	0.43	0.81	50
DOMD(g/kg ODM)	623.2	58.4	441.2	777.7	51

RUMINANT DATABASE

FEED DESCRIPTION : **GRASS HAY, BARN CURED, ME NOT KNOWN** (Source 1)

Determination	Mean	SD	Min	Max	n	Determination	Mean	SD	Min	Max	n
General (g/kg ODM)						**Degradability**					
ODM (fresh)	870.0	22.8	833.5	906.7	30	Dry matter					
TDM (fresh)						a (%)					
CP	126.6	29.0	64.0	172.0	28	b (%)					
MADF	317.2	36.0	259.0	399.0	28	c (h^{-1})					
EE	19.5	5.7	13.0	38.0	28						
AEE						dg (%) @ outflow rate					
TA	86.0	16.6	65.0	117.0	15	0.02h^{-1}					
GE (MJ/kg ODM)	18.4	0.39	17.6	19.1	28	0.05h^{-1}					
						0.08h^{-1}					
NDF ash	610.7	59.7	511.0	725.0	28						
NDF unash						Nitrogen					
ADF ash	326.5	34.0	263.0	400.0	26	a (%)					
ADF unash	352.4	32.4	303.0	431.0	28	b (%)					
						c (h^{-1})					
Energy Values											
						dg (%) @ outflow rate					
DE (MJ/kg ODM)	12.3	1.1	8.9	14.1	28	0.02h^{-1}					
ME (MJ/kg ODM)						0.05h^{-1}					
FE/GE	0.33	0.06	0.22	0.50	28	0.08h^{-1}					
UE/GE											
CH$_4$E/GE	0.08	0.0	0.07	0.08	28						
ME/DE											
ME/GE											

Digestibility Coefficients

Determination	Mean	SD	Min	Max	n
DM	0.68	0.06	0.51	0.78	30
OM	0.69	0.06	0.53	0.80	30
CP	0.64	0.08	0.40	0.75	28
CF	0.73	0.06	0.61	0.87	28
EE	0.52	0.12	0.35	0.84	28
NDF					
ADF					
Cell					
GE	0.67	0.06	0.50	0.78	28
DOMD(g/kg ODM)	642.2	51.8	480.0	735.9	30

RUMINANT DATABASE

FEED DESCRIPTION : **GRASS HAY, BARN CURED, ME < 8** (Source 1)

Determination	Mean	SD	Min	Max	n	Determination	Mean	SD	Min	Max	n
General (g/kg ODM)						**Degradability**					
ODM (fresh)	869.5	4.0	863.5	871.5	4	Dry matter					
TDM (fresh)						a (%)	13.3	3.1	11.1	15.5	2
CP	67.5	17.0	59.0	93.0	4	b (%)	53.3	5.5	49.4	57.2	2
MADF	365.8	37.5	347.0	422.0	4	c (h^{-1})	0.05	0.0	0.05	0.05	2
EE	17.0	0.0	17.0	17.0	4						
AEE						dg (%) @ outflow rate					
TA	69.8	0.50	69.0	70.0	4	$0.02h^{-1}$	51.0	7.1	46.0	56.0	2
GE (MJ/kg ODM)	17.4	0.75	17.0	18.5	4	$0.05h^{-1}$	39.0	5.7	35.0	43.0	2
						$0.08h^{-1}$	33.5	5.0	30.0	37.0	2
NDF ash	644.5	37.0	626.0	700.0	4						
NDF unash						Nitrogen					
ADF ash	367.8	19.5	358.0	397.0	4	a (%)	11.8		11.8	11.8	1
ADF unash	373.0	0.0	373.0	373.0	3	b (%)	72.2		72.2	72.2	1
						c (h^{-1})	0.09		0.09	0.09	1
Energy Values											
						dg (%) @ outflow rate					
DE (MJ/kg ODM)	9.1	0.82	7.9	9.7	4	$0.02h^{-1}$	71.0		71.0	71.0	1
ME (MJ/kg ODM)	7.3	0.83	6.1	7.9	4	$0.05h^{-1}$	58.0		58.0	58.0	1
FE/GE	0.48	0.06	0.43	0.57	4	$0.08h^{-1}$	50.0		50.0	50.0	1
UE/GE	0.03	0.0	0.03	0.03	4						
CH_4E/GE	0.07	0.0	0.06	0.07	4						
ME/DE	0.80	0.02	0.77	0.82	4						
ME/GE	0.42	0.06	0.33	0.46	4						
Digestibility Coefficients											
DM	0.56	0.09	0.42	0.61	4						
OM	0.58	0.07	0.47	0.62	4						
CP	0.38	0.04	0.33	0.41	4						
CF	0.56	0.02	0.53	0.59	4						
EE	0.69	0.08	0.62	0.76	4						
NDF	0.55	0.01	0.54	0.56	3						
ADF											
Cell											
GE	0.53	0.07	0.43	0.57	4						
DOMD(g/kg ODM)	539.8	66.0	441.2	577.7	4						

RUMINANT DATABASE

FEED DESCRIPTION : **GRASS HAY, BARN CURED, ME 8 - 10** (Sources 1, 2)

Determination	Mean	SD	Min	Max	n	Determination	Mean	SD	Min	Max	n
General (g/kg ODM)						**Degradability**					
ODM (fresh)	864.0	26.8	817.4	894.1	9	Dry matter					
TDM (fresh)						a (%)					
CP	113.3	37.8	74.0	185.0	12	b (%)					
MADF	369.6	17.8	349.0	414.0	12	c (h^{-1})					
EE	15.7	2.9	9.0	20.0	12						
AEE						dg (%) @ outflow rate					
TA	67.9	10.8	56.0	87.0	12	0.02h^{-1}					
GE (MJ/kg ODM)	18.6	0.25	18.3	18.9	12	0.05h^{-1}					
						0.08h^{-1}					
NDF ash	671.8	14.4	654.0	701.0	12						
NDF unash						Nitrogen					
ADF ash	392.6	18.4	344.0	421.0	12	a (%)					
ADF unash	396.9	24.1	371.0	448.0	8	b (%)					
						c (h^{-1})					
Energy Values											
						dg (%) @ outflow rate					
DE (MJ/kg ODM)	11.2	0.70	9.8	12.1	9	0.02h^{-1}					
ME (MJ/kg ODM)	9.0	0.50	8.0	9.6	12	0.05h^{-1}					
FE/GE	0.40	0.03	0.34	0.46	12	0.08h^{-1}					
UE/GE	0.04	0.01	0.03	0.06	12						
CH$_4$E/GE	0.07	0.01	0.07	0.08	12						
ME/DE	0.81	0.02	0.78	0.82	9						
ME/GE	0.48	0.03	0.44	0.53	12						

Digestibility Coefficients

Determination	Mean	SD	Min	Max	n
DM	0.60	0.02	0.56	0.63	9
OM	0.63	0.02	0.60	0.67	11
CP	0.59	0.09	0.39	0.68	9
CF	0.68	0.05	0.62	0.74	9
EE	0.45	0.13	0.15	0.56	9
NDF	0.63	0.03	0.61	0.66	3
ADF	0.61	0.02	0.60	0.64	3
Cell	0.65	0.04	0.61	0.69	3
GE	0.60	0.04	0.54	0.66	12
DOMD(g/kg ODM)	589.2	15.9	569.5	614.0	11

RUMINANT DATABASE

FEED DESCRIPTION : **GRASS HAY, BARN CURED, ME > 10** (Sources 1, 2)

Determination	Mean	SD	Min	Max	n	Determination	Mean	SD	Min	Max	n
General (g/kg ODM)						**Degradability**					
ODM (fresh)	847.5	21.5	816.4	865.8	4	Dry matter					
TDM (fresh)						a (%)					
CP	150.0	36.1	98.0	185.0	6	b (%)					
MADF	323.0	61.8	205.0	372.0	6	c (h^{-1})					
EE	18.3	5.9	9.0	24.0	6						
AEE						dg (%) @ outflow rate					
TA	78.8	12.7	57.0	90.0	6	$0.02h^{-1}$					
GE (MJ/kg ODM)	18.8	0.41	18.3	19.4	6	$0.05h^{-1}$					
						$0.08h^{-1}$					
NDF ash	604.2	88.2	437.0	674.0	6						
NDF unash						Nitrogen					
ADF ash	343.2	70.7	207.0	389.0	6	a (%)					
ADF unash	376.5	0.71	376.0	377.0	2	b (%)					
						c (h^{-1})					
Energy Values											
						dg (%) @ outflow rate					
DE (MJ/kg ODM)	13.3	1.7	12.2	15.8	4	$0.02h^{-1}$					
ME (MJ/kg ODM)	10.7	1.1	10.1	13.0	6	$0.05h^{-1}$					
FE/GE	0.31	0.06	0.19	0.36	6	$0.08h^{-1}$					
UE/GE	0.04	0.02	0.03	0.06	6						
CH_4E/GE	0.08	0.01	0.08	0.09	6						
ME/DE	0.82	0.01	0.80	0.83	4						
ME/GE	0.57	0.05	0.53	0.67	6						
Digestibility Coefficients											
DM	0.66	0.09	0.61	0.79	4						
OM	0.70	0.07	0.65	0.84	6						
CP	0.69	0.03	0.66	0.73	4						
CF	0.82	0.13	0.70	0.97	4						
EE	0.49	0.31	0.09	0.84	4						
NDF											
ADF											
Cell											
GE	0.69	0.06	0.64	0.81	6						
DOMD(g/kg ODM)	646.3	66.8	599.3	777.7	6						

RUMINANT DATABASE

FEED DESCRIPTION : **GRASS HAY, SUN CURED** (Sources 1, 2)

Determination	Mean	SD	Min	Max	n
General (g/kg ODM)					
ODM (fresh)	863.8	26.6	791.2	914.7	71
TDM (fresh)					
CP	98.5	30.7	52.0	199.0	77
MADF	369.0	35.9	245.0	437.0	77
EE	16.0	4.9	5.0	30.0	74
AEE	16.2	1.9	14.0	19.0	5
TA	73.0	12.7	44.0	118.0	77
GE (MJ/kg ODM)	18.4	0.41	17.3	19.5	77
NDF ash	678.0	53.9	491.0	820.0	72
NDF unash					
ADF ash	378.8	43.2	244.0	554.0	74
ADF unash	395.0	35.7	305.0	459.0	42
Energy Values					
DE (MJ/kg ODM)	10.7	1.1	7.7	13.2	66
ME (MJ/kg ODM)	8.7	0.90	5.9	10.4	67
FE/GE	0.41	0.06	0.30	0.57	72
UE/GE	0.04	0.02	0.01	0.09	67
CH_4E/GE	0.07	0.01	0.06	0.10	72
ME/DE	0.81	0.02	0.74	0.83	61
ME/GE	0.47	0.05	0.34	0.55	67
Digestibility Coefficients					
DM	0.59	0.06	0.34	0.71	66
OM	0.62	0.06	0.40	0.74	72
CP	0.51	0.10	0.29	0.73	65
CF	0.66	0.07	0.44	0.81	66
EE	0.44	0.12	0.08	0.71	61
NDF	0.65	0.05	0.58	0.70	12
ADF	0.63	0.05	0.54	0.69	12
Cell	0.69	0.05	0.61	0.75	12
GE	0.59	0.06	0.43	0.70	72
DOMD(g/kg ODM)	576.5	48.6	362.0	676.7	72

Determination	Mean	SD	Min	Max	n
Degradability					
Dry matter					
a (%)	22.2		22.2	22.2	1
b (%)	55.5		55.5	55.5	1
$c\ (h^{-1})$	0.05		0.05	0.05	1
dg (%) @ outflow rate					
$0.02h^{-1}$	63.0		63.0	63.0	1
$0.05h^{-1}$	51.0		51.0	51.0	1
$0.08h^{-1}$	45.0		45.0	45.0	1
Nitrogen					
a (%)					
b (%)					
$c\ (h^{-1})$					
dg (%) @ outflow rate					
$0.02h^{-1}$					
$0.05h^{-1}$					
$0.08h^{-1}$					

RUMINANT DATABASE

FEED DESCRIPTION : **GRASS HAY, SUN CURED, ME NOT KNOWN** (Source 1)

Determination	Mean	SD	Min	Max	n	Determination	Mean	SD	Min	Max	n
General (g/kg ODM)						Degradability					
ODM (fresh)	837.1	24.3	791.2	867.3	10	Dry matter					
TDM (fresh)						a (%)					
CP	133.6	40.3	78.0	199.0	10	b (%)					
MADF	348.7	40.0	274.0	398.0	10	c (h^{-1})					
EE	18.6	5.5	14.0	30.0	10						
AEE						dg (%) @ outflow rate					
TA	81.3	19.7	62.0	118.0	10	0.02h^{-1}					
GE (MJ/kg ODM)	18.4	0.56	17.3	19.1	10	0.05h^{-1}					
						0.08h^{-1}					
NDF ash	648.8	36.6	566.0	706.0	10						
NDF unash						Nitrogen					
ADF ash	361.0	37.5	281.0	406.0	10	a (%)					
ADF unash	374.5	40.0	305.0	429.0	10	b (%)					
						c (h^{-1})					
Energy Values											
						dg (%) @ outflow rate					
DE (MJ/kg ODM)	11.7	1.0	10.8	13.2	5	0.02h^{-1}					
ME (MJ/kg ODM)						0.05h^{-1}					
FE/GE	0.37	0.05	0.30	0.43	5	0.08h^{-1}					
UE/GE											
CH$_4$E/GE	0.08	0.01	0.07	0.08	5						
ME/DE											
ME/GE											
Digestibility Coefficients											
DM	0.64	0.05	0.57	0.71	5						
OM	0.66	0.06	0.59	0.74	5						
CP	0.65	0.07	0.57	0.73	5						
CF	0.72	0.08	0.64	0.81	5						
EE	0.50	0.12	0.36	0.68	5						
NDF											
ADF											
Cell											
GE	0.63	0.05	0.57	0.70	5						
DOMD(g/kg ODM)	607.2	48.9	540.7	676.7	5						

RUMINANT DATABASE

FEED DESCRIPTION : **GRASS HAY, SUN CURED, ME < 8** (Source 1)

Determination	Mean	SD	Min	Max	n	Determination	Mean	SD	Min	Max	n
General (g/kg ODM)						**Degradability**					
ODM (fresh)	858.5	16.8	827.0	879.6	15	Dry matter					
TDM (fresh)						a (%)					
CP	84.1	15.2	57.0	120.0	15	b (%)					
MADF	386.5	45.6	245.0	437.0	15	c (h^{-1})					
EE	14.1	2.6	10.0	20.0	15						
AEE						dg (%) @ outflow rate					
TA	71.4	13.9	44.0	96.0	15	0.02h^{-1}					
GE (MJ/kg ODM)	18.2	0.49	17.6	19.5	15	0.05h^{-1}					
						0.08h^{-1}					
NDF ash	709.1	79.5	491.0	820.0	14						
NDF unash						Nitrogen					
ADF ash	400.4	66.0	244.0	554.0	15	a (%)					
ADF unash	426.3	18.2	405.0	443.0	6	b (%)					
						c (h^{-1})					
Energy Values											
						dg (%) @ outflow rate					
DE (MJ/kg ODM)	9.2	0.58	7.7	10.0	15	0.02h^{-1}					
ME (MJ/kg ODM)	7.4	0.49	5.9	7.9	15	0.05h^{-1}					
FE/GE	0.49	0.04	0.45	0.57	15	0.08h^{-1}					
UE/GE	0.03	0.01	0.01	0.06	15						
CH$_4$E/GE	0.07	0.01	0.06	0.07	15						
ME/DE	0.80	0.02	0.76	0.83	15						
ME/GE	0.40	0.03	0.34	0.43	15						

Digestibility Coefficients

Determination	Mean	SD	Min	Max	n
DM	0.52	0.07	0.34	0.60	15
OM	0.55	0.06	0.40	0.64	15
CP	0.44	0.08	0.29	0.59	15
CF	0.61	0.10	0.44	0.79	15
EE	0.35	0.16	0.08	0.71	15
NDF					
ADF					
Cell					
GE	0.51	0.04	0.43	0.55	15
DOMD(g/kg ODM)	519.0	57.1	362.0	598.2	15

RUMINANT DATABASE

FEED DESCRIPTION : **GRASS HAY, SUN CURED, ME 8 - 10** (Sources 1, 2)

Determination	Mean	SD	Min	Max	n	Determination	Mean	SD	Min	Max	n
General (g/kg ODM)						**Degradability**					
ODM (fresh)	871.8	25.9	815.5	914.7	43	Dry matter					
TDM (fresh)						a (%)	22.2		22.2	22.2	1
CP	94.9	26.5	52.0	193.0	49	b (%)	55.5		55.5	55.5	1
MADF	370.0	28.0	316.0	426.0	49	c (h^{-1})	0.05		0.05	0.05	1
EE	16.2	4.8	5.0	27.0	46						
AEE	16.3	2.2	14.0	19.0	4	dg (%) @ outflow rate					
TA	72.0	9.8	48.0	94.0	49	$0.02h^{-1}$	63.0		63.0	63.0	1
GE (MJ/kg ODM)	18.4	0.34	17.8	19.3	49	$0.05h^{-1}$	51.0		51.0	51.0	1
						$0.08h^{-1}$	45.0		45.0	45.0	1
NDF ash	676.6	44.5	558.0	762.0	45						
NDF unash						Nitrogen					
ADF ash	378.1	32.6	309.0	439.0	46	a (%)					
ADF unash	397.4	31.7	348.0	459.0	25	b (%)					
						c (h^{-1})					
Energy Values											
						dg (%) @ outflow rate					
DE (MJ/kg ODM)	11.1	0.58	10.2	12.1	43	$0.02h^{-1}$					
ME (MJ/kg ODM)	9.0	0.50	8.0	9.9	49	$0.05h^{-1}$					
FE/GE	0.40	0.03	0.34	0.45	49	$0.08h^{-1}$					
UE/GE	0.04	0.02	0.02	0.09	49						
CH_4E/GE	0.08	0.01	0.07	0.10	49						
ME/DE	0.81	0.02	0.74	0.83	43						
ME/GE	0.49	0.03	0.44	0.55	49						
Digestibility Coefficients											
DM	0.60	0.04	0.53	0.67	43						
OM	0.63	0.04	0.56	0.69	49						
CP	0.51	0.08	0.34	0.71	42						
CF	0.67	0.05	0.57	0.77	43						
EE	0.47	0.08	0.23	0.60	39						
NDF	0.65	0.05	0.58	0.70	11						
ADF	0.63	0.06	0.54	0.69	11						
Cell	0.69	0.05	0.61	0.75	11						
GE	0.60	0.03	0.55	0.66	49						
DOMD(g/kg ODM)	587.7	29.9	527.0	647.0	49						

RUMINANT DATABASE

FEED DESCRIPTION : **GRASS HAY, SUN CURED, ME > 10** (Source 1)

Determination	Mean	SD	Min	Max	n	Determination	Mean	SD	Min	Max	n
General (g/kg ODM)						**Degradability**					
ODM (fresh)	865.6	28.2	840.2	896.0	3	Dry matter					
TDM (fresh)						a (%)					
CP	113.7	41.2	75.1	157.0	3	b (%)					
MADF	331.3	42.5	289.0	374.0	3	c (h^{-1})					
EE	13.3	9.7	5.0	24.0	3						
AEE	16.0		16.0	16.0	1	dg (%) @ outflow rate					
TA	70.3	17.0	60.0	90.0	3	$0.02h^{-1}$					
GE (MJ/kg ODM)	18.6	0.50	18.3	19.2	3	$0.05h^{-1}$					
						$0.08h^{-1}$					
NDF ash	650.3	18.8	639.0	672.0	3						
NDF unash						Nitrogen					
ADF ash	342.0	18.3	322.0	358.0	3	a (%)					
ADF unash	352.0		352.0	352.0	1	b (%)					
						c (h^{-1})					
Energy Values											
						dg (%) @ outflow rate					
DE (MJ/kg ODM)	12.3	0.31	12.1	12.7	3	$0.02h^{-1}$					
ME (MJ/kg ODM)	10.1	0.20	10.0	10.4	3	$0.05h^{-1}$					
FE/GE	0.34	0.01	0.33	0.34	3	$0.08h^{-1}$					
UE/GE	0.04	0.0	0.04	0.04	3						
CH_4E/GE	0.08	0.0	0.08	0.08	3						
ME/DE	0.82	0.01	0.82	0.83	3						
ME/GE	0.54	0.01	0.54	0.55	3						

Digestibility Coefficients

Determination	Mean	SD	Min	Max	n
DM	0.65	0.01	0.64	0.67	3
OM	0.67	0.01	0.67	0.68	3
CP	0.60	0.10	0.50	0.68	3
CF	0.70	0.02	0.68	0.72	3
EE	0.44	0.14	0.34	0.54	2
NDF	0.68		0.68	0.68	1
ADF	0.65		0.65	0.65	1
Cell	0.72		0.72	0.72	1
GE	0.66	0.0	0.66	0.67	3
DOMD(g/kg ODM)	631.0	16.8	613.0	646.3	3

RUMINANT DATABASE

FEED DESCRIPTION : **LUCERNE HAY** (Source 1)

Determination	Mean	SD	Min	Max	n	Determination	Mean	SD	Min	Max	n
General (g/kg ODM)						**Degradability**					
ODM (fresh)	865.1	8.8	854.4	876.1	5	Dry matter					
TDM (fresh)						a (%)					
CP	183.0	4.2	180.0	186.0	2	b (%)					
MADF	339.8	48.6	291.0	412.0	5	c (h^{-1})					
EE	12.8	3.4	10.0	17.0	5						
AEE						dg (%) @ outflow rate					
TA	95.6	10.2	80.0	105.0	5	$0.02h^{-1}$					
GE (MJ/kg ODM)	18.2	0.55	17.3	18.7	5	$0.05h^{-1}$					
						$0.08h^{-1}$					
NDF ash	493.4	59.1	423.0	574.0	5						
NDF unash						Nitrogen					
ADF ash	374.8	50.4	320.0	448.0	5	a (%)					
ADF unash	381.0	11.3	373.0	389.0	2	b (%)					
						c (h^{-1})					
Energy Values						dg (%) @ outflow rate					
DE (MJ/kg ODM)	11.0	1.1	9.7	12.3	5	$0.02h^{-1}$					
ME (MJ/kg ODM)	8.5	1.0	7.1	9.7	5	$0.05h^{-1}$					
FE/GE	0.40	0.05	0.33	0.45	5	$0.08h^{-1}$					
UE/GE	0.06	0.01	0.05	0.08	5						
CH_4E/GE	0.08	0.01	0.07	0.08	5						
ME/DE	0.77	0.03	0.74	0.81	5						
ME/GE	0.47	0.05	0.41	0.53	5						
Digestibility Coefficients											
DM	0.61	0.05	0.55	0.67	5						
OM	0.64	0.05	0.58	0.69	5						
CP	0.75	0.03	0.73	0.77	2						
CF	0.53	0.04	0.48	0.58	5						
EE	0.30	0.13	0.17	0.51	5						
NDF											
ADF											
Cell											
GE	0.60	0.05	0.55	0.67	5						
DOMD(g/kg ODM)	582.7	34.5	536.5	620.8	5						

RUMINANT DATABASE

FEED DESCRIPTION : **LUCERNE HAY, ME < 8** (Source 1)

Determination	Mean	SD	Min	Max	n	Determination	Mean	SD	Min	Max	n
General (g/kg ODM)						**Degradability**					
ODM (fresh)	864.7	8.8	858.5	870.9	2	Dry matter					
TDM (fresh)						a (%)					
CP	180.0		180.0	180.0	1	b (%)					
MADF	386.5	36.1	361.0	412.0	2	c (h^{-1})					
EE	10.5	0.71	10.0	11.0	2						
AEE						dg (%) @ outflow rate					
TA	88.5	12.0	80.0	97.0	2	0.02h^{-1}					
GE (MJ/kg ODM)	17.9	0.85	17.3	18.5	2	0.05h^{-1}					
						0.08h^{-1}					
NDF ash	547.0	38.2	520.0	574.0	2						
NDF unash						Nitrogen					
ADF ash	421.0	38.2	394.0	448.0	2	a (%)					
ADF unash	389.0		389.0	389.0	1	b (%)					
						c (h^{-1})					
Energy Values											
						dg (%) @ outflow rate					
DE (MJ/kg ODM)	10.0	0.40	9.7	10.2	2	0.02h^{-1}					
ME (MJ/kg ODM)	7.5	0.45	7.1	7.8	2	0.05h^{-1}					
FE/GE	0.45	0.01	0.44	0.45	2	0.08h^{-1}					
UE/GE	0.07	0.01	0.06	0.07	2						
CH$_4$E/GE	0.07	0.0	0.07	0.07	2						
ME/DE	0.75	0.02	0.74	0.76	2						
ME/GE	0.42	0.01	0.41	0.42	2						
Digestibility Coefficients											
DM	0.57	0.03	0.55	0.59	2						
OM	0.60	0.03	0.58	0.62	2						
CP	0.73		0.73	0.73	1						
CF	0.50	0.02	0.48	0.51	2						
EE	0.26	0.03	0.23	0.28	2						
NDF											
ADF											
Cell											
GE	0.56	0.0	0.55	0.56	2						
DOMD(g/kg ODM)	548.7	17.3	536.5	560.9	2						

RUMINANT DATABASE

FEED DESCRIPTION : **LUCERNE HAY, ME 8 - 10** (Source 1)

Determination	Mean	SD	Min	Max	n	Determination	Mean	SD	Min	Max	n
General (g/kg ODM)						**Degradability**					
ODM (fresh)	865.4	10.9	854.4	876.1	3	Dry matter					
TDM (fresh)						a (%)					
CP	186.0		186.0	186.0	1	b (%)					
MADF	308.7	21.1	291.0	332.0	3	c (h^{-1})					
EE	14.3	3.8	10.0	17.0	3						
AEE						dg (%) @ outflow rate					
TA	100.3	7.2	92.0	105.0	3	0.02h^{-1}					
GE (MJ/kg ODM)	18.4	0.30	18.1	18.7	3	0.05h^{-1}					
						0.08h^{-1}					
NDF ash	457.7	38.4	423.0	499.0	3						
NDF unash						Nitrogen					
ADF ash	344.0	28.2	320.0	375.0	3	a (%)					
ADF unash	373.0		373.0	373.0	1	b (%)					
						c (h^{-1})					
Energy Values											
						dg (%) @ outflow rate					
DE (MJ/kg ODM)	11.7	0.52	11.3	12.3	3	0.02h^{-1}					
ME (MJ/kg ODM)	9.2	0.50	8.7	9.7	3	0.05h^{-1}					
FE/GE	0.36	0.03	0.33	0.38	3	0.08h^{-1}					
UE/GE	0.06	0.01	0.05	0.08	3						
CH$_4$E/GE	0.08	0.0	0.08	0.08	3						
ME/DE	0.78	0.03	0.75	0.81	3						
ME/GE	0.50	0.03	0.47	0.53	3						
Digestibility Coefficients											
DM	0.64	0.03	0.62	0.67	3						
OM	0.67	0.03	0.64	0.69	3						
CP	0.77		0.77	0.77	1						
CF	0.55	0.04	0.52	0.58	3						
EE	0.32	0.17	0.17	0.51	3						
NDF											
ADF											
Cell											
GE	0.64	0.03	0.62	0.67	3						
DOMD(g/kg ODM)	605.4	17.3	586.6	620.8	3						

RUMINANT DATABASE

FEED CLASS 11

HIGH TEMPERATURE DRIED GREEN CROPS

RUMINANT DATABASE

FEED DESCRIPTION : **HT DRIED GRASS, SHORT CUTTING CYCLE** (Source 1)

Determination	Mean	SD	Min	Max	n	Determination	Mean	SD	Min	Max	n
General (g/kg ODM)						**Degradability**					
ODM (fresh)	917.2	19.6	890.3	979.4	20	Dry matter					
TDM (fresh)						a (%)					
CP	198.7	23.4	170.0	261.9	20	b (%)					
MADF	276.7	35.6	220.0	347.0	20	c (h^{-1})					
EE	37.3	8.5	12.0	52.0	16						
AEE	48.3	6.0	41.0	57.0	8	dg (%) @ outflow rate					
TA	108.3	22.7	75.0	173.0	20	$0.02h^{-1}$					
GE (MJ/kg ODM)	18.5	0.54	17.6	19.4	20	$0.05h^{-1}$					
						$0.08h^{-1}$					
NDF ash	541.1	66.1	303.0	640.0	20						
NDF unash						Nitrogen					
ADF ash	282.2	26.8	239.0	329.0	16	a (%)					
ADF unash	312.1	37.9	246.0	375.0	16	b (%)					
						c (h^{-1})					
Energy Values											
						dg (%) @ outflow rate					
DE (MJ/kg ODM)	13.2	1.1	10.9	14.9	20	$0.02h^{-1}$					
ME (MJ/kg ODM)	10.7	1.0	8.6	12.0	20	$0.05h^{-1}$					
FE/GE	0.29	0.05	0.22	0.40	20	$0.08h^{-1}$					
UE/GE	0.05	0.02	0.02	0.08	20						
CH_4E/GE	0.08	0.0	0.07	0.08	20						
ME/DE	0.81	0.02	0.78	0.86	20						
ME/GE	0.58	0.04	0.48	0.64	20						
Digestibility Coefficients											
DM	0.72	0.05	0.60	0.79	20						
OM	0.74	0.05	0.63	0.80	20						
CP	0.70	0.04	0.63	0.77	20						
CF	0.74	0.06	0.62	0.84	20						
EE	0.68	0.05	0.57	0.74	11						
NDF	0.78	0.06	0.65	0.85	20						
ADF	0.71	0.06	0.60	0.82	16						
Cell	0.74	0.10	0.44	0.84	16						
GE	0.71	0.05	0.60	0.78	20						
DOMD(g/kg ODM)	666.1	51.1	553.9	742.8	20						

RUMINANT DATABASE

FEED DESCRIPTION : **HT DRIED GRASS, SHORT CUTTING CYCLE, ME 8 - 10** (Source 1)

Determination	Mean	SD	Min	Max	n	Determination	Mean	SD	Min	Max	n

General (g/kg ODM)

Determination	Mean	SD	Min	Max	n
ODM (fresh)	925.6	12.7	906.7	945.4	6
TDM (fresh)					
CP	194.4	17.0	175.7	224.8	6
MADF	312.5	20.2	294.0	347.0	6
EE	39.0	5.9	32.0	48.0	5
AEE	42.0	1.4	41.0	43.0	2
TA	129.9	23.0	109.4	173.0	6
GE (MJ/kg ODM)	18.0	0.26	17.6	18.3	6
NDF ash	573.8	33.2	552.0	640.0	6
NDF unash					
ADF ash	296.0	23.7	269.0	329.0	6
ADF unash	336.0	29.9	287.0	375.0	6

Degradability

Dry matter
a (%)
b (%)
c (h^{-1})

dg (%) @ outflow rate
$0.02h^{-1}$
$0.05h^{-1}$
$0.08h^{-1}$

Nitrogen
a (%)
b (%)
c (h^{-1})

dg (%) @ outflow rate
$0.02h^{-1}$
$0.05h^{-1}$
$0.08h^{-1}$

Energy Values

Determination	Mean	SD	Min	Max	n
DE (MJ/kg ODM)	11.8	0.62	10.9	12.7	6
ME (MJ/kg ODM)	9.4	0.44	8.6	9.9	6
FE/GE	0.34	0.04	0.30	0.40	6
UE/GE	0.06	0.01	0.04	0.08	6
CH_4E/GE	0.08	0.0	0.07	0.08	6
ME/DE	0.79	0.01	0.78	0.81	6
ME/GE	0.52	0.03	0.48	0.55	6

Digestibility Coefficients

Determination	Mean	SD	Min	Max	n
DM	0.66	0.04	0.60	0.70	6
OM	0.69	0.04	0.63	0.73	6
CP	0.68	0.04	0.63	0.73	6
CF	0.68	0.04	0.62	0.73	6
EE	0.67	0.05	0.60	0.74	5
NDF	0.72	0.05	0.65	0.80	6
ADF	0.66	0.05	0.60	0.75	6
Cell	0.66	0.11	0.44	0.76	6
GE	0.66	0.04	0.60	0.70	6
DOMD(g/kg ODM)	605.5	32.8	553.9	651.3	6

FEED CLASS 11

FEED DESCRIPTION : **HT DRIED GRASS, SHORT CUTTING CYCLE, ME > 10** (Source 1)

Determination	Mean	SD	Min	Max	n	Determination	Mean	SD	Min	Max	n
General (g/kg ODM)						**Degradability**					
ODM (fresh)	913.6	21.3	890.3	979.4	14	Dry matter					
TDM (fresh)						a (%)					
CP	200.6	26.0	170.0	261.9	14	b (%)					
MADF	261.3	29.1	220.0	317.0	14	c (h^{-1})					
EE	36.6	9.6	12.0	52.0	11						
AEE	50.3	5.4	41.0	57.0	6	dg (%) @ outflow rate					
TA	99.1	15.7	75.0	130.0	14	$0.02h^{-1}$					
GE (MJ/kg ODM)	18.7	0.48	17.8	19.4	14	$0.05h^{-1}$					
						$0.08h^{-1}$					
NDF ash	527.0	72.5	303.0	610.0	14						
NDF unash						Nitrogen					
ADF ash	273.9	26.1	239.0	313.0	10	a (%)					
ADF unash	297.8	36.0	246.0	343.0	10	b (%)					
						c (h^{-1})					
Energy Values											
						dg (%) @ outflow rate					
DE (MJ/kg ODM)	13.8	0.76	12.6	14.9	14	$0.02h^{-1}$					
ME (MJ/kg ODM)	11.2	0.56	10.3	12.0	14	$0.05h^{-1}$					
FE/GE	0.27	0.03	0.22	0.33	14	$0.08h^{-1}$					
UE/GE	0.05	0.01	0.02	0.08	14						
CH$_4$E/GE	0.08	0.0	0.08	0.08	14						
ME/DE	0.82	0.02	0.79	0.86	14						
ME/GE	0.60	0.02	0.56	0.64	14						
Digestibility Coefficients											
DM	0.74	0.03	0.68	0.79	14						
OM	0.76	0.03	0.69	0.80	14						
CP	0.70	0.04	0.64	0.77	14						
CF	0.77	0.04	0.66	0.84	14						
EE	0.68	0.06	0.57	0.74	6						
NDF	0.80	0.04	0.70	0.85	14						
ADF	0.74	0.05	0.65	0.82	10						
Cell	0.78	0.05	0.70	0.84	10						
GE	0.73	0.03	0.67	0.78	14						
DOMD(g/kg ODM)	692.1	31.4	637.9	742.8	14						

RUMINANT DATABASE

FEED DESCRIPTION : **HT DRIED GRASS, SHORT CUTTING CYCLE, PERENNIAL** (Source 1)

Determination	Mean	SD	Min	Max	n	Determination	Mean	SD	Min	Max	n
General (g/kg ODM)						**Degradability**					
ODM (fresh)	915.6	20.9	890.3	979.4	17	Dry matter					
TDM (fresh)						a (%)					
CP	200.9	24.5	170.0	261.9	17	b (%)					
MADF	267.6	29.8	220.0	317.0	17	c (h^{-1})					
EE	37.6	9.3	12.0	52.0	13						
AEE	49.3	5.6	41.0	57.0	7	dg (%) @ outflow rate					
TA	102.0	15.6	75.0	130.0	17	$0.02h^{-1}$					
GE (MJ/kg ODM)	18.6	0.49	17.8	19.4	17	$0.05h^{-1}$					
						$0.08h^{-1}$					
NDF ash	537.7	71.5	303.0	640.0	17						
NDF unash						Nitrogen					
ADF ash	278.9	26.1	239.0	319.0	13	a (%)					
ADF unash	303.2	35.0	246.0	346.0	13	b (%)					
						c (h^{-1})					
Energy Values											
						dg (%) @ outflow rate					
DE (MJ/kg ODM)	13.5	0.94	11.6	14.9	17	$0.02h^{-1}$					
ME (MJ/kg ODM)	10.9	0.81	9.5	12.0	17	$0.05h^{-1}$					
FE/GE	0.28	0.04	0.22	0.35	17	$0.08h^{-1}$					
UE/GE	0.05	0.02	0.02	0.08	17						
CH_4E/GE	0.08	0.0	0.08	0.08	17						
ME/DE	0.81	0.02	0.78	0.86	17						
ME/GE	0.59	0.03	0.52	0.64	17						

Digestibility Coefficients

Determination	Mean	SD	Min	Max	n
DM	0.73	0.04	0.65	0.79	17
OM	0.75	0.04	0.68	0.80	17
CP	0.70	0.04	0.64	0.77	17
CF	0.76	0.05	0.66	0.84	17
EE	0.67	0.06	0.57	0.74	8
NDF	0.79	0.04	0.70	0.85	17
ADF	0.73	0.06	0.62	0.82	13
Cell	0.77	0.05	0.69	0.84	13
GE	0.72	0.04	0.65	0.78	17
DOMD(g/kg ODM)	680.9	38.4	611.8	742.8	17

FEED CLASS 11

FEED DESCRIPTION : **HT DRIED GRASS, SHORT CUTTING CYCLE, TALL FESCUE** (Source 1)

Determination	Mean	SD	Min	Max	n	Determination	Mean	SD	Min	Max	n
General (g/kg ODM)						**Degradability**					
ODM (fresh)	926.0	5.4	920.1	930.7	3	Dry matter					
TDM (fresh)						a (%)					
CP	186.1	10.6	175.7	196.8	3	b (%)					
MADF	328.0	16.6	316.0	347.0	3	c (h^{-1})					
EE	36.0	4.0	32.0	40.0	3						
AEE	41.0		41.0	41.0	1	dg (%) @ outflow rate					
TA	144.3	25.8	123.0	173.0	3	0.02h^{-1}					
GE (MJ/kg ODM)	17.9	0.28	17.6	18.1	3	0.05h^{-1}					
						0.08h^{-1}					
NDF ash	560.0	7.6	552.0	567.0	3						
NDF unash						Nitrogen					
ADF ash	296.7	30.3	269.0	329.0	3	a (%)					
ADF unash	351.0	25.1	325.0	375.0	3	b (%)					
						c (h^{-1})					
Energy Values											
						dg (%) @ outflow rate					
DE (MJ/kg ODM)	11.5	0.63	10.9	12.2	3	0.02h^{-1}					
ME (MJ/kg ODM)	9.2	0.53	8.6	9.7	3	0.05h^{-1}					
FE/GE	0.36	0.05	0.31	0.40	3	0.08h^{-1}					
UE/GE	0.05	0.01	0.05	0.06	3						
CH$_4$E/GE	0.08	0.01	0.07	0.08	3						
ME/DE	0.80	0.0	0.79	0.80	3						
ME/GE	0.51	0.04	0.48	0.55	3						
Digestibility Coefficients											
DM	0.63	0.03	0.60	0.66	3						
OM	0.67	0.05	0.63	0.72	3						
CP	0.67	0.04	0.63	0.69	3						
CF	0.66	0.05	0.62	0.71	3						
EE	0.69	0.05	0.64	0.74	3						
NDF	0.69	0.04	0.65	0.73	3						
ADF	0.65	0.05	0.60	0.69	3						
Cell	0.60	0.14	0.44	0.69	3						
GE	0.65	0.05	0.60	0.69	3						
DOMD(g/kg ODM)	582.3	25.8	553.9	604.3	3						

RUMINANT DATABASE

FEED DESCRIPTION : **HT DRIED GRASS, UNKNOWN CUTTING CYCLE** (Sources 1, 2)

Determination	Mean	SD	Min	Max	n	Determination	Mean	SD	Min	Max	n
General (g/kg ODM)						**Degradability**					
ODM (fresh)	893.9	27.4	841.0	961.9	79	Dry matter					
TDM (fresh)						a (%)	33.0	2.0	31.6	34.4	2
CP	188.9	38.1	81.9	269.0	113	b (%)	58.7	0.33	58.5	58.9	2
MADF	279.9	36.3	193.0	369.0	112	c (h^{-1})	0.07	0.02	0.06	0.09	2
EE	37.3	7.9	12.0	52.0	112						
AEE	44.8	10.9	20.0	56.0	9	dg (%) @ outflow rate					
TA	93.2	27.5	53.0	280.0	110	0.02h^{-1}	78.5	5.0	75.0	82.0	2
GE (MJ/kg ODM)	18.6	0.57	15.0	19.7	113	0.05h^{-1}	67.0	5.7	63.0	71.0	2
						0.08h^{-1}	60.5	6.4	56.0	65.0	2
NDF ash	537.7	49.1	403.0	692.0	105						
NDF unash						Nitrogen					
ADF ash	297.0	41.3	177.0	406.0	105	a (%)	30.5		30.5	30.5	1
ADF unash	307.9	39.8	213.0	375.0	46	b (%)	63.9		63.9	63.9	1
						c (h^{-1})	0.12		0.12	0.12	1
Energy Values											
						dg (%) @ outflow rate					
DE (MJ/kg ODM)	12.6	1.3	10.4	15.4	70	0.02h^{-1}	85.0		85.0	85.0	1
ME (MJ/kg ODM)	10.4	1.2	8.0	13.4	110	0.05h^{-1}	76.0		76.0	76.0	1
FE/GE	0.32	0.06	0.19	0.44	70	0.08h^{-1}	69.0		69.0	69.0	1
UE/GE	0.06	0.03	0.01	0.13	110						
CH$_4$E/GE	0.08	0.01	0.06	0.10	112						
ME/DE	0.79	0.04	0.69	0.87	68						
ME/GE	0.56	0.07	0.44	0.71	110						
Digestibility Coefficients											
DM	0.67	0.07	0.55	0.82	70						
OM	0.72	0.06	0.60	0.83	102						
CP	0.66	0.08	0.48	0.93	70						
CF	0.70	0.08	0.52	0.86	70						
EE	0.71	0.07	0.48	0.83	70						
NDF	0.82	0.06	0.73	0.88	14						
ADF	0.77	0.05	0.71	0.83	14						
Cell	0.80	0.03	0.74	0.84	11						
GE	0.69	0.07	0.51	0.81	112						
DOMD(g/kg ODM)	652.9	57.0	518.1	770.1	102						

RUMINANT DATABASE

FEED DESCRIPTION : **HT DRIED GRASS, UNKNOWN CUTTING CYCLE, ME 8 - 10** (Sources 1, 2)

Determination	Mean	SD	Min	Max	n	Determination	Mean	SD	Min	Max	n
General (g/kg ODM)						**Degradability**					
ODM (fresh)	898.5	28.8	854.6	961.9	41	Dry matter					
TDM (fresh)						a (%)					
CP	188.4	44.9	81.9	269.0	44	b (%)					
MADF	298.2	34.5	235.0	369.0	43	c (h^{-1})					
EE	36.1	8.6	12.0	52.0	43						
AEE	20.0		20.0	20.0	1	dg (%) @ outflow rate					
TA	106.4	33.9	60.0	280.0	41	$0.02h^{-1}$					
GE (MJ/kg ODM)	18.3	0.68	15.0	18.9	44	$0.05h^{-1}$					
						$0.08h^{-1}$					
NDF ash	552.6	60.1	403.0	692.0	38						
NDF unash						Nitrogen					
ADF ash	309.4	49.8	177.0	406.0	38	a (%)					
ADF unash	319.1	29.9	269.0	375.0	22	b (%)					
						c (h^{-1})					
Energy Values											
						dg (%) @ outflow rate					
DE (MJ/kg ODM)	11.8	0.70	10.4	13.5	39	$0.02h^{-1}$					
ME (MJ/kg ODM)	9.2	0.58	8.0	10.0	44	$0.05h^{-1}$					
FE/GE	0.36	0.04	0.27	0.44	39	$0.08h^{-1}$					
UE/GE	0.06	0.03	0.03	0.13	44						
CH_4E/GE	0.08	0.01	0.06	0.08	44						
ME/DE	0.78	0.04	0.69	0.82	39						
ME/GE	0.50	0.04	0.44	0.60	44						

Digestibility Coefficients

	Mean	SD	Min	Max	n
DM	0.63	0.04	0.55	0.72	39
OM	0.68	0.04	0.60	0.77	42
CP	0.62	0.06	0.48	0.73	39
CF	0.67	0.06	0.52	0.83	39
EE	0.71	0.08	0.48	0.83	39
NDF	0.74	0.01	0.73	0.75	4
ADF	0.71	0.01	0.71	0.72	4
Cell	0.74		0.74	0.74	1
GE	0.64	0.05	0.51	0.73	44
DOMD(g/kg ODM)	605.3	33.4	518.1	687.9	42

RUMINANT DATABASE

FEED DESCRIPTION : **HT DRIED GRASS, UNKNOWN CUTTING CYCLE, ME > 10** (Sources 1, 2)

Determination	Mean	SD	Min	Max	n	Determination	Mean	SD	Min	Max	n
General (g/kg ODM)						**Degradability**					
ODM (fresh)	889.6	25.3	841.0	942.0	37	Dry matter					
TDM (fresh)						a (%)	33.0	2.0	31.6	34.4	2
CP	188.5	33.4	123.0	260.0	66	b (%)	58.7	0.33	58.5	58.9	2
MADF	267.9	32.6	193.0	336.0	66	c (h^{-1})	0.07	0.02	0.06	0.09	2
EE	38.1	7.4	18.0	52.0	66						
AEE	47.9	6.2	40.0	56.0	8	dg (%) @ outflow rate					
TA	84.6	19.1	53.0	133.0	66	0.02h^{-1}	78.5	5.0	75.0	82.0	2
GE (MJ/kg ODM)	18.9	0.35	18.2	19.7	66	0.05h^{-1}	67.0	5.7	63.0	71.0	2
						0.08h^{-1}	60.5	6.4	56.0	65.0	2
NDF ash	528.2	39.4	459.0	631.0	65						
NDF unash						Nitrogen					
ADF ash	289.5	33.9	206.0	368.0	65	a (%)	30.5		30.5	30.5	1
ADF unash	291.8	44.9	213.0	375.0	21	b (%)	63.9		63.9	63.9	1
						c (h^{-1})	0.12		0.12	0.12	1
Energy Values											
						dg (%) @ outflow rate					
DE (MJ/kg ODM)	13.8	0.95	12.4	15.4	29	0.02h^{-1}	85.0		85.0	85.0	1
ME (MJ/kg ODM)	11.2	0.78	10.0	13.4	66	0.05h^{-1}	76.0		76.0	76.0	1
FE/GE	0.27	0.05	0.19	0.37	29	0.08h^{-1}	69.0		69.0	69.0	1
UE/GE	0.05	0.02	0.01	0.11	66						
CH$_4$E/GE	0.08	0.01	0.06	0.10	66						
ME/DE	0.81	0.02	0.74	0.87	29						
ME/GE	0.59	0.04	0.51	0.71	66						

Digestibility Coefficients

Determination	Mean	SD	Min	Max	n
DM	0.73	0.06	0.62	0.82	29
OM	0.75	0.04	0.64	0.83	58
CP	0.71	0.06	0.61	0.93	29
CF	0.75	0.08	0.58	0.86	29
EE	0.71	0.06	0.51	0.80	29
NDF	0.85	0.02	0.81	0.88	10
ADF	0.80	0.03	0.76	0.83	10
Cell	0.80	0.03	0.76	0.84	10
GE	0.72	0.05	0.63	0.81	66
DOMD(g/kg ODM)	688.8	42.7	611.0	770.1	58

RUMINANT DATABASE

FEED DESCRIPTION : **HT DRIED LUCERNE, ALL VARIETIES** (Sources 1, 2)

Determination	Mean	SD	Min	Max	n	Determination	Mean	SD	Min	Max	n
General (g/kg ODM)						**Degradability**					
ODM (fresh)	895.0	24.6	824.7	924.5	22	Dry matter					
TDM (fresh)						a (%)					
CP	199.1	27.7	156.0	268.1	43	b (%)					
MADF	316.1	46.3	211.0	415.0	50	c (h^{-1})					
EE	27.8	7.3	10.0	46.0	50						
AEE						dg (%) @ outflow rate					
TA	102.2	9.6	83.0	114.0	24	0.02h^{-1}					
GE (MJ/kg ODM)	18.7	0.39	18.1	20.5	50	0.05h^{-1}					
						0.08h^{-1}					
NDF ash	465.4	46.1	332.0	548.0	50						
NDF unash						Nitrogen					
ADF ash	336.1	46.1	230.0	430.0	50	a (%)					
ADF unash	327.9	42.5	236.0	413.0	28	b (%)					
						c (h^{-1})					
Energy Values						dg (%) @ outflow rate					
DE (MJ/kg ODM)	11.3	0.96	9.5	13.6	48	0.02h^{-1}					
ME (MJ/kg ODM)	8.8	1.3	5.8	12.1	39	0.05h^{-1}					
FE/GE	0.40	0.05	0.30	0.49	44	0.08h^{-1}					
UE/GE	0.05	0.01	0.03	0.08	39						
CH$_4$E/GE	0.07	0.01	0.04	0.08	50						
ME/DE	0.79	0.06	0.57	0.93	37						
ME/GE	0.47	0.07	0.31	0.64	39						
Digestibility Coefficients											
DM	0.59	0.05	0.48	0.70	50						
OM	0.60	0.05	0.50	0.73	50						
CP	0.67	0.07	0.35	0.75	37						
CF	0.44	0.08	0.31	0.66	44						
EE	0.55	0.13	0.17	0.77	44						
NDF	0.56	0.02	0.54	0.57	2						
ADF	0.57	0.07	0.52	0.61	2						
Cell	0.52	0.01	0.51	0.52	2						
GE	0.60	0.05	0.51	0.70	50						
DOMD(g/kg ODM)	543.6	43.5	451.9	643.4	50						

RUMINANT DATABASE

FEED DESCRIPTION : **HT DRIED LUCERNE, ME < 8** (Source 1)

Determination	Mean	SD	Min	Max	n	Determination	Mean	SD	Min	Max	n
General (g/kg ODM)						**Degradability**					
ODM (fresh)	863.1	54.3	824.7	901.5	2	Dry matter					
TDM (fresh)						a (%)					
CP	177.0	16.6	158.0	193.0	5	b (%)					
MADF	360.8	49.2	296.0	415.0	6	c (h^{-1})					
EE	28.8	12.9	15.0	46.0	6						
AEE						dg (%) @ outflow rate					
TA	108.5	6.4	104.0	113.0	2	0.02h^{-1}					
GE (MJ/kg ODM)	18.5	0.16	18.3	18.7	6	0.05h^{-1}					
						0.08h^{-1}					
NDF ash	495.3	34.4	449.0	548.0	6						
NDF unash						Nitrogen					
ADF ash	384.7	30.8	344.0	430.0	6	a (%)					
ADF unash	377.0	34.8	331.0	413.0	5	b (%)					
						c (h^{-1})					
Energy Values						dg (%) @ outflow rate					
DE (MJ/kg ODM)	9.9	0.43	9.5	10.6	6	0.02h^{-1}					
ME (MJ/kg ODM)	7.0	0.91	5.8	7.9	6	0.05h^{-1}					
FE/GE	0.46	0.03	0.42	0.49	6	0.08h^{-1}					
UE/GE	0.05	0.02	0.03	0.08	6						
CH$_4$E/GE	0.07	0.0	0.07	0.07	6						
ME/DE	0.70	0.09	0.57	0.78	6						
ME/GE	0.38	0.05	0.31	0.43	6						
Digestibility Coefficients											
DM	0.54	0.04	0.48	0.57	6						
OM	0.55	0.04	0.50	0.60	6						
CP	0.63	0.02	0.61	0.66	5						
CF	0.41	0.05	0.33	0.48	6						
EE	0.54	0.19	0.32	0.76	6						
NDF											
ADF											
Cell											
GE	0.54	0.03	0.51	0.58	6						
DOMD(g/kg ODM)	499.2	28.9	451.9	536.7	6						

RUMINANT DATABASE

FEED DESCRIPTION : **HT DRIED LUCERNE, ME 8 - 10** (Sources 1, 2)

Determination	Mean	SD	Min	Max	n
General (g/kg ODM)					
ODM (fresh)	902.1	18.4	866.0	924.5	17
TDM (fresh)					
CP	198.3	22.9	161.0	251.0	23
MADF	323.8	28.0	260.0	363.0	29
EE	25.5	3.7	16.0	34.0	29
AEE	20.0		20.0	20.0	1
TA	103.7	9.5	83.0	114.0	18
GE (MJ/kg ODM)	18.7	0.45	17.7	20.5	29
NDF ash	472.7	32.6	382.0	528.0	29
NDF unash					
ADF ash	339.6	32.0	258.0	392.0	29
ADF unash	327.5	23.3	281.0	367.0	15
Energy Values					
DE (MJ/kg ODM)	11.2	0.52	10.1	12.0	27
ME (MJ/kg ODM)	8.8	0.49	8.0	9.8	29
FE/GE	0.40	0.03	0.32	0.46	27
UE/GE	0.05	0.01	0.04	0.07	29
CH_4E/GE	0.07	0.01	0.07	0.08	29
ME/DE	0.79	0.02	0.76	0.82	27
ME/GE	0.47	0.03	0.43	0.55	29
Digestibility Coefficients					
DM	0.60	0.03	0.56	0.65	27
OM	0.61	0.03	0.57	0.71	27
CP	0.68	0.08	0.35	0.75	21
CF	0.42	0.06	0.31	0.56	27
EE	0.52	0.11	0.17	0.72	27
NDF	0.56	0.02	0.54	0.57	2
ADF	0.57	0.07	0.52	0.61	2
Cell	0.52	0.01	0.51	0.52	2
GE	0.60	0.03	0.54	0.68	29
DOMD(g/kg ODM)	554.2	28.0	506.2	637.8	27

Determination	Mean	SD	Min	Max	n
Degradability					
Dry matter					
a (%)					
b (%)					
c (h^{-1})					
dg (%) @ outflow rate					
$0.02h^{-1}$					
$0.05h^{-1}$					
$0.08h^{-1}$					
Nitrogen					
a (%)					
b (%)					
c (h^{-1})					
dg (%) @ outflow rate					
$0.02h^{-1}$					
$0.05h^{-1}$					
$0.08h^{-1}$					

RUMINANT DATABASE

FEED DESCRIPTION : **HT DRIED LUCERNE, ME > 10** (Sources 1, 2)

Determination	Mean	SD	Min	Max	n	Determination	Mean	SD	Min	Max	n
General (g/kg ODM)						**Degradability**					
ODM (fresh)	874.0	11.9	864.0	890.0	4	Dry matter					
TDM (fresh)						a (%)					
CP	240.7	25.1	214.0	268.1	5	b (%)					
MADF	242.4	9.3	229.0	252.0	5	c (h^{-1})					
EE	25.2	12.2	10.0	39.0	5						
AEE						dg (%) @ outflow rate					
TA	92.0	2.0	91.0	95.0	4	0.02h^{-1}					
GE (MJ/kg ODM)	18.9	0.46	18.1	19.3	5	0.05h^{-1}					
						0.08h^{-1}					
NDF ash	379.6	45.4	332.0	452.0	5						
NDF unash						Nitrogen					
ADF ash	263.2	10.6	250.0	277.0	5	a (%)					
ADF unash	271.0		271.0	271.0	1	b (%)					
						c (h^{-1})					
Energy Values						dg (%) @ outflow rate					
DE (MJ/kg ODM)	13.0	0.46	12.5	13.6	5	0.02h^{-1}					
ME (MJ/kg ODM)	11.4	0.69	10.4	12.1	5	0.05h^{-1}					
FE/GE	0.31		0.31	0.31	1	0.08h^{-1}					
UE/GE	0.05	0.01	0.04	0.06	5						
CH$_4$E/GE	0.06	0.02	0.04	0.08	5						
ME/DE	0.88	0.04	0.83	0.93	5						
ME/GE	0.60	0.03	0.57	0.64	5						
Digestibility Coefficients											
DM	0.67		0.67	0.67	1						
OM	0.71		0.71	0.71	1						
CP	0.66		0.66	0.66	1						
CF	0.66		0.66	0.66	1						
EE	0.67		0.67	0.67	1						
NDF											
ADF											
Cell											
GE	0.69	0.02	0.66	0.70	5						
DOMD(g/kg ODM)	626.9		626.9	626.9	1						

RUMINANT DATABASE

FEED DESCRIPTION : **HT DRIED LUCERNE, VAR ENVER** (Source 1)

Determination	Mean	SD	Min	Max	n	Determination	Mean	SD	Min	Max	n
General (g/kg ODM)						**Degradability**					
ODM (fresh)	903.2	1.2	902.3	904.0	2	Dry matter					
TDM (fresh)						a (%)					
CP	197.5	1.6	196.4	198.6	2	b (%)					
MADF	321.5	20.5	307.0	336.0	2	c (h^{-1})					
EE	26.0	5.7	22.0	30.0	2						
AEE						dg (%) @ outflow rate					
TA	108.5	3.5	106.0	111.0	2	$0.02h^{-1}$					
GE (MJ/kg ODM)	18.6	0.02	18.6	18.6	2	$0.05h^{-1}$					
						$0.08h^{-1}$					
NDF ash	508.5	27.6	489.0	528.0	2						
NDF unash						Nitrogen					
ADF ash	326.5	24.7	309.0	344.0	2	a (%)					
ADF unash	349.0	4.2	346.0	352.0	2	b (%)					
						c (h^{-1})					
Energy Values											
						dg (%) @ outflow rate					
DE (MJ/kg ODM)	11.4	0.59	11.0	11.8	2	$0.02h^{-1}$					
ME (MJ/kg ODM)	9.1	0.38	8.8	9.3	2	$0.05h^{-1}$					
FE/GE	0.39	0.04	0.36	0.41	2	$0.08h^{-1}$					
UE/GE	0.05	0.01	0.04	0.06	2						
CH_4E/GE	0.08	0.01	0.07	0.08	2						
ME/DE	0.79	0.01	0.79	0.80	2						
ME/GE	0.49	0.02	0.47	0.50	2						
Digestibility Coefficients											
DM	0.62	0.03	0.60	0.64	2						
OM	0.63	0.03	0.61	0.65	2						
CP	0.54	0.27	0.35	0.73	2						
CF	0.46	0.01	0.45	0.46	2						
EE	0.57	0.04	0.54	0.59	2						
NDF	0.56	0.02	0.54	0.57	2						
ADF	0.57	0.07	0.52	0.61	2						
Cell	0.52	0.01	0.51	0.52	2						
GE	0.61	0.03	0.59	0.64	2						
DOMD(g/kg ODM)	565.0	26.4	546.3	583.6	2						

RUMINANT DATABASE

FEED DESCRIPTION : **HT DRIED LUCERNE, VAR EUROPE** (Source 1)

Determination	Mean	SD	Min	Max	n	Determination	Mean	SD	Min	Max
General (g/kg ODM)						**Degradability**				
ODM (fresh)	895.8		895.8	895.8	1	Dry matter				
TDM (fresh)						a (%)				
CP	189.7	29.5	156.0	251.0	9	b (%)				
MADF	326.2	33.1	275.0	376.0	9	c (h^{-1})				
EE	28.4	4.5	23.0	36.0	9					
AEE						dg (%) @ outflow rate				
TA	108.0		108.0	108.0	1	$0.02h^{-1}$				
GE (MJ/kg ODM)	18.6	0.23	18.3	19.0	9	$0.05h^{-1}$				
						$0.08h^{-1}$				
NDF ash	474.0	34.1	411.0	526.0	9					
NDF unash						Nitrogen				
ADF ash	340.9	29.2	292.0	401.0	9	a (%)				
ADF unash						b (%)				
						c (h^{-1})				
Energy Values										
						dg (%) @ outflow rate				
DE (MJ/kg ODM)	11.0	0.53	10.4	11.8	9	$0.02h^{-1}$				
ME (MJ/kg ODM)	8.4	0.34	8.1	9.0	6	$0.05h^{-1}$				
FE/GE	0.41	0.03	0.37	0.45	9	$0.08h^{-1}$				
UE/GE	0.06	0.01	0.05	0.07	6					
CH_4E/GE	0.07	0.01	0.07	0.08	9					
ME/DE	0.78	0.01	0.76	0.79	6					
ME/GE	0.45	0.02	0.43	0.47	6					

Digestibility Coefficients

Determination	Mean	SD	Min	Max	n
DM	0.58	0.04	0.50	0.64	10
OM	0.59	0.04	0.51	0.66	10
CP	0.69	0.03	0.66	0.73	9
CF	0.41	0.07	0.31	0.51	9
EE	0.54	0.12	0.33	0.73	9
NDF					
ADF					
Cell					
GE	0.59	0.03	0.55	0.63	9
DOMD(g/kg ODM)	536.3	35.6	461.3	594.0	10

RUMINANT DATABASE

FEED DESCRIPTION : **HT DRIED LUCERNE, VAR VIRTUS** (Source 1)

Determination	Mean	SD	Min	Max	n	Determination	Mean	SD	Min	Max	n
General (g/kg ODM)						**Degradability**					
ODM (fresh)	918.7	5.0	910.6	924.5	6	Dry matter					
TDM (fresh)						a (%)					
CP	198.9	21.5	164.0	232.0	13	b (%)					
MADF	325.9	31.7	269.0	387.0	16	c (h^{-1})					
EE	28.2	5.6	19.0	40.0	16						
AEE						dg (%) @ outflow rate					
TA	102.4	11.5	86.0	114.0	7	$0.02h^{-1}$					
GE (MJ/kg ODM)	18.7	0.31	18.2	19.2	16	$0.05h^{-1}$					
						$0.08h^{-1}$					
NDF ash	474.9	27.2	426.0	510.0	16						
NDF unash						Nitrogen					
ADF ash	345.8	32.4	288.0	416.0	16	a (%)					
ADF unash	331.2	27.8	271.0	370.0	13	b (%)					
						c (h^{-1})					
Energy Values											
						dg (%) @ outflow rate					
DE (MJ/kg ODM)	11.1	0.51	10.2	12.1	16	$0.02h^{-1}$					
ME (MJ/kg ODM)	8.7	0.43	7.9	9.2	12	$0.05h^{-1}$					
FE/GE	0.40	0.03	0.33	0.44	16	$0.08h^{-1}$					
UE/GE	0.05	0.01	0.04	0.06	12						
CH_4E/GE	0.07	0.01	0.07	0.08	16						
ME/DE	0.78	0.01	0.77	0.81	12						
ME/GE	0.46	0.02	0.43	0.50	12						
Digestibility Coefficients											
DM	0.58	0.04	0.51	0.66	21						
OM	0.60	0.04	0.51	0.68	21						
CP	0.69	0.03	0.63	0.74	13						
CF	0.44	0.04	0.35	0.52	16						
EE	0.55	0.13	0.17	0.77	16						
NDF											
ADF											
Cell											
GE	0.60	0.03	0.56	0.67	16						
DOMD(g/kg ODM)	540.7	37.6	464.0	603.5	21						

RUMINANT DATABASE

FEED DESCRIPTION : **HT DRIED RED CLOVER** (Source 1)

Determination	Mean	SD	Min	Max	n	Determination	Mean	SD	Min	Max	n
General (g/kg ODM)						**Degradability**					
ODM (fresh)	879.1		879.1	879.1	1	Dry matter					
TDM (fresh)						a (%)					
CP	177.0		177.0	177.0	1	b (%)					
MADF	295.0		295.0	295.0	1	c (h^{-1})					
EE	23.0		23.0	23.0	1						
AEE						dg (%) @ outflow rate					
TA	91.0		91.0	91.0	1	0.02h^{-1}					
GE (MJ/kg ODM)	18.7		18.7	18.7	1	0.05h^{-1}					
						0.08h^{-1}					
NDF ash	483.0		483.0	483.0	1						
NDF unash						Nitrogen					
ADF ash	330.0		330.0	330.0	1	a (%)					
ADF unash						b (%)					
						c (h^{-1})					
Energy Values											
						dg (%) @ outflow rate					
DE (MJ/kg ODM)	11.3		11.3	11.3	1	0.02h^{-1}					
ME (MJ/kg ODM)	8.9		8.9	8.9	1	0.05h^{-1}					
FE/GE	0.40		0.40	0.40	1	0.08h^{-1}					
UE/GE	0.05		0.05	0.05	1						
CH$_4$E/GE	0.07		0.07	0.07	1						
ME/DE	0.79		0.79	0.79	1						
ME/GE	0.48		0.48	0.48	1						
Digestibility Coefficients											
DM	0.61		0.61	0.61	1						
OM	0.63		0.63	0.63	1						
CP	0.55		0.55	0.55	1						
CF	0.49		0.49	0.49	1						
EE	0.65		0.65	0.65	1						
NDF											
ADF											
Cell											
GE	0.60		0.60	0.60	1						
DOMD(g/kg ODM)	577.0		577.0	577.0	1						

RUMINANT DATABASE

FEED CLASS 12

STRAWS

RUMINANT DATABASE

FEED DESCRIPTION : **AMMONIA TREATED BARLEY STRAW, ALL SEASONS** (Sources 1, 2)

Determination	Mean	SD	Min	Max	n	Determination	Mean	SD	Min	Max	n
General (g/kg ODM)						**Degradability**					
ODM (fresh)	870.6	19.8	843.2	908.0	23	Dry matter					
TDM (fresh)						a (%)	8.8	2.1	6.5	12.2	8
CP	70.0	17.7	46.0	125.0	20	b (%)	62.9	4.9	53.0	67.6	8
MADF	520.5	39.6	415.0	565.0	21	c (h^{-1})	0.04	0.01	0.03	0.06	8
EE	15.4	5.5	7.0	31.0	21						
AEE						dg (%) @ outflow rate					
TA	45.8	11.4	28.0	73.0	21	$0.02h^{-1}$	50.3	4.5	44.0	57.0	8
GE (MJ/kg ODM)	18.7	0.51	18.0	19.7	21	$0.05h^{-1}$	36.3	4.3	31.0	42.0	8
						$0.08h^{-1}$	29.4	3.8	25.0	35.0	8
NDF ash	778.0	56.8	598.0	889.0	21						
NDF unash						Nitrogen					
ADF ash	541.5	41.9	438.0	601.0	21	a (%)					
ADF unash	562.0	47.3	508.0	596.0	3	b (%)					
						c (h^{-1})					
Energy Values											
						dg (%) @ outflow rate					
DE (MJ/kg ODM)	9.8	0.93	8.2	11.7	20	$0.02h^{-1}$					
ME (MJ/kg ODM)	7.7	0.81	6.4	9.3	20	$0.05h^{-1}$					
FE/GE	0.48	0.05	0.39	0.55	21	$0.08h^{-1}$					
UE/GE	0.04	0.01	0.01	0.06	20						
CH_4E/GE	0.07	0.01	0.06	0.09	21						
ME/DE	0.80	0.02	0.76	0.86	19						
ME/GE	0.41	0.04	0.35	0.48	20						
Digestibility Coefficients											
DM	0.53	0.05	0.41	0.61	23						
OM	0.56	0.04	0.46	0.66	22						
CP	0.18	0.08	0.06	0.36	17						
CF	0.68	0.06	0.55	0.77	20						
EE	0.45	0.16	0.12	0.74	19						
NDF											
ADF											
Cell											
GE	0.52	0.05	0.45	0.61	21						
DOMD(g/kg ODM)	536.9	42.4	446.1	628.9	22						

RUMINANT DATABASE

FEED DESCRIPTION : **AMMONIA TREATED SPRING BARLEY STRAW** (Sources 1, 2)

Determination	Mean	SD	Min	Max	n	Determination	Mean	SD	Min	Max	n
General (g/kg ODM)						**Degradability**					
ODM (fresh)	876.5	20.5	844.0	908.0	13	Dry matter					
TDM (fresh)						a (%)	10.8	1.8	8.8	12.2	3
CP	77.6	21.3	54.0	125.0	10	b (%)	63.9	2.5	61.1	65.7	3
MADF	506.9	46.4	415.0	559.0	11	c (h^{-1})	0.04	0.01	0.03	0.04	3
EE	16.7	4.1	11.0	25.0	11						
AEE						dg (%) @ outflow rate					
TA	46.7	8.6	34.0	59.0	11	$0.02h^{-1}$	51.7	5.5	46.0	57.0	3
GE (MJ/kg ODM)	18.7	0.50	18.0	19.7	11	$0.05h^{-1}$	37.3	5.7	31.0	42.0	3
						$0.08h^{-1}$	30.7	5.1	25.0	35.0	3
NDF ash	743.9	54.2	598.0	799.0	11						
NDF unash						Nitrogen					
ADF ash	525.7	42.6	438.0	560.0	11	a (%)					
ADF unash	562.0	47.3	508.0	596.0	3	b (%)					
						c (h^{-1})					
Energy Values											
						dg (%) @ outflow rate					
DE (MJ/kg ODM)	10.1	1.0	8.8	11.7	10	$0.02h^{-1}$					
ME (MJ/kg ODM)	8.0	0.87	6.7	9.3	10	$0.05h^{-1}$					
FE/GE	0.46	0.05	0.39	0.53	11	$0.08h^{-1}$					
UE/GE	0.04	0.02	0.01	0.06	10						
CH_4E/GE	0.07	0.01	0.07	0.09	11						
ME/DE	0.80	0.03	0.76	0.86	9						
ME/GE	0.43	0.05	0.36	0.48	10						
Digestibility Coefficients											
DM	0.54	0.06	0.41	0.61	13						
OM	0.57	0.05	0.46	0.66	12						
CP	0.19	0.10	0.06	0.36	9						
CF	0.69	0.07	0.57	0.77	10						
EE	0.47	0.09	0.38	0.62	9						
NDF											
ADF											
Cell											
GE	0.54	0.05	0.47	0.61	11						
DOMD(g/kg ODM)	551.0	46.1	446.1	628.9	12						

RUMINANT DATABASE

FEED DESCRIPTION : **AMMONIA TREATED WINTER BARLEY STRAW** (Source 1)

Determination	Mean	SD	Min	Max	n	Determination	Mean	SD	Min	Max	n
General (g/kg ODM)						**Degradability**					
ODM (fresh)	866.3	18.1	847.4	890.7	7	Dry matter					
TDM (fresh)						a (%)	7.6	1.1	6.5	9.3	5
CP	63.0	7.4	51.0	73.0	7	b (%)	62.3	6.1	53.0	67.6	5
MADF	546.7	18.8	523.0	565.0	7	c (h^{-1})	0.04	0.01	0.04	0.06	5
EE	15.9	7.0	10.0	31.0	7						
AEE						dg (%) @ outflow rate					
TA	42.9	15.2	28.0	73.0	7	$0.02h^{-1}$	49.4	4.2	44.0	55.0	5
GE (MJ/kg ODM)	18.7	0.37	18.2	19.4	7	$0.05h^{-1}$	35.6	3.8	32.0	42.0	5
						$0.08h^{-1}$	28.6	3.1	26.0	34.0	5
NDF ash	810.0	17.9	785.0	829.0	7						
NDF unash						Nitrogen					
ADF ash	571.6	22.6	538.0	601.0	7	a (%)					
ADF unash						b (%)					
						c (h^{-1})					
Energy Values											
						dg (%) @ outflow rate					
DE (MJ/kg ODM)	9.6	0.63	8.7	10.5	7	$0.02h^{-1}$					
ME (MJ/kg ODM)	7.7	0.62	6.8	8.6	7	$0.05h^{-1}$					
FE/GE	0.49	0.03	0.43	0.53	7	$0.08h^{-1}$					
UE/GE	0.04	0.01	0.03	0.05	7						
CH_4E/GE	0.07	0.0	0.07	0.07	7						
ME/DE	0.79	0.02	0.76	0.82	7						
ME/GE	0.41	0.04	0.37	0.47	7						
Digestibility Coefficients											
DM	0.53	0.04	0.47	0.58	7						
OM	0.55	0.03	0.51	0.58	7						
CP	0.17	0.07	0.07	0.24	6						
CF	0.67	0.04	0.63	0.73	7						
EE	0.51	0.17	0.21	0.74	7						
NDF											
ADF											
Cell											
GE	0.52	0.04	0.47	0.57	7						
DOMD(g/kg ODM)	530.5	21.0	495.7	556.5	7						

RUMINANT DATABASE

FEED DESCRIPTION : **AMMONIA TREATED OATS STRAW, ALL SEASONS** (Source 1)

Determination	Mean	SD	Min	Max	n	Determination	Mean	SD	Min	Max	n
General (g/kg ODM)						**Degradability**					
ODM (fresh)	843.0	47.5	774.3	875.1	4	Dry matter					
TDM (fresh)						a (%)	10.5	2.6	6.8	12.7	4
CP	75.3	22.8	59.0	109.0	4	b (%)	66.9	2.1	65.5	70.1	4
MADF	493.8	87.3	363.0	543.0	4	c (h^{-1})	0.04	0.0	0.04	0.04	4
EE	17.8	8.7	10.0	29.0	4						
AEE						dg (%) @ outflow rate					
TA	66.3	6.2	61.0	75.0	4	0.02h^{-1}	54.5	1.7	52.0	56.0	4
GE (MJ/kg ODM)	18.3	0.33	17.8	18.5	4	0.05h^{-1}	39.8	2.1	37.0	42.0	4
						0.08h^{-1}	32.3	2.2	29.0	34.0	4
NDF ash	735.3	45.4	670.0	774.0	4						
NDF unash						Nitrogen					
ADF ash	522.0	106.1	364.0	584.0	4	a (%)	27.2		27.2	27.2	1
ADF unash						b (%)	54.4		54.4	54.4	1
						c (h^{-1})	0.01		0.01	0.01	1
Energy Values											
						dg (%) @ outflow rate					
DE (MJ/kg ODM)	9.8	0.70	8.9	10.4	4	0.02h^{-1}	50.0		50.0	50.0	1
ME (MJ/kg ODM)	8.0	0.62	7.1	8.4	4	0.05h^{-1}	39.0		39.0	39.0	1
FE/GE	0.46	0.04	0.43	0.52	4	0.08h^{-1}	35.0		35.0	35.0	1
UE/GE	0.03	0.01	0.02	0.04	4						
CH$_4$E/GE	0.07	0.0	0.07	0.07	4						
ME/DE	0.81	0.02	0.80	0.83	4						
ME/GE	0.44	0.04	0.38	0.46	4						

Digestibility Coefficients

Determination	Mean	SD	Min	Max	n
DM	0.58	0.04	0.52	0.61	4
OM	0.59	0.04	0.53	0.62	4
CP	0.26	0.29	0.09	0.69	4
CF	0.69	0.05	0.63	0.74	4
EE	0.47	0.11	0.33	0.58	4
NDF					
ADF					
Cell					
GE	0.54	0.04	0.48	0.57	4
DOMD(g/kg ODM)	550.3	37.5	498.5	587.4	4

RUMINANT DATABASE

FEED DESCRIPTION : **AMMONIA TREATED SPRING OATS STRAW** (Source 1)

Determination	Mean	SD	Min	Max	n	Determination	Mean	SD	Min	Max	n
General (g/kg ODM)						**Degradability**					
ODM (fresh)	875.1		875.1	875.1	1	Dry matter					
TDM (fresh)						a (%)	11.7		11.7	11.7	1
CP	67.0		67.0	67.0	1	b (%)	65.5		65.5	65.5	1
MADF	530.0		530.0	530.0	1	c (h^{-1})	0.04		0.04	0.04	1
EE	29.0		29.0	29.0	1						
AEE						dg (%) @ outflow rate					
TA	66.0		66.0	66.0	1	$0.02h^{-1}$	55.0		55.0	55.0	1
GE (MJ/kg ODM)	18.5		18.5	18.5	1	$0.05h^{-1}$	40.0		40.0	40.0	1
						$0.08h^{-1}$	33.0		33.0	33.0	1
NDF ash	743.0		743.0	743.0	1						
NDF unash						Nitrogen					
ADF ash	584.0		584.0	584.0	1	a (%)					
ADF unash						b (%)					
						c (h^{-1})					
Energy Values											
						dg (%) @ outflow rate					
DE (MJ/kg ODM)	10.2		10.2	10.2	1	$0.02h^{-1}$					
ME (MJ/kg ODM)	8.3		8.3	8.3	1	$0.05h^{-1}$					
FE/GE	0.45		0.45	0.45	1	$0.08h^{-1}$					
UE/GE	0.03		0.03	0.03	1						
CH_4E/GE	0.07		0.07	0.07	1						
ME/DE	0.82		0.82	0.82	1						
ME/GE	0.45		0.45	0.45	1						
Digestibility Coefficients											
DM	0.59		0.59	0.59	1						
OM	0.60		0.60	0.60	1						
CP	0.15		0.15	0.15	1						
CF	0.73		0.73	0.73	1						
EE	0.58		0.58	0.58	1						
NDF											
ADF											
Cell											
GE	0.55		0.55	0.55	1						
DOMD(g/kg ODM)	563.1		563.1	563.1	1						

RUMINANT DATABASE

FEED DESCRIPTION : **AMMONIA TREATED WINTER OATS STRAW** (Source 1)

Determination	Mean	SD	Min	Max	n	Determination	Mean	SD	Min	Max	n
General (g/kg ODM)						**Degradability**					
ODM (fresh)	832.3	52.0	774.3	874.6	3	Dry matter					
TDM (fresh)						a (%)	10.2	3.0	6.8	12.7	3
CP	78.0	27.1	59.0	109.0	3	b (%)	67.4	2.3	65.9	70.1	3
MADF	481.7	102.8	363.0	543.0	3	c (h^{-1})	0.04	0.01	0.04	0.04	3
EE	14.0	5.3	10.0	20.0	3						
AEE						dg (%) @ outflow rate					
TA	66.3	7.6	61.0	75.0	3	$0.02h^{-1}$	54.3	2.1	52.0	56.0	3
GE (MJ/kg ODM)	18.2	0.37	17.8	18.5	3	$0.05h^{-1}$	39.7	2.5	37.0	42.0	3
						$0.08h^{-1}$	32.0	2.6	29.0	34.0	3
NDF ash	732.7	55.2	670.0	774.0	3						
NDF unash						Nitrogen					
ADF ash	501.3	119.6	364.0	583.0	3	a (%)	27.2		27.2	27.2	1
ADF unash						b (%)	54.4		54.4	54.4	1
						c (h^{-1})	0.01		0.01	0.01	1
Energy Values											
						dg (%) @ outflow rate					
DE (MJ/kg ODM)	9.7	0.80	8.9	10.4	3	$0.02h^{-1}$	50.0		50.0	50.0	1
ME (MJ/kg ODM)	7.9	0.71	7.1	8.4	3	$0.05h^{-1}$	39.0		39.0	39.0	1
FE/GE	0.47	0.05	0.43	0.52	3	$0.08h^{-1}$	35.0		35.0	35.0	1
UE/GE	0.03	0.01	0.02	0.04	3						
CH_4E/GE	0.07	0.0	0.07	0.07	3						
ME/DE	0.81	0.02	0.80	0.83	3						
ME/GE	0.43	0.05	0.38	0.46	3						
Digestibility Coefficients											
DM	0.57	0.05	0.52	0.61	3						
OM	0.58	0.05	0.53	0.62	3						
CP	0.30	0.34	0.09	0.69	3						
CF	0.67	0.06	0.63	0.74	3						
EE	0.43	0.09	0.33	0.51	3						
NDF											
ADF											
Cell											
GE	0.53	0.05	0.48	0.57	3						
DOMD(g/kg ODM)	546.1	44.8	498.5	587.4	3						

RUMINANT DATABASE

FEED DESCRIPTION : **AMMONIA TREATED WHEAT STRAW, ALL SEASONS** (Source 1)

Determination	Mean	SD	Min	Max	n	Determination	Mean	SD	Min	Max	n
General (g/kg ODM)						**Degradability**					
ODM (fresh)	868.5	25.7	789.0	899.0	17	Dry matter					
TDM (fresh)						a (%)	15.0	9.7	9.5	38.4	8
CP	68.4	12.2	44.0	90.0	17	b (%)	59.4	6.8	45.8	65.8	8
MADF	532.5	20.2	500.0	569.0	17	c (h^{-1})	0.03	0.01	0.03	0.05	8
EE	13.3	3.3	8.0	23.0	17						
AEE						dg (%) @ outflow rate					
TA	55.5	13.6	37.0	84.0	17	$0.02h^{-1}$	51.4	8.3	46.0	71.0	8
GE (MJ/kg ODM)	18.6	0.47	17.9	19.4	17	$0.05h^{-1}$	37.9	9.6	32.0	61.0	8
						$0.08h^{-1}$	32.0	9.9	27.0	56.0	8
NDF ash	773.2	81.0	567.0	869.0	17						
NDF unash						Nitrogen					
ADF ash	544.2	26.2	498.0	597.0	17	a (%)	74.0		74.0	74.0	1
ADF unash						b (%)	12.8		12.8	12.8	1
						c (h^{-1})	0.16		0.16	0.16	1
Energy Values											
						dg (%) @ outflow rate					
DE (MJ/kg ODM)	9.1	0.65	7.7	10.0	17	$0.02h^{-1}$	85.0		85.0	85.0	1
ME (MJ/kg ODM)	7.3	0.64	5.9	8.5	17	$0.05h^{-1}$	84.0		84.0	84.0	1
FE/GE	0.51	0.04	0.47	0.59	17	$0.08h^{-1}$	82.0		82.0	82.0	1
UE/GE	0.03	0.01	0.01	0.04	17						
CH_4E/GE	0.07	0.01	0.06	0.07	17						
ME/DE	0.80	0.02	0.76	0.85	17						
ME/GE	0.39	0.04	0.31	0.45	17						
Digestibility Coefficients											
DM	0.51	0.04	0.43	0.57	17						
OM	0.53	0.04	0.47	0.59	17						
CP	0.21	0.09	0.08	0.39	15						
CF	0.68	0.06	0.57	0.85	17						
EE	0.35	0.14	0.10	0.57	16						
NDF											
ADF											
Cell											
GE	0.49	0.04	0.41	0.53	17						
DOMD(g/kg ODM)	509.9	35.7	448.9	556.7	17						

RUMINANT DATABASE

FEED DESCRIPTION : **AMMONIA TREATED SPRING WHEAT STRAW** (Source 1)

Determination	Mean	SD	Min	Max	n	Determination	Mean	SD	Min	Max	n
General (g/kg ODM)						**Degradability**					
ODM (fresh)	877.9	9.4	864.1	885.3	4	Dry matter					
TDM (fresh)						a (%)	18.9	13.2	10.9	38.4	4
CP	74.8	9.6	63.0	84.0	4	b (%)	57.0	7.7	45.8	62.9	4
MADF	530.8	11.2	514.0	538.0	4	c (h^{-1})	0.03	0.01	0.03	0.05	4
EE	12.3	0.50	12.0	13.0	4						
AEE						dg (%) @ outflow rate					
TA	63.5	9.7	58.0	78.0	4	$0.02h^{-1}$	54.0	11.6	46.0	71.0	4
GE (MJ/kg ODM)	18.2	0.36	17.9	18.6	4	$0.05h^{-1}$	41.0	13.6	32.0	61.0	4
						$0.08h^{-1}$	35.5	13.9	27.0	56.0	4
NDF ash	782.3	22.8	760.0	807.0	4						
NDF unash						Nitrogen					
ADF ash	548.5	27.1	528.0	587.0	4	a (%)	74.0		74.0	74.0	1
ADF unash						b (%)	12.8		12.8	12.8	1
						c (h^{-1})	0.16		0.16	0.16	1
Energy Values											
						dg (%) @ outflow rate					
DE (MJ/kg ODM)	9.2	0.36	8.8	9.7	4	$0.02h^{-1}$	85.0		85.0	85.0	1
ME (MJ/kg ODM)	7.4	0.32	7.1	7.8	4	$0.05h^{-1}$	84.0		84.0	84.0	1
FE/GE	0.49	0.02	0.47	0.51	4	$0.08h^{-1}$	82.0		82.0	82.0	1
UE/GE	0.03	0.01	0.03	0.04	4						
CH_4E/GE	0.07	0.0	0.07	0.07	4						
ME/DE	0.80	0.0	0.79	0.81	4						
ME/GE	0.41	0.02	0.39	0.43	4						
Digestibility Coefficients											
DM	0.54	0.03	0.51	0.57	4						
OM	0.56	0.02	0.53	0.59	4						
CP	0.25	0.07	0.16	0.30	4						
CF	0.68	0.05	0.63	0.74	4						
EE	0.41	0.07	0.31	0.47	4						
NDF											
ADF											
Cell											
GE	0.51	0.02	0.49	0.53	4						
DOMD(g/kg ODM)	523.7	23.8	502.4	556.7	4						

FEED CLASS 12

RUMINANT DATABASE

FEED DESCRIPTION : **AMMONIA TREATED WINTER WHEAT STRAW** (Source 1)

Determination	Mean	SD	Min	Max	n	Determination	Mean	SD	Min	Max	n
General (g/kg ODM)						**Degradability**					
ODM (fresh)	873.3	18.0	836.9	899.0	11	Dry matter					
TDM (fresh)						a (%)	11.1	2.0	9.5	14.1	4
CP	66.7	13.6	44.0	90.0	11	b (%)	61.8	5.7	53.7	65.8	4
MADF	535.4	22.3	505.0	569.0	11	c (h^{-1})	0.03	0.01	0.03	0.04	4
EE	14.2	3.6	11.0	23.0	11						
AEE						dg (%) @ outflow rate					
TA	52.6	15.2	37.0	84.0	11	$0.02h^{-1}$	48.8	2.5	46.0	52.0	4
GE (MJ/kg ODM)	18.6	0.41	18.0	19.2	11	$0.05h^{-1}$	34.8	2.2	33.0	38.0	4
						$0.08h^{-1}$	28.5	2.4	27.0	32.0	4
NDF ash	778.6	75.8	567.0	851.0	11						
NDF unash						Nitrogen					
ADF ash	544.7	28.9	498.0	597.0	11	a (%)					
ADF unash						b (%)					
						c (h^{-1})					
Energy Values											
						dg (%) @ outflow rate					
DE (MJ/kg ODM)	9.2	0.67	7.7	10.0	11	$0.02h^{-1}$					
ME (MJ/kg ODM)	7.5	0.63	6.2	8.5	11	$0.05h^{-1}$					
FE/GE	0.50	0.03	0.47	0.58	11	$0.08h^{-1}$					
UE/GE	0.03	0.01	0.01	0.04	11						
CH4E/GE	0.07	0.0	0.06	0.07	11						
ME/DE	0.81	0.02	0.77	0.85	11						
ME/GE	0.40	0.03	0.34	0.45	11						
Digestibility Coefficients											
DM	0.51	0.04	0.43	0.57	11						
OM	0.53	0.04	0.47	0.58	11						
CP	0.18	0.10	0.08	0.39	9						
CF	0.69	0.07	0.57	0.85	11						
EE	0.34	0.16	0.10	0.57	10						
NDF											
ADF											
Cell											
GE	0.50	0.03	0.42	0.53	11						
DOMD(g/kg ODM)	508.1	41.0	448.9	556.5	11						

RUMINANT DATABASE

FEED DESCRIPTION : **SODIUM HYDROXIDE TREATED BARLEY STRAW, ALL SEASONS** (Source 1)

Determination	Mean	SD	Min	Max	n	Determination	Mean	SD	Min	Max	n
General (g/kg ODM)						**Degradability**					
ODM (fresh)	805.7	40.6	757.7	875.3	7	Dry matter					
TDM (fresh)						a (%)					
CP	44.6	11.2	33.0	70.0	9	b (%)					
MADF	487.0	33.4	439.0	536.0	10	c (h^{-1})					
EE	12.2	4.6	5.0	22.0	10						
AEE						dg (%) @ outflow rate					
TA	114.8	18.1	92.0	152.0	10	0.02h^{-1}					
GE (MJ/kg ODM)	17.4	0.36	16.8	17.8	10	0.05h^{-1}					
						0.08h^{-1}					
NDF ash	675.9	33.0	627.0	731.0	9						
NDF unash						Nitrogen					
ADF ash	495.7	34.5	443.0	535.0	9	a (%)					
ADF unash	506.0	30.4	461.0	549.0	9	b (%)					
						c (h^{-1})					
Energy Values						dg (%) @ outflow rate					
DE (MJ/kg ODM)	11.4	2.5	7.2	16.8	10	0.02h^{-1}					
ME (MJ/kg ODM)	9.3	1.8	6.1	11.3	7	0.05h^{-1}					
FE/GE	0.38	0.10	0.26	0.60	9	0.08h^{-1}					
UE/GE	0.02	0.01	0.01	0.03	2						
CH$_4$E/GE	0.07	0.01	0.06	0.08	9						
ME/DE	0.86	0.03	0.83	0.89	7						
ME/GE	0.53	0.11	0.34	0.65	7						

Digestibility Coefficients

Determination	Mean	SD	Min	Max	n
DM	0.69	0.08	0.58	0.80	10
OM	0.69	0.10	0.53	0.79	10
CP	0.63	0.31	0.33	0.93	4
CF	0.76	0.07	0.65	0.83	9
EE	0.39	0.30	0.03	0.80	6
NDF	0.75		0.75	0.75	1
ADF	0.71		0.71	0.71	1
Cell	0.78		0.78	0.78	1
GE	0.62	0.10	0.40	0.74	9
DOMD(g/kg ODM)	619.2	79.0	483.3	724.2	10

RUMINANT DATABASE

FEED DESCRIPTION : **SODIUM HYDROXIDE TREATED SPRING BARLEY STRAW** (Source 1)

Determination	Mean	SD	Min	Max	n	Determination	Mean	SD	Min	Max	n
General (g/kg ODM)						**Degradability**					
ODM (fresh)	796.3	31.9	757.7	844.8	5	Dry matter					
TDM (fresh)						a (%)					
CP	43.8	11.7	33.0	70.0	8	b (%)					
MADF	478.4	31.6	439.0	536.0	8	c (h^{-1})					
EE	12.6	4.2	8.0	22.0	8						
AEE						dg (%) @ outflow rate					
TA	116.8	19.9	92.0	152.0	8	0.02h^{-1}					
GE (MJ/kg ODM)	17.4	0.39	16.8	17.8	8	0.05h^{-1}					
						0.08h^{-1}					
NDF ash	668.7	34.4	627.0	731.0	7						
NDF unash						Nitrogen					
ADF ash	486.7	33.8	443.0	529.0	7	a (%)					
ADF unash	502.1	30.0	461.0	549.0	8	b (%)					
						c (h^{-1})					
Energy Values											
						dg (%) @ outflow rate					
DE (MJ/kg ODM)	11.6	2.7	7.2	16.8	8	0.02h^{-1}					
ME (MJ/kg ODM)	9.5	2.1	6.1	11.3	5	0.05h^{-1}					
FE/GE	0.38	0.11	0.26	0.60	7	0.08h^{-1}					
UE/GE	0.01		0.01	0.01	1						
CH$_4$E/GE	0.07	0.01	0.06	0.08	7						
ME/DE	0.86	0.02	0.83	0.89	5						
ME/GE	0.54	0.13	0.34	0.65	5						
Digestibility Coefficients											
DM	0.71	0.08	0.58	0.80	8						
OM	0.71	0.10	0.53	0.79	8						
CP	0.73	0.29	0.40	0.93	3						
CF	0.78	0.05	0.67	0.83	7						
EE	0.42	0.35	0.03	0.80	4						
NDF											
ADF											
Cell											
GE	0.62	0.11	0.40	0.74	7						
DOMD(g/kg ODM)	630.8	81.9	483.3	724.2	8						

RUMINANT DATABASE

FEED DESCRIPTION : **SODIUM HYDROXIDE TREATED WINTER BARLEY STRAW** (Source 1)

Determination	Mean	SD	Min	Max	n	Determination	Mean	SD	Min	Max	n
General (g/kg ODM)						**Degradability**					
ODM (fresh)	829.3	65.1	783.2	875.3	2	Dry matter					
TDM (fresh)						a (%)					
CP	51.3		51.3	51.3	1	b (%)					
MADF	521.5	7.8	516.0	527.0	2	c (h^{-1})					
EE	10.5	7.8	5.0	16.0	2						
AEE						dg (%) @ outflow rate					
TA	107.0	5.7	103.0	111.0	2	$0.02h^{-1}$					
GE (MJ/kg ODM)	17.6	0.28	17.4	17.8	2	$0.05h^{-1}$					
						$0.08h^{-1}$					
NDF ash	701.0	0.0	701.0	701.0	2						
NDF unash						Nitrogen					
ADF ash	527.0	11.3	519.0	535.0	2	a (%)					
ADF unash	537.0		537.0	537.0	1	b (%)					
						c (h^{-1})					
Energy Values											
						dg (%) @ outflow rate					
DE (MJ/kg ODM)	10.4	1.4	9.5	11.4	2	$0.02h^{-1}$					
ME (MJ/kg ODM)	8.8	0.84	8.2	9.4	2	$0.05h^{-1}$					
FE/GE	0.41	0.07	0.36	0.46	2	$0.08h^{-1}$					
UE/GE	0.03		0.03	0.03	1						
CH$_4$E/GE	0.08	0.01	0.07	0.08	2						
ME/DE	0.85	0.03	0.83	0.87	2						
ME/GE	0.50	0.04	0.47	0.53	2						
Digestibility Coefficients											
DM	0.62	0.06	0.58	0.66	2						
OM	0.63	0.07	0.58	0.68	2						
CP	0.33		0.33	0.33	1						
CF	0.68	0.04	0.65	0.71	2						
EE	0.33	0.25	0.15	0.50	2						
NDF	0.75		0.75	0.75	1						
ADF	0.71		0.71	0.71	1						
Cell	0.78		0.78	0.78	1						
GE	0.59	0.07	0.54	0.64	2						
DOMD(g/kg ODM)	572.7	62.1	528.8	616.7	2						

RUMINANT DATABASE

FEED DESCRIPTION : **SODIUM HYDROXIDE TREATED OATS STRAW, ALL SEASONS** (Source 1)

Determination	Mean	SD	Min	Max	n	Determination	Mean	SD	Min	Max	n

General (g/kg ODM)

Determination	Mean	SD	Min	Max	n
ODM (fresh)	786.5	6.8	778.8	791.4	3
TDM (fresh)					
CP	32.0	10.4	20.0	38.0	3
MADF	468.0	51.1	438.0	527.0	3
EE	9.0	1.0	8.0	10.0	3
AEE					
TA	150.0	25.5	122.0	172.0	3
GE (MJ/kg ODM)	16.8	0.36	16.5	17.2	3
NDF ash	625.3	59.8	569.0	688.0	3
NDF unash					
ADF ash	484.3	33.6	462.0	523.0	3
ADF unash					

Energy Values

Determination	Mean	SD	Min	Max	n
DE (MJ/kg ODM)	8.8	3.4	6.5	12.7	3
ME (MJ/kg ODM)	7.6	3.2	5.5	11.3	3
FE/GE	0.48	0.19	0.26	0.61	3
UE/GE					
CH_4E/GE	0.07	0.01	0.06	0.08	3
ME/DE	0.86	0.03	0.84	0.89	3
ME/GE	0.45	0.18	0.33	0.66	3

Digestibility Coefficients

Determination	Mean	SD	Min	Max	n
DM	0.60	0.09	0.52	0.70	3
OM	0.59	0.15	0.48	0.75	3
CP					
CF	0.70	0.11	0.61	0.82	3
EE	0.54	0.31	0.32	0.77	2
NDF					
ADF					
Cell					
GE	0.52	0.19	0.39	0.74	3
DOMD(g/kg ODM)	505.7	137.7	412.0	663.8	3

Degradability

Dry matter
a (%)
b (%)
c (h^{-1})

dg (%) @ outflow rate
0.02h^{-1}
0.05h^{-1}
0.08h^{-1}

Nitrogen
a (%)
b (%)
c (h^{-1})

dg (%) @ outflow rate
0.02h^{-1}
0.05h^{-1}
0.08h^{-1}

RUMINANT DATABASE

FEED DESCRIPTION : **SODIUM HYDROXIDE TREATED SPRING OATS STRAW** (Source 1)

Determination	Mean	SD	Min	Max	n	Determination	Mean	SD	Min	Max	n
General (g/kg ODM)						**Degradability**					
ODM (fresh)	791.4		791.4	791.4	1	Dry matter					
TDM (fresh)						a (%)					
CP	20.0		20.0	20.0	1	b (%)					
MADF	527.0		527.0	527.0	1	c (h^{-1})					
EE	8.0		8.0	8.0	1						
AEE						dg (%) @ outflow rate					
TA	122.0		122.0	122.0	1	$0.02h^{-1}$					
GE (MJ/kg ODM)	17.2		17.2	17.2	1	$0.05h^{-1}$					
						$0.08h^{-1}$					
NDF ash	688.0		688.0	688.0	1						
NDF unash						Nitrogen					
ADF ash	523.0		523.0	523.0	1	a (%)					
ADF unash						b (%)					
						c (h^{-1})					
Energy Values						dg (%) @ outflow rate					
DE (MJ/kg ODM)	12.7		12.7	12.7	1	$0.02h^{-1}$					
ME (MJ/kg ODM)	11.3		11.3	11.3	1	$0.05h^{-1}$					
FE/GE	0.26		0.26	0.26	1	$0.08h^{-1}$					
UE/GE											
CH_4E/GE	0.08		0.08	0.08	1						
ME/DE	0.89		0.89	0.89	1						
ME/GE	0.66		0.66	0.66	1						
Digestibility Coefficients											
DM	0.70		0.70	0.70	1						
OM	0.75		0.75	0.75	1						
CP											
CF	0.82		0.82	0.82	1						
EE											
NDF											
ADF											
Cell											
GE	0.74		0.74	0.74	1						
DOMD(g/kg ODM)	663.8		663.8	663.8	1						

RUMINANT DATABASE

FEED DESCRIPTION : **SODIUM HYDROXIDE TREATED WINTER OATS STRAW** (Source 1)

Determination	Mean	SD	Min	Max	n	Determination	Mean	SD	Min	Max	n
General (g/kg ODM)						**Degradability**					
ODM (fresh)	784.1	7.5	778.8	789.4	2	Dry matter					
TDM (fresh)						a (%)					
CP	38.0	0.0	38.0	38.0	2	b (%)					
MADF	438.5	0.71	438.0	439.0	2	c (h^{-1})					
EE	9.5	0.71	9.0	10.0	2						
AEE						dg (%) @ outflow rate					
TA	164.0	11.3	156.0	172.0	2	0.02h^{-1}					
GE (MJ/kg ODM)	16.6	0.14	16.5	16.7	2	0.05h^{-1}					
						0.08h^{-1}					
NDF ash	594.0	35.4	569.0	619.0	2						
NDF unash						Nitrogen					
ADF ash	465.0	4.2	462.0	468.0	2	a (%)					
ADF unash						b (%)					
						c (h^{-1})					
Energy Values											
						dg (%) @ outflow rate					
DE (MJ/kg ODM)	6.8	0.46	6.5	7.2	2	0.02h^{-1}					
ME (MJ/kg ODM)	5.8	0.42	5.5	6.1	2	0.05h^{-1}					
FE/GE	0.59	0.03	0.57	0.61	2	0.08h^{-1}					
UE/GE											
CH$_4$E/GE	0.06	0.0	0.06	0.06	2						
ME/DE	0.85	0.01	0.84	0.85	2						
ME/GE	0.35	0.03	0.33	0.37	2						
Digestibility Coefficients											
DM	0.55	0.04	0.52	0.57	2						
OM	0.51	0.04	0.48	0.53	2						
CP											
CF	0.64	0.05	0.61	0.68	2						
EE	0.54	0.31	0.32	0.77	2						
NDF											
ADF											
Cell											
GE	0.41	0.03	0.39	0.43	2						
DOMD(g/kg ODM)	426.6	20.7	412.0	441.2	2						

RUMINANT DATABASE

FEED DESCRIPTION : **SODIUM HYDROXIDE TREATED WINTER WHEAT STRAW** (Source 1)

Determination	Mean	SD	Min	Max	n	Determination	Mean	SD	Min	Max	n
General (g/kg ODM)						**Degradability**					
ODM (fresh)	842.4	78.4	517.4	922.8	26	Dry matter					
TDM (fresh)						a (%)					
CP	36.1	6.6	23.0	63.0	27	b (%)					
MADF	505.1	18.8	460.0	538.0	28	c (h^{-1})					
EE	8.7	3.5	6.0	24.0	28						
AEE	11.5	1.6	9.0	16.0	20	dg (%) @ outflow rate					
TA	126.5	26.4	93.0	169.0	28	$0.02h^{-1}$					
GE (MJ/kg ODM)	17.2	0.45	16.3	17.9	28	$0.05h^{-1}$					
						$0.08h^{-1}$					
NDF ash	688.9	41.7	629.0	760.0	25						
NDF unash						Nitrogen					
ADF ash	493.8	40.9	321.0	536.0	24	a (%)					
ADF unash	516.3	39.7	334.0	554.0	27	b (%)					
						c (h^{-1})					
Energy Values											
						dg (%) @ outflow rate					
DE (MJ/kg ODM)	10.4	1.4	8.3	16.3	28	$0.02h^{-1}$					
ME (MJ/kg ODM)	8.6	0.61	7.2	9.6	26	$0.05h^{-1}$					
FE/GE	0.41	0.05	0.33	0.51	27	$0.08h^{-1}$					
UE/GE	0.03	0.01	0.01	0.05	20						
CH_4E/GE	0.07	0.01	0.07	0.08	27						
ME/DE	0.84	0.02	0.79	0.87	26						
ME/GE	0.50	0.04	0.42	0.57	26						
Digestibility Coefficients											
DM	0.64	0.05	0.52	0.78	28						
OM	0.64	0.05	0.56	0.80	28						
CP	0.14	0.20	0.01	0.37	3						
CF	0.80	0.06	0.69	0.90	27						
EE	0.55	0.21	0.14	0.95	24						
NDF	0.76	0.05	0.68	0.85	20						
ADF	0.70	0.05	0.62	0.77	19						
Cell	0.80	0.06	0.65	0.90	20						
GE	0.59	0.05	0.49	0.67	27						
DOMD(g/kg ODM)	570.3	40.7	498.2	698.0	28						

RUMINANT DATABASE

FEED DESCRIPTION : **UNTREATED BARLEY STRAW, ALL SEASONS** (Sources 1, 2)

Determination	Mean	SD	Min	Max	n	Determination	Mean	SD	Min	Max	n
General (g/kg ODM)						**Degradability**					
ODM (fresh)	867.0	26.0	779.7	911.7	53	Dry matter					
TDM (fresh)						a (%)	5.0	1.4	3.4	7.8	8
CP	41.5	12.6	20.0	71.0	51	b (%)	57.0	6.4	47.8	63.7	8
MADF	496.6	37.2	393.0	564.0	52	c (h^{-1})	0.04	0.0	0.03	0.05	8
EE	14.0	5.9	5.0	48.0	53						
AEE						dg (%) @ outflow rate					
TA	56.7	16.8	27.0	97.0	53	$0.02h^{-1}$	43.3	3.8	37.0	48.0	8
GE (MJ/kg ODM)	18.4	0.59	16.9	19.7	53	$0.05h^{-1}$	30.6	2.7	26.0	34.0	8
						$0.08h^{-1}$	24.1	2.2	21.0	27.0	8
NDF ash	810.9	52.0	614.0	878.0	51						
NDF unash						Nitrogen					
ADF ash	508.6	47.0	393.0	595.0	51	a (%)					
ADF unash	521.0	34.2	469.0	571.0	10	b (%)					
						c (h^{-1})					
Energy Values											
						dg (%) @ outflow rate					
DE (MJ/kg ODM)	8.2	1.3	5.1	11.3	51	$0.02h^{-1}$					
ME (MJ/kg ODM)	6.4	1.2	3.4	9.2	51	$0.05h^{-1}$					
FE/GE	0.56	0.07	0.40	0.74	52	$0.08h^{-1}$					
UE/GE	0.03	0.01	0.01	0.05	49						
CH_4E/GE	0.06	0.01	0.05	0.08	52						
ME/DE	0.79	0.04	0.67	0.85	50						
ME/GE	0.35	0.06	0.17	0.48	51						
Digestibility Coefficients											
DM	0.45	0.06	0.30	0.56	53						
OM	0.47	0.06	0.35	0.59	53						
CP	0.19	0.18	-.07	0.80	28						
CF	0.57	0.07	0.42	0.69	51						
EE	0.43	0.21	0.05	0.98	47						
NDF	0.44		0.44	0.44	1						
ADF	0.44		0.44	0.44	1						
Cell	0.51		0.51	0.51	1						
GE	0.44	0.07	0.26	0.60	52						
DOMD(g/kg ODM)	449.9	50.0	338.3	561.1	53						

RUMINANT DATABASE

FEED DESCRIPTION : **UNTREATED SPRING BARLEY STRAW** (Sources 1, 2)

Determination	Mean	SD	Min	Max	n	Determination	Mean	SD	Min	Max	n
General (g/kg ODM)						**Degradability**					
ODM (fresh)	861.9	23.8	779.7	902.8	32	Dry matter					
TDM (fresh)						a (%)	4.6	0.24	4.4	4.8	3
CP	42.6	12.9	20.0	71.0	31	b (%)	62.0	2.6	59.0	63.7	3
MADF	494.2	39.3	393.0	554.0	31	c (h^{-1})	0.04	0.0	0.04	0.04	3
EE	15.4	6.8	9.0	48.0	32						
AEE						dg (%) @ outflow rate					
TA	56.3	16.8	27.0	97.0	32	$0.02h^{-1}$	46.7	1.5	45.0	48.0	3
GE (MJ/kg ODM)	18.5	0.61	16.9	19.7	32	$0.05h^{-1}$	33.0	1.0	32.0	34.0	3
						$0.08h^{-1}$	26.0	1.0	25.0	27.0	3
NDF ash	810.6	50.0	614.0	874.0	30						
NDF unash						Nitrogen					
ADF ash	504.8	47.3	393.0	558.0	30	a (%)					
ADF unash	519.0	35.6	469.0	571.0	9	b (%)					
						c (h^{-1})					
Energy Values											
						dg (%) @ outflow rate					
DE (MJ/kg ODM)	8.4	1.5	5.1	11.3	30	$0.02h^{-1}$					
ME (MJ/kg ODM)	6.6	1.4	3.4	9.2	30	$0.05h^{-1}$					
FE/GE	0.55	0.08	0.40	0.74	31	$0.08h^{-1}$					
UE/GE	0.03	0.01	0.01	0.05	28						
CH_4E/GE	0.07	0.01	0.05	0.08	31						
ME/DE	0.79	0.04	0.67	0.85	29						
ME/GE	0.36	0.07	0.17	0.48	30						

Digestibility Coefficients

Determination	Mean	SD	Min	Max	n
DM	0.46	0.06	0.30	0.56	32
OM	0.49	0.05	0.35	0.59	32
CP	0.25	0.20	-.07	0.80	16
CF	0.57	0.07	0.42	0.69	30
EE	0.46	0.24	0.05	0.98	29
NDF					
ADF					
Cell					
GE	0.45	0.08	0.26	0.60	31
DOMD(g/kg ODM)	461.5	47.5	338.4	561.1	32

RUMINANT DATABASE

FEED DESCRIPTION : **UNTREATED WINTER BARLEY STRAW** (Source 1)

Determination	Mean	SD	Min	Max	n	Determination	Mean	SD	Min	Max	n
General (g/kg ODM)						**Degradability**					
ODM (fresh)	874.4	31.1	804.4	911.7	17	Dry matter					
TDM (fresh)						a (%)	5.3	1.9	3.4	7.8	5
CP	37.6	11.4	26.0	59.0	16	b (%)	54.0	6.3	47.8	63.6	5
MADF	501.9	38.2	419.0	564.0	17	c (h^{-1})	0.04	0.01	0.03	0.05	5
EE	12.1	3.4	5.0	19.0	17						
AEE						dg (%) @ outflow rate					
TA	56.9	17.4	28.0	84.0	17	0.02h^{-1}	41.2	3.2	37.0	45.0	5
GE (MJ/kg ODM)	18.3	0.58	17.4	19.4	17	0.05h^{-1}	29.2	2.4	26.0	32.0	5
						0.08h^{-1}	23.0	2.0	21.0	26.0	5
NDF ash	809.4	61.0	620.0	878.0	17						
NDF unash						Nitrogen					
ADF ash	514.7	52.4	425.0	595.0	17	a (%)					
ADF unash	539.0		539.0	539.0	1	b (%)					
						c (h^{-1})					
Energy Values											
						dg (%) @ outflow rate					
DE (MJ/kg ODM)	7.9	1.0	6.3	10.2	17	0.02h^{-1}					
ME (MJ/kg ODM)	6.2	0.95	4.8	8.1	17	0.05h^{-1}					
FE/GE	0.57	0.05	0.45	0.66	17	0.08h^{-1}					
UE/GE	0.03	0.01	0.01	0.05	17						
CH$_4$E/GE	0.06	0.01	0.06	0.07	17						
ME/DE	0.79	0.03	0.73	0.84	17						
ME/GE	0.34	0.05	0.26	0.44	17						
Digestibility Coefficients											
DM	0.45	0.06	0.35	0.55	17						
OM	0.46	0.05	0.35	0.55	17						
CP	0.15	0.11	0.01	0.33	8						
CF	0.57	0.07	0.45	0.69	17						
EE	0.36	0.14	0.11	0.64	14						
NDF	0.44		0.44	0.44	1						
ADF	0.44		0.44	0.44	1						
Cell	0.51		0.51	0.51	1						
GE	0.43	0.05	0.34	0.55	17						
DOMD(g/kg ODM)	437.2	50.8	338.3	527.0	17						

RUMINANT DATABASE

FEED DESCRIPTION : **UNTREATED OATS STRAW, ALL SEASONS** (Source 1)

Determination	Mean	SD	Min	Max	n	Determination	Mean	SD	Min	Max	n
General (g/kg ODM)						**Degradability**					
ODM (fresh)	846.3	31.1	787.7	869.6	6	Dry matter					
TDM (fresh)						a (%)	9.3	2.9	7.2	13.5	4
CP	34.3	10.6	20.0	48.0	6	b (%)	61.0	10.7	49.7	72.6	4
MADF	513.2	23.2	487.0	544.0	6	c (h^{-1})	0.04	0.01	0.03	0.05	4
EE	13.8	4.9	8.0	21.0	6						
AEE						dg (%) @ outflow rate					
TA	66.2	4.4	63.0	74.0	6	$0.02h^{-1}$	50.0	8.0	44.0	61.0	4
GE (MJ/kg ODM)	18.2	0.25	17.8	18.5	6	$0.05h^{-1}$	36.0	6.2	31.0	45.0	4
						$0.08h^{-1}$	29.3	5.3	25.0	37.0	4
NDF ash	749.2	92.9	587.0	804.0	5						
NDF unash						Nitrogen					
ADF ash	523.4	15.1	500.0	538.0	5	a (%)	29.8		29.8	29.8	1
ADF unash	533.5	12.0	525.0	542.0	2	b (%)	51.0		51.0	51.0	1
						c (h^{-1})	0.01		0.01	0.01	1
Energy Values											
						dg (%) @ outflow rate					
DE (MJ/kg ODM)	8.8	1.6	6.0	10.9	6	$0.02h^{-1}$	45.0		45.0	45.0	1
ME (MJ/kg ODM)	7.2	1.4	4.9	9.0	6	$0.05h^{-1}$	37.0		37.0	37.0	1
FE/GE	0.52	0.09	0.40	0.68	6	$0.08h^{-1}$	35.0		35.0	35.0	1
UE/GE	0.02	0.01	0.01	0.03	5						
CH_4E/GE	0.07	0.01	0.06	0.07	6						
ME/DE	0.82	0.02	0.77	0.84	6						
ME/GE	0.40	0.08	0.27	0.50	6						
Digestibility Coefficients											
DM	0.51	0.08	0.39	0.64	6						
OM	0.53	0.08	0.40	0.65	6						
CP	0.07	0.08	0.0	0.15	3						
CF	0.62	0.11	0.47	0.79	6						
EE	0.42	0.12	0.24	0.54	5						
NDF											
ADF											
Cell											
GE	0.49	0.09	0.32	0.60	6						
DOMD(g/kg ODM)	496.2	73.5	383.3	610.2	6						

RUMINANT DATABASE

FEED DESCRIPTION : **UNTREATED SPRING OATS STRAW** (Source 1)

Determination	Mean	SD	Min	Max	n
General (g/kg ODM)					
ODM (fresh)	812.4	34.9	787.7	837.1	2
TDM (fresh)					
CP	29.0	7.1	24.0	34.0	2
MADF	520.5	24.7	503.0	538.0	2
EE	14.5	9.2	8.0	21.0	2
AEE					
TA	68.5	7.8	63.0	74.0	2
GE (MJ/kg ODM)	18.3	0.21	18.1	18.4	2
NDF ash	804.0		804.0	804.0	1
NDF unash					
ADF ash	517.0		517.0	517.0	1
ADF unash	542.0		542.0	542.0	1
Energy Values					
DE (MJ/kg ODM)	9.4	0.11	9.3	9.4	2
ME (MJ/kg ODM)	7.6	0.55	7.2	7.9	2
FE/GE	0.49	0.0	0.49	0.49	2
UE/GE	0.02	0.01	0.01	0.02	2
CH$_4$E/GE	0.07	0.0	0.07	0.07	2
ME/DE	0.81	0.05	0.77	0.84	2
ME/GE	0.41	0.03	0.40	0.43	2
Digestibility Coefficients					
DM	0.52	0.02	0.50	0.53	2
OM	0.55	0.01	0.54	0.55	2
CP	0.07		0.07	0.07	1
CF	0.62	0.08	0.57	0.68	2
EE	0.24		0.24	0.24	1
NDF					
ADF					
Cell					
GE	0.51	0.0	0.51	0.51	2
DOMD(g/kg ODM)	510.7	0.63	510.2	511.1	2

Degradability

Determination	Mean	SD	Min	Max	n
Dry matter					
a (%)	8.6		8.6	8.6	1
b (%)	67.2		67.2	67.2	1
c (h^{-1})	0.03		0.03	0.03	1
dg (%) @ outflow rate					
0.02h^{-1}	51.0		51.0	51.0	1
0.05h^{-1}	35.0		35.0	35.0	1
0.08h^{-1}	28.0		28.0	28.0	1
Nitrogen					
a (%)					
b (%)					
c (h^{-1})					
dg (%) @ outflow rate					
0.02h^{-1}					
0.05h^{-1}					
0.08h^{-1}					

RUMINANT DATABASE

FEED DESCRIPTION : **UNTREATED WINTER OATS STRAW** (Source 1)

Determination	Mean	SD	Min	Max	n	Determination	Mean	SD	Min	Max	n
General (g/kg ODM)						**Degradability**					
ODM (fresh)	863.2	8.0	853.1	869.6	4	Dry matter					
TDM (fresh)						a (%)	9.5	3.5	7.2	13.5	3
CP	37.0	11.9	20.0	48.0	4	b (%)	59.0	12.1	49.7	72.6	3
MADF	509.5	25.3	487.0	544.0	4	c (h^{-1})	0.04	0.01	0.04	0.05	3
EE	13.5	3.3	9.0	17.0	4						
AEE						dg (%) @ outflow rate					
TA	65.0	2.7	63.0	69.0	4	0.02h^{-1}	49.7	9.8	44.0	61.0	3
GE (MJ/kg ODM)	18.1	0.28	17.8	18.5	4	0.05h^{-1}	36.3	7.6	31.0	45.0	3
						0.08h^{-1}	29.7	6.4	25.0	37.0	3
NDF ash	735.5	101.3	587.0	804.0	4						
NDF unash						Nitrogen					
ADF ash	525.0	17.0	500.0	538.0	4	a (%)	29.8		29.8	29.8	1
ADF unash	525.0		525.0	525.0	1	b (%)	51.0		51.0	51.0	1
						c (h^{-1})	0.01		0.01	0.01	1
Energy Values											
						dg (%) @ outflow rate					
DE (MJ/kg ODM)	8.5	2.0	6.0	10.9	4	0.02h^{-1}	45.0		45.0	45.0	1
ME (MJ/kg ODM)	7.0	1.7	4.9	9.0	4	0.05h^{-1}	37.0		37.0	37.0	1
FE/GE	0.53	0.12	0.40	0.68	4	0.08h^{-1}	35.0		35.0	35.0	1
UE/GE	0.02	0.01	0.01	0.03	3						
CH$_4$E/GE	0.07	0.01	0.06	0.07	4						
ME/DE	0.83	0.0	0.82	0.83	4						
ME/GE	0.39	0.10	0.27	0.50	4						
Digestibility Coefficients											
DM	0.51	0.10	0.39	0.64	4						
OM	0.52	0.10	0.40	0.65	4						
CP	0.08	0.11	0.0	0.15	2						
CF	0.62	0.13	0.47	0.79	4						
EE	0.46	0.07	0.39	0.54	4						
NDF											
ADF											
Cell											
GE	0.47	0.12	0.32	0.60	4						
DOMD(g/kg ODM)	488.9	93.8	383.3	610.2	4						

RUMINANT DATABASE

FEED DESCRIPTION : **UNTREATED OILSEED RAPE STRAW** (Source 1)

Determination	Mean	SD	Min	Max	n	Determination	Mean	SD	Min	Max	n
General (g/kg ODM)						**Degradability**					
ODM (fresh)	864.5	14.0	854.6	874.4	2	Dry matter					
TDM (fresh)						a (%)					
CP	62.0	5.7	58.0	66.0	2	b (%)					
MADF	524.0	36.8	498.0	550.0	2	c (h^{-1})					
EE	19.0	2.8	17.0	21.0	2						
AEE						dg (%) @ outflow rate					
TA	87.5	23.3	71.0	104.0	2	0.02h^{-1}					
GE (MJ/kg ODM)	18.5	0.99	17.8	19.2	2	0.05h^{-1}					
						0.08h^{-1}					
NDF ash	802.5	106.8	727.0	878.0	2						
NDF unash						Nitrogen					
ADF ash	581.5	47.4	548.0	615.0	2	a (%)					
ADF unash						b (%)					
						c (h^{-1})					
Energy Values											
						dg (%) @ outflow rate					
DE (MJ/kg ODM)	7.5	2.3	5.9	9.2	2	0.02h^{-1}					
ME (MJ/kg ODM)	5.5	2.4	3.8	7.2	2	0.05h^{-1}					
FE/GE	0.60	0.11	0.52	0.67	2	0.08h^{-1}					
UE/GE	0.05	0.01	0.04	0.06	2						
CH$_4$E/GE	0.07	0.01	0.06	0.07	2						
ME/DE	0.72	0.10	0.65	0.79	2						
ME/GE	0.30	0.11	0.22	0.38	2						
Digestibility Coefficients											
DM	0.43	0.01	0.42	0.44	2						
OM	0.46	0.02	0.44	0.47	2						
CP	0.64	0.19	0.50	0.77	2						
CF	0.38	0.0	0.38	0.38	2						
EE	0.58		0.58	0.58	1						
NDF											
ADF											
Cell											
GE	0.40	0.11	0.33	0.48	2						
DOMD(g/kg ODM)	415.6	7.8	410.1	421.1	2						

RUMINANT DATABASE

FEED DESCRIPTION : **UNTREATED WINTER TRITICALE STRAW** (Source 1)

Determination	Mean	SD	Min	Max	n	Determination	Mean	SD	Min	Max	n
General (g/kg ODM)						**Degradability**					
ODM (fresh)	873.1		873.1	873.1	1	Dry matter					
TDM (fresh)						a (%)					
CP	41.0		41.0	41.0	1	b (%)					
MADF	462.0		462.0	462.0	1	c (h^{-1})					
EE	15.0		15.0	15.0	1						
AEE						dg (%) @ outflow rate					
TA	37.0		37.0	37.0	1	0.02h^{-1}					
GE (MJ/kg ODM)	17.8		17.8	17.8	1	0.05h^{-1}					
						0.08h^{-1}					
NDF ash	622.0		622.0	622.0	1						
NDF unash						Nitrogen					
ADF ash						a (%)					
ADF unash						b (%)					
						c (h^{-1})					
Energy Values											
						dg (%) @ outflow rate					
DE (MJ/kg ODM)	7.2		7.2	7.2	1	0.02h^{-1}					
ME (MJ/kg ODM)	5.6		5.6	5.6	1	0.05h^{-1}					
FE/GE	0.60		0.60	0.60	1	0.08h^{-1}					
UE/GE	0.03		0.03	0.03	1						
CH$_4$E/GE	0.06		0.06	0.06	1						
ME/DE	0.78		0.78	0.78	1						
ME/GE	0.32		0.32	0.32	1						
Digestibility Coefficients											
DM	0.43		0.43	0.43	1						
OM	0.46		0.46	0.46	1						
CP	0.03		0.03	0.03	1						
CF	0.55		0.55	0.55	1						
EE	0.57		0.57	0.57	1						
NDF											
ADF											
Cell											
GE	0.40		0.40	0.40	1						
DOMD(g/kg ODM)	444.5		444.5	444.5	1						

RUMINANT DATABASE

FEED DESCRIPTION : **UNTREATED WHEAT STRAW, ALL SEASONS** (Source 1)

Determination	Mean	SD	Min	Max	n	Determination	Mean	SD	Min	Max	n
General (g/kg ODM)						**Degradability**					
ODM (fresh)	872.3	30.6	700.5	929.6	69	Dry matter					
TDM (fresh)						a (%)	9.2	8.0	3.8	30.2	9
CP	38.9	10.2	22.0	78.1	68	b (%)	54.6	4.7	47.7	59.0	9
MADF	514.9	29.2	436.0	566.0	70	c (h^{-1})	0.04	0.01	0.03	0.06	9
EE	11.9	4.1	2.0	21.0	70						
AEE	9.0	1.4	8.0	11.0	4	dg (%) @ outflow rate					
TA	69.2	20.5	25.0	120.0	69	$0.02h^{-1}$	44.9	11.1	36.0	73.0	9
GE (MJ/kg ODM)	18.2	0.49	17.3	19.4	70	$0.05h^{-1}$	32.9	11.3	24.0	62.0	9
						$0.08h^{-1}$	27.1	10.8	18.0	55.0	9
NDF ash	809.3	39.3	674.0	925.0	66						
NDF unash						Nitrogen					
ADF ash	502.2	36.8	400.0	565.0	63	a (%)					
ADF unash	539.7	39.7	433.0	604.0	22	b (%)					
						c (h^{-1})					
Energy Values											
						dg (%) @ outflow rate					
DE (MJ/kg ODM)	7.7	1.3	4.5	11.4	70	$0.02h^{-1}$					
ME (MJ/kg ODM)	6.1	1.2	3.2	9.4	69	$0.05h^{-1}$					
FE/GE	0.58	0.07	0.38	0.76	70	$0.08h^{-1}$					
UE/GE	0.03	0.02	0.01	0.06	66						
CH_4E/GE	0.06	0.01	0.05	0.07	70						
ME/DE	0.78	0.04	0.67	0.86	69						
ME/GE	0.33	0.06	0.17	0.51	69						
Digestibility Coefficients											
DM	0.43	0.06	0.28	0.53	70						
OM	0.46	0.05	0.31	0.58	70						
CP	0.23	0.16	0.02	0.70	27						
CF	0.57	0.08	0.39	0.85	69						
EE	0.41	0.20	0.07	0.86	59						
NDF	0.56	0.08	0.50	0.70	5						
ADF	0.47	0.14	0.23	0.56	5						
Cell	0.61	0.02	0.59	0.64	4						
GE	0.42	0.07	0.24	0.62	70						
DOMD(g/kg ODM)	428.9	47.6	301.5	541.0	70						

RUMINANT DATABASE

FEED DESCRIPTION : **UNTREATED SPRING WHEAT STRAW** (Source 1)

Determination	Mean	SD	Min	Max	n	Determination	Mean	SD	Min	Max	n
General (g/kg ODM)						**Degradability**					
ODM (fresh)	882.6	13.3	866.0	894.1	4	Dry matter					
TDM (fresh)						a (%)	7.3	1.5	5.6	8.9	4
CP	36.5	7.9	25.0	43.0	4	b (%)	53.8	6.1	47.7	59.0	4
MADF	513.3	23.4	485.0	533.0	4	c (h^{-1})	0.04	0.0	0.04	0.04	4
EE	13.8	2.2	11.0	16.0	4						
AEE						dg (%) @ outflow rate					
TA	63.5	9.3	53.0	75.0	4	$0.02h^{-1}$	42.5	4.2	38.0	48.0	4
GE (MJ/kg ODM)	17.8	0.32	17.5	18.3	4	$0.05h^{-1}$	30.5	3.3	27.0	35.0	4
						$0.08h^{-1}$	25.0	2.9	22.0	29.0	4
NDF ash	818.3	24.3	792.0	844.0	4						
NDF unash						Nitrogen					
ADF ash	534.5	26.9	503.0	565.0	4	a (%)					
ADF unash						b (%)					
						c (h^{-1})					
Energy Values											
						dg (%) @ outflow rate					
DE (MJ/kg ODM)	7.2	0.67	6.3	7.8	4	$0.02h^{-1}$					
ME (MJ/kg ODM)	5.7	0.61	4.9	6.3	4	$0.05h^{-1}$					
FE/GE	0.60	0.04	0.56	0.64	4	$0.08h^{-1}$					
UE/GE	0.02	0.0	0.02	0.02	4						
CH_4E/GE	0.06	0.0	0.06	0.06	4						
ME/DE	0.80	0.01	0.78	0.80	4						
ME/GE	0.32	0.03	0.28	0.35	4						
Digestibility Coefficients											
DM	0.42	0.05	0.37	0.47	4						
OM	0.45	0.05	0.39	0.50	4						
CP	0.20	0.08	0.14	0.25	2						
CF	0.55	0.05	0.49	0.61	4						
EE	0.33	0.02	0.32	0.36	4						
NDF											
ADF											
Cell											
GE	0.40	0.04	0.36	0.44	4						
DOMD(g/kg ODM)	425.9	61.1	365.3	492.2	4						

RUMINANT DATABASE

FEED DESCRIPTION : **UNTREATED WINTER WHEAT STRAW** (Source 1)

Determination	Mean	SD	Min	Max	n	Determination	Mean	SD	Min	Max	n
General (g/kg ODM)						**Degradability**					
ODM (fresh)	871.7	32.3	700.5	929.6	61	Dry matter					
TDM (fresh)						a (%)	10.7	11.0	3.8	30.2	5
CP	39.1	10.5	22.0	78.1	60	b (%)	55.3	3.8	49.5	58.8	5
MADF	514.9	29.9	436.0	566.0	62	c (h^{-1})	0.04	0.01	0.03	0.06	5
EE	11.7	4.1	2.0	21.0	62						
AEE	9.0	1.4	8.0	11.0	4	dg (%) @ outflow rate					
TA	70.7	20.3	29.0	120.0	61	$0.02h^{-1}$	46.8	14.9	36.0	73.0	5
GE (MJ/kg ODM)	18.2	0.48	17.3	19.1	62	$0.05h^{-1}$	34.8	15.4	24.0	62.0	5
						$0.08h^{-1}$	28.8	14.9	18.0	55.0	5
NDF ash	806.4	37.9	674.0	870.0	58						
NDF unash						Nitrogen					
ADF ash	498.8	36.5	400.0	558.0	56	a (%)					
ADF unash	541.5	39.7	433.0	604.0	21	b (%)					
						c (h^{-1})					
Energy Values											
						dg (%) @ outflow rate					
DE (MJ/kg ODM)	7.7	1.2	4.5	10.8	62	$0.02h^{-1}$					
ME (MJ/kg ODM)	6.0	1.1	3.2	9.2	61	$0.05h^{-1}$					
FE/GE	0.58	0.07	0.40	0.76	62	$0.08h^{-1}$					
UE/GE	0.03	0.02	0.01	0.06	58						
CH_4E/GE	0.06	0.01	0.05	0.07	62						
ME/DE	0.78	0.04	0.67	0.86	61						
ME/GE	0.33	0.06	0.17	0.51	61						
Digestibility Coefficients											
DM	0.43	0.06	0.28	0.53	62						
OM	0.46	0.05	0.31	0.58	62						
CP	0.24	0.16	0.02	0.70	23						
CF	0.57	0.08	0.39	0.85	61						
EE	0.40	0.20	0.07	0.82	51						
NDF	0.56	0.08	0.50	0.70	5						
ADF	0.47	0.14	0.23	0.56	5						
Cell	0.61	0.02	0.59	0.64	4						
GE	0.42	0.07	0.24	0.60	62						
DOMD(g/kg ODM)	429.1	47.9	301.5	541.0	62						

RUMINANT DATABASE

FEED CLASS 20

FRESH HERBAGES AND FORAGES FED FRESH

RUMINANT DATABASE

FEED DESCRIPTION : **CABBAGE, FRESH** (Sources 1, 2)

Determination	Mean	SD	Min	Max	n	Determination	Mean	SD	Min	Max	n
General (g/kg ODM)						**Degradability**					
ODM (fresh)	106.5	13.3	84.0	119.0	5	Dry matter					
TDM (fresh)						a (%)					
CP	206.6	12.3	192.0	221.0	5	b (%)					
MADF	128.4	14.9	107.0	143.0	5	c (h^{-1})					
EE	17.2	7.7	9.0	28.0	5						
AEE						dg (%) @ outflow rate					
TA	107.6	18.9	90.0	134.0	5	0.02h^{-1}					
GE (MJ/kg ODM)	17.6	0.96	16.6	19.1	5	0.05h^{-1}					
						0.08h^{-1}					
NDF ash	243.8	191.7	141.0	586.0	5						
NDF unash						Nitrogen					
ADF ash	136.0	14.6	119.0	158.0	5	a (%)					
ADF unash						b (%)					
						c (h^{-1})					
Energy Values											
						dg (%) @ outflow rate					
DE (MJ/kg ODM)	15.8	1.3	14.5	17.8	5	0.02h^{-1}					
ME (MJ/kg ODM)	13.7	0.82	12.6	14.7	5	0.05h^{-1}					
FE/GE	0.10	0.03	0.07	0.13	5	0.08h^{-1}					
UE/GE	0.05	0.01	0.04	0.06	5						
CH$_4$E/GE	0.07	0.02	0.05	0.09	5						
ME/DE	0.87	0.02	0.83	0.89	5						
ME/GE	0.78	0.02	0.76	0.80	5						

Digestibility Coefficients

Determination	Mean	SD	Min	Max	n
DM	0.87	0.02	0.85	0.89	5
OM	0.92	0.01	0.90	0.93	5
CP	0.87	0.02	0.86	0.90	5
CF					
EE	0.68		0.68	0.68	1
NDF					
ADF					
Cell					
GE	0.90	0.03	0.87	0.93	5
DOMD(g/kg ODM)	781.2	78.0	649.2	843.0	5

RUMINANT DATABASE

FEED DESCRIPTION : **FORAGE SORGHUM/SUDANGRASS HYBRID, VAR TOPGRASS** (Source 1)

Determination	Mean	SD	Min	Max	n	Determination	Mean	SD	Min	Max	n
General (g/kg ODM)						**Degradability**					
ODM (fresh)	174.0		174.0	174.0	1	Dry matter					
TDM (fresh)						a (%)					
CP	137.0		137.0	137.0	1	b (%)					
MADF	345.0		345.0	345.0	1	c (h^{-1})					
EE	12.0		12.0	12.0	1						
AEE						dg (%) @ outflow rate					
TA	75.0		75.0	75.0	1	$0.02h^{-1}$					
GE (MJ/kg ODM)	19.4		19.4	19.4	1	$0.05h^{-1}$					
						$0.08h^{-1}$					
NDF ash	627.0		627.0	627.0	1						
NDF unash						Nitrogen					
ADF ash	370.0		370.0	370.0	1	a (%)					
ADF unash						b (%)					
						c (h^{-1})					
Energy Values											
						dg (%) @ outflow rate					
DE (MJ/kg ODM)	13.3		13.3	13.3	1	$0.02h^{-1}$					
ME (MJ/kg ODM)	10.9		10.9	10.9	1	$0.05h^{-1}$					
FE/GE	0.31		0.31	0.31	1	$0.08h^{-1}$					
UE/GE	0.05		0.05	0.05	1						
CH_4E/GE	0.08		0.08	0.08	1						
ME/DE	0.82		0.82	0.82	1						
ME/GE	0.56		0.56	0.56	1						
Digestibility Coefficients											
DM	0.64		0.64	0.64	1						
OM	0.67		0.67	0.67	1						
CP	0.74		0.74	0.74	1						
CF	0.69		0.69	0.69	1						
EE	0.70		0.70	0.70	1						
NDF											
ADF											
Cell											
GE	0.69		0.69	0.69	1						
DOMD(g/kg ODM)	624.4		624.4	624.4	1						

RUMINANT DATABASE

FEED DESCRIPTION : **FRESH GRASS, ALL SPECIES** (Source 1)

Determination	Mean	SD	Min	Max	n	Determination	Mean	SD	Min	Max	n
General (g/kg ODM)						**Degradability**					
ODM (fresh)	196.6	46.8	112.7	424.0	244	Dry matter					
TDM (fresh)						a (%)	25.2	12.3	2.2	52.4	54
CP	156.1	51.4	54.0	360.6	216	b (%)	61.6	10.1	40.4	82.7	54
MADF	272.5	46.1	181.0	380.0	243	c (h^{-1})	0.08	0.03	0.03	0.14	54
EE	21.7	5.5	11.0	43.0	244						
AEE						dg (%) @ outflow rate					
TA	78.0	16.9	18.0	151.0	243	$0.02h^{-1}$	73.5	9.8	45.0	89.0	54
GE (MJ/kg ODM)	18.7	0.45	17.5	19.9	244	$0.05h^{-1}$	62.1	11.2	32.0	82.0	54
						$0.08h^{-1}$	55.2	11.7	25.0	77.0	54
NDF ash	577.3	59.2	415.0	765.0	242						
NDF unash						Nitrogen					
ADF ash	295.9	47.7	184.0	483.0	242	a (%)	20.5	12.2	0.96	46.0	51
ADF unash	305.2	39.8	200.0	410.0	162	b (%)	71.4	11.9	44.2	91.3	51
						c (h^{-1})	0.13	0.06	0.04	0.47	51
Energy Values											
						dg (%) @ outflow rate					
DE (MJ/kg ODM)	13.8	1.5	9.4	17.1	244	$0.02h^{-1}$	81.5	6.8	61.0	93.0	51
ME (MJ/kg ODM)	11.2	1.2	7.2	14.1	243	$0.05h^{-1}$	70.9	8.4	47.0	87.0	51
FE/GE	0.26	0.08	0.09	0.48	244	$0.08h^{-1}$	63.5	9.3	41.0	82.0	51
UE/GE	0.06	0.02	0.02	0.12	242						
CH_4E/GE	0.08	0.01	0.02	0.09	244						
ME/DE	0.81	0.03	0.74	0.88	243						
ME/GE	0.60	0.07	0.39	0.78	243						

Digestibility Coefficients

Determination	Mean	SD	Min	Max	n
DM	0.73	0.08	0.52	0.85	243
OM	0.77	0.07	0.57	0.88	243
CP	0.70	0.12	0.27	0.95	211
CF	0.79	0.10	0.24	0.97	244
EE	0.52	0.15	0.16	0.94	243
NDF	0.81	0.07	0.62	0.97	70
ADF	0.78	0.07	0.61	0.95	70
Cell	0.81	0.07	0.67	0.94	70
GE	0.74	0.09	0.16	0.87	244
DOMD(g/kg ODM)	709.7	54.7	539.6	828.5	243

RUMINANT DATABASE

FEED DESCRIPTION : **FRESH GRASS, ALL SPECIES, ME < 8** (Source 1)

Determination	Mean	SD	Min	Max	n	Determination	Mean	SD	Min	Max	n
General (g/kg ODM)						**Degradability**					
ODM (fresh)	204.3	55.3	156.8	265.0	3	Dry matter					
TDM (fresh)						a (%)	8.1		8.1	8.1	1
CP	96.5	2.1	95.0	98.0	2	b (%)	70.9		70.9	70.9	1
MADF	349.0	11.8	336.0	359.0	3	c (h^{-1})	0.09		0.09	0.09	1
EE	16.3	5.0	11.0	21.0	3						
AEE						dg (%) @ outflow rate					
TA	69.0	9.5	59.0	78.0	3	$0.02h^{-1}$	66.0		66.0	66.0	1
GE (MJ/kg ODM)	18.1	0.23	17.8	18.2	3	$0.05h^{-1}$	54.0		54.0	54.0	1
						$0.08h^{-1}$	46.0		46.0	46.0	1
NDF ash	658.7	13.2	647.0	673.0	3						
NDF unash						Nitrogen					
ADF ash	351.3	32.2	316.0	379.0	3	a (%)	15.8		15.8	15.8	1
ADF unash						b (%)	72.0		72.0	72.0	1
						c (h^{-1})	0.13		0.13	0.13	1
Energy Values											
						dg (%) @ outflow rate					
DE (MJ/kg ODM)	9.7	0.21	9.4	9.9	3	$0.02h^{-1}$	78.0		78.0	78.0	1
ME (MJ/kg ODM)	7.5	0.32	7.2	7.8	3	$0.05h^{-1}$	68.0		68.0	68.0	1
FE/GE	0.47	0.02	0.45	0.48	3	$0.08h^{-1}$	60.0		60.0	60.0	1
UE/GE	0.05	0.01	0.05	0.06	3						
CH_4E/GE	0.07	0.0	0.07	0.07	3						
ME/DE	0.77	0.02	0.76	0.79	3						
ME/GE	0.41	0.02	0.39	0.44	3						
Digestibility Coefficients											
DM	0.56	0.03	0.52	0.58	3						
OM	0.60	0.04	0.57	0.64	3						
CP	0.41	0.12	0.33	0.49	2						
CF	0.63	0.02	0.61	0.64	3						
EE	0.52	0.03	0.49	0.56	3						
NDF											
ADF											
Cell											
GE	0.53	0.02	0.52	0.55	3						
DOMD(g/kg ODM)	564.4	33.9	539.6	603.1	3						

RUMINANT DATABASE

FEED DESCRIPTION : **FRESH GRASS, ALL SPECIES, ME 8 - 10** (Source 1)

Determination	Mean	SD	Min	Max	n	Determination	Mean	SD	Min	Max	n
General (g/kg ODM)						**Degradability**					
ODM (fresh)	217.5	49.6	112.7	347.9	38	Dry matter					
TDM (fresh)						a (%)	19.7	7.2	7.9	33.4	9
CP	119.9	41.1	71.0	255.6	34	b (%)	58.7	5.3	46.4	63.5	9
MADF	314.5	31.8	226.0	378.0	38	c (h^{-1})	0.05	0.02	0.03	0.08	9
EE	18.7	4.9	11.0	33.0	38						
AEE						dg (%) @ outflow rate					
TA	68.9	13.3	18.0	105.0	38	$0.02h^{-1}$	60.4	9.9	45.0	74.0	9
GE (MJ/kg ODM)	18.5	0.36	17.8	19.2	38	$0.05h^{-1}$	48.1	10.4	32.0	62.0	9
						$0.08h^{-1}$	41.4	10.3	25.0	54.0	9
NDF ash	627.1	40.8	519.0	687.0	37						
NDF unash						Nitrogen					
ADF ash	329.1	32.2	240.0	381.0	37	a (%)	19.1	8.2	7.9	35.5	8
ADF unash	320.1	30.7	242.0	376.0	20	b (%)	65.7	5.3	58.6	73.5	8
						c (h^{-1})	0.10	0.03	0.04	0.12	8
Energy Values											
						dg (%) @ outflow rate					
DE (MJ/kg ODM)	11.7	0.53	10.5	13.0	38	$0.02h^{-1}$	72.9	8.7	61.0	83.0	8
ME (MJ/kg ODM)	9.5	0.34	8.7	10.0	38	$0.05h^{-1}$	61.8	9.5	47.0	73.0	8
FE/GE	0.36	0.03	0.30	0.40	38	$0.08h^{-1}$	54.4	9.0	41.0	65.0	8
UE/GE	0.05	0.02	0.03	0.09	38						
CH_4E/GE	0.08	0.01	0.07	0.08	38						
ME/DE	0.81	0.02	0.75	0.84	38						
ME/GE	0.51	0.03	0.47	0.56	38						
Digestibility Coefficients											
DM	0.65	0.04	0.58	0.77	38						
OM	0.68	0.04	0.62	0.81	38						
CP	0.62	0.09	0.32	0.80	31						
CF	0.70	0.05	0.59	0.83	38						
EE	0.49	0.16	0.16	0.78	38						
NDF	0.71	0.06	0.62	0.82	8						
ADF	0.67	0.04	0.61	0.74	8						
Cell	0.73	0.05	0.67	0.81	8						
GE	0.64	0.03	0.60	0.70	38						
DOMD(g/kg ODM)	637.0	31.2	580.0	757.1	38						

RUMINANT DATABASE

FEED DESCRIPTION : **FRESH GRASS, ALL SPECIES, ME 10 - 12** (Source 1)

Determination	Mean	SD	Min	Max	n	Determination	Mean	SD	Min	Max	n
General (g/kg ODM)						**Degradability**					
ODM (fresh)	192.4	47.1	121.7	424.0	137	Dry matter					
TDM (fresh)						a (%)	23.9	12.9	2.2	48.2	24
CP	150.1	44.8	54.0	274.4	119	b (%)	62.2	10.5	44.0	82.7	24
MADF	279.4	38.1	185.0	380.0	136	c (h^{-1})	0.08	0.03	0.04	0.14	24
EE	21.4	5.1	12.0	39.0	137						
AEE						dg (%) @ outflow rate					
TA	78.1	17.0	47.0	151.0	136	0.02h^{-1}	73.1	7.6	59.0	89.0	24
GE (MJ/kg ODM)	18.7	0.40	17.9	19.8	137	0.05h^{-1}	61.7	9.4	48.0	82.0	24
						0.08h^{-1}	54.7	10.1	43.0	77.0	24
NDF ash	582.1	53.2	420.0	765.0	136						
NDF unash						Nitrogen					
ADF ash	300.9	44.0	195.0	483.0	136	a (%)	20.5	13.2	0.96	44.4	24
ADF unash	309.4	40.5	200.0	410.0	108	b (%)	71.3	12.2	44.2	89.3	24
						c (h^{-1})	0.13	0.05	0.06	0.24	24
Energy Values											
						dg (%) @ outflow rate					
DE (MJ/kg ODM)	13.7	0.76	11.9	15.4	137	0.02h^{-1}	81.4	4.9	75.0	92.0	24
ME (MJ/kg ODM)	11.1	0.54	10.0	12.0	137	0.05h^{-1}	70.8	7.3	59.0	86.0	24
FE/GE	0.26	0.05	0.18	0.37	137	0.08h^{-1}	63.4	8.7	49.0	82.0	24
UE/GE	0.06	0.02	0.03	0.12	136						
CH$_4$E/GE	0.08	0.01	0.08	0.09	137						
ME/DE	0.81	0.03	0.74	0.88	137						
ME/GE	0.59	0.03	0.53	0.65	137						
Digestibility Coefficients											
DM	0.72	0.05	0.55	0.81	137						
OM	0.76	0.05	0.67	0.85	137						
CP	0.70	0.10	0.38	0.95	117						
CF	0.78	0.08	0.24	0.89	137						
EE	0.51	0.13	0.19	0.76	136						
NDF	0.81	0.05	0.70	0.93	46						
ADF	0.77	0.04	0.67	0.87	46						
Cell	0.80	0.05	0.69	0.89	46						
GE	0.74	0.05	0.63	0.82	137						
DOMD(g/kg ODM)	706.7	34.4	622.6	780.4	137						

RUMINANT DATABASE

FEED DESCRIPTION : **FRESH GRASS, ALL SPECIES, ME > 12** (Source 1)

Determination	Mean	SD	Min	Max	n	Determination	Mean	SD	Min	Max	n
General (g/kg ODM)						**Degradability**					
ODM (fresh)	193.4	41.9	116.6	363.0	65	Dry matter					
TDM (fresh)						a (%)	30.1	12.0	16.2	52.4	20
CP	189.8	49.9	72.0	360.6	61	b (%)	61.6	11.4	40.4	76.4	20
MADF	229.8	33.4	181.0	310.0	65	c (h^{-1})	0.09	0.02	0.05	0.13	20
EE	24.6	5.3	16.0	43.0	65						
AEE						dg (%) @ outflow rate					
TA	83.6	16.8	45.0	150.0	65	$0.02h^{-1}$	80.3	4.8	69.0	89.0	20
GE (MJ/kg ODM)	18.9	0.53	17.5	19.9	65	$0.05h^{-1}$	69.4	6.8	56.0	82.0	20
						$0.08h^{-1}$	62.5	8.0	48.0	77.0	20
NDF ash	534.5	51.0	415.0	619.0	65						
NDF unash						Nitrogen					
ADF ash	263.6	44.2	184.0	398.0	65	a (%)	21.4	13.0	4.0	46.0	18
ADF unash	282.4	34.5	208.0	353.0	33	b (%)	74.0	13.3	48.0	91.3	18
						c (h^{-1})	0.15	0.09	0.05	0.47	18
Energy Values											
						dg (%) @ outflow rate					
DE (MJ/kg ODM)	15.5	0.58	14.4	17.1	65	$0.02h^{-1}$	85.5	4.4	73.0	93.0	18
ME (MJ/kg ODM)	12.6	0.49	12.0	14.1	65	$0.05h^{-1}$	75.2	6.3	61.0	87.0	18
FE/GE	0.19	0.03	0.13	0.25	65	$0.08h^{-1}$	67.9	7.5	55.0	82.0	18
UE/GE	0.06	0.02	0.02	0.09	65						
CH_4E/GE	0.09	0.01	0.08	0.09	65						
ME/DE	0.82	0.02	0.78	0.86	65						
ME/GE	0.67	0.03	0.61	0.78	65						
Digestibility Coefficients											
DM	0.79	0.04	0.64	0.85	65						
OM	0.83	0.04	0.67	0.88	65						
CP	0.77	0.09	0.27	0.89	61						
CF	0.86	0.05	0.62	0.97	65						
EE	0.54	0.13	0.21	0.94	65						
NDF	0.89	0.05	0.80	0.97	16						
ADF	0.86	0.05	0.78	0.95	16						
Cell	0.89	0.04	0.82	0.94	16						
GE	0.81	0.03	0.75	0.87	65						
DOMD(g/kg ODM)	764.9	31.2	647.9	828.5	65						

RUMINANT DATABASE

FEED DESCRIPTION : **FRESH GRASS, HYBRID RYEGRASS, VAR AUGUSTA** (Source 1)

Determination	Mean	SD	Min	Max	n	Determination	Mean	SD	Min	Max	n
General (g/kg ODM)						**Degradability**					
ODM (fresh)	162.7	22.1	121.7	180.7	6	Dry matter					
TDM (fresh)						a (%)					
CP	180.6	57.9	126.7	274.4	6	b (%)					
MADF	270.7	31.7	224.0	308.0	6	c (h^{-1})					
EE	18.0	3.3	14.0	22.0	6						
AEE						dg (%) @ outflow rate					
TA	100.7	18.2	76.0	127.0	6	0.02h^{-1}					
GE (MJ/kg ODM)	18.5	0.38	17.9	18.9	6	0.05h^{-1}					
						0.08h^{-1}					
NDF ash	586.2	37.3	550.0	637.0	6						
NDF unash						Nitrogen					
ADF ash	316.3	26.8	280.0	349.0	6	a (%)					
ADF unash	322.5	25.9	287.0	353.0	6	b (%)					
						c (h^{-1})					
Energy Values											
						dg (%) @ outflow rate					
DE (MJ/kg ODM)	14.2	0.85	13.0	15.0	6	0.02h^{-1}					
ME (MJ/kg ODM)	11.5	0.73	10.6	12.4	6	0.05h^{-1}					
FE/GE	0.24	0.04	0.20	0.30	6	0.08h^{-1}					
UE/GE	0.06	0.01	0.04	0.08	6						
CH$_4$E/GE	0.09	0.01	0.08	0.09	6						
ME/DE	0.81	0.02	0.79	0.83	6						
ME/GE	0.62	0.04	0.57	0.67	6						
Digestibility Coefficients											
DM	0.77	0.03	0.72	0.80	6						
OM	0.79	0.03	0.73	0.82	6						
CP	0.74	0.07	0.66	0.83	6						
CF	0.84	0.05	0.75	0.87	6						
EE	0.43	0.09	0.27	0.54	6						
NDF	0.84	0.05	0.74	0.87	6						
ADF	0.81	0.05	0.73	0.87	6						
Cell	0.85	0.07	0.71	0.89	6						
GE	0.77	0.04	0.70	0.80	6						
DOMD(g/kg ODM)	718.8	27.5	677.7	757.0	6						

RUMINANT DATABASE

FEED DESCRIPTION : **FRESH GRASS, ITALIAN RYGRASS, VAR RvP** (Source 1)

Determination	Mean	SD	Min	Max	n	Determination	Mean	SD	Min	Max	n
General (g/kg ODM)						**Degradability**					
ODM (fresh)	222.9	55.1	141.0	363.0	30	Dry matter					
TDM (fresh)						a (%)	41.3	15.9	2.2	52.4	10
CP	127.8	44.4	54.0	248.0	24	b (%)	49.7	13.3	40.4	82.7	10
MADF	245.3	45.9	184.0	325.0	30	c (h^{-1})	0.10	0.03	0.05	0.13	10
EE	22.2	6.2	13.0	43.0	30						
AEE						dg (%) @ outflow rate					
TA	72.6	14.7	45.0	104.0	30	$0.02h^{-1}$	82.3	6.9	69.0	89.0	10
GE (MJ/kg ODM)	18.6	0.43	17.9	19.3	30	$0.05h^{-1}$	74.2	9.4	56.0	82.0	10
						$0.08h^{-1}$	68.7	10.9	48.0	77.0	10
NDF ash	508.4	56.5	415.0	592.0	29						
NDF unash						Nitrogen					
ADF ash	278.7	66.7	184.0	483.0	29	a (%)	36.1	12.8	4.1	46.0	9
ADF unash	276.9	38.3	200.0	326.0	16	b (%)	56.6	12.0	44.2	85.7	9
						c (h^{-1})	0.17	0.06	0.05	0.24	9
Energy Values											
						dg (%) @ outflow rate					
DE (MJ/kg ODM)	13.9	1.2	11.7	15.6	30	$0.02h^{-1}$	85.7	6.9	73.0	93.0	9
ME (MJ/kg ODM)	11.4	1.0	9.3	13.2	30	$0.05h^{-1}$	78.4	9.3	61.0	87.0	9
FE/GE	0.25	0.06	0.14	0.37	30	$0.08h^{-1}$	73.2	10.4	55.0	82.0	9
UE/GE	0.05	0.02	0.02	0.12	30						
CH_4E/GE	0.08	0.0	0.08	0.09	30						
ME/DE	0.82	0.03	0.75	0.86	30						
ME/GE	0.61	0.05	0.50	0.72	30						
Digestibility Coefficients											
DM	0.73	0.05	0.63	0.81	30						
OM	0.77	0.05	0.66	0.84	30						
CP	0.64	0.12	0.27	0.79	24						
CF	0.75	0.07	0.62	0.91	30						
EE	0.61	0.08	0.44	0.77	30						
NDF											
ADF											
Cell											
GE	0.75	0.06	0.63	0.86	30						
DOMD(g/kg ODM)	715.8	45.3	624.3	778.6	30						

RUMINANT DATABASE

FEED DESCRIPTION : **FRESH GRASS, PERENNIAL RYEGRASS, VAR AJAX** (Source 1)

Determination	Mean	SD	Min	Max	n	Determination	Mean	SD	Min	Max	n
General (g/kg ODM)						**Degradability**					
ODM (fresh)	199.8	41.2	144.0	276.0	12	Dry matter					
TDM (fresh)						a (%)					
CP	125.4	39.8	72.0	195.0	12	b (%)					
MADF	306.3	42.4	235.0	380.0	12	c (h^{-1})					
EE	22.9	3.7	17.0	29.0	12						
AEE						dg (%) @ outflow rate					
TA	72.4	11.0	56.0	91.0	12	0.02h^{-1}					
GE (MJ/kg ODM)	18.5	0.37	17.9	19.0	12	0.05h^{-1}					
						0.08h^{-1}					
NDF ash	580.3	43.9	498.0	633.0	12						
NDF unash						Nitrogen					
ADF ash	297.5	42.4	231.0	354.0	12	a (%)					
ADF unash	298.3	37.8	242.0	351.0	8	b (%)					
						c (h^{-1})					
Energy Values						dg (%) @ outflow rate					
DE (MJ/kg ODM)	13.5	1.3	11.6	15.8	12	0.02h^{-1}					
ME (MJ/kg ODM)	10.8	1.1	9.4	12.6	12	0.05h^{-1}					
FE/GE	0.27	0.07	0.17	0.38	12	0.08h^{-1}					
UE/GE	0.06	0.02	0.04	0.09	12						
CH$_4$E/GE	0.08	0.01	0.08	0.09	12						
ME/DE	0.80	0.02	0.75	0.83	12						
ME/GE	0.58	0.05	0.50	0.66	12						
Digestibility Coefficients											
DM	0.69	0.05	0.61	0.77	12						
OM	0.75	0.07	0.65	0.84	12						
CP	0.67	0.08	0.56	0.78	10						
CF	0.78	0.08	0.66	0.94	12						
EE	0.55	0.09	0.37	0.65	12						
NDF											
ADF											
Cell											
GE	0.73	0.07	0.62	0.83	12						
DOMD(g/kg ODM)	698.1	56.2	613.5	777.0	12						

RUMINANT DATABASE

FEED DESCRIPTION : **FRESH GRASS, PERENNIAL RYEGRASS, VAR MELLE** (Source 1)

Determination	Mean	SD	Min	Max	n	Determination	Mean	SD	Min	Max	n
General (g/kg ODM)						**Degradability**					
ODM (fresh)	209.8	51.9	148.0	279.0	8	Dry matter					
TDM (fresh)						a (%)					
CP	224.8	66.7	163.0	360.6	8	b (%)					
MADF	254.0	37.7	183.0	313.0	8	c (h^{-1})					
EE	21.0	2.7	18.0	25.0	8						
AEE						dg (%) @ outflow rate					
TA	92.9	9.8	81.0	110.0	8	0.02h^{-1}					
GE (MJ/kg ODM)	18.8	0.31	18.5	19.5	8	0.05h^{-1}					
						0.08h^{-1}					
NDF ash	572.8	26.6	533.0	618.0	8						
NDF unash						Nitrogen					
ADF ash	293.5	28.7	234.0	325.0	8	a (%)					
ADF unash	314.6	33.2	243.0	352.0	8	b (%)					
						c (h^{-1})					
Energy Values											
						dg (%) @ outflow rate					
DE (MJ/kg ODM)	14.0	1.6	11.6	16.5	8	0.02h^{-1}					
ME (MJ/kg ODM)	11.3	1.4	9.1	13.5	8	0.05h^{-1}					
FE/GE	0.25	0.07	0.15	0.36	8	0.08h^{-1}					
UE/GE	0.06	0.01	0.05	0.07	8						
CH$_4$E/GE	0.08	0.01	0.08	0.09	8						
ME/DE	0.81	0.02	0.78	0.82	8						
ME/GE	0.60	0.06	0.49	0.69	8						
Digestibility Coefficients											
DM	0.76	0.06	0.66	0.85	8						
OM	0.79	0.06	0.68	0.88	8						
CP	0.79	0.06	0.72	0.89	8						
CF	0.82	0.09	0.68	0.95	8						
EE	0.31	0.09	0.22	0.46	8						
NDF	0.83	0.08	0.69	0.95	8						
ADF	0.80	0.08	0.65	0.93	8						
Cell	0.83	0.07	0.71	0.93	8						
GE	0.75	0.07	0.64	0.85	8						
DOMD(g/kg ODM)	717.9	52.2	619.3	790.3	8						

FEED DESCRIPTION : **FRESH GRASS, PERENNIAL RYGRASS, VAR S23** (Source 1)

Determination	Mean	SD	Min	Max	n	Determination	Mean	SD	Min	Max	n
General (g/kg ODM)						**Degradability**					
ODM (fresh)	197.0	32.6	146.0	236.0	12	Dry matter					
TDM (fresh)						a (%)					
CP	101.8	25.8	68.0	138.0	6	b (%)					
MADF	265.1	48.0	205.0	331.0	12	c (h^{-1})					
EE	27.3	6.2	19.0	39.0	12						
AEE						dg (%) @ outflow rate					
TA	81.5	10.4	66.0	102.0	12	$0.02h^{-1}$					
GE (MJ/kg ODM)	18.4	0.28	17.9	18.9	12	$0.05h^{-1}$					
						$0.08h^{-1}$					
NDF ash	572.0	54.8	510.0	664.4	12						
NDF unash						Nitrogen					
ADF ash	289.3	48.4	226.0	373.0	12	a (%)					
ADF unash	270.8	45.8	208.0	341.0	8	b (%)					
						c (h^{-1})					
Energy Values						dg (%) @ outflow rate					
DE (MJ/kg ODM)	14.0	1.2	12.0	16.3	12	$0.02h^{-1}$					
ME (MJ/kg ODM)	11.5	1.1	9.9	13.5	12	$0.05h^{-1}$					
FE/GE	0.24	0.06	0.14	0.33	12	$0.08h^{-1}$					
UE/GE	0.05	0.02	0.03	0.09	12						
CH_4E/GE	0.08	0.01	0.08	0.09	12						
ME/DE	0.82	0.02	0.78	0.85	12						
ME/GE	0.62	0.05	0.55	0.71	12						
Digestibility Coefficients											
DM	0.75	0.06	0.65	0.85	12						
OM	0.78	0.07	0.67	0.87	12						
CP	0.67	0.04	0.62	0.70	3						
CF	0.79	0.18	0.24	0.89	12						
EE	0.57	0.07	0.48	0.66	12						
NDF											
ADF											
Cell											
GE	0.76	0.06	0.67	0.86	12						
DOMD(g/kg ODM)	721.4	55.7	622.6	798.5	12						

RUMINANT DATABASE

FEED DESCRIPTION : **FRESH GRASS, PERENNIAL RYEGRASS, VAR S24** (Source 1)

Determination	Mean	SD	Min	Max	n	Determination	Mean	SD	Min	Max	n
General (g/kg ODM)						**Degradability**					
ODM (fresh)	206.0	62.5	133.0	424.0	24	Dry matter					
TDM (fresh)						a (%)					
CP	126.5	39.5	77.0	212.0	17	b (%)					
MADF	289.5	48.8	195.0	359.0	23	c (h^{-1})					
EE	20.0	5.1	13.0	33.0	24						
AEE						dg (%) @ outflow rate					
TA	69.1	13.1	47.0	96.0	24	0.02h^{-1}					
GE (MJ/kg ODM)	18.7	0.37	17.9	19.3	24	0.05h^{-1}					
						0.08h^{-1}					
NDF ash	615.6	62.3	502.0	765.0	24						
NDF unash						Nitrogen					
ADF ash	333.2	36.0	270.0	389.0	24	a (%)					
ADF unash	322.8	39.1	273.0	384.0	12	b (%)					
						c (h^{-1})					
Energy Values											
						dg (%) @ outflow rate					
DE (MJ/kg ODM)	13.7	1.4	9.7	15.7	24	0.02h^{-1}					
ME (MJ/kg ODM)	11.1	1.2	7.4	12.5	24	0.05h^{-1}					
FE/GE	0.27	0.07	0.17	0.47	24	0.08h^{-1}					
UE/GE	0.06	0.02	0.04	0.09	23						
CH$_4$E/GE	0.08	0.01	0.07	0.09	24						
ME/DE	0.81	0.02	0.77	0.88	24						
ME/GE	0.59	0.06	0.41	0.68	24						
Digestibility Coefficients											
DM	0.71	0.07	0.52	0.79	24						
OM	0.75	0.07	0.57	0.85	24						
CP	0.64	0.13	0.38	0.79	17						
CF	0.77	0.08	0.59	0.90	24						
EE	0.60	0.08	0.43	0.78	24						
NDF											
ADF											
Cell											
GE	0.73	0.07	0.53	0.83	24						
DOMD(g/kg ODM)	705.9	63.1	539.6	793.3	24						

RUMINANT DATABASE

FEED DESCRIPTION : **FRESH GRASS, TALL FESCUE, VAR DOVEY** (Source 1)

Determination	Mean	SD	Min	Max	n	Determination	Mean	SD	Min	Max	n
General (g/kg ODM)						**Degradability**					
ODM (fresh)	187.7	33.2	155.0	241.0	6	Dry matter					
TDM (fresh)						a (%)					
CP	142.7	42.1	97.0	208.0	6	b (%)					
MADF	302.8	22.6	267.0	323.0	6	c (h^{-1})					
EE	20.2	2.5	17.0	22.0	6						
AEE						dg (%) @ outflow rate					
TA	76.7	10.4	62.0	90.0	6	$0.02h^{-1}$					
GE (MJ/kg ODM)	18.4	0.36	17.8	18.8	6	$0.05h^{-1}$					
						$0.08h^{-1}$					
NDF ash	647.0	22.5	605.0	672.0	6						
NDF unash						Nitrogen					
ADF ash	311.7	29.0	263.0	345.0	6	a (%)					
ADF unash	317.3	14.4	298.0	331.0	6	b (%)					
						c (h^{-1})					
Energy Values						dg (%) @ outflow rate					
DE (MJ/kg ODM)	12.6	1.3	10.7	13.8	6	$0.02h^{-1}$					
ME (MJ/kg ODM)	10.0	0.91	8.8	11.0	6	$0.05h^{-1}$					
FE/GE	0.32	0.06	0.26	0.40	6	$0.08h^{-1}$					
UE/GE	0.06	0.02	0.04	0.08	6						
CH_4E/GE	0.08	0.0	0.07	0.08	6						
ME/DE	0.80	0.02	0.78	0.82	6						
ME/GE	0.54	0.05	0.49	0.59	6						
Digestibility Coefficients											
DM	0.64	0.04	0.58	0.70	6						
OM	0.71	0.05	0.63	0.77	6						
CP	0.65	0.11	0.49	0.80	6						
CF	0.77	0.07	0.67	0.85	6						
EE	0.66	0.06	0.59	0.78	6						
NDF											
ADF											
Cell											
GE	0.68	0.06	0.60	0.74	6						
DOMD(g/kg ODM)	659.0	42.7	591.0	705.4	6						

FEED DESCRIPTION : **FRESH GRASS, TALL FESCUE, VAR S170** (Source 1)

Determination	Mean	SD	Min	Max	n
General (g/kg ODM)					
ODM (fresh)	207.0	40.9	153.0	267.0	12
TDM (fresh)					
CP	151.8	44.5	98.0	229.0	12
MADF	284.9	30.9	231.0	336.0	12
EE	20.3	3.6	17.0	29.0	12
AEE					
TA	81.6	8.6	70.0	95.0	12
GE (MJ/kg ODM)	18.6	0.38	18.0	19.1	12
NDF ash	613.0	27.8	543.0	656.0	12
NDF unash					
ADF ash	303.0	24.8	263.0	335.0	12
ADF unash	298.6	25.0	255.0	332.0	11
Energy Values					
DE (MJ/kg ODM)	13.1	1.6	9.4	15.0	12
ME (MJ/kg ODM)	10.3	1.3	7.2	11.7	12
FE/GE	0.30	0.08	0.21	0.48	12
UE/GE	0.07	0.02	0.04	0.10	12
CH_4E/GE	0.08	0.01	0.07	0.09	12
ME/DE	0.79	0.02	0.75	0.82	12
ME/GE	0.55	0.06	0.39	0.63	12
Digestibility Coefficients					
DM	0.67	0.05	0.57	0.73	12
OM	0.73	0.05	0.64	0.79	12
CP	0.65	0.13	0.33	0.81	12
CF	0.75	0.06	0.64	0.83	12
EE	0.60	0.08	0.49	0.76	11
NDF					
ADF					
Cell					
GE	0.70	0.08	0.52	0.79	12
DOMD(g/kg ODM)	671.8	42.0	603.1	723.3	12

Determination	Mean	SD	Min	Max	n
Degradability					
Dry matter					
a (%)					
b (%)					
c (h^{-1})					
dg (%) @ outflow rate					
$0.02h^{-1}$					
$0.05h^{-1}$					
$0.08h^{-1}$					
Nitrogen					
a (%)					
b (%)					
c (h^{-1})					
dg (%) @ outflow rate					
$0.02h^{-1}$					
$0.05h^{-1}$					
$0.08h^{-1}$					

RUMINANT DATABASE

FEED DESCRIPTION : **KALE, BITTERN** (Sources 1, 2)

Determination	Mean	SD	Min	Max	n	Determination	Mean	SD	Min	Max	n
General (g/kg ODM)						**Degradability**					
ODM (fresh)	133.2	26.1	114.7	151.6	2	Dry matter					
TDM (fresh)						a (%)					
CP	163.6	17.6	151.2	176.0	2	b (%)					
MADF	195.2	37.9	168.4	222.0	2	c (h^{-1})					
EE	21.9	3.0	19.8	24.0	2						
AEE						dg (%) @ outflow rate					
TA	114.5	16.3	103.0	126.0	2	$0.02h^{-1}$					
GE (MJ/kg ODM)	17.2	0.24	17.0	17.3	2	$0.05h^{-1}$					
						$0.08h^{-1}$					
NDF ash	257.6	51.5	221.2	294.0	2						
NDF unash						Nitrogen					
ADF ash	206.7	28.7	186.4	227.0	2	a (%)					
ADF unash						b (%)					
						c (h^{-1})					
Energy Values											
						dg (%) @ outflow rate					
DE (MJ/kg ODM)	13.8		13.8	13.8	1	$0.02h^{-1}$					
ME (MJ/kg ODM)	11.8	0.90	11.2	12.4	2	$0.05h^{-1}$					
FE/GE	0.18	0.02	0.17	0.19	2	$0.08h^{-1}$					
UE/GE	0.06	0.02	0.04	0.07	2						
CH_4E/GE	0.08	0.01	0.08	0.09	2						
ME/DE	0.81		0.81	0.81	1						
ME/GE	0.69	0.04	0.66	0.72	2						
Digestibility Coefficients											
DM	0.82		0.82	0.82	1						
OM	0.85	0.01	0.84	0.86	2						
CP	0.85	0.02	0.83	0.86	2						
CF	0.68		0.68	0.68	1						
EE	0.70		0.70	0.70	1						
NDF											
ADF											
Cell											
GE	0.82	0.01	0.81	0.83	2						
DOMD(g/kg ODM)	753.6	20.4	739.1	768.0	2						

RUMINANT DATABASE

FEED DESCRIPTION : **KALE, DWARF THOUSAND HEAD** (Source 2)

Determination	Mean	SD	Min	Max	n
General (g/kg ODM)					
ODM (fresh)	157.7		157.7	157.7	1
TDM (fresh)					
CP	158.3		158.3	158.3	1
MADF	194.3		194.3	194.3	1
EE	20.4		20.4	20.4	1
AEE					
TA	105.0		105.0	105.0	1
GE (MJ/kg ODM)	17.4		17.4	17.4	1
NDF ash	236.3		236.3	236.3	1
NDF unash					
ADF ash	200.7		200.7	200.7	1
ADF unash					
Energy Values					
DE (MJ/kg ODM)					
ME (MJ/kg ODM)	11.6		11.6	11.6	1
FE/GE	0.18		0.18	0.18	1
UE/GE	0.05		0.05	0.05	1
CH$_4$E/GE	0.10		0.10	0.10	1
ME/DE					
ME/GE	0.67		0.67	0.67	1
Digestibility Coefficients					
DM					
OM	0.85		0.85	0.85	1
CP	0.82		0.82	0.82	1
CF					
EE					
NDF					
ADF					
Cell					
GE	0.82		0.82	0.82	1
DOMD(g/kg ODM)	756.0		756.0	756.0	1

Determination	Mean	SD	Min	Max	n
Degradability					
Dry matter					
a (%)					
b (%)					
c (h^{-1})					
dg (%) @ outflow rate					
0.02h^{-1}					
0.05h^{-1}					
0.08h^{-1}					
Nitrogen					
a (%)					
b (%)					
c (h^{-1})					
dg (%) @ outflow rate					
0.02h^{-1}					
0.05h^{-1}					
0.08h^{-1}					

RUMINANT DATABASE

FEED DESCRIPTION : **KALE, MARIS KESTREL** (Sources 1, 2)

Determination	Mean	SD	Min	Max	n	Determination	Mean	SD	Min	Max	n
General (g/kg ODM)						**Degradability**					
ODM (fresh)	134.9	1.6	133.7	136.0	2	Dry matter					
TDM (fresh)						a (%)					
CP	166.4	33.4	142.7	190.0	2	b (%)					
MADF	161.7	1.8	160.4	163.0	2	c (h^{-1})					
EE	18.4	0.56	18.0	18.8	2						
AEE						dg (%) @ outflow rate					
TA	117.8	0.35	117.5	118.0	2	0.02h^{-1}					
GE (MJ/kg ODM)	17.2	0.43	16.9	17.5	2	0.05h^{-1}					
						0.08h^{-1}					
NDF ash	232.2	45.1	200.3	264.0	2						
NDF unash						Nitrogen					
ADF ash	182.2	12.4	173.4	191.0	2	a (%)					
ADF unash						b (%)					
						c (h^{-1})					
Energy Values						dg (%) @ outflow rate					
DE (MJ/kg ODM)	15.6		15.6	15.6	1	0.02h^{-1}					
ME (MJ/kg ODM)	12.7	0.13	12.6	12.8	2	0.05h^{-1}					
FE/GE	0.12	0.02	0.11	0.14	2	0.08h^{-1}					
UE/GE	0.05	0.02	0.04	0.07	2						
CH$_4$E/GE	0.08	0.01	0.08	0.09	2						
ME/DE	0.82		0.82	0.82	1						
ME/GE	0.74	0.01	0.73	0.75	2						
Digestibility Coefficients											
DM	0.87		0.87	0.87	1						
OM	0.89	0.01	0.89	0.90	2						
CP	0.86	0.04	0.83	0.88	2						
CF	0.83		0.83	0.83	1						
EE	0.64		0.64	0.64	1						
NDF											
ADF											
Cell											
GE	0.87	0.02	0.86	0.89	2						
DOMD(g/kg ODM)	789.3	8.8	783.0	795.5	2						

RUMINANT DATABASE

FEED DESCRIPTION : **KALE, MARROW STEM** (Sources 1, 2)

Determination	Mean	SD	Min	Max	n
General (g/kg ODM)					
ODM (fresh)	117.7	2.3	116.1	119.3	2
TDM (fresh)					
CP	152.2	8.2	146.4	158.0	2
MADF	229.5	24.7	212.0	247.0	2
EE	19.1	2.7	17.2	21.0	2
AEE					
TA	175.4	73.0	123.7	227.0	2
GE (MJ/kg ODM)	16.7	0.09	16.7	16.8	2
NDF ash	350.3	117.0	267.5	433.0	2
NDF unash					
ADF ash	243.0	21.2	228.0	258.0	2
ADF unash					
Energy Values					
DE (MJ/kg ODM)	13.2		13.2	13.2	1
ME (MJ/kg ODM)	11.0	0.36	10.7	11.2	2
FE/GE	0.21	0.01	0.21	0.22	2
UE/GE	0.05	0.02	0.04	0.06	2
CH_4E/GE	0.09	0.01	0.08	0.09	2
ME/DE	0.81		0.81	0.81	1
ME/GE	0.65	0.03	0.64	0.67	2
Digestibility Coefficients					
DM	0.80		0.80	0.80	1
OM	0.81	0.01	0.80	0.82	2
CP	0.84	0.02	0.82	0.85	2
CF	0.65		0.65	0.65	1
EE	0.66		0.66	0.66	1
NDF					
ADF					
Cell					
GE	0.79	0.01	0.78	0.79	2
DOMD(g/kg ODM)	669.6	69.8	620.2	719.0	2

Determination	Mean	SD	Min	Max	n
Degradability					
Dry matter					
a (%)					
b (%)					
c (h^{-1})					
dg (%) @ outflow rate					
$0.02h^{-1}$					
$0.05h^{-1}$					
$0.08h^{-1}$					
Nitrogen					
a (%)					
b (%)					
c (h^{-1})					
dg (%) @ outflow rate					
$0.02h^{-1}$					
$0.05h^{-1}$					
$0.08h^{-1}$					

RUMINANT DATABASE

FEED DESCRIPTION : **KALE, MERLIN** (Source 2)

Determination	Mean	SD	Min	Max	n	Determination	Mean	SD	Min	Max	n
General (g/kg ODM)						**Degradability**					
ODM (fresh)	120.8		120.8	120.8	1	Dry matter					
TDM (fresh)						a (%)					
CP	147.0		147.0	147.0	1	b (%)					
MADF	184.3		184.3	184.3	1	c (h^{-1})					
EE	18.3		18.3	18.3	1						
AEE						dg (%) @ outflow rate					
TA	123.6		123.6	123.6	1	$0.02h^{-1}$					
GE (MJ/kg ODM)	16.7		16.7	16.7	1	$0.05h^{-1}$					
						$0.08h^{-1}$					
NDF ash	228.8		228.8	228.8	1						
NDF unash						Nitrogen					
ADF ash	198.5		198.5	198.5	1	a (%)					
ADF unash						b (%)					
						c (h^{-1})					
Energy Values											
						dg (%) @ outflow rate					
DE (MJ/kg ODM)						$0.02h^{-1}$					
ME (MJ/kg ODM)	11.9		11.9	11.9	1	$0.05h^{-1}$					
FE/GE	0.15		0.15	0.15	1	$0.08h^{-1}$					
UE/GE	0.04		0.04	0.04	1						
CH_4E/GE	0.10		0.10	0.10	1						
ME/DE											
ME/GE	0.71		0.71	0.71	1						

Digestibility Coefficients

Determination	Mean	SD	Min	Max	n
DM					
OM	0.88		0.88	0.88	1
CP	0.84		0.84	0.84	1
CF					
EE					
NDF					
ADF					
Cell					
GE	0.85		0.85	0.85	1
DOMD(g/kg ODM)	770.0		770.0	770.0	1

RUMINANT DATABASE

FEED DESCRIPTION : **KALE, THOUSAND HEAD** (Sources 1, 2)

Determination	Mean	SD	Min	Max	n	Determination	Mean	SD	Min	Max	n
General (g/kg ODM)						**Degradability**					
ODM (fresh)	143.2	8.6	137.1	149.2	2	Dry matter					
TDM (fresh)						a (%)					
CP	187.5	72.8	136.0	239.0	2	b (%)					
MADF	174.3	23.6	157.7	191.0	2	c (h^{-1})					
EE	20.2	2.5	18.5	22.0	2						
AEE						dg (%) @ outflow rate					
TA	117.0	12.7	108.0	126.0	2	0.02h^{-1}					
GE (MJ/kg ODM)	17.3	0.38	17.1	17.6	2	0.05h^{-1}					
						0.08h^{-1}					
NDF ash	259.3	87.2	197.7	321.0	2						
NDF unash						Nitrogen					
ADF ash	198.0	41.0	169.0	227.0	2	a (%)					
ADF unash						b (%)					
						c (h^{-1})					
Energy Values											
						dg (%) @ outflow rate					
DE (MJ/kg ODM)	14.3		14.3	14.3	1	0.02h^{-1}					
ME (MJ/kg ODM)	11.9	0.95	11.2	12.6	2	0.05h^{-1}					
FE/GE	0.16	0.02	0.15	0.18	2	0.08h^{-1}					
UE/GE	0.06	0.04	0.04	0.09	2						
CH$_4$E/GE	0.09	0.01	0.08	0.09	2						
ME/DE	0.78		0.78	0.78	1						
ME/GE	0.69	0.07	0.64	0.74	2						
Digestibility Coefficients											
DM	0.82		0.82	0.82	1						
OM	0.87	0.02	0.85	0.88	2						
CP	0.85	0.0	0.85	0.85	2						
CF	0.68		0.68	0.68	1						
EE	0.77		0.77	0.77	1						
NDF											
ADF											
Cell											
GE	0.84	0.03	0.81	0.86	2						
DOMD(g/kg ODM)	765.0	31.2	742.9	787.0	2						

RUMINANT DATABASE

FEED DESCRIPTION : **WHITE CLOVER, VAR BLANCA** (Source 1)

Determination	Mean	SD	Min	Max	n	Determination	Mean	SD	Min	Max	n
General (g/kg ODM)						**Degradability**					
ODM (fresh)	117.5	7.8	112.0	123.0	2	Dry matter					
TDM (fresh)						a (%)					
CP	297.5	5.0	294.0	301.0	2	b (%)					
MADF	228.5	24.7	211.0	246.0	2	c (h^{-1})					
EE	25.5	5.0	22.0	29.0	2						
AEE						dg (%) @ outflow rate					
TA	92.5	13.4	83.0	102.0	2	$0.02h^{-1}$					
GE (MJ/kg ODM)	19.6	0.28	19.4	19.8	2	$0.05h^{-1}$					
						$0.08h^{-1}$					
NDF ash	399.5	30.4	378.0	421.0	2						
NDF unash						Nitrogen					
ADF ash	252.5	20.5	238.0	267.0	2	a (%)					
ADF unash	255.5	21.9	240.0	271.0	2	b (%)					
						c (h^{-1})					
Energy Values											
						dg (%) @ outflow rate					
DE (MJ/kg ODM)	15.0	0.26	14.8	15.2	2	$0.02h^{-1}$					
ME (MJ/kg ODM)	11.6	0.25	11.4	11.7	2	$0.05h^{-1}$					
FE/GE	0.24	0.01	0.23	0.24	2	$0.08h^{-1}$					
UE/GE	0.09	0.0	0.09	0.09	2						
CH_4E/GE	0.08	0.0	0.08	0.08	2						
ME/DE	0.77	0.0	0.77	0.78	2						
ME/GE	0.59	0.0	0.59	0.59	2						
Digestibility Coefficients											
DM	0.69	0.03	0.67	0.71	2						
OM	0.77	0.01	0.76	0.77	2						
CP											
CF	0.68	0.04	0.66	0.71	2						
EE	0.63	0.25	0.46	0.81	2						
NDF											
ADF											
Cell											
GE	0.76	0.0	0.76	0.77	2						
DOMD(g/kg ODM)	699.3	21.8	683.9	714.7	2						

RUMINANT DATABASE

FEED CLASS 30

SILAGES

RUMINANT DATABASE

FEED DESCRIPTION : **BARLEY WHOLE CROP SILAGE** (Source 1)

Determination	Mean	SD	Min	Max	n	Determination	Mean	SD	Min	Max	n

General (g/kg ODM)

Degradability

ODM (fresh)	394.0	137.0	199.0	520.0	4	Dry matter
TDM (fresh)	414.8	128.5	230.0	528.0	4	a (%)
CP	90.3	12.0	80.0	106.0	4	b (%)
MADF	252.0	40.6	211.0	308.0	4	c (h^{-1})
EE	19.8	8.5	13.0	32.0	4	
AEE						dg (%) @ outflow rate
TA	77.8	37.1	41.0	126.0	4	0.02h^{-1}
GE (MJ/kg TDM)	17.9	0.95	17.0	19.2	4	0.05h^{-1}
						0.08h^{-1}
NDF ash	575.0	82.9	485.0	669.0	4	
NDF unash						Nitrogen
ADF ash	274.3	40.7	216.0	308.0	4	a (%)
ADF unash						b (%)
						c (h^{-1})

Energy Values

						dg (%) @ outflow rate
DE (MJ/kg TDM)	11.0	1.9	8.2	12.6	4	0.02h^{-1}
ME (MJ/kg TDM)	9.1	2.1	6.0	10.9	4	0.05h^{-1}
FE/GE	0.39	0.12	0.26	0.54	4	0.08h^{-1}
UE/GE	0.03	0.02	0.02	0.06	4	
CH$_4$E/GE	0.08	0.01	0.07	0.08	4	
ME/DE	0.82	0.06	0.73	0.86	4	
ME/GE	0.48	0.14	0.29	0.61	4	

Digestibility Coefficients

DM	0.61	0.14	0.43	0.76	4
OM	0.63	0.14	0.45	0.77	4
CP	0.40	0.12	0.30	0.56	4
CF	0.52	0.25	0.24	0.84	4
EE	0.58	0.14	0.39	0.72	4
NDF					
ADF					
Cell					
GE	0.61	0.12	0.46	0.74	4
DOMD(g/kg TDM)	607.7	77.6	508.8	690.8	4

RUMINANT DATABASE

FEED DESCRIPTION : **BEAN WHOLE CROP SILAGE** (Source 1)

Determination	Mean	SD	Min	Max	n	Determination	Mean	SD	Min	Max	n
General (g/kg ODM)						**Degradability**					
ODM (fresh)	228.5	17.7	216.0	241.0	2	Dry matter					
TDM (fresh)	237.0	19.8	223.0	251.0	2	a (%)					
CP	172.5	6.4	168.0	177.0	2	b (%)					
MADF	470.5	16.3	459.0	482.0	2	c (h^{-1})					
EE	12.5	0.71	12.0	13.0	2						
AEE						dg (%) @ outflow rate					
TA	123.0	4.2	120.0	126.0	2	0.02h^{-1}					
GE (MJ/kg TDM)	17.0	0.72	16.5	17.5	2	0.05h^{-1}					
						0.08h^{-1}					
NDF ash	565.5	31.8	543.0	588.0	2						
NDF unash						Nitrogen					
ADF ash	500.0	32.5	477.0	523.0	2	a (%)					
ADF unash						b (%)					
						c (h^{-1})					
Energy Values											
						dg (%) @ outflow rate					
DE (MJ/kg TDM)	9.4	0.13	9.3	9.5	2	0.02h^{-1}					
ME (MJ/kg TDM)	7.3	0.26	7.1	7.5	2	0.05h^{-1}					
FE/GE	0.45	0.03	0.43	0.47	2	0.08h^{-1}					
UE/GE	0.05	0.0	0.05	0.05	2						
CH$_4$E/GE	0.07	0.0	0.07	0.07	2						
ME/DE	0.78	0.02	0.77	0.79	2						
ME/GE	0.41	0.03	0.39	0.43	2						
Digestibility Coefficients											
DM	0.52	0.05	0.48	0.55	2						
OM	0.57	0.04	0.54	0.59	2						
CP	0.67	0.01	0.66	0.67	2						
CF	0.54	0.0	0.54	0.54	2						
EE	0.79	0.01	0.79	0.80	2						
NDF											
ADF											
Cell											
GE	0.55	0.03	0.53	0.57	2						
DOMD(g/kg TDM)	513.3	29.5	492.5	534.1	2						

RUMINANT DATABASE

FEED DESCRIPTION : **GRASS SILAGE** (Sources 1, 2)

Determination	Mean	SD	Min	Max	n	Determination	Mean	SD	Min	Max	n
General (g/kg ODM)						**Degradability**					
ODM (fresh)	255.0	80.3	159.0	622.0	231	Dry matter					
TDM (fresh)	280.2	80.3	175.0	629.0	218	a (%)	35.3	10.3	15.0	51.7	33
CP	168.4	39.0	82.0	303.0	231	b (%)	49.3	10.5	25.1	79.4	33
MADF	348.7	42.0	230.0	460.6	230	c (h^{-1})	0.06	0.02	0.02	0.12	33
EE	42.6	11.4	15.0	90.0	226						
AEE	43.3	12.1	28.0	68.0	14	dg (%) @ outflow rate					
TA	92.7	17.4	54.0	183.0	231	0.02h^{-1}	70.8	8.0	54.0	84.0	33
GE (MJ/kg TDM)	19.0	0.97	14.7	21.7	218	0.05h^{-1}	60.8	9.3	39.0	77.0	33
						0.08h^{-1}	55.2	9.7	33.0	72.0	33
NDF ash	582.1	69.4	399.0	855.0	217						
NDF unash						Nitrogen					
ADF ash	362.6	46.8	226.0	513.0	204	a (%)	61.9	9.1	45.3	75.8	16
ADF unash	371.7	45.5	278.0	525.0	94	b (%)	26.8	11.2	10.1	53.4	16
						c (h^{-1})	0.13	0.09	0.03	0.40	16
Energy Values											
						dg (%) @ outflow rate					
DE (MJ/kg TDM)	13.5	1.4	8.7	17.1	218	0.02h^{-1}	82.9	6.6	72.0	93.0	16
ME (MJ/kg TDM)	10.9	1.2	7.0	14.0	218	0.05h^{-1}	78.4	7.8	63.0	90.0	16
FE/GE	0.29	0.07	0.19	0.48	231	0.08h^{-1}	75.5	8.4	58.0	87.0	16
UE/GE	0.05	0.02	0.01	0.10	231						
CH$_4$E/GE	0.08	0.01	0.06	0.10	231						
ME/DE	0.81	0.03	0.74	0.87	218						
ME/GE	0.52	0.06	0.38	0.68	218						

Digestibility Coefficients

Determination	Mean	SD	Min	Max	n
DM	0.67	0.08	0.48	0.81	184
OM	0.71	0.07	0.52	0.83	231
CP	0.67	0.10	0.34	0.82	184
CF	0.77	0.09	0.50	0.90	184
EE	0.70	0.09	0.36	0.86	176
NDF	0.76	0.07	0.61	0.90	49
ADF	0.76	0.07	0.60	0.90	42
Cell	0.80	0.05	0.67	0.91	42
GE	0.71	0.07	0.52	0.81	231
DOMD(g/kg TDM)	677.9	56.4	491.2	782.1	218

RUMINANT DATABASE

FEED DESCRIPTION : **GRASS SILAGE, BIG BALE** (Source 1)

Determination	Mean	SD	Min	Max	n	Determination	Mean	SD	Min	Max	n
General (g/kg ODM)						**Degradability**					
ODM (fresh)	349.6	113.1	172.7	622.0	32	Dry matter					
TDM (fresh)	368.4	110.4	195.0	629.0	31	a (%)	32.1	11.7	18.6	50.1	9
CP	158.7	48.7	82.0	249.0	32	b (%)	50.8	15.1	25.1	79.4	9
MADF	344.9	35.4	271.0	424.0	32	c (h^{-1})	0.04	0.01	0.02	0.06	9
EE	31.0	9.2	15.0	47.0	32						
AEE	39.8	13.9	28.0	55.0	4	dg (%) @ outflow rate					
TA	91.2	16.5	58.0	130.0	32	$0.02h^{-1}$	64.1	9.1	54.0	79.0	9
GE (MJ/kg TDM)	18.9	1.1	15.9	21.0	31	$0.05h^{-1}$	53.1	10.1	39.0	70.0	9
						$0.08h^{-1}$	47.8	10.6	33.0	65.0	9
NDF ash	605.3	57.0	485.0	723.0	32						
NDF unash						Nitrogen					
ADF ash	357.9	38.3	290.0	450.0	31	a (%)	57.9	10.3	45.3	70.6	4
ADF unash	376.3	40.4	294.0	453.0	31	b (%)	28.3	16.8	17.6	53.4	4
						c (h^{-1})	0.09	0.04	0.03	0.12	4
Energy Values											
						dg (%) @ outflow rate					
DE (MJ/kg TDM)	12.7	1.6	8.7	17.1	31	$0.02h^{-1}$	77.8	7.6	72.0	89.0	4
ME (MJ/kg TDM)	10.3	1.4	7.0	14.0	31	$0.05h^{-1}$	72.5	9.7	63.0	86.0	4
FE/GE	0.33	0.07	0.19	0.48	32	$0.08h^{-1}$	69.3	10.3	58.0	83.0	4
UE/GE	0.05	0.01	0.03	0.08	32						
CH_4E/GE	0.08	0.01	0.07	0.09	32						
ME/DE	0.81	0.02	0.76	0.84	31						
ME/GE	0.51	0.05	0.38	0.61	31						
Digestibility Coefficients											
DM	0.65	0.06	0.51	0.81	32						
OM	0.68	0.06	0.52	0.82	32						
CP	0.65	0.10	0.39	0.80	32						
CF	0.72	0.08	0.50	0.89	32						
EE	0.63	0.10	0.36	0.82	32						
NDF	0.76	0.09	0.66	0.90	10						
ADF	0.74	0.07	0.64	0.83	9						
Cell	0.77	0.06	0.69	0.86	9						
GE	0.67	0.07	0.52	0.81	32						
DOMD(g/kg TDM)	641.4	58.6	514.6	774.3	31						

FEED CLASS 30

FEED DESCRIPTION : **GRASS SILAGE, BIG BALE, ME 8 - 10 (ODM BASIS)** (Source 1)

Determination	Mean	SD	Min	Max	n	Determination	Mean	SD	Min	Max	n

General (g/kg ODM)

						Degradability					
ODM (fresh)	390.2	130.0	206.3	580.0	8	**Dry matter**					
TDM (fresh)	406.0	123.3	227.0	585.0	8	a (%)	22.1	5.7	18.6	28.7	3
CP	150.5	48.4	93.0	223.3	8	b (%)	62.0	15.7	48.8	79.4	3
MADF	355.1	24.8	313.0	392.0	8	c (h^{-1})	0.04	0.02	0.02	0.05	3
EE	27.6	8.5	15.0	39.0	8						
AEE						dg (%) @ outflow rate					
TA	90.2	16.0	71.0	113.6	8	$0.02h^{-1}$	59.3	8.4	54.0	69.0	3
GE (MJ/kg TDM)	18.1	1.1	15.9	19.3	8	$0.05h^{-1}$	46.7	9.3	39.0	57.0	3
						$0.08h^{-1}$	40.3	8.7	33.0	50.0	3
NDF ash	625.5	42.4	559.0	667.0	8						
NDF unash						**Nitrogen**					
ADF ash	362.5	32.1	300.0	406.0	8	a (%)	45.3		45.3	45.3	1
ADF unash	378.1	40.8	306.0	440.0	8	b (%)	53.4		53.4	53.4	1
						c (h^{-1})	0.03		0.03	0.03	1

Energy Values

						dg (%) @ outflow rate					
DE (MJ/kg TDM)	11.1	0.68	9.9	11.7	8	$0.02h^{-1}$	75.0		75.0	75.0	1
ME (MJ/kg TDM)	8.8	0.57	8.1	9.6	8	$0.05h^{-1}$	63.0		63.0	63.0	1
FE/GE	0.39	0.04	0.34	0.44	8	$0.08h^{-1}$	58.0		58.0	58.0	1
UE/GE	0.05	0.02	0.03	0.08	8						
CH₄E/GE	0.08	0.01	0.07	0.08	8						
ME/DE	0.80	0.03	0.76	0.83	8						
ME/GE	0.47	0.03	0.43	0.52	8						

Digestibility Coefficients

DM	0.61	0.04	0.55	0.66	8
OM	0.64	0.03	0.59	0.68	8
CP	0.60	0.11	0.39	0.71	8
CF	0.71	0.04	0.63	0.76	8
EE	0.60	0.10	0.45	0.77	8
NDF	0.69		0.69	0.69	1
ADF	0.64		0.64	0.64	1
Cell	0.69		0.69	0.69	1
GE	0.61	0.04	0.56	0.66	8
DOMD(g/kg TDM)	607.5	37.4	544.1	657.8	8

FEED DESCRIPTION : **GRASS SILAGE, BIG BALE , ME 10 - 12 (ODM BASIS)** (Source 1)

Determination	Mean	SD	Min	Max	n	Determination	Mean	SD	Min	Max	n
General (g/kg ODM)						**Degradability**					
ODM (fresh)	360.0	99.5	189.0	622.0	18	Dry matter					
TDM (fresh)	378.1	98.0	212.0	629.0	17	a (%)	35.1	10.7	26.5	50.1	5
CP	159.9	49.8	82.0	249.0	18	b (%)	45.8	13.6	25.1	62.7	5
MADF	344.6	33.6	271.0	398.0	18	c (h^{-1})	0.03	0.01	0.03	0.04	5
EE	31.6	9.4	16.0	47.0	18						
AEE	28.0	0.0	28.0	28.0	2	dg (%) @ outflow rate					
TA	89.4	17.6	58.0	130.0	18	$0.02h^{-1}$	64.0	7.5	56.0	76.0	5
GE (MJ/kg TDM)	19.2	0.70	17.7	20.9	17	$0.05h^{-1}$	53.6	7.5	46.0	66.0	5
						$0.08h^{-1}$	48.8	8.2	41.0	62.0	5
NDF ash	609.2	48.5	511.0	685.0	18						
NDF unash						Nitrogen					
ADF ash	356.1	41.4	290.0	450.0	17	a (%)	57.9	0.12	57.8	57.9	2
ADF unash	373.8	43.0	294.0	445.0	17	b (%)	19.0	2.1	17.6	20.5	2
						c (h^{-1})	0.10	0.01	0.09	0.11	2
Energy Values											
						dg (%) @ outflow rate					
DE (MJ/kg TDM)	13.0	0.62	12.1	14.0	17	$0.02h^{-1}$	73.5	2.1	72.0	75.0	2
ME (MJ/kg TDM)	10.6	0.59	9.4	11.5	17	$0.05h^{-1}$	70.5	2.1	69.0	72.0	2
FE/GE	0.32	0.03	0.25	0.36	18	$0.08h^{-1}$	68.0	1.4	67.0	69.0	2
UE/GE	0.05	0.01	0.03	0.07	18						
CH_4E/GE	0.08	0.0	0.08	0.08	18						
ME/DE	0.81	0.02	0.78	0.83	17						
ME/GE	0.52	0.03	0.46	0.58	17						

Digestibility Coefficients

	Mean	SD	Min	Max	n
DM	0.65	0.04	0.58	0.74	18
OM	0.68	0.04	0.60	0.77	18
CP	0.65	0.09	0.48	0.80	18
CF	0.73	0.06	0.62	0.85	18
EE	0.63	0.10	0.36	0.76	18
NDF	0.74	0.09	0.66	0.90	5
ADF	0.71	0.03	0.66	0.74	4
Cell	0.74	0.02	0.72	0.76	4
GE	0.68	0.03	0.64	0.75	18
DOMD(g/kg TDM)	639.1	36.9	557.0	709.6	17

RUMINANT DATABASE

FEED DESCRIPTION : **GRASS SILAGE, BIG BALE, ME 12 - 14 (ODM BASIS)** (Source 1)

Determination	Mean	SD	Min	Max	n	Determination	Mean	SD	Min	Max	n

General (g/kg ODM)

	Mean	SD	Min	Max	n
ODM (fresh)	230.4	64.7	172.7	339.0	5
TDM (fresh)	254.8	67.6	195.0	367.0	5
CP	180.2	45.6	106.0	228.2	5
MADF	314.2	30.2	283.0	354.0	5
EE	36.6	7.4	24.0	42.0	5
AEE	51.5	5.0	48.0	55.0	2
TA	97.4	16.0	78.0	110.0	5
GE (MJ/kg TDM)	19.4	1.2	17.7	21.0	5
NDF ash	535.2	39.2	485.0	575.0	5
NDF unash					
ADF ash	341.2	20.2	312.0	357.0	5
ADF unash	366.4	17.9	347.0	395.0	5

Energy Values

	Mean	SD	Min	Max	n
DE (MJ/kg TDM)	15.1	1.2	14.3	17.1	5
ME (MJ/kg TDM)	12.2	1.1	11.3	14.0	5
FE/GE	0.23	0.04	0.19	0.28	5
UE/GE	0.06	0.01	0.04	0.07	5
CH4E/GE	0.09	0.01	0.08	0.09	5
ME/DE	0.81	0.02	0.79	0.84	5
ME/GE	0.57	0.04	0.51	0.61	5

Digestibility Coefficients

	Mean	SD	Min	Max	n
DM	0.75	0.05	0.69	0.81	5
OM	0.77	0.05	0.71	0.82	5
CP	0.76	0.02	0.73	0.78	5
CF	0.74	0.17	0.50	0.89	5
EE	0.70	0.10	0.55	0.82	5
NDF	0.80	0.08	0.71	0.88	4
ADF	0.79	0.06	0.72	0.83	4
Cell	0.82	0.04	0.78	0.86	4
GE	0.78	0.04	0.72	0.81	5
DOMD(g/kg TDM)	729.1	44.0	675.3	774.3	5

Degradability

Dry matter

	Mean	SD	Min	Max	n
a (%)	47.3		47.3	47.3	1
b (%)	42.1		42.1	42.1	1
c (h^{-1})	0.06		0.06	0.06	1

dg (%) @ outflow rate

	Mean	SD	Min	Max	n
$0.02h^{-1}$	79.0		79.0	79.0	1
$0.05h^{-1}$	70.0		70.0	70.0	1
$0.08h^{-1}$	65.0		65.0	65.0	1

Nitrogen

	Mean	SD	Min	Max	n
a (%)	70.6		70.6	70.6	1
b (%)	21.6		21.6	21.6	1
c (h^{-1})	0.12		0.12	0.12	1

dg (%) @ outflow rate

	Mean	SD	Min	Max	n
$0.02h^{-1}$	89.0		89.0	89.0	1
$0.05h^{-1}$	86.0		86.0	86.0	1
$0.08h^{-1}$	83.0		83.0	83.0	1

RUMINANT DATABASE

FEED DESCRIPTION : **GRASS SILAGE, CLAMP** (Sources 1, 2)

Determination	Mean	SD	Min	Max	n	Determination	Mean	SD	Min	Max	n
General (g/kg ODM)						**Degradability**					
ODM (fresh)	241.6	63.1	159.0	515.0	185	Dry matter					
TDM (fresh)	266.6	64.3	175.0	522.0	180	a (%)	36.3	10.0	15.0	51.7	22
CP	170.1	37.5	87.0	303.0	185	b (%)	48.8	8.9	38.4	69.6	22
MADF	349.3	42.5	230.0	460.6	185	c (h^{-1})	0.07	0.02	0.05	0.12	22
EE	44.5	10.7	22.0	90.0	185						
AEE	38.7	9.3	31.0	49.0	3	dg (%) @ outflow rate					
TA	92.7	17.7	54.0	183.0	185	$0.02h^{-1}$	73.4	6.2	63.0	84.0	22
GE (MJ/kg TDM)	19.0	0.97	14.7	21.7	180	$0.05h^{-1}$	63.8	7.4	49.0	77.0	22
						$0.08h^{-1}$	58.0	8.1	42.0	72.0	22
NDF ash	578.4	70.1	399.0	855.0	174						
NDF unash						Nitrogen					
ADF ash	362.7	46.5	226.0	474.5	165	a (%)	62.9	9.0	48.2	75.8	11
ADF unash	364.1	41.2	278.0	445.0	58	b (%)	26.1	10.1	10.1	43.7	11
						c (h^{-1})	0.14	0.11	0.05	0.40	11
Energy Values											
						dg (%) @ outflow rate					
DE (MJ/kg TDM)	13.6	1.4	8.8	16.7	180	$0.02h^{-1}$	84.1	5.4	76.0	93.0	11
ME (MJ/kg TDM)	11.0	1.2	7.0	13.7	180	$0.05h^{-1}$	79.7	6.2	70.0	90.0	11
FE/GE	0.29	0.06	0.19	0.48	185	$0.08h^{-1}$	77.0	6.9	66.0	87.0	11
UE/GE	0.06	0.02	0.01	0.10	185						
CH_4E/GE	0.08	0.01	0.06	0.10	185						
ME/DE	0.81	0.03	0.74	0.87	180						
ME/GE	0.52	0.06	0.38	0.68	180						
Digestibility Coefficients											
DM	0.67	0.07	0.48	0.79	138						
OM	0.71	0.06	0.52	0.83	185						
CP	0.67	0.10	0.34	0.82	138						
CF	0.77	0.07	0.54	0.89	138						
EE	0.71	0.07	0.48	0.86	136						
NDF	0.76	0.06	0.61	0.85	31						
ADF	0.77	0.06	0.60	0.85	28						
Cell	0.81	0.04	0.67	0.86	28						
GE	0.71	0.06	0.52	0.81	185						
DOMD(g/kg TDM)	684.1	53.2	491.2	782.1	180						

RUMINANT DATABASE

FEED DESCRIPTION : **GRASS SILAGE, CLAMP, ME 8 - 10 (ODM BASIS)** (Source 1)

Determination	Mean	SD	Min	Max	n	Determination	Mean	SD	Min	Max	n
General (g/kg ODM)						**Degradability**					
ODM (fresh)	326.9	106.6	168.0	515.0	12	Dry matter					
TDM (fresh)	350.8	100.6	211.0	522.0	12	a (%)					
CP	159.5	55.3	106.0	291.0	12	b (%)					
MADF	387.6	18.6	358.0	414.0	12	c (h^{-1})					
EE	30.7	4.6	23.0	40.0	12						
AEE						dg (%) @ outflow rate					
TA	98.4	22.8	71.0	140.0	12	0.02h^{-1}					
GE (MJ/kg TDM)	18.0	1.3	14.7	20.2	12	0.05h^{-1}					
						0.08h^{-1}					
NDF ash	602.6	78.7	399.0	692.0	10						
NDF unash						Nitrogen					
ADF ash	386.6	20.4	361.0	413.0	9	a (%)					
ADF unash	431.3	9.6	422.0	441.0	4	b (%)					
						c (h^{-1})					
Energy Values											
						dg (%) @ outflow rate					
DE (MJ/kg TDM)	10.4	0.80	8.8	11.3	12	0.02h^{-1}					
ME (MJ/kg TDM)	8.4	0.60	7.0	9.0	12	0.05h^{-1}					
FE/GE	0.42	0.03	0.39	0.48	12	0.08h^{-1}					
UE/GE	0.04	0.01	0.01	0.06	12						
CH$_4$E/GE	0.07	0.0	0.07	0.07	12						
ME/DE	0.81	0.02	0.77	0.85	12						
ME/GE	0.43	0.03	0.38	0.47	12						
Digestibility Coefficients											
DM	0.55	0.04	0.48	0.62	12						
OM	0.59	0.04	0.52	0.64	12						
CP	0.54	0.15	0.34	0.81	12						
CF	0.66	0.07	0.54	0.75	12						
EE	0.65	0.07	0.53	0.76	11						
NDF											
ADF											
Cell											
GE	0.58	0.03	0.52	0.61	12						
DOMD(g/kg TDM)	571.8	57.5	491.2	675.0	12						

RUMINANT DATABASE

FEED DESCRIPTION : **GRASS SILAGE, CLAMP, ME 10 - 12 (ODM BASIS)** (Sources 1, 2)

Determination	Mean	SD	Min	Max	n	Determination	Mean	SD	Min	Max	n
General (g/kg ODM)						**Degradability**					
ODM (fresh)	249.3	61.2	163.0	448.0	66	Dry matter					
TDM (fresh)	274.3	64.7	175.0	460.3	63	a (%)	35.7	8.2	15.0	41.2	9
CP	165.1	38.5	87.0	298.7	66	b (%)	46.5	7.7	39.8	64.9	9
MADF	350.9	42.3	250.0	460.6	66	c (h^{-1})	0.06	0.01	0.05	0.08	9
EE	42.2	8.5	22.0	63.0	66						
AEE	49.0		49.0	49.0	1	dg (%) @ outflow rate					
TA	94.3	21.4	54.0	183.0	66	$0.02h^{-1}$	70.9	5.2	63.0	78.0	9
GE (MJ/kg TDM)	18.8	0.95	16.0	21.6	63	$0.05h^{-1}$	61.6	6.3	49.0	69.0	9
						$0.08h^{-1}$	56.1	6.6	42.0	64.0	9
NDF ash	595.8	77.3	443.0	855.0	59						
NDF unash						Nitrogen					
ADF ash	364.7	50.7	270.0	474.5	56	a (%)	62.4	7.8	48.2	69.7	6
ADF unash	362.8	34.1	310.0	428.0	21	b (%)	24.8	12.1	10.1	43.7	6
						c (h^{-1})	0.18	0.14	0.05	0.40	6
Energy Values											
						dg (%) @ outflow rate					
DE (MJ/kg TDM)	12.8	0.79	11.1	15.7	63	$0.02h^{-1}$	83.0	5.0	76.0	89.0	6
ME (MJ/kg TDM)	10.3	0.63	8.8	12.5	63	$0.05h^{-1}$	79.0	5.0	74.0	86.0	6
FE/GE	0.32	0.04	0.25	0.38	66	$0.08h^{-1}$	76.5	5.7	70.0	84.0	6
UE/GE	0.06	0.02	0.03	0.10	66						
CH_4E/GE	0.08	0.0	0.07	0.10	66						
ME/DE	0.80	0.03	0.74	0.86	63						
ME/GE	0.50	0.04	0.43	0.68	63						
Digestibility Coefficients											
DM	0.65	0.04	0.54	0.73	55						
OM	0.69	0.05	0.58	0.79	66						
CP	0.65	0.07	0.45	0.77	55						
CF	0.75	0.06	0.65	0.87	55						
EE	0.70	0.07	0.48	0.86	55						
NDF	0.69	0.05	0.61	0.74	6						
ADF	0.69	0.06	0.60	0.76	5						
Cell	0.76	0.06	0.67	0.82	5						
GE	0.68	0.04	0.62	0.75	66						
DOMD(g/kg TDM)	659.5	34.2	581.8	729.0	63						

RUMINANT DATABASE

FEED DESCRIPTION : **GRASS SILAGE, CLAMP, ME 12 - 14 (ODM BASIS)** (Sources 1, 2)

Determination	Mean	SD	Min	Max	n	Determination	Mean	SD	Min	Max	n
General (g/kg ODM)						**Degradability**					
ODM (fresh)	227.2	48.7	159.0	446.0	107	Dry matter					
TDM (fresh)	252.3	49.9	183.3	474.0	105	a (%)	36.7	11.5	16.7	51.7	13
CP	174.4	34.1	102.9	303.0	107	b (%)	50.4	9.6	38.4	69.6	13
MADF	344.0	42.5	230.0	422.6	107	c (h^{-1})	0.07	0.02	0.05	0.12	13
EE	47.4	10.9	23.0	90.0	107						
AEE	33.5	3.5	31.0	36.0	2	dg (%) @ outflow rate					
TA	91.0	14.1	62.0	137.6	107	$0.02h^{-1}$	75.1	6.4	64.0	84.0	13
GE (MJ/kg TDM)	19.3	0.83	17.0	21.7	105	$0.05h^{-1}$	65.3	8.0	53.0	77.0	13
						$0.08h^{-1}$	59.3	8.9	45.0	72.0	13
NDF ash	566.3	62.7	420.0	682.5	105						
NDF unash						Nitrogen					
ADF ash	359.4	45.4	226.0	441.4	100	a (%)	63.5	11.2	50.2	75.8	5
ADF unash	356.7	40.7	278.0	445.0	33	b (%)	27.6	8.1	20.6	40.3	5
						c (h^{-1})	0.09	0.03	0.05	0.12	5
Energy Values											
						dg (%) @ outflow rate					
DE (MJ/kg TDM)	14.4	0.79	12.8	16.7	105	$0.02h^{-1}$	85.4	6.2	79.0	93.0	5
ME (MJ/kg TDM)	11.7	0.64	10.4	13.7	105	$0.05h^{-1}$	80.6	8.0	70.0	90.0	5
FE/GE	0.25	0.04	0.19	0.32	107	$0.08h^{-1}$	77.6	8.8	66.0	87.0	5
UE/GE	0.06	0.02	0.03	0.09	107						
CH_4E/GE	0.08	0.01	0.06	0.09	107						
ME/DE	0.82	0.02	0.77	0.87	105						
ME/GE	0.55	0.04	0.46	0.63	105						
Digestibility Coefficients											
DM	0.71	0.05	0.57	0.79	71						
OM	0.74	0.05	0.63	0.83	107						
CP	0.71	0.08	0.42	0.82	71						
CF	0.81	0.05	0.68	0.89	71						
EE	0.74	0.05	0.57	0.82	70						
NDF	0.78	0.05	0.66	0.85	25						
ADF	0.79	0.04	0.71	0.85	23						
Cell	0.82	0.03	0.77	0.86	23						
GE	0.75	0.04	0.68	0.81	107						
DOMD(g/kg TDM)	711.7	35.1	608.8	782.1	105						

RUMINANT DATABASE

FEED DESCRIPTION : **LUCERNE SILAGE** (Source 1)

Determination	Mean	SD	Min	Max	n	Determination	Mean	SD	Min	Max	n
General (g/kg ODM)						**Degradability**					
ODM (fresh)	338.1	101.3	238.0	512.0	8	Dry matter					
TDM (fresh)	359.9	94.2	267.0	523.0	8	a (%)	40.0	1.6	38.6	41.7	3
CP	193.6	27.4	149.0	230.0	8	b (%)	33.7	1.7	32.4	35.6	3
MADF	375.9	60.0	322.0	490.0	8	c (h^{-1})	0.13	0.02	0.11	0.15	3
EE	24.5	4.4	18.0	33.0	8						
AEE						dg (%) @ outflow rate					
TA	105.0	8.5	95.0	119.0	8	$0.02h^{-1}$	69.0	0.0	69.0	69.0	3
GE (MJ/kg TDM)	18.5	0.82	17.1	19.4	8	$0.05h^{-1}$	64.0	0.0	64.0	64.0	3
						$0.08h^{-1}$	60.3	0.58	60.0	61.0	3
NDF ash	495.2	81.9	403.0	606.0	6						
NDF unash						Nitrogen					
ADF ash	406.2	77.5	342.0	531.0	6	a (%)	66.3	2.0	64.1	68.1	3
ADF unash	346.5	5.0	343.0	350.0	2	b (%)	25.2	2.2	23.7	27.8	3
						c (h^{-1})	0.17	0.04	0.12	0.19	3
Energy Values											
						dg (%) @ outflow rate					
DE (MJ/kg TDM)	10.3	2.1	5.7	12.6	8	$0.02h^{-1}$	88.7	1.5	87.0	90.0	3
ME (MJ/kg TDM)	8.0	2.0	3.6	10.2	8	$0.05h^{-1}$	85.7	1.5	84.0	87.0	3
FE/GE	0.45	0.10	0.35	0.67	8	$0.08h^{-1}$	83.3	2.1	81.0	85.0	3
UE/GE	0.05	0.01	0.04	0.07	8						
CH_4E/GE	0.07	0.0	0.06	0.08	8						
ME/DE	0.77	0.06	0.62	0.81	8						
ME/GE	0.41	0.11	0.16	0.50	8						
Digestibility Coefficients											
DM	0.53	0.09	0.33	0.62	8						
OM	0.58	0.09	0.38	0.66	8						
CP	0.68	0.06	0.56	0.76	8						
CF	0.54	0.13	0.36	0.81	8						
EE	0.61	0.02	0.58	0.64	8						
NDF											
ADF											
Cell											
GE	0.55	0.10	0.33	0.65	8						
DOMD(g/kg TDM)	557.1	45.7	491.6	622.5	8						

271

RUMINANT DATABASE

FEED DESCRIPTION : **MAIZE SILAGE** (Sources 1, 2)

Determination	Mean	SD	Min	Max	n	Determination	Mean	SD	Min	Max	n
General (g/kg ODM)						**Degradability**					
ODM (fresh)	251.6	47.2	161.0	317.0	26	Dry matter					
TDM (fresh)	278.4	45.9	191.0	350.0	26	a (%)	39.1		39.1	39.1	1
CP	100.8	15.9	81.9	154.0	26	b (%)	41.8		41.8	41.8	1
MADF	264.7	55.9	204.0	383.0	26	c (h^{-1})	0.10		0.10	0.10	1
EE	28.9	6.7	14.0	39.0	26						
AEE						dg (%) @ outflow rate					
TA	53.9	13.0	39.0	91.5	26	$0.02h^{-1}$	74.0		74.0	74.0	1
GE (MJ/kg TDM)	18.2	0.73	16.3	19.1	26	$0.05h^{-1}$	67.0		67.0	67.0	1
						$0.08h^{-1}$	63.0		63.0	63.0	1
NDF ash	480.0	90.8	376.0	680.0	25						
NDF unash						Nitrogen					
ADF ash	277.1	51.3	217.0	386.0	25	a (%)	65.5		65.5	65.5	1
ADF unash	377.2	33.0	324.0	408.0	6	b (%)	19.3		19.3	19.3	1
						c (h^{-1})	0.20		0.20	0.20	1
Energy Values											
						dg (%) @ outflow rate					
DE (MJ/kg TDM)	11.7	1.2	9.3	13.0	10	$0.02h^{-1}$	83.0		83.0	83.0	1
ME (MJ/kg TDM)	10.5	1.1	7.2	12.1	26	$0.05h^{-1}$	81.0		81.0	81.0	1
FE/GE	0.39	0.07	0.29	0.53	26	$0.08h^{-1}$	79.0		79.0	79.0	1
UE/GE	0.04	0.02	0.02	0.09	26						
CH_4E/GE	0.08	0.01	0.07	0.09	26						
ME/DE	0.81	0.03	0.76	0.84	10						
ME/GE	0.52	0.05	0.38	0.62	26						
Digestibility Coefficients											
DM	0.62	0.04	0.56	0.67	10						
OM	0.75	0.08	0.57	0.86	26						
CP	0.61	0.08	0.51	0.71	10						
CF	0.63	0.08	0.46	0.73	10						
EE	0.76	0.11	0.60	0.89	10						
NDF	0.61	0.06	0.53	0.69	5						
ADF	0.62	0.05	0.56	0.70	5						
Cell	0.65	0.07	0.57	0.74	5						
GE	0.69	0.04	0.55	0.74	26						
DOMD(g/kg TDM)	742.5	70.7	583.4	842.4	26						

RUMINANT DATABASE

FEED DESCRIPTION : **MAIZE SILAGE, ME 8 - 10 (ODM BASIS)** (Source 1)

Determination	Mean	SD	Min	Max	n	Determination	Mean	SD	Min	Max	n
General (g/kg ODM)						**Degradability**					
ODM (fresh)	250.5	24.7	233.0	268.0	2	Dry matter					
TDM (fresh)	273.0	18.4	260.0	286.0	2	a (%)					
CP	100.5	0.71	100.0	101.0	2	b (%)					
MADF	240.5	16.3	229.0	252.0	2	c (h^{-1})					
EE	27.5	0.71	27.0	28.0	2						
AEE						dg (%) @ outflow rate					
TA	50.0	2.8	48.0	52.0	2	0.02h^{-1}					
GE (MJ/kg TDM)	17.2	1.3	16.3	18.1	2	0.05h^{-1}					
						0.08h^{-1}					
NDF ash	480.5	33.2	457.0	504.0	2						
NDF unash						Nitrogen					
ADF ash	252.5	17.7	240.0	265.0	2	a (%)					
ADF unash						b (%)					
						c (h^{-1})					
Energy Values											
						dg (%) @ outflow rate					
DE (MJ/kg TDM)	11.3	1.3	10.3	12.2	2	0.02h^{-1}					
ME (MJ/kg TDM)	8.8	0.50	8.5	9.2	2	0.05h^{-1}					
FE/GE	0.35	0.03	0.33	0.37	2	0.08h^{-1}					
UE/GE	0.07	0.04	0.04	0.09	2						
CH$_4$E/GE	0.08	0.0	0.08	0.08	2						
ME/DE	0.79	0.05	0.76	0.82	2						
ME/GE	0.47	0.01	0.47	0.48	2						
Digestibility Coefficients											
DM	0.63	0.04	0.60	0.66	2						
OM	0.67	0.04	0.64	0.70	2						
CP	0.56	0.06	0.51	0.60	2						
CF	0.56	0.14	0.46	0.66	2						
EE	0.86	0.04	0.83	0.89	2						
NDF											
ADF											
Cell											
GE	0.65	0.03	0.63	0.67	2						
DOMD(g/kg TDM)	672.7	28.9	652.3	693.1	2						

RUMINANT DATABASE

FEED DESCRIPTION : **MAIZE SILAGE, ME 10 - 12 (ODM BASIS)** (Sources 1, 2)

Determination	Mean	SD	Min	Max	n	Determination	Mean	SD	Min	Max	n
General (g/kg ODM)						**Degradability**					
ODM (fresh)	240.9	47.1	161.0	316.0	11	Dry matter					
TDM (fresh)	267.6	43.4	191.0	336.0	11	a (%)	39.1		39.1	39.1	1
CP	103.8	20.9	81.9	154.0	11	b (%)	41.8		41.8	41.8	1
MADF	281.1	55.4	221.0	380.0	11	c (h^{-1})	0.10		0.10	0.10	1
EE	27.3	6.2	15.0	36.0	11						
AEE						dg (%) @ outflow rate					
TA	55.7	15.3	39.0	91.5	11	$0.02h^{-1}$	74.0		74.0	74.0	1
GE (MJ/kg TDM)	18.1	0.77	16.5	19.1	11	$0.05h^{-1}$	67.0		67.0	67.0	1
						$0.08h^{-1}$	63.0		63.0	63.0	1
NDF ash	504.7	88.3	392.0	634.0	10						
NDF unash						Nitrogen					
ADF ash	290.2	47.9	238.0	365.0	10	a (%)	65.5		65.5	65.5	1
ADF unash	364.5	33.9	324.0	407.0	4	b (%)	19.3		19.3	19.3	1
						c (h^{-1})	0.20		0.20	0.20	1
Energy Values											
						dg (%) @ outflow rate					
DE (MJ/kg TDM)	12.1	0.73	11.4	13.0	6	$0.02h^{-1}$	83.0		83.0	83.0	1
ME (MJ/kg TDM)	10.2	0.63	9.0	10.8	11	$0.05h^{-1}$	81.0		81.0	81.0	1
FE/GE	0.39	0.08	0.29	0.53	11	$0.08h^{-1}$	79.0		79.0	79.0	1
UE/GE	0.04	0.01	0.02	0.07	11						
CH_4E/GE	0.08	0.01	0.07	0.09	11						
ME/DE	0.82	0.02	0.78	0.84	6						
ME/GE	0.51	0.04	0.43	0.56	11						

Digestibility Coefficients

Determination	Mean	SD	Min	Max	n
DM	0.64	0.03	0.59	0.67	6
OM	0.72	0.07	0.62	0.83	11
CP	0.61	0.09	0.51	0.71	6
CF	0.65	0.05	0.60	0.73	6
EE	0.78	0.09	0.61	0.86	6
NDF	0.63	0.06	0.59	0.69	3
ADF	0.64	0.05	0.60	0.70	3
Cell	0.67	0.06	0.63	0.74	3
GE	0.68	0.02	0.65	0.71	11
DOMD(g/kg TDM)	718.3	56.6	632.7	813.8	11

RUMINANT DATABASE

FEED DESCRIPTION : **MAIZE SILAGE, ME 12 - 14 (ODM BASIS)** (Sources 1, 2)

Determination	Mean	SD	Min	Max	n	Determination	Mean	SD	Min	Max	n
General (g/kg ODM)						**Degradability**					
ODM (fresh)	267.1	46.9	166.0	317.0	12	Dry matter					
TDM (fresh)	295.3	46.1	195.0	350.0	12	a (%)					
CP	97.7	12.3	82.0	119.1	12	b (%)					
MADF	245.3	51.0	204.0	383.0	12	c (h^{-1})					
EE	31.8	5.9	15.0	39.0	12						
AEE						dg (%) @ outflow rate					
TA	52.4	12.6	41.0	86.3	12	0.02h^{-1}					
GE (MJ/kg TDM)	18.6	0.16	18.3	18.8	12	0.05h^{-1}					
						0.08h^{-1}					
NDF ash	445.5	84.5	376.0	680.0	12						
NDF unash						Nitrogen					
ADF ash	261.3	47.1	217.0	378.0	12	a (%)					
ADF unash	408.0		408.0	408.0	1	b (%)					
						c (h^{-1})					
Energy Values											
						dg (%) @ outflow rate					
DE (MJ/kg TDM)	13.0		13.0	13.0	1	0.02h^{-1}					
ME (MJ/kg TDM)	11.3	0.45	10.4	12.1	12	0.05h^{-1}					
FE/GE	0.38	0.05	0.30	0.47	12	0.08h^{-1}					
UE/GE	0.03	0.01	0.02	0.06	12						
CH$_4$E/GE	0.08	0.01	0.07	0.09	12						
ME/DE	0.80		0.80	0.80	1						
ME/GE	0.55	0.04	0.48	0.62	12						
Digestibility Coefficients											
DM	0.61		0.61	0.61	1						
OM	0.81	0.05	0.65	0.86	12						
CP	0.68		0.68	0.68	1						
CF	0.69		0.69	0.69	1						
EE	0.67		0.67	0.67	1						
NDF	0.65		0.65	0.65	1						
ADF	0.65		0.65	0.65	1						
Cell	0.70		0.70	0.70	1						
GE	0.72	0.02	0.68	0.74	12						
DOMD(g/kg TDM)	789.5	46.6	654.9	842.4	12						

RUMINANT DATABASE

FEED DESCRIPTION : **MIXED CLOVER SILAGE** (Sources 1, 2)

Determination	Mean	SD	Min	Max	n	Determination	Mean	SD	Min	Max	n
General (g/kg ODM)						**Degradability**					
ODM (fresh)	217.2	43.2	156.0	301.0	10	**Dry matter**					
TDM (fresh)	235.8	42.8	182.0	322.0	10	a (%)	33.1	8.0	22.6	40.3	4
CP	233.5	64.3	165.0	395.0	10	b (%)	48.1	8.1	39.3	55.4	4
MADF	330.6	32.7	263.0	379.0	10	c (h^{-1})	0.10	0.03	0.07	0.14	4
EE	36.2	11.7	15.0	54.0	10						
AEE						dg (%) @ outflow rate					
TA	116.1	19.0	93.0	156.0	10	$0.02h^{-1}$	73.0	1.4	71.0	74.0	4
GE (MJ/kg TDM)	18.0	1.5	16.2	21.7	10	$0.05h^{-1}$	64.8	2.2	63.0	68.0	4
						$0.08h^{-1}$	59.5	3.1	57.0	64.0	4
NDF ash	439.9	75.2	294.0	564.0	10						
NDF unash						**Nitrogen**					
ADF ash	341.5	45.6	266.0	408.0	9	a (%)	42.4	2.1	40.3	44.6	3
ADF unash	350.0	28.3	330.0	370.0	2	b (%)	47.5	3.0	44.1	49.8	3
						c (h^{-1})	0.12	0.04	0.10	0.16	3
Energy Values											
						dg (%) @ outflow rate					
DE (MJ/kg TDM)	12.5	1.2	11.0	14.6	10	$0.02h^{-1}$	83.0	1.0	82.0	84.0	3
ME (MJ/kg TDM)	9.8	1.1	8.5	11.8	10	$0.05h^{-1}$	76.0	1.7	75.0	78.0	3
FE/GE	0.31	0.04	0.24	0.37	10	$0.08h^{-1}$	70.7	2.9	69.0	74.0	3
UE/GE	0.07	0.01	0.06	0.08	10						
CH_4E/GE	0.08	0.01	0.06	0.08	10						
ME/DE	0.78	0.02	0.77	0.81	10						
ME/GE	0.50	0.05	0.45	0.59	10						
Digestibility Coefficients											
DM	0.64	0.06	0.58	0.74	9						
OM	0.69	0.06	0.61	0.79	10						
CP	0.74	0.05	0.65	0.81	9						
CF	0.70	0.10	0.55	0.83	9						
EE	0.62	0.12	0.40	0.72	9						
NDF											
ADF											
Cell											
GE	0.69	0.04	0.63	0.76	10						
DOMD(g/kg TDM)	644.1	56.6	564.1	734.6	10						

RUMINANT DATABASE

FEED DESCRIPTION : **PEA WHOLE CROP SILAGE** (Source 1)

Determination	Mean	SD	Min	Max	n	Determination	Mean	SD	Min	Max	n
General (g/kg ODM)						**Degradability**					
ODM (fresh)	253.4	48.0	174.0	303.0	5	Dry matter					
TDM (fresh)	275.6	50.3	193.0	320.0	5	a (%)					
CP	178.9	47.1	123.8	222.0	5	b (%)					
MADF	377.0	48.3	298.0	429.0	5	c (h^{-1})					
EE	35.4	11.7	19.0	49.0	5						
AEE						dg (%) @ outflow rate					
TA	142.8	64.1	72.0	218.0	5	$0.02h^{-1}$					
GE (MJ/kg TDM)	17.8	1.9	15.0	20.0	5	$0.05h^{-1}$					
						$0.08h^{-1}$					
NDF ash	280.0		280.0	280.0	1						
NDF unash						Nitrogen					
ADF ash	239.0		239.0	239.0	1	a (%)					
ADF unash	408.6	49.6	353.0	484.0	5	b (%)					
						c (h^{-1})					
Energy Values											
						dg (%) @ outflow rate					
DE (MJ/kg TDM)	11.0	2.0	8.8	14.2	5	$0.02h^{-1}$					
ME (MJ/kg TDM)	7.7	0.92	6.5	8.8	4	$0.05h^{-1}$					
FE/GE	0.38	0.11	0.25	0.47	5	$0.08h^{-1}$					
UE/GE	0.05	0.02	0.04	0.07	4						
CH_4E/GE	0.07	0.01	0.06	0.08	5						
ME/DE	0.71	0.12	0.53	0.79	4						
ME/GE	0.39	0.03	0.36	0.41	4						
Digestibility Coefficients											
DM	0.54	0.07	0.44	0.62	4						
OM	0.59	0.08	0.52	0.71	4						
CP	0.59	0.07	0.48	0.66	5						
CF	0.56	0.09	0.46	0.69	5						
EE	0.62	0.11	0.47	0.78	5						
NDF											
ADF											
Cell											
GE	0.57	0.09	0.50	0.72	5						
DOMD(g/kg TDM)	544.5	77.8	448.6	635.4	4						

RUMINANT DATABASE

FEED CLASS 40

ENERGY FEEDS

RUMINANT DATABASE

FEED DESCRIPTION : **APPLES, FRESH** (Source 1)

Determination	Mean	SD	Min	Max	n	Determination	Mean	SD	Min	Max	n
General (g/kg ODM)						**Degradability**					
ODM (fresh)	135.6	13.5	126.0	145.1	2	Dry matter					
TDM (fresh)						a (%)					
CP	38.3	8.1	32.6	44.0	2	b (%)					
MADF	101.0	29.7	80.0	122.0	2	c (h^{-1})					
EE	12.0	2.8	10.0	14.0	2						
AEE						dg (%) @ outflow rate					
TA	20.0	2.8	18.0	22.0	2	$0.02h^{-1}$					
GE (MJ/kg ODM)	16.8	0.0	16.8	16.8	2	$0.05h^{-1}$					
						$0.08h^{-1}$					
NDF ash	126.0	12.7	117.0	135.0	2						
NDF unash						Nitrogen					
ADF ash	117.0	17.0	105.0	129.0	2	a (%)					
ADF unash	108.5	23.3	92.0	125.0	2	b (%)					
						c (h^{-1})					
Energy Values											
						dg (%) @ outflow rate					
DE (MJ/kg ODM)	13.7	1.4	12.8	14.7	2	$0.02h^{-1}$					
ME (MJ/kg ODM)	11.9	1.2	11.1	12.7	2	$0.05h^{-1}$					
FE/GE	0.19	0.08	0.13	0.24	2	$0.08h^{-1}$					
UE/GE	0.03	0.01	0.02	0.03	2						
CH_4E/GE	0.09	0.01	0.08	0.09	2						
ME/DE	0.86	0.0	0.86	0.86	2						
ME/GE	0.71	0.07	0.66	0.76	2						
Digestibility Coefficients											
DM	0.85	0.06	0.81	0.89	2						
OM	0.87	0.04	0.84	0.90	2						
CP	0.24		0.24	0.24	1						
CF	0.46	0.14	0.36	0.56	2						
EE	0.58		0.58	0.58	1						
NDF											
ADF											
Cell											
GE	0.82	0.08	0.77	0.87	2						
DOMD(g/kg ODM)	856.1	46.1	823.5	888.7	2						

RUMINANT DATABASE

FEED DESCRIPTION : **APPLE POMACE** (Source 1)

Determination	Mean	SD	Min	Max	n	Determination	Mean	SD	Min	Max	n
General (g/kg ODM)						**Degradability**					
ODM (fresh)	242.0	32.8	204.0	282.0	5	Dry matter					
TDM (fresh)	243.5	23.3	227.0	260.0	2	a (%)					
CP	69.0	8.7	64.0	79.0	3	b (%)					
MADF	375.2	34.3	346.0	430.0	5	c (h^{-1})					
EE	27.4	3.8	23.0	32.0	5						
AEE	28.5	5.8	20.0	33.0	4	dg (%) @ outflow rate					
TA	18.2	3.1	15.0	22.0	5	$0.02h^{-1}$					
GE (MJ/kg ODM)	19.8	1.2	19.0	21.8	5	$0.05h^{-1}$					
						$0.08h^{-1}$					
NDF ash	488.6	53.4	425.0	540.0	5						
NDF unash						Nitrogen					
ADF ash	414.6	72.4	355.0	522.0	5	a (%)					
ADF unash	389.3	53.9	344.0	449.0	3	b (%)					
						c (h^{-1})					
Energy Values											
						dg (%) @ outflow rate					
DE (MJ/kg ODM)	10.9	0.42	10.3	11.4	5	$0.02h^{-1}$					
ME (MJ/kg ODM)	9.1	0.50	8.6	9.9	5	$0.05h^{-1}$					
FE/GE	0.45	0.04	0.40	0.51	5	$0.08h^{-1}$					
UE/GE	0.02	0.01	0.01	0.03	5						
CH_4E/GE	0.07	0.0	0.07	0.07	5						
ME/DE	0.83	0.02	0.82	0.86	5						
ME/GE	0.46	0.04	0.40	0.52	5						
Digestibility Coefficients											
DM	0.60	0.07	0.49	0.69	5						
OM	0.61	0.08	0.50	0.69	5						
CP	0.24	0.21	0.09	0.39	2						
CF	0.50	0.10	0.37	0.65	5						
EE	0.65	0.22	0.27	0.82	5						
NDF											
ADF											
Cell											
GE	0.55	0.04	0.49	0.60	5						
DOMD(g/kg ODM)	607.7	72.0	496.9	683.0	5						

RUMINANT DATABASE

FEED DESCRIPTION : **BARLEY GRAIN, ALL SEASONS** (Sources 1, 2)

Determination	Mean	SD	Min	Max	n	Determination	Mean	SD	Min	Max	n
General (g/kg ODM)						**Degradability**					
ODM (fresh)	865.3	15.1	801.0	888.4	45	Dry matter					
TDM (fresh)						a (%)	31.0	5.6	18.6	41.4	16
CP	129.0	13.0	103.1	160.0	45	b (%)	55.8	5.9	46.4	68.1	16
MADF	61.6	9.7	35.0	89.0	45	c (h^{-1})	0.40	0.15	0.02	0.51	16
EE	15.4	6.2	5.0	40.0	45						
AEE	27.7	5.0	14.0	32.0	30	dg (%) @ outflow rate					
TA	27.5	7.0	22.0	52.0	45	$0.02h^{-1}$	82.7	9.2	54.0	89.0	16
GE (MJ/kg ODM)	18.4	0.20	18.0	18.9	45	$0.05h^{-1}$	78.8	11.1	44.0	85.0	16
						$0.08h^{-1}$	75.5	11.6	40.0	83.0	16
NDF ash	200.7	49.3	133.4	366.0	45						
NDF unash						Nitrogen					
ADF ash	65.8	9.8	49.0	91.0	45	a (%)	24.5	4.8	15.3	34.2	13
ADF unash	69.1	11.0	51.0	98.0	26	b (%)	69.7	4.6	60.0	78.7	13
						c (h^{-1})	0.35	0.06	0.23	0.44	13
Energy Values											
						dg (%) @ outflow rate					
DE (MJ/kg ODM)	15.8	0.40	15.0	16.8	29	$0.02h^{-1}$	90.3	1.1	89.0	92.0	13
ME (MJ/kg ODM)	13.3	0.50	12.1	14.3	45	$0.05h^{-1}$	85.2	1.4	83.0	87.0	13
FE/GE	0.14	0.02	0.08	0.18	29	$0.08h^{-1}$	80.9	1.5	78.0	83.0	13
UE/GE	0.04	0.02	0.01	0.08	45						
CH_4E/GE	0.10	0.02	0.08	0.14	45						
ME/DE	0.85	0.02	0.81	0.87	29						
ME/GE	0.72	0.03	0.64	0.78	45						
Digestibility Coefficients											
DM	0.84	0.03	0.73	0.87	30						
OM	0.86	0.05	0.59	0.89	30						
CP	0.77	0.04	0.66	0.84	45						
CF	0.46	0.18	0.09	0.78	29						
EE	0.91	0.08	0.66	1.0	28						
NDF	0.57	0.09	0.42	0.80	25						
ADF	0.50	0.10	0.27	0.78	25						
Cell	0.53	0.15	0.15	0.84	24						
GE	0.85	0.03	0.77	0.92	45						
DOMD(g/kg ODM)	838.4	53.2	568.5	873.7	30						

RUMINANT DATABASE

FEED DESCRIPTION : **BARLEY GRAIN, SPRING** (Sources 1, 2)

Determination	Mean	SD	Min	Max	n	Determination	Mean	SD	Min	Max	n
General (g/kg ODM)						**Degradability**					
ODM (fresh)	868.4	12.0	825.4	885.6	32	Dry matter					
TDM (fresh)						a (%)	33.5	4.2	29.2	41.4	9
CP	127.6	12.2	103.1	160.0	32	b (%)	55.3	4.9	47.7	61.6	9
MADF	60.7	9.1	35.0	78.0	32	c (h^{-1})	0.48	0.04	0.43	0.51	9
EE	14.1	5.6	5.0	25.0	32						
AEE	29.6	2.1	24.0	32.0	16	dg (%) @ outflow rate					
TA	26.9	6.6	22.0	50.0	32	0.02h^{-1}	86.6	1.8	83.0	89.0	9
GE (MJ/kg ODM)	18.4	0.18	18.0	18.8	32	0.05h^{-1}	83.6	1.7	80.0	85.0	9
						0.08h^{-1}	80.9	1.5	78.0	83.0	9
NDF ash	198.8	38.1	133.4	274.0	32						
NDF unash						Nitrogen					
ADF ash	65.1	9.7	50.0	86.0	32	a (%)	25.8	4.6	17.3	34.2	9
ADF unash	66.6	10.1	51.0	88.0	16	b (%)	68.6	4.5	60.0	75.4	9
						c (h^{-1})	0.36	0.06	0.29	0.44	9
Energy Values											
						dg (%) @ outflow rate					
DE (MJ/kg ODM)	15.8	0.23	15.5	16.3	16	0.02h^{-1}	90.7	1.1	89.0	92.0	9
ME (MJ/kg ODM)	13.2	0.49	12.1	13.9	32	0.05h^{-1}	85.8	1.3	83.0	87.0	9
FE/GE	0.14	0.01	0.12	0.16	16	0.08h^{-1}	81.4	1.3	79.0	83.0	9
UE/GE	0.04	0.02	0.01	0.08	32						
CH$_4$E/GE	0.10	0.02	0.08	0.14	32						
ME/DE	0.85	0.02	0.81	0.87	16						
ME/GE	0.72	0.03	0.64	0.76	32						
Digestibility Coefficients											
DM	0.85	0.01	0.83	0.87	16						
OM	0.87	0.01	0.85	0.89	16						
CP	0.77	0.04	0.66	0.84	32						
CF	0.49	0.16	0.28	0.78	16						
EE	0.92	0.09	0.66	1.0	16						
NDF	0.58	0.09	0.42	0.80	16						
ADF	0.51	0.11	0.27	0.78	16						
Cell	0.55	0.14	0.19	0.84	16						
GE	0.85	0.02	0.77	0.88	32						
DOMD(g/kg ODM)	851.9	11.4	836.5	871.4	16						

RUMINANT DATABASE

FEED DESCRIPTION : **BARLEY GRAIN, WINTER** (Source 1)

Determination	Mean	SD	Min	Max	n	Determination	Mean	SD	Min	Max	n
General (g/kg ODM)						**Degradability**					
ODM (fresh)	863.0	11.9	852.4	888.4	8	Dry matter					
TDM (fresh)						a (%)	27.6	4.2	21.9	31.2	4
CP	136.4	16.1	117.7	160.0	8	b (%)	61.2	5.4	55.0	68.1	4
MADF	68.0	10.5	55.2	89.0	8	c (h^{-1})	0.45	0.06	0.37	0.51	4
EE	16.5	1.4	14.0	18.0	8						
AEE	30.0	1.5	28.0	32.0	8	dg (%) @ outflow rate					
TA	26.2	3.2	23.0	32.0	8	$0.02h^{-1}$	86.0	1.4	84.0	87.0	4
GE (MJ/kg ODM)	18.5	0.21	18.2	18.9	8	$0.05h^{-1}$	82.8	1.3	81.0	84.0	4
						$0.08h^{-1}$	79.3	0.96	78.0	80.0	4
NDF ash	180.1	32.2	145.7	238.0	8						
NDF unash						Nitrogen					
ADF ash	69.3	10.4	59.0	91.0	8	a (%)	21.7	4.6	15.3	26.3	4
ADF unash	73.3	11.8	61.0	98.0	8	b (%)	72.3	4.4	69.1	78.7	4
						c (h^{-1})	0.33	0.07	0.23	0.36	4
Energy Values											
						dg (%) @ outflow rate					
DE (MJ/kg ODM)	15.9	0.49	15.1	16.6	8	$0.02h^{-1}$	89.5	0.58	89.0	90.0	4
ME (MJ/kg ODM)	13.5	0.48	12.7	14.2	8	$0.05h^{-1}$	84.0	0.82	83.0	85.0	4
FE/GE	0.14	0.03	0.09	0.18	8	$0.08h^{-1}$	79.5	1.0	78.0	80.0	4
UE/GE	0.04	0.01	0.03	0.05	8						
CH_4E/GE	0.09	0.0	0.09	0.09	8						
ME/DE	0.85	0.01	0.83	0.86	8						
ME/GE	0.73	0.03	0.68	0.78	8						
Digestibility Coefficients											
DM	0.84	0.02	0.81	0.87	8						
OM	0.86	0.02	0.83	0.89	8						
CP	0.77	0.02	0.73	0.81	8						
CF	0.38	0.20	0.09	0.71	8						
EE	0.92	0.06	0.81	0.97	8						
NDF	0.56	0.09	0.43	0.69	8						
ADF	0.49	0.08	0.39	0.62	8						
Cell	0.49	0.19	0.15	0.69	7						
GE	0.86	0.03	0.82	0.91	8						
DOMD(g/kg ODM)	842.0	21.0	813.3	873.7	8						

RUMINANT DATABASE

FEED DESCRIPTION : **CASSAVA MEAL** (Sources 1, 2)

Determination	Mean	SD	Min	Max	n	Determination	Mean	SD	Min	Max	n
General (g/kg ODM)						**Degradability**					
ODM (fresh)	885.4	2.4	883.7	887.1	2	Dry matter					
TDM (fresh)						a (%)					
CP	27.6	1.5	26.0	29.0	5	b (%)					
MADF	73.0	25.1	32.0	92.0	5	c (h^{-1})					
EE	4.4	1.8	2.0	7.0	5						
AEE	6.0	1.4	5.0	7.0	2	dg (%) @ outflow rate					
TA	50.4	16.1	22.0	62.0	5	0.02h^{-1}					
GE (MJ/kg ODM)	16.8	0.19	16.6	17.1	5	0.05h^{-1}					
						0.08h^{-1}					
NDF ash	113.6	91.5	48.0	275.0	5						
NDF unash						Nitrogen					
ADF ash	63.0	22.5	37.0	76.0	3	a (%)					
ADF unash	98.0		98.0	98.0	1	b (%)					
						c (h^{-1})					
Energy Values											
						dg (%) @ outflow rate					
DE (MJ/kg ODM)	14.9	0.49	14.5	15.2	2	0.02h^{-1}					
ME (MJ/kg ODM)	12.6	0.42	12.1	12.9	5	0.05h^{-1}					
FE/GE	0.11	0.02	0.09	0.12	2	0.08h^{-1}					
UE/GE	0.02	0.02	0.01	0.04	4						
CH$_4$E/GE	0.13	0.04	0.09	0.18	5						
ME/DE	0.87	0.02	0.85	0.88	2						
ME/GE	0.75	0.03	0.73	0.78	5						
Digestibility Coefficients											
DM	0.80	0.01	0.79	0.80	2						
OM	0.89	0.03	0.86	0.95	5						
CP											
CF	0.38	0.10	0.31	0.45	2						
EE											
NDF											
ADF											
Cell											
GE	0.89	0.03	0.86	0.93	5						
DOMD(g/kg ODM)	851.7	44.8	821.2	930.0	5						

RUMINANT DATABASE

FEED DESCRIPTION : **CITRUS PULP, DRIED** (Sources 1, 2)

Determination	Mean	SD	Min	Max	n
General (g/kg ODM)					
ODM (fresh)	885.0	6.4	875.0	892.4	8
TDM (fresh)					
CP	71.6	3.2	68.0	78.5	8
MADF	221.3	11.0	203.0	239.0	8
EE	23.8	7.4	16.0	40.0	8
AEE	17.8	5.5	14.0	27.0	5
TA	64.8	4.7	60.0	73.0	8
GE (MJ/kg ODM)	17.5	0.17	17.3	17.9	8
NDF ash	248.8	31.2	198.0	290.0	8
NDF unash					
ADF ash	242.3	15.8	220.0	266.0	8
ADF unash	245.5	19.7	217.0	262.0	4
Energy Values					
DE (MJ/kg ODM)	15.0	0.72	13.7	15.9	6
ME (MJ/kg ODM)	12.6	0.87	11.3	14.2	8
FE/GE	0.14	0.04	0.09	0.21	8
UE/GE	0.05	0.02	0.03	0.07	8
CH$_4$E/GE	0.09	0.01	0.05	0.10	8
ME/DE	0.83	0.01	0.82	0.84	6
ME/GE	0.72	0.05	0.66	0.82	8
Digestibility Coefficients					
DM	0.83	0.03	0.78	0.87	8
OM	0.88	0.03	0.83	0.93	8
CP	0.56	0.06	0.44	0.63	8
CF	0.85	0.07	0.73	0.90	6
EE	0.84	0.07	0.72	0.92	6
NDF	0.86	0.04	0.83	0.91	3
ADF	0.89	0.02	0.88	0.91	3
Cell	0.91	0.02	0.89	0.92	3
GE	0.86	0.04	0.79	0.91	8
DOMD(g/kg ODM)	824.8	35.3	770.5	875.0	8

Determination	Mean	SD	Min	Max	n
Degradability					
Dry matter					
a (%)	24.3		24.3	24.3	1
b (%)	75.4		75.4	75.4	1
c (h^{-1})	0.08		0.08	0.08	1
dg (%) @ outflow rate					
0.02h^{-1}	84.0		84.0	84.0	1
0.05h^{-1}	70.0		70.0	70.0	1
0.08h^{-1}	62.0		62.0	62.0	1
Nitrogen					
a (%)					
b (%)					
c (h^{-1})					
dg (%) @ outflow rate					
0.02h^{-1}					
0.05h^{-1}					
0.08h^{-1}					

RUMINANT DATABASE

FEED DESCRIPTION : **COFFEE RESIDUE, FRESH** (Source 1)

Determination	Mean	SD	Min	Max	n	Determination	Mean	SD	Min	Max	n

General (g/kg ODM)

ODM (fresh)	315.4		315.4	315.4	1
TDM (fresh)					
CP	107.0		107.0	107.0	1
MADF	691.0		691.0	691.0	1
EE	211.0		211.0	211.0	1
AEE	199.0		199.0	199.0	1
TA	6.0		6.0	6.0	1
GE (MJ/kg ODM)	25.2		25.2	25.2	1
NDF ash	740.0		740.0	740.0	1
NDF unash					
ADF ash	696.0		696.0	696.0	1
ADF unash					

Degradability

Dry matter
a (%)
b (%)
c (h^{-1})

dg (%) @ outflow rate
$0.02h^{-1}$
$0.05h^{-1}$
$0.08h^{-1}$

Nitrogen
a (%)
b (%)
c (h^{-1})

dg (%) @ outflow rate
$0.02h^{-1}$
$0.05h^{-1}$
$0.08h^{-1}$

Energy Values

DE (MJ/kg ODM)	13.8		13.8	13.8	1
ME (MJ/kg ODM)	10.0		10.0	10.0	1
FE/GE	0.45		0.45	0.45	1
UE/GE	0.08		0.08	0.08	1
CH_4E/GE	0.07		0.07	0.07	1
ME/DE	0.73		0.73	0.73	1
ME/GE	0.40		0.40	0.40	1

Digestibility Coefficients

DM	0.52		0.52	0.52	1
OM	0.57		0.57	0.57	1
CP					
CF	0.54		0.54	0.54	1
EE	0.95		0.95	0.95	1
NDF					
ADF					
Cell					
GE	0.55		0.55	0.55	1
DOMD(g/kg ODM)	572.3		572.3	572.3	1

RUMINANT DATABASE

FEED DESCRIPTION : **FODDER BEET, FRESH** (Source 1)

Determination	Mean	SD	Min	Max	n	Determination	Mean	SD	Min	Max	n
General (g/kg ODM)						**Degradability**					
ODM (fresh)	182.8	18.6	158.7	214.1	10	Dry matter					
TDM (fresh)						a (%)					
CP	62.9	9.5	51.0	80.3	10	b (%)					
MADF	91.1	18.1	62.0	120.0	10	c (h^{-1})					
EE	2.6	1.2	1.0	4.0	10						
AEE	3.7	1.1	2.6	5.0	4	dg (%) @ outflow rate					
TA	81.3	19.9	50.0	105.0	10	0.02h^{-1}					
GE (MJ/kg ODM)	16.0	0.37	15.6	16.6	10	0.05h^{-1}					
						0.08h^{-1}					
NDF ash	135.9	22.6	105.0	172.0	10						
NDF unash						Nitrogen					
ADF ash	71.6	10.1	54.0	84.0	10	a (%)					
ADF unash	113.5	16.3	97.0	128.0	4	b (%)					
						c (h^{-1})					
Energy Values											
						dg (%) @ outflow rate					
DE (MJ/kg ODM)	14.1	0.34	13.6	14.6	10	0.02h^{-1}					
ME (MJ/kg ODM)	11.9	0.29	11.6	12.4	10	0.05h^{-1}					
FE/GE	0.12	0.01	0.10	0.14	10	0.08h^{-1}					
UE/GE	0.04	0.01	0.03	0.05	10						
CH$_4$E/GE	0.09	0.0	0.09	0.09	10						
ME/DE	0.85	0.01	0.84	0.86	10						
ME/GE	0.74	0.01	0.73	0.76	10						
Digestibility Coefficients											
DM	0.86	0.01	0.85	0.88	10						
OM	0.90	0.01	0.88	0.92	10						
CP	0.51	0.07	0.36	0.62	10						
CF	0.71	0.08	0.59	0.82	9						
EE	0.34	0.16	0.11	0.52	5						
NDF	0.74	0.11	0.60	0.84	4						
ADF	0.76	0.12	0.60	0.88	4						
Cell	0.85	0.10	0.71	0.92	4						
GE	0.88	0.01	0.86	0.90	10						
DOMD(g/kg ODM)	829.2	17.7	802.3	853.6	10						

RUMINANT DATABASE

FEED DESCRIPTION : **GRAPE JUICE CONCENTRATE** (Source 1)

Determination	Mean	SD	Min	Max	n	Determination	Mean	SD	Min	Max	n
General (g/kg ODM)						**Degradability**					
ODM (fresh)	599.0		599.0	599.0	1	Dry matter					
TDM (fresh)						a (%)					
CP						b (%)					
MADF						c (h^{-1})					
EE	2.3		2.3	2.3	1						
AEE						dg (%) @ outflow rate					
TA	15.0		15.0	15.0	1	$0.02h^{-1}$					
GE (MJ/kg ODM)	16.0		16.0	16.0	1	$0.05h^{-1}$					
						$0.08h^{-1}$					
NDF ash											
NDF unash						Nitrogen					
ADF ash						a (%)					
ADF unash						b (%)					
						c (h^{-1})					
Energy Values											
						dg (%) @ outflow rate					
DE (MJ/kg ODM)	15.8		15.8	15.8	1	$0.02h^{-1}$					
ME (MJ/kg ODM)	13.4		13.4	13.4	1	$0.05h^{-1}$					
FE/GE	0.01		0.01	0.01	1	$0.08h^{-1}$					
UE/GE	0.05		0.05	0.05	1						
CH_4E/GE	0.10		0.10	0.10	1						
ME/DE	0.85		0.85	0.85	1						
ME/GE	0.84		0.84	0.84	1						
Digestibility Coefficients											
DM	0.84		0.84	0.84	1						
OM	0.94		0.94	0.94	1						
CP											
CF											
EE											
NDF											
ADF											
Cell											
GE	0.99		0.99	0.99	1						
DOMD(g/kg ODM)	929.9		929.9	929.9	1						

RUMINANT DATABASE

FEED DESCRIPTION : **MAIZE FIBRE** (Source 1)

Determination	Mean	SD	Min	Max	n	Determination	Mean	SD	Min	Max	n
General (g/kg ODM)						**Degradability**					
ODM (fresh)	378.0	28.3	344.0	415.8	5	Dry matter					
TDM (fresh)	377.7	31.5	334.6	410.0	5	a (%)					
CP	147.2	38.5	110.7	211.8	5	b (%)					
MADF	145.8	25.0	106.0	175.0	5	c (h^{-1})					
EE	31.2	8.0	24.0	44.0	5						
AEE	42.0	5.9	35.0	49.0	4	dg (%) @ outflow rate					
TA	21.8	28.1	9.0	72.0	5	0.02h^{-1}					
GE (MJ/kg ODM)	19.9	0.85	18.5	20.7	5	0.05h^{-1}					
						0.08h^{-1}					
NDF ash	538.0	100.7	362.0	597.0	5						
NDF unash						Nitrogen					
ADF ash	154.2	21.3	120.0	176.0	5	a (%)					
ADF unash	153.6	26.1	111.0	178.0	5	b (%)					
						c (h^{-1})					
Energy Values											
						dg (%) @ outflow rate					
DE (MJ/kg ODM)	15.9	0.62	15.1	16.7	5	0.02h^{-1}					
ME (MJ/kg ODM)	13.4	0.85	12.2	14.5	5	0.05h^{-1}					
FE/GE	0.20	0.03	0.17	0.23	5	0.08h^{-1}					
UE/GE	0.04	0.02	0.02	0.07	5						
CH$_4$E/GE	0.09	0.0	0.08	0.09	5						
ME/DE	0.84	0.02	0.81	0.87	5						
ME/GE	0.67	0.03	0.65	0.72	5						
Digestibility Coefficients											
DM	0.78	0.01	0.77	0.80	5						
OM	0.80	0.02	0.78	0.83	5						
CP	0.73	0.06	0.66	0.79	5						
CF	0.74	0.04	0.69	0.78	5						
EE	0.74	0.06	0.69	0.84	5						
NDF	0.78	0.02	0.75	0.80	5						
ADF	0.71	0.03	0.69	0.73	2						
Cell	0.77	0.05	0.74	0.81	2						
GE	0.80	0.02	0.77	0.83	5						
DOMD(g/kg ODM)	787.2	15.4	770.2	811.1	5						

RUMINANT DATABASE

FEED DESCRIPTION : **MAIZE GLUTEN FEED** (Sources 1, 2)

Determination	Mean	SD	Min	Max	n	Determination	Mean	SD	Min	Max	n
General (g/kg ODM)						**Degradability**					
ODM (fresh)	883.6	10.9	864.0	907.9	23	Dry matter					
TDM (fresh)						a (%)	43.5	5.1	34.0	49.0	6
CP	220.2	13.0	201.0	252.4	23	b (%)	50.6	7.4	41.4	63.2	6
MADF	110.2	17.3	72.0	141.0	23	c (h^{-1})	0.07	0.01	0.06	0.08	6
EE	46.2	18.4	17.0	80.0	23						
AEE	52.3	17.5	29.0	81.0	23	dg (%) @ outflow rate					
TA	71.5	16.8	34.0	95.0	23	0.02h^{-1}	82.5	3.0	77.0	85.0	6
GE (MJ/kg ODM)	19.2	0.48	18.5	20.2	23	0.05h^{-1}	72.8	3.4	69.0	77.0	6
						0.08h^{-1}	67.0	3.7	62.0	71.0	6
NDF ash	385.7	38.8	327.0	451.0	23						
NDF unash						Nitrogen					
ADF ash	118.6	15.9	81.0	147.0	23	a (%)	60.9	3.6	55.4	64.3	5
ADF unash	131.6	18.8	99.0	162.0	17	b (%)	35.7	3.6	31.3	39.9	5
						c (h^{-1})	0.09	0.02	0.07	0.11	5
Energy Values											
						dg (%) @ outflow rate					
DE (MJ/kg ODM)	15.8	0.65	14.2	17.1	18	0.02h^{-1}	90.0	1.0	89.0	91.0	5
ME (MJ/kg ODM)	12.9	0.65	11.3	14.2	22	0.05h^{-1}	84.0	1.4	83.0	86.0	5
FE/GE	0.18	0.04	0.12	0.26	22	0.08h^{-1}	80.0	1.4	79.0	82.0	5
UE/GE	0.06	0.01	0.05	0.09	22						
CH$_4$E/GE	0.09	0.01	0.07	0.09	22						
ME/DE	0.81	0.02	0.78	0.84	18						
ME/GE	0.67	0.04	0.59	0.74	22						
Digestibility Coefficients											
DM	0.78	0.05	0.67	0.87	22						
OM	0.82	0.04	0.74	0.89	22						
CP	0.77	0.05	0.66	0.84	22						
CF	0.68	0.16	0.22	0.97	18						
EE	0.90	0.05	0.75	0.98	18						
NDF	0.76	0.08	0.59	0.88	14						
ADF	0.72	0.12	0.41	0.88	14						
Cell	0.73	0.13	0.45	0.93	14						
GE	0.82	0.04	0.74	0.88	22						
DOMD(g/kg ODM)	765.2	40.7	689.7	863.6	22						

RUMINANT DATABASE

FEED DESCRIPTION : **MAIZE GRAIN** (Source 2)

Determination	Mean	SD	Min	Max	n	Determination	Mean	SD	Min	Max	n
General (g/kg ODM)						**Degradability**					
ODM (fresh)						Dry matter					
TDM (fresh)						a (%)					
CP	104.4	5.1	98.0	118.0	16	b (%)					
MADF	28.3	3.1	24.0	35.0	16	c (h^{-1})					
EE	39.7	5.9	30.0	51.0	16						
AEE						dg (%) @ outflow rate					
TA	14.1	1.4	13.0	17.0	16	0.02h^{-1}					
GE (MJ/kg ODM)	18.9	0.11	18.7	19.1	16	0.05h^{-1}					
						0.08h^{-1}					
NDF ash	109.1	17.2	91.0	147.0	16						
NDF unash						Nitrogen					
ADF ash	29.8	4.6	23.0	38.0	16	a (%)					
ADF unash						b (%)					
						c (h^{-1})					
Energy Values											
						dg (%) @ outflow rate					
DE (MJ/kg ODM)						0.02h^{-1}					
ME (MJ/kg ODM)	13.8	0.53	12.7	14.9	16	0.05h^{-1}					
FE/GE						0.08h^{-1}					
UE/GE	0.03	0.01	0.01	0.05	16						
CH$_4$E/GE	0.11	0.01	0.08	0.13	16						
ME/DE											
ME/GE	0.73	0.03	0.67	0.79	16						
Digestibility Coefficients											
DM											
OM	0.89	0.03	0.83	0.94	16						
CP											
CF											
EE											
NDF											
ADF											
Cell											
GE	0.87	0.03	0.81	0.92	16						
DOMD(g/kg ODM)	879.4	31.1	816.0	929.5	16						

RUMINANT DATABASE

FEED DESCRIPTION : **NAKED OATS GRAIN, ALL SEASONS** (Source 1)

Determination	Mean	SD	Min	Max	n	Determination	Mean	SD	Min	Max	n
General (g/kg ODM)						**Degradability**					
ODM (fresh)	867.4	26.2	801.0	888.9	10	Dry matter					
TDM (fresh)						a (%)	76.7	5.3	70.9	81.3	3
CP	133.0	18.3	103.0	164.0	10	b (%)	17.2	3.5	13.3	20.1	3
MADF	36.2	18.3	15.0	70.0	10	c (h^{-1})	0.34	0.07	0.27	0.41	3
EE	89.9	9.2	71.0	100.0	10						
AEE	99.1	14.0	65.0	113.0	9	dg (%) @ outflow rate					
TA	21.9	2.9	18.0	27.0	10	0.02h^{-1}	93.0	4.6	88.0	97.0	3
GE (MJ/kg ODM)	20.0	0.29	19.5	20.4	10	0.05h^{-1}	91.7	4.2	87.0	95.0	3
						0.08h^{-1}	90.7	4.2	86.0	94.0	3
NDF ash	113.9	36.6	59.0	164.0	10						
NDF unash						Nitrogen					
ADF ash	40.2	17.8	20.0	70.0	10	a (%)	73.6	4.6	69.8	78.7	3
ADF unash	41.4	19.3	19.0	71.0	10	b (%)	23.1	3.9	18.6	25.6	3
						c (h^{-1})	0.36	0.08	0.28	0.44	3
Energy Values											
						dg (%) @ outflow rate					
DE (MJ/kg ODM)	17.3	0.59	16.4	18.3	10	0.02h^{-1}	95.7	1.5	94.0	97.0	3
ME (MJ/kg ODM)	14.8	0.36	14.1	15.3	10	0.05h^{-1}	93.7	1.5	92.0	95.0	3
FE/GE	0.13	0.03	0.08	0.20	10	0.08h^{-1}	92.3	1.2	91.0	93.0	3
UE/GE	0.03	0.01	0.02	0.07	10						
CH$_4$E/GE	0.09	0.0	0.09	0.09	10						
ME/DE	0.86	0.01	0.82	0.87	10						
ME/GE	0.74	0.02	0.69	0.77	10						
Digestibility Coefficients											
DM	0.85	0.04	0.77	0.91	10						
OM	0.87	0.04	0.79	0.93	10						
CP	0.78	0.04	0.71	0.83	10						
CF	0.33	0.11	0.16	0.45	9						
EE	0.94	0.02	0.90	0.96	10						
NDF	0.54	0.17	0.35	0.73	4						
ADF	0.44	0.38	0.15	0.96	4						
Cell											
GE	0.87	0.03	0.80	0.92	10						
DOMD(g/kg ODM)	857.0	35.9	784.0	909.6	10						

RUMINANT DATABASE

FEED DESCRIPTION : **NAKED OATS GRAIN, SPRING** (Source 1)

Determination	Mean	SD	Min	Max	n	Determination	Mean	SD	Min	Max	n
General (g/kg ODM)						**Degradability**					
ODM (fresh)	859.6	28.0	801.0	882.5	7	Dry matter					
TDM (fresh)						a (%)	76.7	5.3	70.9	81.3	3
CP	126.9	18.8	103.0	164.0	7	b (%)	17.2	3.5	13.3	20.1	3
MADF	43.0	17.7	15.0	70.0	7	c (h^{-1})	0.34	0.07	0.27	0.41	3
EE	92.4	9.9	71.0	100.0	7						
AEE	98.5	17.1	65.0	113.0	6	dg (%) @ outflow rate					
TA	22.1	3.5	18.0	27.0	7	$0.02h^{-1}$	93.0	4.6	88.0	97.0	3
GE (MJ/kg ODM)	20.1	0.32	19.5	20.4	7	$0.05h^{-1}$	91.7	4.2	87.0	95.0	3
						$0.08h^{-1}$	90.7	4.2	86.0	94.0	3
NDF ash	130.0	27.7	93.0	164.0	7						
NDF unash						Nitrogen					
ADF ash	43.6	19.2	20.0	70.0	7	a (%)	73.6	4.6	69.8	78.7	3
ADF unash	43.3	20.9	19.0	71.0	7	b (%)	23.1	3.9	18.6	25.6	3
						c (h^{-1})	0.36	0.08	0.28	0.44	3
Energy Values											
						dg (%) @ outflow rate					
DE (MJ/kg ODM)	17.2	0.58	16.4	17.8	7	$0.02h^{-1}$	95.7	1.5	94.0	97.0	3
ME (MJ/kg ODM)	14.8	0.43	14.1	15.3	7	$0.05h^{-1}$	93.7	1.5	92.0	95.0	3
FE/GE	0.14	0.03	0.11	0.20	7	$0.08h^{-1}$	92.3	1.2	91.0	93.0	3
UE/GE	0.03	0.01	0.02	0.04	7						
CH_4E/GE	0.09	0.0	0.09	0.09	7						
ME/DE	0.86	0.01	0.85	0.87	7						
ME/GE	0.74	0.02	0.69	0.77	7						
Digestibility Coefficients											
DM	0.84	0.04	0.77	0.91	7						
OM	0.86	0.04	0.79	0.91	7						
CP	0.78	0.04	0.71	0.83	7						
CF	0.32	0.12	0.16	0.44	7						
EE	0.93	0.02	0.90	0.96	7						
NDF	0.63		0.63	0.63	1						
ADF	0.18		0.18	0.18	1						
Cell											
GE	0.86	0.03	0.80	0.89	7						
DOMD(g/kg ODM)	848.1	37.1	784.0	897.9	7						

RUMINANT DATABASE

FEED DESCRIPTION : **NAKED OATS GRAIN, WINTER** (Source 1)

Determination	Mean	SD	Min	Max	n	Determination	Mean	SD	Min	Max	n
General (g/kg ODM)						**Degradability**					
ODM (fresh)	885.6	5.5	879.3	888.9	3	Dry matter					
TDM (fresh)						a (%)					
CP	147.3	2.1	145.4	149.5	3	b (%)					
MADF	20.3	4.2	17.0	25.0	3	c (h^{-1})					
EE	84.0	3.0	81.0	87.0	3						
AEE	100.3	6.4	93.0	105.0	3	dg (%) @ outflow rate					
TA	21.3	1.2	20.0	22.0	3	0.02h^{-1}					
GE (MJ/kg ODM)	19.9	0.20	19.7	20.1	3	0.05h^{-1}					
						0.08h^{-1}					
NDF ash	76.3	26.6	59.0	107.0	3						
NDF unash						Nitrogen					
ADF ash	32.3	13.7	23.0	48.0	3	a (%)					
ADF unash	37.0	17.8	23.0	57.0	3	b (%)					
						c (h^{-1})					
Energy Values											
						dg (%) @ outflow rate					
DE (MJ/kg ODM)	17.5	0.63	17.1	18.3	3	0.02h^{-1}					
ME (MJ/kg ODM)	14.9	0.15	14.7	15.0	3	0.05h^{-1}					
FE/GE	0.12	0.03	0.08	0.14	3	0.08h^{-1}					
UE/GE	0.04	0.03	0.02	0.07	3						
CH$_4$E/GE	0.09	0.0	0.09	0.09	3						
ME/DE	0.85	0.03	0.82	0.87	3						
ME/GE	0.75	0.0	0.75	0.75	3						
Digestibility Coefficients											
DM	0.87	0.03	0.85	0.91	3						
OM	0.89	0.03	0.87	0.93	3						
CP	0.80	0.03	0.76	0.82	3						
CF	0.37	0.11	0.29	0.45	2						
EE	0.94	0.02	0.93	0.95	3						
NDF	0.51	0.20	0.35	0.73	3						
ADF	0.52	0.41	0.15	0.96	3						
Cell											
GE	0.88	0.03	0.86	0.92	3						
DOMD(g/kg ODM)	877.7	27.6	861.2	909.6	3						

RUMINANT DATABASE

FEED DESCRIPTION : **OATS GRAIN, ALL SEASONS** (Sources 1, 2)

Determination	Mean	SD	Min	Max	n	Determination	Mean	SD	Min	Max	n
General (g/kg ODM)						**Degradability**					
ODM (fresh)	854.7	18.5	820.0	889.4	21	Dry matter					
TDM (fresh)						a (%)	58.0	6.9	51.3	64.3	4
CP	104.8	12.6	79.4	132.5	21	b (%)	17.2	4.2	11.5	20.7	4
MADF	134.0	18.1	117.0	154.6	5	c (h^{-1})	0.23	0.13	0.08	0.35	4
EE	40.5	15.7	16.0	67.0	21						
AEE	69.8	5.4	63.0	75.0	5	dg (%) @ outflow rate					
TA	25.4	2.0	22.0	30.0	21	$0.02h^{-1}$	73.3	3.3	71.0	78.0	4
GE (MJ/kg ODM)	19.6	0.19	19.1	19.8	21	$0.05h^{-1}$	71.5	3.1	69.0	76.0	4
						$0.08h^{-1}$	70.5	3.1	68.0	75.0	4
NDF ash	312.2	21.4	256.0	342.0	21						
NDF unash						Nitrogen					
ADF ash	148.1	12.6	131.0	177.0	21	a (%)	72.0	3.3	68.8	76.5	4
ADF unash	146.2	7.3	136.0	155.0	5	b (%)	23.4	3.0	20.2	27.0	4
						c (h^{-1})	0.40	0.01	0.39	0.42	4
Energy Values											
						dg (%) @ outflow rate					
DE (MJ/kg ODM)	14.6	1.1	13.0	15.6	5	$0.02h^{-1}$	94.5	2.4	91.0	96.0	4
ME (MJ/kg ODM)	12.1	0.77	10.6	13.4	21	$0.05h^{-1}$	92.8	1.9	90.0	94.0	4
FE/GE	0.25	0.06	0.19	0.34	5	$0.08h^{-1}$	91.5	1.9	89.0	93.0	4
UE/GE	0.03	0.01	0.02	0.05	21						
CH_4E/GE	0.08	0.02	0.06	0.13	21						
ME/DE	0.85	0.01	0.83	0.86	5						
ME/GE	0.62	0.04	0.55	0.69	21						

Digestibility Coefficients

Determination	Mean	SD	Min	Max	n
DM	0.74	0.05	0.66	0.79	5
OM	0.76	0.05	0.68	0.81	5
CP	0.73	0.04	0.66	0.77	5
CF	0.35	0.18	0.12	0.56	5
EE	0.96	0.02	0.93	0.98	5
NDF	0.40	0.14	0.23	0.52	5
ADF	0.40	0.14	0.19	0.57	5
Cell	0.39	0.18	0.14	0.60	5
GE	0.72	0.04	0.66	0.81	21
DOMD(g/kg ODM)	739.6	54.0	659.3	791.8	5

RUMINANT DATABASE

FEED DESCRIPTION : **OATS GRAIN, SPRING** (Source 2)

Determination	Mean	SD	Min	Max	n	Determination	Mean	SD	Min	Max	n
General (g/kg ODM)						**Degradability**					
ODM (fresh)	847.1	14.7	820.0	869.0	15	Dry matter					
TDM (fresh)						a (%)					
CP	103.5	14.0	79.4	132.5	15	b (%)					
MADF						c (h^{-1})					
EE	34.3	12.4	16.0	62.0	15						
AEE						dg (%) @ outflow rate					
TA	25.2	1.8	22.0	28.0	15	0.02h^{-1}					
GE (MJ/kg ODM)	19.6	0.20	19.1	19.8	15	0.05h^{-1}					
						0.08h^{-1}					
NDF ash	320.2	15.2	283.0	342.0	15						
NDF unash						Nitrogen					
ADF ash	150.7	13.1	133.0	177.0	15	a (%)					
ADF unash						b (%)					
						c (h^{-1})					
Energy Values											
						dg (%) @ outflow rate					
DE (MJ/kg ODM)						0.02h^{-1}					
ME (MJ/kg ODM)	11.9	0.72	10.6	13.4	15	0.05h^{-1}					
FE/GE						0.08h^{-1}					
UE/GE	0.03	0.01	0.02	0.04	15						
CH$_4$E/GE	0.08	0.02	0.06	0.13	15						
ME/DE											
ME/GE	0.61	0.04	0.55	0.68	15						

Digestibility Coefficients

	Mean	SD	Min	Max	n
DM					
OM					
CP					
CF					
EE					
NDF					
ADF					
Cell					
GE	0.71	0.04	0.66	0.78	15

DOMD(g/kg ODM)

RUMINANT DATABASE

FEED DESCRIPTION : **OATS GRAIN, WINTER** (Sources 1, 2)

Determination	Mean	SD	Min	Max	n	Determination	Mean	SD	Min	Max	n
General (g/kg ODM)						**Degradability**					
ODM (fresh)	873.7	12.6	851.0	889.4	6	Dry matter					
TDM (fresh)						a (%)	58.0	6.9	51.3	64.3	4
CP	108.0	8.2	98.5	120.6	6	b (%)	17.2	4.2	11.5	20.7	4
MADF	134.0	18.1	117.0	154.6	5	c (h^{-1})	0.23	0.13	0.08	0.35	4
EE	56.0	12.4	33.0	67.0	6						
AEE	69.8	5.4	63.0	75.0	5	dg (%) @ outflow rate					
TA	25.8	2.5	23.0	30.0	6	$0.02h^{-1}$	73.3	3.3	71.0	78.0	4
GE (MJ/kg ODM)	19.5	0.18	19.3	19.7	6	$0.05h^{-1}$	71.5	3.1	69.0	76.0	4
						$0.08h^{-1}$	70.5	3.1	68.0	75.0	4
NDF ash	292.3	22.7	256.0	312.0	6						
NDF unash						Nitrogen					
ADF ash	141.5	8.8	131.0	153.0	6	a (%)	72.0	3.3	68.8	76.5	4
ADF unash	146.2	7.3	136.0	155.0	5	b (%)	23.4	3.0	20.2	27.0	4
						c (h^{-1})	0.40	0.01	0.39	0.42	4
Energy Values											
						dg (%) @ outflow rate					
DE (MJ/kg ODM)	14.6	1.1	13.0	15.6	5	$0.02h^{-1}$	94.5	2.4	91.0	96.0	4
ME (MJ/kg ODM)	12.5	0.81	11.1	13.4	6	$0.05h^{-1}$	92.8	1.9	90.0	94.0	4
FE/GE	0.25	0.06	0.19	0.34	5	$0.08h^{-1}$	91.5	1.9	89.0	93.0	4
UE/GE	0.03	0.01	0.02	0.05	6						
CH_4E/GE	0.08	0.01	0.07	0.09	6						
ME/DE	0.85	0.01	0.83	0.86	5						
ME/GE	0.64	0.04	0.56	0.69	6						
Digestibility Coefficients											
DM	0.74	0.05	0.66	0.79	5						
OM	0.76	0.05	0.68	0.81	5						
CP	0.73	0.04	0.66	0.77	5						
CF	0.35	0.18	0.12	0.56	5						
EE	0.96	0.02	0.93	0.98	5						
NDF	0.40	0.14	0.23	0.52	5						
ADF	0.40	0.14	0.19	0.57	5						
Cell	0.39	0.18	0.14	0.60	5						
GE	0.74	0.06	0.66	0.81	6						
DOMD(g/kg ODM)	739.6	54.0	659.3	791.8	5						

RUMINANT DATABASE

FEED DESCRIPTION : **OLIVE PULP MEAL** (Source 1)

Determination	Mean	SD	Min	Max	n	Determination	Mean	SD	Min	Max	n

General (g/kg ODM)

Degradability

ODM (fresh)	881.1		881.1	881.1	1	Dry matter					
TDM (fresh)						a (%)					
CP	108.0		108.0	108.0	1	b (%)					
MADF	523.0		523.0	523.0	1	c (h^{-1})					
EE	18.0		18.0	18.0	1						
AEE	16.0		16.0	16.0	1	dg (%) @ outflow rate					
TA	76.0		76.0	76.0	1	$0.02h^{-1}$					
GE (MJ/kg ODM)	20.0		20.0	20.0	1	$0.05h^{-1}$					
						$0.08h^{-1}$					
NDF ash	684.0		684.0	684.0	1						
NDF unash						Nitrogen					
ADF ash	543.0		543.0	543.0	1	a (%)					
ADF unash	567.0		567.0	567.0	1	b (%)					
						c (h^{-1})					

Energy Values

						dg (%) @ outflow rate					
DE (MJ/kg ODM)	5.4		5.4	5.4	1	$0.02h^{-1}$					
ME (MJ/kg ODM)	4.3		4.3	4.3	1	$0.05h^{-1}$					
FE/GE	0.73		0.73	0.73	1	$0.08h^{-1}$					
UE/GE											
CH_4E/GE	0.05		0.05	0.05	1						
ME/DE	0.79		0.79	0.79	1						
ME/GE	0.21		0.21	0.21	1						

Digestibility Coefficients

DM	0.17		0.17	0.17	1
OM	0.21		0.21	0.21	1
CP					
CF	0.13		0.13	0.13	1
EE	0.84		0.84	0.84	1
NDF					
ADF					
Cell					
GE	0.27		0.27	0.27	1
DOMD(g/kg ODM)	198.5		198.5	198.5	1

RUMINANT DATABASE

FEED DESCRIPTION : **PECTIN EXTRACTED FRUITS** (Source 1)

Determination	Mean	SD	Min	Max	n	Determination	Mean	SD	Min	Max	n
General (g/kg ODM)						**Degradability**					
ODM (fresh)	163.5	13.4	154.0	173.0	2	Dry matter					
TDM (fresh)	166.5	13.4	157.0	176.0	2	a (%)					
CP	105.0	1.4	104.0	106.0	2	b (%)					
MADF	624.5	21.9	609.0	640.0	2	c (h^{-1})					
EE	35.5	0.71	35.0	36.0	2						
AEE	41.5	2.1	40.0	43.0	2	dg (%) @ outflow rate					
TA	13.0	4.2	10.0	16.0	2	0.02h^{-1}					
GE (MJ/kg ODM)	20.7	0.78	20.1	21.2	2	0.05h^{-1}					
						0.08h^{-1}					
NDF ash	767.0	4.2	764.0	770.0	2						
NDF unash						Nitrogen					
ADF ash	708.0	4.2	705.0	711.0	2	a (%)					
ADF unash	674.5	2.1	673.0	676.0	2	b (%)					
						c (h^{-1})					
Energy Values											
						dg (%) @ outflow rate					
DE (MJ/kg ODM)	11.7	0.61	11.3	12.1	2	0.02h^{-1}					
ME (MJ/kg ODM)	9.9	0.80	9.3	10.5	2	0.05h^{-1}					
FE/GE	0.43	0.04	0.40	0.46	2	0.08h^{-1}					
UE/GE	0.02	0.01	0.01	0.02	2						
CH$_4$E/GE	0.07	0.0	0.07	0.07	2						
ME/DE	0.84	0.03	0.83	0.86	2						
ME/GE	0.48	0.06	0.44	0.52	2						
Digestibility Coefficients											
DM	0.56	0.04	0.53	0.59	2						
OM	0.61	0.04	0.58	0.63	2						
CP	0.23	0.06	0.19	0.28	2						
CF	0.67	0.08	0.62	0.73	2						
EE	0.77	0.25	0.59	0.95	2						
NDF											
ADF											
Cell											
GE	0.57	0.05	0.54	0.60	2						
DOMD(g/kg ODM)	603.1	30.6	581.5	624.7	2						

RUMINANT DATABASE

FEED DESCRIPTION : **POTATOES, FRESH** (Source 2)

Determination	Mean	SD	Min	Max	n		Determination	Mean	SD	Min	Max	n
General (g/kg ODM)							**Degradability**					
ODM (fresh)	203.9	7.2	198.8	209.0	2		Dry matter					
TDM (fresh)							a (%)					
CP	108.2	7.0	103.3	113.2	2		b (%)					
MADF	39.2	0.65	38.8	39.7	2		c (h^{-1})					
EE	2.4	0.11	2.3	2.5	2							
AEE							dg (%) @ outflow rate					
TA	52.8	2.2	51.3	54.3	2		$0.02h^{-1}$					
GE (MJ/kg ODM)	17.2	0.09	17.2	17.3	2		$0.05h^{-1}$					
							$0.08h^{-1}$					
NDF ash	73.2	3.6	70.7	75.8	2							
NDF unash							Nitrogen					
ADF ash	43.6	1.2	42.8	44.5	2		a (%)					
ADF unash							b (%)					
							c (h^{-1})					
Energy Values												
							dg (%) @ outflow rate					
DE (MJ/kg ODM)							$0.02h^{-1}$					
ME (MJ/kg ODM)	13.4	0.02	13.3	13.4	2		$0.05h^{-1}$					
FE/GE							$0.08h^{-1}$					
UE/GE	0.03	0.0	0.03	0.03	2							
CH$_4$E/GE	0.10	0.01	0.10	0.11	2							
ME/DE												
ME/GE	0.77	0.01	0.77	0.78	2							
Digestibility Coefficients												
DM												
OM	0.93	0.0	0.93	0.93	2							
CP												
CF												
EE												
NDF												
ADF												
Cell												
GE	0.90	0.0	0.90	0.91	2							
DOMD(g/kg ODM)	882.0		882.0	882.0	1							

FEED CLASS 40

FEED DESCRIPTION : **POTATO, PROCESSING WASTE** (Source 1)

Determination	Mean	SD	Min	Max	n	Determination	Mean	SD	Min	Max	n
General (g/kg ODM)						**Degradability**					
ODM (fresh)	982.5		982.5	982.5	1	Dry matter					
TDM (fresh)						a (%)					
CP	91.0		91.0	91.0	1	b (%)					
MADF	28.0		28.0	28.0	1	c (h^{-1})					
EE	22.0		22.0	22.0	1						
AEE						dg (%) @ outflow rate					
TA	92.0		92.0	92.0	1	0.02h^{-1}					
GE (MJ/kg ODM)	16.5		16.5	16.5	1	0.05h^{-1}					
						0.08h^{-1}					
NDF ash											
NDF unash						Nitrogen					
ADF ash						a (%)					
ADF unash	33.0		33.0	33.0	1	b (%)					
						c (h^{-1})					
Energy Values											
						dg (%) @ outflow rate					
DE (MJ/kg ODM)	12.0		12.0	12.0	1	0.02h^{-1}					
ME (MJ/kg ODM)	10.5		10.5	10.5	1	0.05h^{-1}					
FE/GE	0.27		0.27	0.27	1	0.08h^{-1}					
UE/GE	0.01		0.01	0.01	1						
CH$_4$E/GE	0.08		0.08	0.08	1						
ME/DE	0.87		0.87	0.87	1						
ME/GE	0.64		0.64	0.64	1						
Digestibility Coefficients											
DM	0.66		0.66	0.66	1						
OM	0.69		0.69	0.69	1						
CP	0.49		0.49	0.49	1						
CF											
EE											
NDF											
ADF											
Cell											
GE	0.73		0.73	0.73	1						
DOMD(g/kg ODM)	633.7		633.7	633.7	1						

RUMINANT DATABASE

FEED DESCRIPTION : **RICE BRAN MEAL, EXPELLED** (Source 2)

Determination	Mean	SD	Min	Max	n	Determination	Mean	SD	Min	Max	n
General (g/kg ODM)						**Degradability**					
ODM (fresh)	902.0		902.0	902.0	1	Dry matter					
TDM (fresh)						a (%)					
CP	128.0		128.0	128.0	1	b (%)					
MADF	229.0		229.0	229.0	1	c (h^{-1})					
EE	90.0		90.0	90.0	1						
AEE						dg (%) @ outflow rate					
TA	113.0		113.0	113.0	1	$0.02h^{-1}$					
GE (MJ/kg ODM)	18.9		18.9	18.9	1	$0.05h^{-1}$					
						$0.08h^{-1}$					
NDF ash	370.0		370.0	370.0	1						
NDF unash						Nitrogen					
ADF ash	242.0		242.0	242.0	1	a (%)					
ADF unash						b (%)					
						c (h^{-1})					
Energy Values											
						dg (%) @ outflow rate					
DE (MJ/kg ODM)						$0.02h^{-1}$					
ME (MJ/kg ODM)	11.0		11.0	11.0	1	$0.05h^{-1}$					
FE/GE	0.35		0.35	0.35	1	$0.08h^{-1}$					
UE/GE	0.03		0.03	0.03	1						
CH_4E/GE	0.04		0.04	0.04	1						
ME/DE											
ME/GE	0.58		0.58	0.58	1						
Digestibility Coefficients											
DM	0.60		0.60	0.60	1						
OM	0.66		0.66	0.66	1						
CP	0.65		0.65	0.65	1						
CF											
EE											
NDF											
ADF											
Cell											
GE	0.65		0.65	0.65	1						
DOMD(g/kg ODM)	585.0		585.0	585.0	1						

RUMINANT DATABASE

FEED DESCRIPTION : **RICE BRAN MEAL, EXTRACTED** (Source 2)

Determination	Mean	SD	Min	Max	n
General (g/kg ODM)					
ODM (fresh)	886.0	10.1	875.0	895.0	3
TDM (fresh)					
CP	165.3	5.1	161.0	171.0	3
MADF	277.7	35.9	254.0	319.0	3
EE	7.0	2.0	5.0	9.0	3
AEE					
TA	160.3	10.6	149.0	170.0	3
GE (MJ/kg ODM)	16.7	0.29	16.5	17.0	3
NDF ash	487.3	76.7	408.0	561.0	3
NDF unash					
ADF ash	298.3	36.5	272.0	340.0	3
ADF unash					
Energy Values					
DE (MJ/kg ODM)					
ME (MJ/kg ODM)	7.1	0.32	6.7	7.3	3
FE/GE	0.47	0.03	0.44	0.51	3
UE/GE	0.04	0.01	0.03	0.05	3
CH_4E/GE	0.06	0.01	0.06	0.07	3
ME/DE					
ME/GE	0.43	0.02	0.41	0.44	3
Digestibility Coefficients					
DM	0.48	0.03	0.44	0.50	3
OM	0.55	0.03	0.51	0.57	3
CP	0.60	0.05	0.55	0.65	3
CF					
EE					
NDF					
ADF					
Cell					
GE	0.53	0.03	0.50	0.54	3
DOMD(g/kg ODM)	460.7	29.2	427.0	478.0	3

Determination	Mean	SD	Min	Max	n
Degradability					
Dry matter					
a (%)					
b (%)					
c (h^{-1})					
dg (%) @ outflow rate					
$0.02h^{-1}$					
$0.05h^{-1}$					
$0.08h^{-1}$					
Nitrogen					
a (%)					
b (%)					
c (h^{-1})					
dg (%) @ outflow rate					
$0.02h^{-1}$					
$0.05h^{-1}$					
$0.08h^{-1}$					

RUMINANT DATABASE

FEED DESCRIPTION : **SAINFOIN, LOW TEMP DRIED**   (Source 1)

Determination	Mean	SD	Min	Max	n	Determination	Mean	SD	Min	Max	n

General (g/kg ODM)

						Degradability					
ODM (fresh)	854.1		854.1	854.1	1	Dry matter					
TDM (fresh)						a (%)					
CP	189.0		189.0	189.0	1	b (%)					
MADF	256.0		256.0	256.0	1	c (h^{-1})					
EE	19.0		19.0	19.0	1						
AEE	17.0		17.0	17.0	1	dg (%) @ outflow rate					
TA	78.0		78.0	78.0	1	$0.02h^{-1}$					
GE (MJ/kg ODM)	20.0		20.0	20.0	1	$0.05h^{-1}$					
						$0.08h^{-1}$					
NDF ash	448.0		448.0	448.0	1						
NDF unash						Nitrogen					
ADF ash						a (%)					
ADF unash	306.0		306.0	306.0	1	b (%)					
						c (h^{-1})					

Energy Values

						dg (%) @ outflow rate					
DE (MJ/kg ODM)	13.8		13.8	13.8	1	$0.02h^{-1}$					
ME (MJ/kg ODM)	10.9		10.9	10.9	1	$0.05h^{-1}$					
FE/GE	0.31		0.31	0.31	1	$0.08h^{-1}$					
UE/GE	0.07		0.07	0.07	1						
CH_4E/GE	0.08		0.08	0.08	1						
ME/DE	0.79		0.79	0.79	1						
ME/GE	0.55		0.55	0.55	1						

Digestibility Coefficients

DM	0.63		0.63	0.63	1
OM	0.70		0.70	0.70	1
CP	0.51		0.51	0.51	1
CF	0.61		0.61	0.61	1
EE	0.88		0.88	0.88	1
NDF					
ADF					
Cell					
GE	0.69		0.69	0.69	1
DOMD(g/kg ODM)	652.3		652.3	652.3	1

RUMINANT DATABASE

FEED DESCRIPTION : **SORGHUM GRAIN** (Source 2)

Determination	Mean	SD	Min	Max	n	Determination	Mean	SD	Min	Max	n
General (g/kg ODM)						**Degradability**					
ODM (fresh)						Dry matter					
TDM (fresh)						a (%)					
CP	109.5	4.1	106.0	114.0	4	b (%)					
MADF	48.8	10.6	41.0	64.0	4	c (h^{-1})					
EE	32.3	2.6	30.0	35.0	4						
AEE						dg (%) @ outflow rate					
TA	17.0	1.4	16.0	19.0	4	$0.02h^{-1}$					
GE (MJ/kg ODM)	18.7	0.12	18.6	18.9	4	$0.05h^{-1}$					
						$0.08h^{-1}$					
NDF ash	107.3	2.2	105.0	110.0	4						
NDF unash						Nitrogen					
ADF ash	57.0	10.2	49.0	71.0	4	a (%)					
ADF unash						b (%)					
						c (h^{-1})					
Energy Values						dg (%) @ outflow rate					
DE (MJ/kg ODM)						$0.02h^{-1}$					
ME (MJ/kg ODM)	13.2	0.99	12.1	14.4	4	$0.05h^{-1}$					
FE/GE	0.17	0.04	0.12	0.22	4	$0.08h^{-1}$					
UE/GE	0.02	0.01	0.01	0.03	4						
CH_4E/GE	0.11	0.02	0.09	0.13	4						
ME/DE											
ME/GE	0.71	0.05	0.65	0.77	4						
Digestibility Coefficients											
DM											
OM	0.86	0.04	0.82	0.91	4						
CP											
CF											
EE											
NDF											
ADF											
Cell											
GE	0.83	0.04	0.79	0.88	4						
DOMD(g/kg ODM)	850.0	38.5	807.0	895.0	4						

RUMINANT DATABASE

FEED DESCRIPTION : **SUGAR BEET FEED DRIED, MOLASSED** (Source 2)

Determination	Mean	SD	Min	Max	n	Determination	Mean	SD	Min	Max	n
General (g/kg ODM)						**Degradability**					
ODM (fresh)	891.4	2.3	889.0	894.1	6	Dry matter					
TDM (fresh)						a (%)					
CP	120.7	13.0	102.2	139.0	14	b (%)					
MADF	173.9	7.0	164.0	191.0	14	c (h^{-1})					
EE	4.6	1.5	3.0	8.0	14						
AEE	3.8	1.2	3.0	6.0	6	dg (%) @ outflow rate					
TA	84.9	6.4	75.0	99.0	14	$0.02h^{-1}$					
GE (MJ/kg ODM)	17.1	0.21	16.5	17.4	14	$0.05h^{-1}$					
						$0.08h^{-1}$					
NDF ash	313.3	28.3	271.0	362.0	14						
NDF unash						Nitrogen					
ADF ash	178.6	7.2	164.0	190.0	14	a (%)					
ADF unash	189.2	7.5	175.0	195.0	6	b (%)					
						c (h^{-1})					
Energy Values											
						dg (%) @ outflow rate					
DE (MJ/kg ODM)	15.0	0.26	14.6	15.3	6	$0.02h^{-1}$					
ME (MJ/kg ODM)	12.5	0.36	11.7	13.1	14	$0.05h^{-1}$					
FE/GE	0.13	0.02	0.11	0.16	14	$0.08h^{-1}$					
UE/GE	0.04	0.01	0.02	0.05	14						
CH_4E/GE	0.10	0.01	0.08	0.12	14						
ME/DE	0.84	0.0	0.83	0.85	6						
ME/GE	0.74	0.02	0.68	0.77	14						
Digestibility Coefficients											
DM	0.87	0.02	0.85	0.88	6						
OM	0.90	0.01	0.87	0.92	14						
CP	0.71	0.03	0.67	0.75	6						
CF	0.92	0.04	0.87	0.98	6						
EE	0.21	0.06	0.16	0.25	2						
NDF	0.92	0.01	0.90	0.93	3						
ADF	0.55	0.10	0.49	0.66	3						
Cell											
GE	0.87	0.02	0.84	0.89	14						
DOMD(g/kg ODM)	823.1	12.3	798.0	846.0	14						

RUMINANT DATABASE

FEED DESCRIPTION : **SUGAR BEET FEED, DRIED, UNMOLASSED** (Source 1)

Determination	Mean	SD	Min	Max	n	Determination	Mean	SD	Min	Max	n
General (g/kg ODM)						Degradability					
ODM (fresh)	856.1	40.1	826.2	901.7	3	Dry matter					
TDM (fresh)						a (%)					
CP	77.2		77.2	77.2	1	b (%)					
MADF	206.7	47.6	172.0	261.0	3	c (h^{-1})					
EE	6.7	2.9	5.0	10.0	3						
AEE	5.0	1.4	4.0	6.0	2	dg (%) @ outflow rate					
TA	68.3	21.5	46.0	89.0	3	0.02h^{-1}					
GE (MJ/kg ODM)	17.1	0.50	16.6	17.6	3	0.05h^{-1}					
						0.08h^{-1}					
NDF ash	372.3	111.5	304.0	501.0	3						
NDF unash						Nitrogen					
ADF ash	212.7	60.6	170.0	282.0	3	a (%)					
ADF unash	224.3	57.5	179.0	289.0	3	b (%)					
						c (h^{-1})					
Energy Values											
						dg (%) @ outflow rate					
DE (MJ/kg ODM)	15.3	0.37	14.9	15.6	3	0.02h^{-1}					
ME (MJ/kg ODM)	12.9	0.28	12.6	13.2	3	0.05h^{-1}					
FE/GE	0.11	0.04	0.08	0.16	3	0.08h^{-1}					
UE/GE	0.05	0.01	0.04	0.05	3						
CH$_4$E/GE	0.09	0.0	0.09	0.09	3						
ME/DE	0.84	0.01	0.84	0.85	3						
ME/GE	0.75	0.03	0.72	0.78	3						
Digestibility Coefficients											
DM	0.84	0.01	0.84	0.85	3						
OM	0.89	0.02	0.87	0.90	3						
CP	0.54		0.54	0.54	1						
CF	0.80	0.03	0.78	0.83	3						
EE	0.22	0.08	0.16	0.28	2						
NDF	0.86		0.86	0.86	1						
ADF	0.86		0.86	0.86	1						
Cell	0.87		0.87	0.87	1						
GE	0.89	0.04	0.84	0.92	3						
DOMD(g/kg ODM)	832.1	9.5	821.7	840.3	3						

RUMINANT DATABASE

FEED DESCRIPTION : **SUGAR BEET FEED, ENSILED** (Source 1)

Determination	Mean	SD	Min	Max	n	Determination	Mean	SD	Min	Max	n
General (g/kg ODM)						**Degradability**					
ODM (fresh)	163.0	15.9	142.0	178.0	4	Dry matter					
TDM (fresh)	174.5	15.9	154.0	191.0	4	a (%)					
CP	111.3	6.3	104.0	119.0	4	b (%)					
MADF	289.8	7.3	282.0	296.0	4	c (h^{-1})					
EE	6.5	3.4	2.0	10.0	4						
AEE	10.3	3.1	7.0	13.0	3	dg (%) @ outflow rate					
TA	92.5	24.1	72.0	127.0	4	$0.02h^{-1}$					
GE (MJ/kg ODM)	17.0	0.78	16.0	17.7	4	$0.05h^{-1}$					
						$0.08h^{-1}$					
NDF ash	418.0	35.7	384.0	458.0	4						
NDF unash						Nitrogen					
ADF ash	272.5	11.7	257.0	285.0	4	a (%)					
ADF unash	302.5	19.4	276.0	317.0	4	b (%)					
						c (h^{-1})					
Energy Values											
						dg (%) @ outflow rate					
DE (MJ/kg ODM)	13.6	0.85	12.6	14.5	4	$0.02h^{-1}$					
ME (MJ/kg ODM)	11.5	0.84	10.5	12.3	4	$0.05h^{-1}$					
FE/GE	0.20	0.05	0.13	0.24	4	$0.08h^{-1}$					
UE/GE	0.04	0.02	0.02	0.05	4						
CH_4E/GE	0.09	0.0	0.08	0.09	4						
ME/DE	0.85	0.01	0.83	0.86	4						
ME/GE	0.68	0.04	0.64	0.74	4						
Digestibility Coefficients											
DM	0.77	0.06	0.72	0.85	4						
OM	0.83	0.04	0.79	0.89	4						
CP	0.59	0.14	0.42	0.75	4						
CF	0.87	0.04	0.84	0.93	4						
EE	0.33	0.09	0.27	0.42	3						
NDF											
ADF											
Cell											
GE	0.80	0.05	0.76	0.87	4						
DOMD(g/kg ODM)	756.6	42.4	724.8	817.0	4						

RUMINANT DATABASE

FEED DESCRIPTION : **SUGAR BEET FEED, PRESSED** (Source 1)

Determination	Mean	SD	Min	Max	n	Determination	Mean	SD	Min	Max	n
General (g/kg ODM)						**Degradability**					
ODM (fresh)	189.0	14.4	174.0	205.0	5	Dry matter					
TDM (fresh)						a (%)					
CP	98.5	0.71	98.0	99.0	2	b (%)					
MADF	271.8	15.2	252.0	294.0	5	c (h^{-1})					
EE	5.6	0.55	5.0	6.0	5						
AEE	5.0	0.0	5.0	5.0	4	dg (%) @ outflow rate					
TA	82.2	17.1	65.0	110.0	5	0.02h^{-1}					
GE (MJ/kg ODM)	17.0	0.28	16.6	17.3	5	0.05h^{-1}					
						0.08h^{-1}					
NDF ash	523.3	45.5	489.0	590.0	4						
NDF unash						Nitrogen					
ADF ash	251.0	6.3	243.0	258.0	4	a (%)					
ADF unash	288.0	16.7	263.0	309.0	5	b (%)					
						c (h^{-1})					
Energy Values						dg (%) @ outflow rate					
DE (MJ/kg ODM)	13.7	0.81	12.8	14.6	5	0.02h^{-1}					
ME (MJ/kg ODM)	11.7	0.86	10.6	12.5	5	0.05h^{-1}					
FE/GE	0.20	0.05	0.15	0.26	5	0.08h^{-1}					
UE/GE	0.03	0.01	0.02	0.05	5						
CH$_4$E/GE	0.09	0.01	0.08	0.09	5						
ME/DE	0.85	0.02	0.83	0.86	5						
ME/GE	0.69	0.05	0.61	0.73	5						
Digestibility Coefficients											
DM	0.74	0.06	0.68	0.79	5						
OM	0.82	0.04	0.77	0.86	5						
CP	0.48	0.04	0.45	0.51	2						
CF	0.85	0.06	0.78	0.90	5						
EE	0.16	0.14	0.02	0.30	3						
NDF											
ADF											
Cell											
GE	0.80	0.05	0.74	0.85	5						
DOMD(g/kg ODM)	761.0	40.3	708.0	798.5	5						

RUMINANT DATABASE

FEED DESCRIPTION : **SWEDES** (Source 2)

Determination	Mean	SD	Min	Max	n	Determination	Mean	SD	Min	Max	n
General (g/kg ODM)						**Degradability**					
ODM (fresh)	104.5	13.1	95.3	113.8	2	Dry matter					
TDM (fresh)						a (%)					
CP	90.5	8.1	84.8	96.3	2	b (%)					
MADF	114.3	7.0	109.4	119.3	2	c (h^{-1})					
EE	3.8	0.28	3.6	4.0	2						
AEE						dg (%) @ outflow rate					
TA	60.1	8.0	54.4	65.8	2	$0.02h^{-1}$					
GE (MJ/kg ODM)	17.3	0.07	17.3	17.4	2	$0.05h^{-1}$					
						$0.08h^{-1}$					
NDF ash	140.4	1.6	139.2	141.5	2						
NDF unash						Nitrogen					
ADF ash	125.4	6.5	120.8	130.0	2	a (%)					
ADF unash						b (%)					
						c (h^{-1})					
Energy Values											
						dg (%) @ outflow rate					
DE (MJ/kg ODM)						$0.02h^{-1}$					
ME (MJ/kg ODM)	14.0	0.08	13.9	14.0	2	$0.05h^{-1}$					
FE/GE						$0.08h^{-1}$					
UE/GE	0.02	0.0	0.02	0.03	2						
CH_4E/GE	0.09	0.0	0.08	0.09	2						
ME/DE											
ME/GE	0.81	0.0	0.80	0.81	2						
Digestibility Coefficients											
DM											
OM	0.93	0.0	0.93	0.93	2						
CP											
CF											
EE											
NDF											
ADF											
Cell											
GE	0.92	0.0	0.91	0.92	2						
DOMD(g/kg ODM)	876.1	7.8	870.5	881.6	2						

RUMINANT DATABASE

FEED DESCRIPTION : **TRIPLE NUTS** (Source 2)

Determination	Mean	SD	Min	Max	n	Determination	Mean	SD	Min	Max	n
General (g/kg ODM)						**Degradability**					
ODM (fresh)						**Dry matter**					
TDM (fresh)						a (%)					
CP	204.0	1.4	202.0	205.0	4	b (%)					
MADF	157.8	1.3	156.0	159.0	4	c (h^{-1})					
EE	4.8	1.7	3.0	7.0	4						
AEE						dg (%) @ outflow rate					
TA	109.5	2.6	107.0	113.0	4	$0.02h^{-1}$					
GE (MJ/kg ODM)	16.2	0.03	16.1	16.2	4	$0.05h^{-1}$					
						$0.08h^{-1}$					
NDF ash	261.5	3.4	258.0	266.0	4						
NDF unash						**Nitrogen**					
ADF ash	167.5	4.7	164.0	174.0	4	a (%)					
ADF unash						b (%)					
						c (h^{-1})					
Energy Values											
						dg (%) @ outflow rate					
DE (MJ/kg ODM)						$0.02h^{-1}$					
ME (MJ/kg ODM)	12.0	0.66	11.4	12.8	4	$0.05h^{-1}$					
FE/GE	0.13	0.04	0.09	0.17	4	$0.08h^{-1}$					
UE/GE	0.04	0.01	0.03	0.05	4						
CH_4E/GE	0.11	0.01	0.11	0.12	4						
ME/DE											
ME/GE	0.74	0.04	0.70	0.79	4						
Digestibility Coefficients											
DM											
OM	0.90	0.03	0.87	0.94	4						
CP											
CF											
EE											
NDF											
ADF											
Cell											
GE	0.87	0.04	0.83	0.91	4						
DOMD(g/kg ODM)	802.8	29.5	773.0	837.0	4						

RUMINANT DATABASE

FEED DESCRIPTION : **TRITICALE GRAIN, WINTER** (Source 1)

Determination	Mean	SD	Min	Max	n	Determination	Mean	SD	Min	Max	n
General (g/kg ODM)						**Degradability**					
ODM (fresh)	856.9	8.2	845.4	868.9	9	Dry matter					
TDM (fresh)						a (%)	66.9	2.4	65.2	68.6	2
CP	131.3	13.8	109.0	147.0	9	b (%)	25.4	3.7	22.8	28.0	2
MADF	32.0	4.7	26.0	41.0	9	c (h^{-1})	0.39	0.01	0.39	0.40	2
EE	14.7	1.5	12.0	17.0	9						
AEE	20.4	1.9	18.0	24.0	9	dg (%) @ outflow rate					
TA	20.9	2.0	18.0	25.0	9	$0.02h^{-1}$	91.0	1.4	90.0	92.0	2
GE (MJ/kg ODM)	18.2	0.29	17.7	18.6	9	$0.05h^{-1}$	89.5	0.71	89.0	90.0	2
						$0.08h^{-1}$	88.0	1.4	87.0	89.0	2
NDF ash	113.2	19.3	83.0	147.0	9						
NDF unash						Nitrogen					
ADF ash	36.1	6.1	27.0	44.0	9	a (%)	59.1	4.0	56.3	61.9	2
ADF unash	34.5	5.2	28.0	45.0	8	b (%)	36.3	4.1	33.4	39.2	2
						c (h^{-1})	0.24	0.01	0.24	0.25	2
Energy Values											
						dg (%) @ outflow rate					
DE (MJ/kg ODM)	16.2	0.77	15.1	17.5	9	$0.02h^{-1}$	92.5	0.71	92.0	93.0	2
ME (MJ/kg ODM)	13.8	0.76	12.8	15.2	9	$0.05h^{-1}$	89.5	0.71	89.0	90.0	2
FE/GE	0.11	0.04	0.04	0.16	9	$0.08h^{-1}$	86.5	0.71	86.0	87.0	2
UE/GE	0.04	0.01	0.03	0.05	9						
CH_4E/GE	0.09	0.01	0.09	0.10	9						
ME/DE	0.85	0.01	0.84	0.87	9						
ME/GE	0.76	0.04	0.72	0.83	9						
Digestibility Coefficients											
DM	0.87	0.02	0.84	0.90	9						
OM	0.89	0.02	0.86	0.92	9						
CP	0.79	0.05	0.72	0.86	9						
CF	0.71	0.23	0.39	0.94	4						
EE	0.73	0.14	0.44	0.84	8						
NDF	0.77	0.21	0.54	0.95	3						
ADF											
Cell											
GE	0.89	0.03	0.84	0.96	9						
DOMD(g/kg ODM)	877.8	21.0	847.0	907.3	9						

RUMINANT DATABASE

FEED DESCRIPTION : **WHEAT BRAN** (Source 2)

Determination	Mean	SD	Min	Max	n	Determination	Mean	SD	Min	Max	n
General (g/kg ODM)						**Degradability**					
ODM (fresh)	880.3	7.8	874.0	890.0	4	Dry matter					
TDM (fresh)						a (%)					
CP	177.8	13.3	167.0	197.0	4	b (%)					
MADF	140.0	17.3	118.0	160.0	4	c (h^{-1})					
EE	46.0	6.1	40.0	53.0	4						
AEE						dg (%) @ outflow rate					
TA	68.3	4.6	62.0	73.0	4	0.02h^{-1}					
GE (MJ/kg ODM)	18.9	0.10	18.7	19.0	4	0.05h^{-1}					
						0.08h^{-1}					
NDF ash	495.8	60.1	429.0	550.0	4						
NDF unash						Nitrogen					
ADF ash	151.3	18.5	128.0	173.0	4	a (%)					
ADF unash						b (%)					
						c (h^{-1})					
Energy Values											
						dg (%) @ outflow rate					
DE (MJ/kg ODM)						0.02h^{-1}					
ME (MJ/kg ODM)	10.8	0.65	10.2	11.7	4	0.05h^{-1}					
FE/GE						0.08h^{-1}					
UE/GE	0.05	0.01	0.04	0.06	4						
CH$_4$E/GE	0.09	0.01	0.08	0.10	4						
ME/DE											
ME/GE	0.57	0.03	0.54	0.62	4						
Digestibility Coefficients											
DM											
OM	0.75	0.04	0.70	0.81	4						
CP											
CF											
EE											
NDF											
ADF											
Cell											
GE	0.71	0.04	0.67	0.77	4						
DOMD(g/kg ODM)	697.8	46.0	651.0	761.0	4						

RUMINANT DATABASE

FEED DESCRIPTION : **WHEAT FEED** (Sources 1, 2)

Determination	Mean	SD	Min	Max	n	Determination	Mean	SD	Min	Max	n
General (g/kg ODM)						**Degradability**					
ODM (fresh)	879.2	10.3	861.3	898.0	8	Dry matter					
TDM (fresh)						a (%)					
CP	181.0	14.9	159.0	197.0	8	b (%)					
MADF	108.5	25.3	54.0	141.0	8	c (h^{-1})					
EE	43.8	13.3	31.0	73.0	8						
AEE	50.3	1.7	48.0	52.0	4	dg (%) @ outflow rate					
TA	51.1	7.4	34.0	58.0	8	0.02h^{-1}					
GE (MJ/kg ODM)	19.1	0.22	18.7	19.3	8	0.05h^{-1}					
						0.08h^{-1}					
NDF ash	348.4	61.9	243.0	435.0	8						
NDF unash						Nitrogen					
ADF ash	111.9	23.4	61.0	138.0	8	a (%)					
ADF unash	118.0	7.0	110.6	127.5	4	b (%)					
						c (h^{-1})					
Energy Values											
						dg (%) @ outflow rate					
DE (MJ/kg ODM)	14.3	0.47	13.8	14.9	4	0.02h^{-1}					
ME (MJ/kg ODM)	11.9	1.0	11.2	14.3	8	0.05h^{-1}					
FE/GE	0.25	0.02	0.22	0.27	4	0.08h^{-1}					
UE/GE	0.05	0.02	0.02	0.07	8						
CH$_4$E/GE	0.08	0.01	0.07	0.09	8						
ME/DE	0.82	0.01	0.80	0.82	4						
ME/GE	0.62	0.05	0.59	0.74	8						
Digestibility Coefficients											
DM	0.73	0.02	0.71	0.76	4						
OM	0.77	0.04	0.71	0.86	8						
CP	0.75	0.01	0.74	0.77	4						
CF	0.48	0.10	0.35	0.57	4						
EE	0.79	0.06	0.71	0.84	4						
NDF	0.54	0.03	0.50	0.56	4						
ADF	0.40	0.07	0.32	0.49	4						
Cell	0.41	0.12	0.24	0.53	4						
GE	0.75	0.05	0.68	0.84	8						
DOMD(g/kg ODM)	730.5	47.8	665.0	830.0	8						

RUMINANT DATABASE

FEED DESCRIPTION : **WHEAT GRAIN, ALL SEASONS** (Sources 1, 2)

Determination	Mean	SD	Min	Max	n	Determination	Mean	SD	Min	Max	n
General (g/kg ODM)						**Degradability**					
ODM (fresh)	863.4	9.2	846.0	887.0	26	Dry matter					
TDM (fresh)						a (%)	61.9	5.0	54.7	71.9	8
CP	126.1	16.6	97.0	157.0	26	b (%)	32.2	4.6	23.6	38.4	8
MADF	29.0	4.1	20.0	38.0	26	c (h^{-1})	0.38	0.05	0.28	0.42	8
EE	18.5	3.4	14.0	30.0	26						
AEE	22.7	1.4	21.0	26.0	10	dg (%) @ outflow rate					
TA	17.6	1.6	15.0	22.0	26	$0.02h^{-1}$	92.4	1.3	91.0	94.0	8
GE (MJ/kg ODM)	18.3	0.15	18.0	18.7	26	$0.05h^{-1}$	90.4	1.7	88.0	93.0	8
						$0.08h^{-1}$	88.5	1.9	87.0	92.0	8
NDF ash	123.3	16.5	96.0	175.0	26						
NDF unash						Nitrogen					
ADF ash	31.7	3.9	24.0	40.0	26	a (%)	45.0	5.7	39.1	53.2	7
ADF unash	37.4	8.3	27.0	57.0	10	b (%)	51.0	4.8	44.5	55.9	7
						c (h^{-1})	0.38	0.11	0.22	0.51	7
Energy Values											
						dg (%) @ outflow rate					
DE (MJ/kg ODM)	16.4	0.36	15.8	16.8	10	$0.02h^{-1}$	93.3	2.1	91.0	97.0	7
ME (MJ/kg ODM)	13.7	0.62	12.3	14.7	26	$0.05h^{-1}$	89.7	2.5	87.0	94.0	7
FE/GE	0.11	0.02	0.08	0.14	10	$0.08h^{-1}$	86.6	3.3	83.0	92.0	7
UE/GE	0.03	0.02	0.01	0.06	26						
CH_4E/GE	0.10	0.02	0.07	0.14	26						
ME/DE	0.86	0.02	0.83	0.89	10						
ME/GE	0.75	0.04	0.67	0.80	26						

Digestibility Coefficients

	Mean	SD	Min	Max	n
DM	0.89	0.02	0.85	0.92	10
OM	0.90	0.02	0.87	0.94	26
CP	0.77	0.05	0.66	0.87	26
CF	0.67	0.21	0.31	0.92	9
EE	0.86	0.09	0.70	0.97	10
NDF	0.60	0.12	0.47	0.80	10
ADF	0.54	0.20	0.32	0.91	10
Cell	0.63	0.19	0.42	0.94	8
GE	0.88	0.03	0.83	0.92	26
DOMD(g/kg ODM)	888.7	20.6	850.0	922.7	26

RUMINANT DATABASE

FEED DESCRIPTION : **WHEAT GRAIN, SPRING** (Source 2)

Determination	Mean	SD	Min	Max	n	Determination	Mean	SD	Min	Max	n
General (g/kg ODM)						**Degradability**					
ODM (fresh)	871.0		871.0	871.0	1	Dry matter					
TDM (fresh)						a (%)					
CP	137.0		137.0	137.0	1	b (%)					
MADF	29.0		29.0	29.0	1	c (h^{-1})					
EE	30.0		30.0	30.0	1						
AEE						dg (%) @ outflow rate					
TA	19.0		19.0	19.0	1	$0.02h^{-1}$					
GE (MJ/kg ODM)	18.5		18.5	18.5	1	$0.05h^{-1}$					
						$0.08h^{-1}$					
NDF ash	134.0		134.0	134.0	1						
NDF unash						Nitrogen					
ADF ash	36.0		36.0	36.0	1	a (%)					
ADF unash						b (%)					
						c (h^{-1})					
Energy Values											
						dg (%) @ outflow rate					
DE (MJ/kg ODM)						$0.02h^{-1}$					
ME (MJ/kg ODM)	13.4		13.4	13.4	1	$0.05h^{-1}$					
FE/GE						$0.08h^{-1}$					
UE/GE	0.04		0.04	0.04	1						
CH4E/GE	0.13		0.13	0.13	1						
ME/DE											
ME/GE	0.72		0.72	0.72	1						
Digestibility Coefficients											
DM											
OM	0.91		0.91	0.91	1						
CP	0.79		0.79	0.79	1						
CF											
EE											
NDF											
ADF											
Cell											
GE	0.88		0.88	0.88	1						
DOMD(g/kg ODM)	890.0		890.0	890.0	1						

RUMINANT DATABASE

FEED DESCRIPTION : **WHEAT GRAIN, WINTER** (Sources 1, 2)

Determination	Mean	SD	Min	Max	n	Determination	Mean	SD	Min	Max	n
General (g/kg ODM)						**Degradability**					
ODM (fresh)	863.1	9.3	846.0	887.0	25	Dry matter					
TDM (fresh)						a (%)	61.9	5.0	54.7	71.9	8
CP	125.6	16.8	97.0	157.0	25	b (%)	32.2	4.6	23.6	38.4	8
MADF	29.0	4.2	20.0	38.0	25	c (h^{-1})	0.38	0.05	0.28	0.42	8
EE	18.0	2.6	14.0	23.0	25						
AEE	22.7	1.4	21.0	26.0	10	dg (%) @ outflow rate					
TA	17.5	1.6	15.0	22.0	25	$0.02h^{-1}$	92.4	1.3	91.0	94.0	8
GE (MJ/kg ODM)	18.3	0.15	18.0	18.7	25	$0.05h^{-1}$	90.4	1.7	88.0	93.0	8
						$0.08h^{-1}$	88.5	1.9	87.0	92.0	8
NDF ash	122.8	16.6	96.0	175.0	25						
NDF unash						Nitrogen					
ADF ash	31.6	3.9	24.0	40.0	25	a (%)	45.0	5.7	39.1	53.2	7
ADF unash	37.4	8.3	27.0	57.0	10	b (%)	51.0	4.8	44.5	55.9	7
						c (h^{-1})	0.38	0.11	0.22	0.51	7
Energy Values											
						dg (%) @ outflow rate					
DE (MJ/kg ODM)	16.4	0.36	15.8	16.8	10	$0.02h^{-1}$	93.3	2.1	91.0	97.0	7
ME (MJ/kg ODM)	13.7	0.62	12.3	14.7	25	$0.05h^{-1}$	89.7	2.5	87.0	94.0	7
FE/GE	0.11	0.02	0.08	0.14	10	$0.08h^{-1}$	86.6	3.3	83.0	92.0	7
UE/GE	0.03	0.02	0.01	0.06	25						
CH_4E/GE	0.10	0.02	0.07	0.14	25						
ME/DE	0.86	0.02	0.83	0.89	10						
ME/GE	0.75	0.04	0.67	0.80	25						
Digestibility Coefficients											
DM	0.89	0.02	0.85	0.92	10						
OM	0.90	0.02	0.87	0.94	25						
CP	0.77	0.05	0.66	0.87	25						
CF	0.67	0.21	0.31	0.92	9						
EE	0.86	0.09	0.70	0.97	10						
NDF	0.60	0.12	0.47	0.80	10						
ADF	0.54	0.20	0.32	0.91	10						
Cell	0.63	0.19	0.42	0.94	8						
GE	0.88	0.03	0.83	0.92	25						
DOMD(g/kg ODM)	888.6	21.0	850.0	922.7	25						

RUMINANT DATABASE

FEED DESCRIPTION : **WHEAT OFFALS** (Source 2)

Determination	Mean	SD	Min	Max	n	Determination	Mean	SD	Min	Max	n
General (g/kg ODM)						**Degradability**					
ODM (fresh)	877.6	6.3	864.0	886.0	8	Dry matter					
TDM (fresh)						a (%)					
CP	184.6	17.4	163.0	211.0	8	b (%)					
MADF	101.6	30.2	53.0	150.0	8	c (h^{-1})					
EE	46.9	5.9	41.0	59.0	8						
AEE						dg (%) @ outflow rate					
TA	51.0	11.6	31.0	71.0	8	0.02h^{-1}					
GE (MJ/kg ODM)	19.1	0.15	18.8	19.3	8	0.05h^{-1}					
						0.08h^{-1}					
NDF ash	353.6	81.7	238.0	505.0	8						
NDF unash						Nitrogen					
ADF ash	103.5	26.9	58.0	147.0	8	a (%)					
ADF unash						b (%)					
						c (h^{-1})					
Energy Values											
						dg (%) @ outflow rate					
DE (MJ/kg ODM)						0.02h^{-1}					
ME (MJ/kg ODM)	11.9	0.95	10.6	13.9	8	0.05h^{-1}					
FE/GE						0.08h^{-1}					
UE/GE	0.04	0.01	0.03	0.05	8						
CH$_4$E/GE	0.09	0.01	0.07	0.10	8						
ME/DE											
ME/GE	0.62	0.05	0.56	0.73	8						
Digestibility Coefficients											
DM											
OM	0.77	0.04	0.73	0.87	8						
CP											
CF											
EE											
NDF											
ADF											
Cell											
GE	0.75	0.04	0.71	0.84	8						
DOMD(g/kg ODM)	732.1	48.1	691.0	843.0	8						

RUMINANT DATABASE

FEED CLASS 50

PROTEIN SUPPLEMENTS

RUMINANT DATABASE

FEED DESCRIPTION : **BEANS, FIELD SPRING** (Sources 1, 2)

Determination	Mean	SD	Min	Max	n	Determination	Mean	SD	Min	Max	n
General (g/kg ODM)						**Degradability**					
ODM (fresh)	865.4		865.4	865.4	1	Dry matter					
TDM (fresh)						a (%)	33.7		33.7	33.7	1
CP	333.1	33.5	264.8	369.0	9	b (%)	55.4		55.4	55.4	1
MADF	110.1	7.4	101.0	120.0	9	c (h^{-1})	0.12		0.12	0.12	1
EE	12.0	3.0	8.0	17.0	9						
AEE	16.0		16.0	16.0	1	dg (%) @ outflow rate					
TA	37.2	3.1	32.0	42.0	9	$0.02h^{-1}$	81.0		81.0	81.0	1
GE (MJ/kg ODM)	18.6	0.16	18.2	18.8	9	$0.05h^{-1}$	73.0		73.0	73.0	1
						$0.08h^{-1}$	67.0		67.0	67.0	1
NDF ash	186.4	27.8	118.2	210.0	9						
NDF unash						Nitrogen					
ADF ash	122.5	9.5	110.0	138.0	8	a (%)	41.9		41.9	41.9	1
ADF unash						b (%)	56.2		56.2	56.2	1
						c (h^{-1})	0.16		0.16	0.16	1
Energy Values											
						dg (%) @ outflow rate					
DE (MJ/kg ODM)	15.6		15.6	15.6	1	$0.02h^{-1}$	92.0		92.0	92.0	1
ME (MJ/kg ODM)	13.4	0.65	12.5	14.5	9	$0.05h^{-1}$	84.0		84.0	84.0	1
FE/GE	0.14		0.14	0.14	1	$0.08h^{-1}$	79.0		79.0	79.0	1
UE/GE	0.07	0.01	0.06	0.08	9						
CH_4E/GE	0.12	0.02	0.09	0.15	9						
ME/DE	0.81		0.81	0.81	1						
ME/GE	0.72	0.03	0.67	0.78	9						
Digestibility Coefficients											
DM	0.86		0.86	0.86	1						
OM	0.91	0.02	0.88	0.94	9						
CP	0.84		0.84	0.84	1						
CF	0.82		0.82	0.82	1						
EE	0.97		0.97	0.97	1						
NDF	0.48		0.48	0.48	1						
ADF											
Cell											
GE	0.91	0.03	0.86	0.93	9						
DOMD(g/kg ODM)	871.7	26.9	813.0	896.0	9						

RUMINANT DATABASE

FEED DESCRIPTION : **BEANS, FIELD WINTER** (Sources 1, 2)

Determination	Mean	SD	Min	Max	n	Determination	Mean	SD	Min	Max	n
General (g/kg ODM)						**Degradability**					
ODM (fresh)	847.8	8.7	841.6	853.9	2	Dry matter					
TDM (fresh)						a (%)					
CP	267.4	11.7	253.0	283.0	6	b (%)					
MADF	128.8	20.2	115.0	169.0	6	c (h^{-1})					
EE	13.4	2.2	10.0	16.0	5						
AEE	18.0	0.0	18.0	18.0	2	dg (%) @ outflow rate					
TA	34.9	4.3	30.0	42.8	6	0.02h^{-1}					
GE (MJ/kg ODM)	18.4	0.25	17.9	18.6	6	0.05h^{-1}					
						0.08h^{-1}					
NDF ash	167.3	21.8	130.0	186.0	6						
NDF unash						Nitrogen					
ADF ash	123.8	4.3	118.0	127.0	4	a (%)					
ADF unash						b (%)					
						c (h^{-1})					
Energy Values											
						dg (%) @ outflow rate					
DE (MJ/kg ODM)	15.7	0.79	15.1	16.2	2	0.02h^{-1}					
ME (MJ/kg ODM)	13.1	0.45	12.5	13.6	6	0.05h^{-1}					
FE/GE	0.15	0.02	0.13	0.16	2	0.08h^{-1}					
UE/GE	0.05	0.01	0.04	0.07	6						
CH$_4$E/GE	0.11	0.02	0.09	0.14	6						
ME/DE	0.82	0.01	0.82	0.83	2						
ME/GE	0.71	0.02	0.69	0.73	6						
Digestibility Coefficients											
DM	0.85	0.03	0.83	0.87	2						
OM	0.91	0.04	0.86	0.96	6						
CP	0.82	0.0	0.81	0.82	2						
CF	0.81	0.08	0.75	0.86	2						
EE											
NDF	0.58	0.02	0.57	0.59	2						
ADF											
Cell											
GE	0.88	0.03	0.84	0.91	6						
DOMD(g/kg ODM)	879.9	40.3	825.8	929.0	6						

RUMINANT DATABASE

FEED DESCRIPTION : **BREWERS GRAINS** (Source 2)

Determination	Mean	SD	Min	Max	n	Determination	Mean	SD	Min	Max	n
General (g/kg ODM)						**Degradability**					
ODM (fresh)	272.8	15.0	257.0	299.0	6	Dry matter					
TDM (fresh)	276.8	15.5	260.0	304.0	6	a (%)					
CP	244.6	34.0	195.6	276.2	6	b (%)					
MADF	218.5	19.5	190.0	241.0	6	c (h^{-1})					
EE	77.2	9.7	65.5	92.5	6						
AEE						dg (%) @ outflow rate					
TA	41.1	6.2	30.3	49.8	6	$0.02h^{-1}$					
GE (MJ/kg TDM)	20.9	0.31	20.5	21.3	6	$0.05h^{-1}$					
						$0.08h^{-1}$					
NDF ash	572.3	61.7	499.0	643.0	6						
NDF unash						Nitrogen					
ADF ash	244.2	19.1	216.0	266.0	6	a (%)					
ADF unash						b (%)					
						c (h^{-1})					
Energy Values											
						dg (%) @ outflow rate					
DE (MJ/kg TDM)						$0.02h^{-1}$					
ME (MJ/kg TDM)	11.5	0.65	10.7	12.2	6	$0.05h^{-1}$					
FE/GE	0.38	0.03	0.34	0.42	6	$0.08h^{-1}$					
UE/GE	0.04	0.0	0.03	0.05	6						
CH_4E/GE	0.04	0.0	0.03	0.05	6						
ME/DE											
ME/GE	0.54	0.03	0.51	0.57	6						
Digestibility Coefficients											
DM											
OM	0.60	0.03	0.55	0.64	6						
CP	0.77	0.03	0.73	0.81	6						
CF											
EE											
NDF											
ADF											
Cell											
GE	0.61	0.03	0.57	0.64	6						
DOMD(g/kg TDM)	589.4	34.4	543.3	628.0	6						

RUMINANT DATABASE

FEED DESCRIPTION : **COPRA, EXPELLED** (Source 2)

Determination	Mean	SD	Min	Max	n	Determination	Mean	SD	Min	Max	n
General (g/kg ODM)						**Degradability**					
ODM (fresh)	900.0	8.5	894.0	906.0	2	Dry matter					
TDM (fresh)						a (%)					
CP	225.0	11.3	217.0	233.0	2	b (%)					
MADF	250.0	8.5	244.0	256.0	2	c (h^{-1})					
EE	101.5	41.7	72.0	131.0	2						
AEE						dg (%) @ outflow rate					
TA	62.0	1.4	61.0	63.0	2	$0.02h^{-1}$					
GE (MJ/kg ODM)	19.9	1.0	19.2	20.6	2	$0.05h^{-1}$					
						$0.08h^{-1}$					
NDF ash	517.0	21.2	502.0	532.0	2						
NDF unash						Nitrogen					
ADF ash	281.0	11.3	273.0	289.0	2	a (%)					
ADF unash						b (%)					
						c (h^{-1})					
Energy Values											
						dg (%) @ outflow rate					
DE (MJ/kg ODM)						$0.02h^{-1}$					
ME (MJ/kg ODM)	12.9	0.51	12.5	13.3	2	$0.05h^{-1}$					
FE/GE	0.28	0.08	0.22	0.34	2	$0.08h^{-1}$					
UE/GE	0.03	0.0	0.03	0.03	2						
CH_4E/GE	0.04	0.03	0.02	0.06	2						
ME/DE											
ME/GE	0.65	0.06	0.61	0.69	2						

Digestibility Coefficients

Determination	Mean	SD	Min	Max	n
DM	0.71	0.10	0.64	0.77	2
OM	0.71	0.11	0.64	0.79	2
CP	0.77	0.06	0.73	0.82	2
CF					
EE					
NDF					
ADF					
Cell					
GE	0.72	0.08	0.66	0.78	2
DOMD(g/kg ODM)	669.0	99.0	599.0	739.0	2

RUMINANT DATABASE

FEED DESCRIPTION : **COTTONSEED MEAL** (Source 1)

Determination	Mean	SD	Min	Max	n	Determination	Mean	SD	Min	Max	n
General (g/kg ODM)						**Degradability**					
ODM (fresh)	923.6	16.1	901.5	940.3	4	Dry matter					
TDM (fresh)						a (%)	28.7		28.7	28.7	1
CP	374.8	18.2	355.9	399.0	4	b (%)	52.9		52.9	52.9	1
MADF	245.0	36.1	200.0	283.0	4	c (h^{-1})	0.06		0.06	0.06	1
EE	66.1	7.2	56.0	72.0	4						
AEE	68.5	3.9	65.0	74.0	4	dg (%) @ outflow rate					
TA	62.3	2.5	59.0	65.0	4	$0.02h^{-1}$	67.0		67.0	67.0	1
GE (MJ/kg ODM)	20.4	0.21	20.2	20.7	4	$0.05h^{-1}$	56.0		56.0	56.0	1
						$0.08h^{-1}$	50.0		50.0	50.0	1
NDF ash	420.8	50.0	376.0	467.0	4						
NDF unash						Nitrogen					
ADF ash	273.0	23.7	253.0	303.0	4	a (%)	33.2		33.2	33.2	1
ADF unash	279.5	22.4	257.0	309.0	4	b (%)	60.4		60.4	60.4	1
						c (h^{-1})	0.06		0.06	0.06	1
Energy Values											
						dg (%) @ outflow rate					
DE (MJ/kg ODM)	13.9	1.6	11.9	15.9	4	$0.02h^{-1}$	79.0		79.0	79.0	1
ME (MJ/kg ODM)	11.1	1.5	9.3	12.9	4	$0.05h^{-1}$	66.0		66.0	66.0	1
FE/GE	0.32	0.07	0.23	0.41	4	$0.08h^{-1}$	59.0		59.0	59.0	1
UE/GE	0.06	0.01	0.05	0.07	4						
CH$_4$E/GE	0.08	0.01	0.07	0.08	4						
ME/DE	0.80	0.02	0.78	0.81	4						
ME/GE	0.54	0.07	0.46	0.62	4						
Digestibility Coefficients											
DM	0.64	0.08	0.55	0.73	4						
OM	0.66	0.08	0.57	0.76	4						
CP	0.77	0.03	0.75	0.82	4						
CF	0.43	0.12	0.28	0.54	4						
EE	0.96	0.01	0.95	0.97	2						
NDF	0.49	0.11	0.39	0.62	4						
ADF	0.39	0.12	0.28	0.54	4						
Cell	0.45	0.18	0.31	0.69	4						
GE	0.68	0.07	0.59	0.77	4						
DOMD(g/kg ODM)	626.7	72.1	539.5	716.0	4						

RUMINANT DATABASE

FEED DESCRIPTION : **DISTILLERS DARK GRAINS, BARLEY BASED** (Source 2)

Determination	Mean	SD	Min	Max	n	Determination	Mean	SD	Min	Max	n
General (g/kg ODM)						**Degradability**					
ODM (fresh)	890.0	12.7	881.0	899.0	2	Dry matter					
TDM (fresh)						a (%)					
CP	266.5	21.9	251.0	282.0	2	b (%)					
MADF	166.5	14.8	156.0	177.0	2	c (h^{-1})					
EE	65.0	4.2	62.0	68.0	2						
AEE						dg (%) @ outflow rate					
TA	56.5	0.71	56.0	57.0	2	$0.02h^{-1}$					
GE (MJ/kg ODM)	21.2	0.06	21.1	21.2	2	$0.05h^{-1}$					
						$0.08h^{-1}$					
NDF ash	419.5	21.9	404.0	435.0	2						
NDF unash						Nitrogen					
ADF ash	174.5	13.4	165.0	184.0	2	a (%)					
ADF unash						b (%)					
						c (h^{-1})					
Energy Values											
						dg (%) @ outflow rate					
DE (MJ/kg ODM)						$0.02h^{-1}$					
ME (MJ/kg ODM)	12.2	0.18	12.1	12.4	2	$0.05h^{-1}$					
FE/GE						$0.08h^{-1}$					
UE/GE	0.04	0.01	0.04	0.05	2						
CH_4E/GE	0.05	0.0	0.05	0.05	2						
ME/DE											
ME/GE	0.58	0.01	0.57	0.58	2						
Digestibility Coefficients											
DM											
OM	0.65	0.0	0.65	0.65	2						
CP											
CF											
EE											
NDF											
ADF											
Cell											
GE	0.67	0.0	0.67	0.67	2						
DOMD(g/kg ODM)	612.0	0.0	612.0	612.0	2						

RUMINANT DATABASE

FEED DESCRIPTION : **DISTILLERS DARK GRAINS, MAIZE BASED** (Sources 1, 2)

Determination	Mean	SD	Min	Max	n	Determination	Mean	SD	Min	Max	n
General (g/kg ODM)						**Degradability**					
ODM (fresh)	889.4	27.7	857.8	930.0	5	Dry matter					
TDM (fresh)						a (%)	43.4		43.4	43.4	1
CP	317.4	70.1	261.0	437.0	5	b (%)	42.5		42.5	42.5	1
MADF	165.4	48.0	116.0	225.0	5	c (h^{-1})	0.06		0.06	0.06	1
EE	109.6	18.6	90.0	130.0	5						
AEE	108.5	0.71	108.0	109.0	2	dg (%) @ outflow rate					
TA	46.4	15.7	20.0	58.0	5	0.02h^{-1}	75.0		75.0	75.0	1
GE (MJ/kg ODM)	22.4	0.79	21.7	23.7	5	0.05h^{-1}	67.0		67.0	67.0	1
						0.08h^{-1}	62.0		62.0	62.0	1
NDF ash	342.6	83.0	232.0	412.0	5						
NDF unash						Nitrogen					
ADF ash	215.6	55.7	151.0	261.0	5	a (%)	31.9		31.9	31.9	1
ADF unash	272.5	6.4	268.0	277.0	2	b (%)	45.6		45.6	45.6	1
						c (h^{-1})	0.05		0.05	0.05	1
Energy Values											
						dg (%) @ outflow rate					
DE (MJ/kg ODM)	17.9	0.26	17.7	18.1	2	0.02h^{-1}	65.0		65.0	65.0	1
ME (MJ/kg ODM)	14.7	0.85	13.6	15.4	5	0.05h^{-1}	55.0		55.0	55.0	1
FE/GE	0.18	0.01	0.17	0.18	2	0.08h^{-1}	50.0		50.0	50.0	1
UE/GE	0.06	0.02	0.04	0.09	5						
CH$_4$E/GE	0.05	0.04	0.02	0.09	5						
ME/DE	0.81	0.04	0.79	0.84	2						
ME/GE	0.66	0.04	0.60	0.70	5						

Digestibility Coefficients

Determination	Mean	SD	Min	Max	n
DM	0.80	0.01	0.79	0.80	2
OM	0.76	0.07	0.67	0.83	5
CP	0.78	0.02	0.77	0.80	2
CF	0.79	0.09	0.73	0.85	2
EE	0.92	0.02	0.90	0.94	2
NDF	0.81	0.06	0.77	0.85	2
ADF	0.82	0.03	0.80	0.84	2
Cell	0.73	0.01	0.73	0.74	2
GE	0.77	0.06	0.67	0.83	5
DOMD(g/kg ODM)	726.2	61.1	636.0	790.8	5

FEED DESCRIPTION : **DISTILLERS DARK GRAINS, WHEAT BASED** (Source 1)

Determination	Mean	SD	Min	Max	n	Determination	Mean	SD	Min	Max	n
General (g/kg ODM)						**Degradability**					
ODM (fresh)	873.1	22.1	845.2	905.9	5	Dry matter					
TDM (fresh)						a (%)	75.1	8.3	63.3	81.2	4
CP	321.2	14.5	299.5	335.6	5	b (%)	17.3	7.0	10.5	26.9	4
MADF	230.6	36.5	187.0	276.0	5	c (h^{-1})	0.11	0.07	0.04	0.20	4
EE	52.6	5.4	48.0	61.0	5						
AEE	67.4	3.4	64.0	73.0	5	dg (%) @ outflow rate					
TA	54.4	7.0	46.0	65.0	5	$0.02h^{-1}$	88.8	4.8	82.0	93.0	4
GE (MJ/kg ODM)	21.7	0.61	21.0	22.6	5	$0.05h^{-1}$	85.5	6.6	76.0	90.0	4
						$0.08h^{-1}$	83.8	7.5	73.0	89.0	4
NDF ash	309.2	62.0	230.0	382.0	5						
NDF unash						Nitrogen					
ADF ash	243.8	28.2	207.0	275.0	5	a (%)	84.0	8.9	71.4	92.2	4
ADF unash	246.0	24.9	210.0	274.0	5	b (%)	11.7	7.0	5.2	21.4	4
						c (h^{-1})	0.17	0.10	0.05	0.28	4
Energy Values											
						dg (%) @ outflow rate					
DE (MJ/kg ODM)	15.8	0.27	15.4	16.1	5	$0.02h^{-1}$	93.5	4.4	87.0	97.0	4
ME (MJ/kg ODM)	12.4	0.28	12.2	12.8	5	$0.05h^{-1}$	91.8	6.7	82.0	97.0	4
FE/GE	0.27	0.03	0.25	0.30	5	$0.08h^{-1}$	90.5	7.2	80.0	96.0	4
UE/GE	0.07	0.01	0.06	0.08	5						
CH_4E/GE	0.08	0.0	0.08	0.08	5						
ME/DE	0.79	0.01	0.78	0.80	5						
ME/GE	0.57	0.02	0.54	0.60	5						
Digestibility Coefficients											
DM	0.70	0.04	0.66	0.74	5						
OM	0.74	0.04	0.70	0.77	5						
CP	0.61	0.06	0.53	0.68	5						
CF	0.58	0.02	0.55	0.61	5						
EE	0.94	0.02	0.93	0.97	5						
NDF	0.59	0.12	0.43	0.72	5						
ADF	0.67	0.05	0.59	0.73	5						
Cell	0.76	0.05	0.69	0.82	5						
GE	0.73	0.03	0.70	0.75	5						
DOMD(g/kg ODM)	698.6	33.3	662.6	735.6	5						

RUMINANT DATABASE

FEED DESCRIPTION : **DRAFF, BARLEY BASED** (Source 2)

Determination	Mean	SD	Min	Max	n	Determination	Mean	SD	Min	Max	n

General (g/kg ODM)

						Degradability					
ODM (fresh)	248.0	7.1	243.0	253.0	2	Dry matter					
TDM (fresh)	255.0		255.0	255.0	1	a (%)					
CP	210.5	5.0	207.0	214.0	2	b (%)					
MADF	274.0		274.0	274.0	1	c (h^{-1})					
EE	86.0	2.8	84.0	88.0	2						
AEE						dg (%) @ outflow rate					
TA	34.0	1.4	33.0	35.0	2	$0.02h^{-1}$					
GE (MJ/kg ODM)	21.5	0.14	21.4	21.6	2	$0.05h^{-1}$					
						$0.08h^{-1}$					
NDF ash	672.5	23.3	656.0	689.0	2						
NDF unash						Nitrogen					
ADF ash	294.0	42.4	264.0	324.0	2	a (%)					
ADF unash						b (%)					
						c (h^{-1})					

Energy Values

						dg (%) @ outflow rate					
DE (MJ/kg ODM)						$0.02h^{-1}$					
ME (MJ/kg ODM)	10.2	0.92	9.5	10.8	2	$0.05h^{-1}$					
FE/GE	0.46	0.03	0.43	0.48	2	$0.08h^{-1}$					
UE/GE	0.04	0.0	0.03	0.04	2						
CH$_4$E/GE	0.03	0.0	0.03	0.03	2						
ME/DE											
ME/GE	0.47	0.04	0.44	0.50	2						

Digestibility Coefficients

	Mean	SD	Min	Max	n
DM	0.51		0.51	0.51	1
OM	0.52	0.03	0.50	0.54	2
CP	0.74	0.01	0.73	0.75	2
CF					
EE					
NDF					
ADF					
Cell					
GE	0.54	0.03	0.52	0.57	2
DOMD(g/kg ODM)	499.5	24.7	482.0	517.0	2

RUMINANT DATABASE

FEED DESCRIPTION : **FISHMEAL, CHILEAN** (Sources 1, 2)

Determination	Mean	SD	Min	Max	n	Determination	Mean	SD	Min	Max	n
General (g/kg ODM)						**Degradability**					
ODM (fresh)	916.8	28.6	898.7	959.1	4	Dry matter					
TDM (fresh)						a (%)					
CP	716.9	14.3	701.8	736.0	4	b (%)					
MADF						c (h^{-1})					
EE	82.5	18.0	64.0	104.0	4						
AEE	105.0	13.5	91.0	118.0	3	dg (%) @ outflow rate					
TA	176.8	13.7	161.0	194.0	4	0.02h^{-1}					
GE (MJ/kg ODM)	20.3	0.58	19.6	20.8	4	0.05h^{-1}					
						0.08h^{-1}					
NDF ash											
NDF unash						Nitrogen					
ADF ash						a (%)					
ADF unash						b (%)					
						c (h^{-1})					
Energy Values											
						dg (%) @ outflow rate					
DE (MJ/kg ODM)	19.6	0.52	19.1	20.1	3	0.02h^{-1}					
ME (MJ/kg ODM)	14.9	0.54	14.4	15.6	4	0.05h^{-1}					
FE/GE	0.05	0.03	0.01	0.08	4	0.08h^{-1}					
UE/GE	0.14	0.04	0.10	0.17	4						
CH$_4$E/GE	0.08	0.03	0.04	0.10	4						
ME/DE	0.76	0.03	0.73	0.79	3						
ME/GE	0.73	0.02	0.72	0.75	4						
Digestibility Coefficients											
DM	0.87	0.03	0.84	0.92	4						
OM	0.96	0.04	0.92	1.0	4						
CP	0.91	0.02	0.89	0.93	4						
CF											
EE	0.97	0.03	0.95	0.99	2						
NDF											
ADF											
Cell											
GE	0.95	0.03	0.92	0.99	4						
DOMD(g/kg ODM)	792.2	19.7	776.8	821.0	4						

RUMINANT DATABASE

FEED DESCRIPTION : **FISHMEAL, HERRING** (Sources 1, 2)

Determination	Mean	SD	Min	Max	n	Determination	Mean	SD	Min	Max	n
General (g/kg ODM)						**Degradability**					
ODM (fresh)	929.6	13.6	920.0	939.2	2	Dry matter					
TDM (fresh)						a (%)					
CP	782.3	59.0	740.5	824.0	2	b (%)					
MADF						c (h^{-1})					
EE	78.5	5.0	75.0	82.0	2						
AEE	73.0		73.0	73.0	1	dg (%) @ outflow rate					
TA	126.0	5.7	122.0	130.0	2	0.02h^{-1}					
GE (MJ/kg ODM)	22.1	0.20	22.0	22.3	2	0.05h^{-1}					
						0.08h^{-1}					
NDF ash											
NDF unash						Nitrogen					
ADF ash						a (%)					
ADF unash						b (%)					
						c (h^{-1})					
Energy Values											
						dg (%) @ outflow rate					
DE (MJ/kg ODM)	20.0		20.0	20.0	1	0.02h^{-1}					
ME (MJ/kg ODM)	16.4	2.0	14.9	17.8	2	0.05h^{-1}					
FE/GE	0.07	0.04	0.04	0.09	2	0.08h^{-1}					
UE/GE	0.14	0.01	0.13	0.14	2						
CH$_4$E/GE	0.06	0.04	0.03	0.09	2						
ME/DE	0.75		0.75	0.75	1						
ME/GE	0.74	0.09	0.68	0.80	2						
Digestibility Coefficients											
DM	0.83	0.05	0.79	0.86	2						
OM	0.92	0.05	0.88	0.95	2						
CP	0.96	0.02	0.94	0.97	2						
CF											
EE											
NDF											
ADF											
Cell											
GE	0.93	0.04	0.91	0.96	2						
DOMD(g/kg ODM)	805.0	45.2	773.1	837.0	2						

RUMINANT DATABASE

FEED DESCRIPTION : **FISHMEAL, MIXED MEAL** (Source 1)

Determination	Mean	SD	Min	Max	n	Determination	Mean	SD	Min	Max	n
General (g/kg ODM)						**Degradability**					
ODM (fresh)	931.5	0.92	930.4	932.0	3	Dry matter					
TDM (fresh)						a (%)	37.2	5.5	33.3	41.1	2
CP	700.7	12.9	686.0	710.0	3	b (%)	57.0	4.7	53.7	60.3	2
MADF						c (h^{-1})	0.01	0.0	0.01	0.02	2
EE	89.0	32.1	68.0	126.0	3						
AEE	86.0	13.0	78.0	101.0	3	dg (%) @ outflow rate					
TA	213.7	10.4	202.0	222.0	3	$0.02h^{-1}$	61.0	0.0	61.0	61.0	2
GE (MJ/kg ODM)	19.7	0.30	19.4	20.0	3	$0.05h^{-1}$	50.0	1.4	49.0	51.0	2
						$0.08h^{-1}$	46.0	2.8	44.0	48.0	2
NDF ash											
NDF unash						Nitrogen					
ADF ash						a (%)					
ADF unash						b (%)					
						c (h^{-1})					
Energy Values											
						dg (%) @ outflow rate					
DE (MJ/kg ODM)	19.7	0.26	19.4	19.9	3	$0.02h^{-1}$					
ME (MJ/kg ODM)	15.2	0.11	15.1	15.3	3	$0.05h^{-1}$					
FE/GE						$0.08h^{-1}$					
UE/GE	0.13	0.02	0.11	0.14	3						
CH4E/GE	0.10	0.0	0.10	0.10	3						
ME/DE	0.77	0.02	0.76	0.79	3						
ME/GE	0.77	0.02	0.75	0.79	3						
Digestibility Coefficients											
DM	0.73	0.02	0.71	0.74	3						
OM	0.96	0.02	0.94	0.98	3						
CP	0.93	0.02	0.91	0.95	3						
CF											
EE	0.74	0.20	0.51	0.86	3						
NDF											
ADF											
Cell											
GE	1.0	0.0	1.0	1.0	3						
DOMD(g/kg ODM)	762.1	21.8	737.5	778.9	3						

RUMINANT DATABASE

FEED DESCRIPTION : **FISHMEAL, OFFAL MEAL-WHITE** (Source 1)

Determination	Mean	SD	Min	Max	n	Determination	Mean	SD	Min	Max	n
General (g/kg ODM)						**Degradability**					
ODM (fresh)	920.6	14.6	911.8	937.5	3	Dry matter					
TDM (fresh)						a (%)	34.5		34.5	34.5	1
CP	718.9	8.3	711.8	728.0	3	b (%)	49.0		49.0	49.0	1
MADF						c (h^{-1})	0.02		0.02	0.02	1
EE	74.3	3.1	71.0	77.0	3						
AEE	90.0	5.3	84.0	94.0	3	dg (%) @ outflow rate					
TA	205.7	11.9	192.0	214.0	3	$0.02h^{-1}$	56.0		56.0	56.0	1
GE (MJ/kg ODM)	20.0	0.30	19.7	20.3	3	$0.05h^{-1}$	46.0		46.0	46.0	1
						$0.08h^{-1}$	43.0		43.0	43.0	1
NDF ash											
NDF unash						Nitrogen					
ADF ash						a (%)					
ADF unash						b (%)					
						c (h^{-1})					
Energy Values											
						dg (%) @ outflow rate					
DE (MJ/kg ODM)	18.0	1.2	16.8	19.2	3	$0.02h^{-1}$					
ME (MJ/kg ODM)	13.4	1.2	12.1	14.5	3	$0.05h^{-1}$					
FE/GE	0.10	0.07	0.03	0.17	3	$0.08h^{-1}$					
UE/GE	0.14	0.01	0.13	0.15	3						
CH_4E/GE	0.09	0.01	0.09	0.10	3						
ME/DE	0.74	0.02	0.72	0.76	3						
ME/GE	0.67	0.07	0.59	0.73	3						
Digestibility Coefficients											
DM	0.77	0.05	0.73	0.83	3						
OM	0.92	0.05	0.87	0.98	3						
CP	0.93	0.02	0.91	0.94	3						
CF											
EE	0.97	0.02	0.94	0.98	3						
NDF											
ADF	0.85		0.85	0.85	1						
Cell											
GE	0.90	0.07	0.83	0.97	3						
DOMD(g/kg ODM)	736.8	45.2	707.7	788.8	3						

FEED DESCRIPTION : **FISHMEAL, WHITE** (Sources 1, 2)

Determination	Mean	SD	Min	Max	n	Determination	Mean	SD	Min	Max	n
General (g/kg ODM)						**Degradability**					
ODM (fresh)	917.8	20.5	893.0	955.0	6	Dry matter					
TDM (fresh)						a (%)	33.2	0.12	33.1	33.2	2
CP	693.8	25.2	672.0	738.0	6	b (%)	45.9	12.3	37.2	54.6	2
MADF						c (h^{-1})	0.01	0.0	0.01	0.01	2
EE	81.2	15.4	63.0	98.0	6						
AEE	90.8	14.9	73.0	107.0	4	dg (%) @ outflow rate					
TA	205.0	23.2	169.0	229.0	6	0.02h^{-1}	51.0	2.8	49.0	53.0	2
GE (MJ/kg ODM)	19.9	0.75	19.1	21.0	6	0.05h^{-1}	42.0	1.4	41.0	43.0	2
						0.08h^{-1}	39.5	0.71	39.0	40.0	2
NDF ash											
NDF unash						Nitrogen					
ADF ash						a (%)	29.9		29.9	29.9	1
ADF unash						b (%)	63.2		63.2	63.2	1
						c (h^{-1})	0.02		0.02	0.02	1
Energy Values											
						dg (%) @ outflow rate					
DE (MJ/kg ODM)	19.0	1.4	17.2	21.0	5	0.02h^{-1}	59.0		59.0	59.0	1
ME (MJ/kg ODM)	14.2	1.7	12.1	17.0	6	0.05h^{-1}	46.0		46.0	46.0	1
FE/GE	0.07	0.05	0.02	0.14	5	0.08h^{-1}	41.0		41.0	41.0	1
UE/GE	0.15	0.03	0.09	0.18	6						
CH$_4$E/GE	0.09	0.03	0.03	0.10	6						
ME/DE	0.74	0.04	0.70	0.81	5						
ME/GE	0.71	0.07	0.61	0.81	6						
Digestibility Coefficients											
DM	0.81	0.07	0.73	0.91	6						
OM	0.94	0.05	0.85	0.97	6						
CP	0.92	0.02	0.90	0.94	6						
CF											
EE	0.97	0.01	0.97	0.98	2						
NDF											
ADF											
Cell											
GE	0.95	0.05	0.86	1.0	6						
DOMD(g/kg ODM)	751.4	44.2	682.7	802.6	6						

RUMINANT DATABASE

FEED DESCRIPTION : **GROUNDNUT MEAL** (Source 2)

Determination	Mean	SD	Min	Max	n	Determination	Mean	SD	Min	Max	n
General (g/kg ODM)						**Degradability**					
ODM (fresh)						Dry matter					
TDM (fresh)						a (%)					
CP	494.5	26.2	476.0	513.0	2	b (%)					
MADF	128.5	9.2	122.0	135.0	2	c (h^{-1})					
EE	70.0	12.7	61.0	79.0	2						
AEE						dg (%) @ outflow rate					
TA	71.5	19.1	58.0	85.0	2	0.02h^{-1}					
GE (MJ/kg ODM)	20.5	0.44	20.2	20.9	2	0.05h^{-1}					
						0.08h^{-1}					
NDF ash	180.1	45.2	148.1	212.0	2						
NDF unash						Nitrogen					
ADF ash	145.5	3.5	143.0	148.0	2	a (%)					
ADF unash						b (%)					
						c (h^{-1})					
Energy Values											
						dg (%) @ outflow rate					
DE (MJ/kg ODM)						0.02h^{-1}					
ME (MJ/kg ODM)	13.7	0.61	13.3	14.2	2	0.05h^{-1}					
FE/GE						0.08h^{-1}					
UE/GE	0.10	0.01	0.10	0.11	2						
CH$_4$E/GE	0.08	0.0	0.08	0.08	2						
ME/DE											
ME/GE	0.67	0.02	0.66	0.68	2						

Digestibility Coefficients

Determination	Mean	SD	Min	Max	n
DM					
OM	0.83	0.01	0.83	0.84	2
CP					
CF					
EE					
NDF					
ADF					
Cell					
GE	0.87	0.01	0.86	0.88	2
DOMD(g/kg ODM)	772.0	22.6	756.0	788.0	2

RUMINANT DATABASE

FEED DESCRIPTION : **MAIZE GERM MEAL** (Source 2)

Determination	Mean	SD	Min	Max	n	Determination	Mean	SD	Min	Max	n
General (g/kg ODM)						**Degradability**					
ODM (fresh)						Dry matter					
TDM (fresh)						a (%)					
CP	115.3	4.3	111.0	119.0	4	b (%)					
MADF	63.3	7.7	54.0	71.0	4	c (h^{-1})					
EE	113.0	13.3	102.0	129.0	4						
AEE						dg (%) @ outflow rate					
TA	32.0	3.6	29.0	37.0	4	$0.02h^{-1}$					
GE (MJ/kg ODM)	20.2	0.39	19.7	20.5	4	$0.05h^{-1}$					
						$0.08h^{-1}$					
NDF ash	264.3	42.6	222.0	319.0	4						
NDF unash						Nitrogen					
ADF ash	70.0	9.4	61.0	80.0	4	a (%)					
ADF unash						b (%)					
						c (h^{-1})					
Energy Values											
						dg (%) @ outflow rate					
DE (MJ/kg ODM)						$0.02h^{-1}$					
ME (MJ/kg ODM)	14.5	1.5	13.1	15.8	4	$0.05h^{-1}$					
FE/GE						$0.08h^{-1}$					
UE/GE	0.02	0.01	0.02	0.03	4						
CH4E/GE	0.06	0.01	0.05	0.08	4						
ME/DE											
ME/GE	0.72	0.06	0.66	0.77	4						
Digestibility Coefficients											
DM											
OM	0.79	0.04	0.76	0.82	4						
CP											
CF											
EE											
NDF											
ADF											
Cell											
GE	0.78	0.05	0.73	0.82	4						
DOMD(g/kg ODM)	764.3	33.8	733.0	794.0	4						

RUMINANT DATABASE

FEED DESCRIPTION : **MAIZE GLUTEN MEAL** (Source 1)

Determination	Mean	SD	Min	Max	n	Determination	Mean	SD	Min	Max	n
General (g/kg ODM)						**Degradability**					
ODM (fresh)	905.5	13.6	891.6	922.8	5	Dry matter					
TDM (fresh)						a (%)	11.7	5.1	7.6	17.4	3
CP	665.7	33.2	616.1	699.5	5	b (%)	77.9	18.0	57.2	88.6	3
MADF	136.4	99.5	14.0	283.0	5	c (h^{-1})	0.05	0.05	0.02	0.11	3
EE	31.2	10.6	22.0	45.0	5						
AEE	65.0	24.0	48.0	82.0	2	dg (%) @ outflow rate					
TA	12.6	5.2	8.0	21.0	5	0.02h^{-1}	60.3	6.7	53.0	66.0	3
GE (MJ/kg ODM)	23.8	0.69	23.3	24.9	5	0.05h^{-1}	44.3	11.7	34.0	57.0	3
						0.08h^{-1}	36.7	12.9	26.0	51.0	3
NDF ash	189.7	59.8	127.0	246.0	3						
NDF unash						Nitrogen					
ADF ash	204.6	38.2	161.0	255.0	5	a (%)	8.3	7.5	3.0	13.6	2
ADF unash	187.8	81.9	69.0	256.0	4	b (%)	75.8	15.0	65.2	86.4	2
						c (h^{-1})	0.03	0.02	0.02	0.05	2
Energy Values											
						dg (%) @ outflow rate					
DE (MJ/kg ODM)	23.0	0.40	22.4	23.5	5	0.02h^{-1}	54.0	7.1	49.0	59.0	2
ME (MJ/kg ODM)	17.5	0.41	17.0	18.2	5	0.05h^{-1}	37.5	10.6	30.0	45.0	2
FE/GE	0.04	0.03	0.01	0.08	5	0.08h^{-1}	29.5	10.6	22.0	37.0	2
UE/GE	0.13	0.01	0.12	0.15	5						
CH$_4$E/GE	0.10	0.0	0.09	0.10	5						
ME/DE	0.76	0.01	0.75	0.77	5						
ME/GE	0.74	0.02	0.71	0.75	5						
Digestibility Coefficients											
DM	0.94	0.04	0.90	0.99	5						
OM	0.96	0.03	0.92	0.99	5						
CP	0.95	0.02	0.94	0.97	5						
CF	0.25		0.25	0.25	1						
EE	0.74	0.08	0.65	0.86	5						
NDF	0.93		0.93	0.93	1						
ADF	0.94		0.94	0.94	1						
Cell	0.91		0.91	0.91	1						
GE	0.97	0.03	0.92	0.99	5						
DOMD(g/kg ODM)	944.0	30.7	911.2	991.3	5						

RUMINANT DATABASE

FEED DESCRIPTION : **MEAT AND BONE MEAL** (Source 2)

Determination	Mean	SD	Min	Max	n	Determination	Mean	SD	Min	Max	n
General (g/kg ODM)						**Degradability**					
ODM (fresh)	926.5	13.4	917.0	936.0	2	Dry matter					
TDM (fresh)						a (%)					
CP	566.0	52.3	529.0	603.0	2	b (%)					
MADF						c (h^{-1})					
EE	91.5	118.1	8.0	175.0	2						
AEE						dg (%) @ outflow rate					
TA	291.0	58.0	250.0	332.0	2	0.02h^{-1}					
GE (MJ/kg ODM)	17.5	3.3	15.2	19.9	2	0.05h^{-1}					
						0.08h^{-1}					
NDF ash											
NDF unash						Nitrogen					
ADF ash						a (%)					
ADF unash						b (%)					
						c (h^{-1})					
Energy Values											
						dg (%) @ outflow rate					
DE (MJ/kg ODM)						0.02h^{-1}					
ME (MJ/kg ODM)	12.3	1.9	11.0	13.7	2	0.05h^{-1}					
FE/GE	0.09	0.0	0.09	0.10	2	0.08h^{-1}					
UE/GE	0.11	0.01	0.10	0.12	2						
CH$_4$E/GE	0.09	0.02	0.08	0.11	2						
ME/DE											
ME/GE	0.71	0.03	0.69	0.72	2						
Digestibility Coefficients											
DM	0.66	0.0	0.66	0.66	2						
OM	0.94	0.01	0.93	0.94	2						
CP	0.86	0.03	0.84	0.88	2						
CF											
EE											
NDF											
ADF											
Cell											
GE	0.91	0.0	0.91	0.91	2						
DOMD(g/kg ODM)	664.0	60.8	621.0	707.0	2						

339

RUMINANT DATABASE

FEED DESCRIPTION : **PALM KERNEL MEAL** (Source 1)

Determination	Mean	SD	Min	Max	n	Determination	Mean	SD	Min	Max	n
General (g/kg ODM)						**Degradability**					
ODM (fresh)	895.1	23.2	851.9	918.1	7	Dry matter					
TDM (fresh)						a (%)	15.0	5.6	8.9	22.1	6
CP	169.6	22.4	140.3	192.8	7	b (%)	77.3	8.1	70.0	88.4	6
MADF	425.4	43.9	392.0	505.0	7	c (h^{-1})	0.04	0.01	0.03	0.05	6
EE	82.7	8.2	69.0	96.0	7						
AEE	76.0	10.3	58.0	87.0	6	dg (%) @ outflow rate					
TA	43.6	3.3	39.3	50.0	7	$0.02h^{-1}$	65.7	7.5	58.0	75.0	6
GE (MJ/kg ODM)	20.4	0.44	19.6	20.9	7	$0.05h^{-1}$	48.5	6.7	42.0	59.0	6
						$0.08h^{-1}$	40.2	6.3	34.0	51.0	6
NDF ash	692.7	39.0	637.0	731.0	7						
NDF unash						Nitrogen					
ADF ash	469.7	38.1	428.0	518.0	7	a (%)	18.1	6.4	11.7	24.5	3
ADF unash	490.2	36.6	438.0	530.0	6	b (%)	84.4	3.3	81.6	88.0	3
						c (h^{-1})	0.03	0.01	0.03	0.04	3
Energy Values											
						dg (%) @ outflow rate					
DE (MJ/kg ODM)	13.9	1.4	11.6	15.5	7	$0.02h^{-1}$	70.7	7.4	65.0	79.0	3
ME (MJ/kg ODM)	11.6	1.3	9.5	13.0	7	$0.05h^{-1}$	52.0	7.0	47.0	60.0	3
FE/GE	0.32	0.08	0.22	0.44	7	$0.08h^{-1}$	43.0	7.0	38.0	51.0	3
UE/GE	0.04	0.01	0.03	0.04	7						
CH_4E/GE	0.08	0.01	0.07	0.09	7						
ME/DE	0.83	0.01	0.81	0.84	7						
ME/GE	0.57	0.07	0.46	0.66	7						

Digestibility Coefficients

Determination	Mean	SD	Min	Max	n
DM	0.65	0.10	0.49	0.76	7
OM	0.67	0.10	0.51	0.78	7
CP	0.75	0.08	0.59	0.83	7
CF	0.22	0.15	0.0	0.43	7
EE	0.98	0.01	0.96	0.99	4
NDF	0.62	0.12	0.44	0.77	7
ADF	0.53	0.13	0.34	0.73	7
Cell	0.56	0.12	0.35	0.74	7
GE	0.68	0.08	0.56	0.78	7
DOMD(g/kg ODM)	646.1	94.2	485.5	751.1	7

RUMINANT DATABASE

FEED DESCRIPTION : **PEAS, FIELD** (Source 2)

Determination	Mean	SD	Min	Max	n	Determination	Mean	SD	Min	Max	n
General (g/kg ODM)						**Degradability**					
ODM (fresh)	867.5	6.4	863.0	872.0	2	Dry matter					
TDM (fresh)						a (%)					
CP	260.7	16.2	235.0	284.0	6	b (%)					
MADF	82.5	9.7	69.0	99.0	6	c (h^{-1})					
EE	14.2	3.4	11.0	20.0	6						
AEE						dg (%) @ outflow rate					
TA	31.5	2.6	28.0	35.0	6	0.02h^{-1}					
GE (MJ/kg ODM)	18.5	0.12	18.3	18.6	6	0.05h^{-1}					
						0.08h^{-1}					
NDF ash	126.8	24.9	100.0	173.0	6						
NDF unash						Nitrogen					
ADF ash	84.2	12.0	71.0	105.0	6	a (%)					
ADF unash						b (%)					
						c (h^{-1})					
Energy Values						dg (%) @ outflow rate					
						0.02h^{-1}					
DE (MJ/kg ODM)						0.05h^{-1}					
ME (MJ/kg ODM)	13.5	0.58	12.7	14.4	6	0.08h^{-1}					
FE/GE	0.08	0.0	0.08	0.08	2						
UE/GE	0.06	0.01	0.04	0.07	6						
CH$_4$E/GE	0.13	0.03	0.09	0.18	6						
ME/DE											
ME/GE	0.73	0.03	0.69	0.78	6						
Digestibility Coefficients											
DM	0.92	0.0	0.92	0.92	2						
OM	0.94	0.02	0.91	0.96	6						
CP	0.89	0.0	0.89	0.89	2						
CF											
EE											
NDF											
ADF											
Cell											
GE	0.92	0.01	0.90	0.93	6						
DOMD(g/kg ODM)	909.3	15.2	886.0	932.0	6						

RUMINANT DATABASE

FEED DESCRIPTION : **POT ALE SYRUP** (Source 2)

Determination	Mean	SD	Min	Max	n	Determination	Mean	SD	Min	Max	n
General (g/kg ODM)						**Degradability**					
ODM (fresh)	483.0		483.0	483.0	1	Dry matter					
TDM (fresh)	509.0		509.0	509.0	1	a (%)					
CP	374.0		374.0	374.0	1	b (%)					
MADF						c (h^{-1})					
EE	2.0		2.0	2.0	1						
AEE						dg (%) @ outflow rate					
TA	95.0		95.0	95.0	1	$0.02h^{-1}$					
GE (MJ/kg ODM)	20.0		20.0	20.0	1	$0.05h^{-1}$					
						$0.08h^{-1}$					
NDF ash	6.0		6.0	6.0	1						
NDF unash						Nitrogen					
ADF ash						a (%)					
ADF unash						b (%)					
						c (h^{-1})					
Energy Values											
						dg (%) @ outflow rate					
DE (MJ/kg ODM)						$0.02h^{-1}$					
ME (MJ/kg ODM)	15.4		15.4	15.4	1	$0.05h^{-1}$					
FE/GE	0.11		0.11	0.11	1	$0.08h^{-1}$					
UE/GE	0.07		0.07	0.07	1						
CH4E/GE	0.09		0.09	0.09	1						
ME/DE											
ME/GE	0.77		0.77	0.77	1						
Digestibility Coefficients											
DM											
OM	0.89		0.89	0.89	1						
CP	0.78		0.78	0.78	1						
CF											
EE											
NDF											
ADF											
Cell											
GE	0.89		0.89	0.89	1						
DOMD(g/kg ODM)	805.0		805.0	805.0	1						

342

RUMINANT DATABASE

FEED DESCRIPTION : **RAPESEED MEAL** (Sources 1, 2)

Determination	Mean	SD	Min	Max	n	Determination	Mean	SD	Min	Max	n
General (g/kg ODM)						**Degradability**					
ODM (fresh)	898.2	11.5	881.5	927.7	12	Dry matter					
TDM (fresh)						a (%)	32.7	4.9	26.3	38.9	6
CP	399.6	22.4	350.9	432.0	12	b (%)	51.7	4.5	46.0	59.2	6
MADF	198.9	17.4	179.0	241.0	12	c (h^{-1})	0.11	0.03	0.07	0.16	6
EE	34.8	21.4	6.8	87.0	12						
AEE	53.1	20.9	25.0	83.0	8	dg (%) @ outflow rate					
TA	79.4	9.7	68.0	97.0	12	$0.02h^{-1}$	76.0	2.8	72.0	79.0	6
GE (MJ/kg ODM)	19.7	0.40	19.1	20.5	12	$0.05h^{-1}$	67.7	4.3	61.0	73.0	6
						$0.08h^{-1}$	61.8	5.0	54.0	68.0	6
NDF ash	308.8	61.3	247.0	459.0	12						
NDF unash						Nitrogen					
ADF ash	218.9	39.4	187.0	324.0	12	a (%)	32.3	8.2	21.4	41.7	6
ADF unash	234.8	48.9	200.0	340.0	8	b (%)	60.8	7.9	52.4	73.8	6
						c (h^{-1})	0.16	0.05	0.08	0.23	6
Energy Values											
						dg (%) @ outflow rate					
DE (MJ/kg ODM)	15.2	0.89	14.0	16.1	9	$0.02h^{-1}$	85.8	3.1	81.0	89.0	6
ME (MJ/kg ODM)	12.0	0.83	10.6	13.2	12	$0.05h^{-1}$	77.8	5.7	68.0	84.0	6
FE/GE	0.23	0.05	0.16	0.31	12	$0.08h^{-1}$	71.8	7.2	59.0	79.0	6
UE/GE	0.08	0.02	0.06	0.12	12						
CH_4E/GE	0.08	0.01	0.06	0.09	12						
ME/DE	0.79	0.03	0.73	0.82	9						
ME/GE	0.61	0.05	0.54	0.68	12						
Digestibility Coefficients											
DM	0.72	0.05	0.63	0.79	12						
OM	0.76	0.04	0.68	0.84	12						
CP	0.84	0.05	0.76	0.95	12						
CF	0.38	0.15	0.21	0.57	8						
EE	0.84	0.13	0.57	0.96	7						
NDF	0.53	0.15	0.35	0.73	7						
ADF	0.36	0.10	0.25	0.52	7						
Cell	0.49	0.13	0.28	0.69	7						
GE	0.77	0.05	0.69	0.84	12						
DOMD(g/kg ODM)	707.9	41.8	621.4	767.6	12						

RUMINANT DATABASE

FEED DESCRIPTION : **SOYABEAN, FULL FAT** (Source 2)

Determination	Mean	SD	Min	Max	n	Determination	Mean	SD	Min	Max	n
General (g/kg ODM)						**Degradability**					
ODM (fresh)	901.5	15.1	892.0	924.0	4	Dry matter					
TDM (fresh)						a (%)					
CP	407.5	11.8	395.0	423.0	4	b (%)					
MADF	94.3	25.1	70.0	125.0	4	c (h^{-1})					
EE	209.8	15.2	200.0	232.0	4						
AEE	232.3	7.0	225.0	239.0	3	dg (%) @ outflow rate					
TA	53.5	1.7	51.0	55.0	4	0.02h^{-1}					
GE (MJ/kg ODM)	23.9	0.18	23.7	24.1	4	0.05h^{-1}					
						0.08h^{-1}					
NDF ash	124.0	19.4	105.0	144.0	4						
NDF unash						Nitrogen					
ADF ash	97.3	24.1	78.0	129.0	4	a (%)					
ADF unash						b (%)					
						c (h^{-1})					
Energy Values											
						dg (%) @ outflow rate					
DE (MJ/kg ODM)						0.02h^{-1}					
ME (MJ/kg ODM)	15.5	0.37	15.1	16.0	4	0.05h^{-1}					
FE/GE	0.24	0.02	0.21	0.26	4	0.08h^{-1}					
UE/GE	0.08	0.01	0.07	0.09	4						
CH$_4$E/GE	0.03	0.01	0.02	0.03	4						
ME/DE											
ME/GE	0.65	0.01	0.64	0.67	4						
Digestibility Coefficients											
DM	0.71	0.03	0.68	0.75	4						
OM	0.73	0.03	0.70	0.77	4						
CP	0.92	0.02	0.90	0.94	4						
CF											
EE											
NDF											
ADF											
Cell											
GE	0.76	0.02	0.74	0.79	4						
DOMD(g/kg ODM)	689.5	28.3	665.0	729.0	4						

RUMINANT DATABASE

FEED DESCRIPTION : **SOYABEAN MEAL, EXTRACTED** (Sources 1, 2)

Determination	Mean	SD	Min	Max	n	Determination	Mean	SD	Min	Max	n
General (g/kg ODM)						**Degradability**					
ODM (fresh)						**Dry matter**					
TDM (fresh)						a (%)					
CP	497.3	21.1	471.0	524.0	6	b (%)					
MADF	105.3	16.0	86.0	126.0	6	c (h^{-1})					
EE	17.3	4.5	14.0	26.0	6						
AEE						dg (%) @ outflow rate					
TA	69.5	5.1	64.0	79.0	6	0.02h^{-1}					
GE (MJ/kg ODM)	19.6	0.17	19.4	19.9	6	0.05h^{-1}					
						0.08h^{-1}					
NDF ash	154.3	24.5	126.0	185.0	6						
NDF unash						**Nitrogen**					
ADF ash	120.7	17.9	97.0	139.0	6	a (%)					
ADF unash						b (%)					
						c (h^{-1})					
Energy Values											
						dg (%) @ outflow rate					
DE (MJ/kg ODM)						0.02h^{-1}					
ME (MJ/kg ODM)	13.3	0.54	12.6	14.0	6	0.05h^{-1}					
FE/GE						0.08h^{-1}					
UE/GE	0.12	0.01	0.10	0.14	6						
CH$_4$E/GE	0.11	0.01	0.10	0.12	6						
ME/DE											
ME/GE	0.68	0.03	0.64	0.71	6						
Digestibility Coefficients											
DM											
OM	0.91	0.03	0.86	0.94	6						
CP											
CF											
EE											
NDF											
ADF											
Cell											
GE	0.91	0.02	0.89	0.94	6						
DOMD(g/kg ODM)	843.8	32.6	800.0	877.0	6						

RUMINANT DATABASE

FEED DESCRIPTION : **SUNFLOWER SEED MEAL** (Source 1)

Determination	Mean	SD	Min	Max	n	Determination	Mean	SD	Min	Max	n
General (g/kg ODM)						**Degradability**					
ODM (fresh)	897.6	7.7	886.6	905.1	6	Dry matter					
TDM (fresh)						a (%)	24.7	3.9	18.8	29.1	5
CP	335.5	31.4	301.8	390.1	6	b (%)	46.8	9.4	39.2	58.6	5
MADF	292.7	26.5	252.0	331.0	6	c (h^{-1})	0.11	0.04	0.05	0.16	5
EE	23.0	10.7	9.0	35.0	6						
AEE	26.8	6.2	20.0	35.0	4	dg (%) @ outflow rate					
TA	71.2	7.8	59.0	80.0	6	$0.02h^{-1}$	63.2	2.8	60.0	67.0	5
GE (MJ/kg ODM)	19.5	0.29	19.0	19.8	6	$0.05h^{-1}$	55.4	1.1	54.0	57.0	5
						$0.08h^{-1}$	50.4	1.8	48.0	53.0	5
NDF ash	473.3	29.7	445.0	525.0	6						
NDF unash						Nitrogen					
ADF ash	328.2	28.2	294.0	372.0	6	a (%)	30.2	9.3	18.2	39.6	5
ADF unash	330.3	27.5	293.0	373.0	6	b (%)	64.9	9.1	56.0	76.4	5
						c (h^{-1})	0.17	0.06	0.12	0.27	5
Energy Values											
						dg (%) @ outflow rate					
DE (MJ/kg ODM)	12.8	1.0	11.7	14.2	6	$0.02h^{-1}$	87.8	3.0	84.0	92.0	5
ME (MJ/kg ODM)	9.6	0.96	8.6	11.0	6	$0.05h^{-1}$	79.6	5.6	73.0	87.0	5
FE/GE	0.34	0.06	0.27	0.40	6	$0.08h^{-1}$	73.6	7.5	65.0	83.0	5
UE/GE	0.09	0.01	0.07	0.10	6						
CH_4E/GE	0.08	0.0	0.07	0.08	6						
ME/DE	0.75	0.02	0.72	0.77	6						
ME/GE	0.49	0.05	0.44	0.56	6						
Digestibility Coefficients											
DM	0.63	0.05	0.57	0.70	6						
OM	0.65	0.05	0.58	0.72	6						
CP	0.87	0.01	0.85	0.88	6						
CF	0.29	0.08	0.21	0.41	6						
EE	0.71	0.25	0.20	0.88	6						
NDF	0.45	0.08	0.37	0.54	4						
ADF	0.37	0.08	0.29	0.47	4						
Cell	0.37	0.11	0.29	0.52	4						
GE	0.66	0.05	0.60	0.73	6						
DOMD(g/kg ODM)	603.4	46.8	549.1	674.7	6						

PIG DATABASE

FEED CLASS 11

HIGH TEMPERATURE DRIED GREEN CROPS

PIG DATABASE

FEED DESCRIPTION : **HT DRIED GRASS** (Source 4)

Determination	Mean	SD	Min	Max	n	Determination	Mean	SD	Min	Max	n
General (g/kg ODM)						**Ileal digestibility coefficients for amino acids**					
ODM (fresh)	907.6		907.6	907.6	1	Ala					
CP	122.6		122.6	122.6	1	Arg					
CF	193.1		193.1	193.1	1	Asp					
EE	30.0		30.0	30.0	1	Cys					
AEE						Glu					
TA	161.4		161.4	161.4	1	Gly					
GE (MJ/kg ODM)	16.9		16.9	16.9	1	His					
						Ile					
						Leu					
NDF ash						Lys					
NDF unash						Meth					
ADF ash						Phe					
ADF unash						Pro					
						Pro.OH					
						Ser					
WSC						Thr					
Sugars	156.0		156.0	156.0	1	Tryp					
						Tyr					
Energy Values						Val					
DE (MJ/kg ODM)	6.6		6.6	6.6	1						

Faecal Digestibility Coefficients

DM
OM
CP
CF
EE
NDF
ADF
Cell
GE

PIG DATABASE

FEED CLASS 40

ENERGY FEEDS

PIG DATABASE

FEED DESCRIPTION : **BARLEY GRAIN, ALL SEASONS** (Source 4)

Determination	Mean	SD	Min	Max	n	Determination	Mean	SD	Min	Max	n
General (g/kg ODM)						**Ileal digestibility coefficients for amino acids**					
ODM (fresh)	872.1	7.3	862.0	888.0	10	Ala					
CP	127.8	23.3	100.0	170.6	10	Arg					
CF	41.8	3.5	36.3	48.7	10	Asp					
EE	15.7	1.8	13.4	19.1	10	Cys					
AEE	15.3	1.3	13.8	17.8	10	Glu					
TA	25.3	3.4	20.1	32.5	10	Gly					
GE (MJ/kg ODM)	18.6	0.17	18.3	18.8	10	His					
						Ile					
						Leu					
NDF ash	247.7	13.2	237.8	274.8	8	Lys					
NDF unash						Meth					
ADF ash						Phe					
ADF unash						Pro					
						Pro.OH					
						Ser					
WSC						Thr					
Sugars	28.5	2.1	27.0	30.0	2	Tryp					
						Tyr					
Energy Values						Val					
DE (MJ/kg ODM)	15.4	0.23	15.1	15.9	10						

Faecal Digestibility Coefficients

DM
OM
CP
CF
EE
NDF
ADF
Cell
GE

PIG DATABASE

FEED DESCRIPTION : **BARLEY GRAIN, SPRING** (Source 4)

Determination	Mean	SD	Min	Max	n	Determination	Mean	SD	Min	Max	n
General (g/kg ODM)						**Ileal digestibility coefficients**					
						for amino acids					
ODM (fresh)	872.9	7.1	866.0	888.0	8	Ala					
CP	129.6	23.7	100.0	170.6	8	Arg					
CF	42.9	2.9	39.5	48.7	8	Asp					
EE	16.0	1.9	13.4	19.1	8	Cys					
AEE	15.6	1.3	14.1	17.8	8	Glu					
TA	25.7	3.7	20.1	32.5	8	Gly					
GE (MJ/kg ODM)	18.6	0.18	18.3	18.8	8	His					
						Ile					
						Leu					
NDF ash	250.3	14.5	238.1	274.8	6	Lys					
NDF unash						Meth					
ADF ash						Phe					
ADF unash						Pro					
						Pro.OH					
						Ser					
WSC						Thr					
Sugars	28.5	2.1	27.0	30.0	2	Tryp					
						Tyr					
Energy Values						Val					
DE (MJ/kg ODM)	15.5	0.26	15.1	15.9	8						

Faecal Digestibility Coefficients

DM
OM
CP
CF
EE
NDF
ADF
Cell
GE

FEED DESCRIPTION : **BARLEY GRAIN, WINTER** (Source 4)

Determination	Mean	SD	Min	Max	n	Determination	Mean	SD	Min	Max	n

General (g/kg ODM)

**Ileal digestibility coefficients
for amino acids**

Determination	Mean	SD	Min	Max	n	Determination
ODM (fresh)	869.0	9.9	862.0	876.0	2	Ala
CP	121.0	28.8	100.6	141.3	2	Arg
CF	37.4	1.6	36.3	38.5	2	Asp
EE	14.6	1.4	13.6	15.6	2	Cys
AEE	14.2	0.57	13.8	14.6	2	Glu
TA	23.6	1.6	22.5	24.7	2	Gly
GE (MJ/kg ODM)	18.5	0.15	18.4	18.6	2	His
						Ile
						Leu
NDF ash	239.7	2.6	237.8	241.5	2	Lys
NDF unash						Meth
ADF ash						Phe
ADF unash						Pro
						Pro.OH
						Ser
WSC						Thr
Sugars						Tryp
						Tyr
						Val

Energy Values

Determination	Mean	SD	Min	Max	n
DE (MJ/kg ODM)	15.4	0.04	15.4	15.4	2

Faecal Digestibility Coefficients

DM
OM
CP
CF
EE
NDF
ADF
Cell
GE

PIG DATABASE

FEED DESCRIPTION : **MAIZE GRAIN** (Source 4)

Determination	Mean	SD	Min	Max	n	Determination	Mean	SD	Min	Max	n
General (g/kg ODM)						**Ileal digestibility coefficients for amino acids**					
ODM (fresh)	864.3	8.0	855.0	874.7	7	Ala					
CP	98.6	8.2	82.5	106.9	7	Arg					
CF	21.1	3.1	17.8	26.0	7	Asp					
EE	35.4	8.2	21.8	48.1	7	Cys					
AEE	38.2	6.2	31.3	49.2	6	Glu					
TA	17.0	3.1	11.3	20.7	7	Gly					
GE (MJ/kg ODM)	18.8	0.10	18.6	18.9	7	His					
						Ile					
						Leu					
NDF ash	156.3	13.8	143.3	175.7	4	Lys					
NDF unash						Meth					
ADF ash						Phe					
ADF unash						Pro					
						Pro.OH					
						Ser					
WSC						Thr					
Sugars	25.0	3.5	21.0	27.0	3	Tryp					
						Tyr					
Energy Values						Val					
DE (MJ/kg ODM)	16.5	0.37	16.1	17.1	7						

Faecal Digestibility Coefficients

DM
OM
CP
CF
EE
NDF
ADF
Cell
GE

PIG DATABASE

FEED DESCRIPTION : **OATS GRAIN, SPRING** (Source 4)

Determination	Mean	SD	Min	Max	n	Determination	Mean	SD	Min	Max	n

General (g/kg ODM)

Ileal digestibility coefficients for amino acids

Determination	Mean	SD	Min	Max	n	Determination
ODM (fresh)	885.4	9.1	876.0	894.2	3	Ala
CP	126.0	19.8	113.0	148.8	3	Arg
CF	97.5	6.8	93.5	105.4	3	Asp
EE	23.7	5.8	17.8	29.4	3	Cys
AEE	30.7	2.7	29.0	33.8	3	Glu
TA	30.9	3.0	27.9	33.9	3	Gly
GE (MJ/kg ODM)	19.5	0.24	19.3	19.8	3	His
						Ile
						Leu
NDF ash	357.1	9.1	350.6	363.5	2	Lys
NDF unash						Meth
ADF ash						Phe
ADF unash						Pro
						Pro.OH
						Ser
WSC						Thr
Sugars	21.0		21.0	21.0	1	Tryp
						Tyr
Energy Values						Val

Determination	Mean	SD	Min	Max	n
DE (MJ/kg ODM)	12.8	0.40	12.5	13.3	3

Faecal Digestibility Coefficients

DM
OM
CP
CF
EE
NDF
ADF
Cell
GE

PIG DATABASE

FEED DESCRIPTION : **RYE GRAIN** (Source 4)

Determination	Mean	SD	Min	Max	n	Determination	Mean	SD	Min	Max	n
General (g/kg ODM)						Ileal digestibility coefficients for amino acids					
ODM (fresh)	868.5	5.0	865.0	872.0	2	Ala					
CP	119.1	19.0	105.6	132.5	2	Arg					
CF	20.3	0.28	20.1	20.5	2	Asp					
EE	11.6	1.4	10.6	12.6	2	Cys					
AEE	29.1	0.14	29.0	29.2	2	Glu					
TA	18.0	0.57	17.6	18.4	2	Gly					
GE (MJ/kg ODM)	18.5	0.38	18.2	18.8	2	His					
						Ile					
						Leu					
NDF ash	357.1	9.1	350.6	363.5	2	Lys					
NDF unash						Meth					
ADF ash						Phe					
ADF unash						Pro					
						Pro.OH					
						Ser					
WSC						Thr					
Sugars						Tryp					
						Tyr					
Energy Values						Val					
DE (MJ/kg ODM)	15.3	0.30	15.0	15.5	2						

Faecal Digestibility Coefficients

DM
OM
CP
CF
EE
NDF
ADF
Cell
GE

PIG DATABASE

FEED DESCRIPTION : **SORGHUM GRAIN** (Source 4)

Determination	Mean	SD	Min	Max	n	Determination	Mean	SD	Min	Max	n
General (g/kg ODM)						**Ileal digestibility coefficients for amino acids**					
ODM (fresh)	897.4		897.4	897.4	1	Ala					
CP	128.7		128.7	128.7	1	Arg					
CF	19.7		19.7	19.7	1	Asp					
EE	21.8		21.8	21.8	1	Cys					
AEE						Glu					
TA	16.9		16.9	16.9	1	Gly					
GE (MJ/kg ODM)	18.5		18.5	18.5	1	His					
						Ile					
						Leu					
NDF ash						Lys					
NDF unash						Meth					
ADF ash						Phe					
ADF unash						Pro					
						Pro.OH					
						Ser					
WSC						Thr					
Sugars	15.0		15.0	15.0	1	Tryp					
						Tyr					
Energy Values						Val					
DE (MJ/kg ODM)	16.6		16.6	16.6	1						

Faecal Digestibility Coefficients

DM
OM
CP
CF
EE
NDF
ADF
Cell
GE

PIG DATABASE

FEED DESCRIPTION : **WHEAT BRAN** (Source 4)

Determination	Mean	SD	Min	Max	n	Determination	Mean	SD	Min	Max	n
General (g/kg ODM)						**Ileal digestibility coefficients for amino acids**					
ODM (fresh)	896.0		896.0	896.0	1	Ala					
CP	140.9		140.9	140.9	1	Arg					
CF	119.7		119.7	119.7	1	Asp					
EE	32.8		32.8	32.8	1	Cys					
AEE						Glu					
TA	64.2		64.2	64.2	1	Gly					
GE (MJ/kg ODM)	18.8		18.8	18.8	1	His					
						Ile					
						Leu					
NDF ash						Lys					
NDF unash						Meth					
ADF ash						Phe					
ADF unash						Pro					
						Pro.OH					
						Ser					
WSC						Thr					
Sugars	51.0		51.0	51.0	1	Tryp					
						Tyr					
Energy Values						Val					
DE (MJ/kg ODM)	9.0		9.0	9.0	1						

Faecal Digestibility Coefficients

DM
OM
CP
CF
EE
NDF
ADF
Cell
GE

PIG DATABASE

FEED DESCRIPTION : **WHEAT GRAIN, ALL SEASONS** (Source 4)

Determination	Mean	SD	Min	Max	n	Determination	Mean	SD	Min	Max	n
General (g/kg ODM)						**Ileal digestibility coefficients for amino acids**					
ODM (fresh)	864.5	12.5	848.0	888.0	9	Ala					
CP	135.7	19.4	101.3	161.3	9	Arg					
CF	20.3	1.8	17.0	22.6	9	Asp					
EE	15.3	2.3	12.0	18.1	9	Cys					
AEE	19.2	1.7	15.7	22.1	9	Glu					
TA	15.0	2.5	11.7	20.0	9	Gly					
GE (MJ/kg ODM)	18.4	0.40	17.9	19.0	9	His					
						Ile					
						Leu					
NDF ash	152.3	8.3	133.3	157.0	8	Lys					
NDF unash						Meth					
ADF ash						Phe					
ADF unash						Pro					
						Pro.OH					
						Ser					
WSC						Thr					
Sugars	30.0		30.0	30.0	1	Tryp					
						Tyr					
Energy Values						Val					
DE (MJ/kg ODM)	16.1	0.42	15.1	16.4	9						

Faecal Digestibility Coefficients

DM
OM
CP
CF
EE
NDF
ADF
Cell
GE

PIG DATABASE

FEED DESCRIPTION : **WHEAT GRAIN, SPRING** (Source 4)

Determination	Mean	SD	Min	Max	n	Determination	Mean	SD	Min	Max	n
General (g/kg ODM)						**Ileal digestibility coefficients for amino acids**					
ODM (fresh)	857.0		857.0	857.0	1	Ala					
CP	155.0		155.0	155.0	1	Arg					
CF	21.6		21.6	21.6	1	Asp					
EE	18.1		18.1	18.1	1	Cys					
AEE	20.7		20.7	20.7	1	Glu					
TA	16.7		16.7	16.7	1	Gly					
GE (MJ/kg ODM)	19.0		19.0	19.0	1	His					
						Ile					
						Leu					
NDF ash	155.9		155.9	155.9	1	Lys					
NDF unash						Meth					
ADF ash						Phe					
ADF unash						Pro					
						Pro.OH					
WSC						Ser					
Sugars						Thr					
						Tryp					
Energy Values						Tyr					
						Val					
DE (MJ/kg ODM)	16.4		16.4	16.4	1						

Faecal Digestibility Coefficients

DM
OM
CP
CF
EE
NDF
ADF
Cell
GE

PIG DATABASE

FEED DESCRIPTION : **WHEAT GRAIN, WINTER** (Source 4)

Determination	Mean	SD	Min	Max	n	Determination	Mean	SD	Min	Max	n
General (g/kg ODM)						**Ileal digestibility coefficients for amino acids**					
ODM (fresh)	865.5	13.1	848.0	888.0	8	Ala					
CP	133.3	19.2	101.3	161.3	8	Arg					
CF	20.2	1.8	17.0	22.6	8	Asp					
EE	14.9	2.2	12.0	17.2	8	Cys					
AEE	19.0	1.8	15.7	22.1	8	Glu					
TA	14.8	2.6	11.7	20.0	8	Gly					
GE (MJ/kg ODM)	18.3	0.34	17.9	19.0	8	His					
						Ile					
						Leu					
NDF ash	151.7	8.8	133.3	157.0	7	Lys					
NDF unash						Meth					
ADF ash						Phe					
ADF unash						Pro					
						Pro.OH					
						Ser					
WSC						Thr					
Sugars	30.0		30.0	30.0	1	Tryp					
						Tyr					
Energy Values						Val					
DE (MJ/kg ODM)	16.0	0.42	15.1	16.4	8						

Faecal Digestibility Coefficients

DM
OM
CP
CF
EE
NDF
ADF
Cell
GE

PIG DATABASE

FEED DESCRIPTION : **WHEAT MIDDLINGS** (Source 4)

Determination	Mean	SD	Min	Max	n	Determination	Mean	SD	Min	Max	n

General (g/kg ODM)

Determination	Mean	SD	Min	Max	n
ODM (fresh)	878.7		878.7	878.7	1
CP	174.5		174.5	174.5	1
CF	71.3		71.3	71.3	1
EE	39.3		39.3	39.3	1
AEE	37.4		37.4	37.4	1
TA	47.5		47.5	47.5	1
GE (MJ/kg ODM)	19.2		19.2	19.2	1

NDF ash
NDF unash
ADF ash
ADF unash

Determination	Mean	SD	Min	Max	n
WSC					
Sugars	65.0		65.0	65.0	1

Energy Values

Determination	Mean	SD	Min	Max	n
DE (MJ/kg ODM)	13.5		13.5	13.5	1

Faecal Digestibility Coefficients

DM
OM
CP
CF
EE
NDF
ADF
Cell
GE

Ileal digestibility coefficients for amino acids

Ala
Arg
Asp
Cys
Glu
Gly
His
Ile
Leu
Lys
Meth
Phe
Pro
Pro.OH
Ser
Thr
Tryp
Tyr
Val

PIG DATABASE

FEED CLASS 50

PROTEIN SUPPLEMENTS

PIG DATABASE

FEED DESCRIPTION : **BEANS, FIELD SPRING** (Source 4)

Determination	Mean	SD	Min	Max	n	Determination	Mean	SD	Min	Max	n
General (g/kg ODM)						**Ileal digestibility coefficients for amino acids**					
ODM (fresh)	857.4		857.4	857.4	1	Ala					
CP	297.6		297.6	297.6	1	Arg					
CF	69.4		69.4	69.4	1	Asp					
EE	22.1		22.1	22.1	1	Cys					
AEE						Glu					
TA	33.9		33.9	33.9	1	Gly					
GE (MJ/kg ODM)	18.8		18.8	18.8	1	His					
						Ile					
						Leu					
NDF ash						Lys					
NDF unash						Meth					
ADF ash						Phe					
ADF unash						Pro					
						Pro.OH					
						Ser					
WSC						Thr					
Sugars	47.0		47.0	47.0	1	Tryp					
						Tyr					
Energy Values						Val					
DE (MJ/kg ODM)	14.7		14.7	14.7	1						

Faecal Digestibility Coefficients

DM
OM
CP
CF
EE
NDF
ADF
Cell
GE

PIG DATABASE

FEED DESCRIPTION : **COPRA, EXPELLED** (Sources 2, 4)

Determination	Mean	SD	Min	Max	n	Determination	Mean	SD	Min	Max	n
General (g/kg ODM)						**Ileal digestibility coefficients for amino acids**					
ODM (fresh)	950.5	5.8	943.0	956.0	4	Ala					
CP	184.8	26.3	154.0	218.0	4	Arg					
CF	82.5	14.4	68.0	100.0	4	Asp					
EE	201.3	102.4	91.0	333.0	4	Cys					
AEE						Glu					
TA	46.5	5.1	43.0	54.0	4	Gly					
GE (MJ/kg ODM)	21.9	2.1	19.7	24.6	4	His					
						Ile					
						Leu					
NDF ash						Lys					
NDF unash						Meth					
ADF ash						Phe					
ADF unash						Pro					
						Pro.OH					
						Ser					
WSC						Thr					
Sugars						Tryp					
						Tyr					
Energy Values						Val					

DE (MJ/kg ODM)   18.1   1.8   15.5   19.7   4

Faecal Digestibility Coefficients

DM
OM
CP
CF
EE
NDF
ADF
Cell
GE

PIG DATABASE

FEED DESCRIPTION : **COPRA, EXTRACTED** (Source 4)

Determination	Mean	SD	Min	Max	n	Determination	Mean	SD	Min	Max	n

General (g/kg ODM)

Ileal digestibility coefficients for amino acids

Determination	Mean	SD	Min	Max	n	Determination
ODM (fresh)	899.0		899.0	899.0	1	Ala
CP	246.0		246.0	246.0	1	Arg
CF	108.0		108.0	108.0	1	Asp
EE	4.0		4.0	4.0	1	Cys
AEE						Glu
TA	62.0		62.0	62.0	1	Gly
GE (MJ/kg ODM)	18.3		18.3	18.3	1	His
						Ile
						Leu
NDF ash						Lys
NDF unash						Meth
ADF ash						Phe
ADF unash						Pro
						Pro.OH
						Ser
WSC						Thr
Sugars						Tryp
						Tyr

Energy Values

Val

	Mean	SD	Min	Max	n
DE (MJ/kg ODM)	12.7		12.7	12.7	1

Faecal Digestibility Coefficients

DM
OM
CP
CF
EE
NDF
ADF
Cell
GE

369

PIG DATABASE

FEED DESCRIPTION : **COPRA, FULL FAT** (Source 4)

Determination	Mean	SD	Min	Max	n	Determination	Mean	SD	Min	Max	n
General (g/kg ODM)						Ileal digestibility coefficients for amino acids					
ODM (fresh)	959.0		959.0	959.0	1	Ala					
CP	76.0		76.0	76.0	1	Arg					
CF	35.0		35.0	35.0	1	Asp					
EE	662.0		662.0	662.0	1	Cys					
AEE						Glu					
TA	12.0		12.0	12.0	1	Gly					
GE (MJ/kg ODM)	34.4		34.4	34.4	1	His					
						Ile					
						Leu					
NDF ash						Lys					
NDF unash						Meth					
ADF ash						Phe					
ADF unash						Pro					
						Pro.OH					
						Ser					
WSC						Thr					
Sugars						Tryp					
						Tyr					
Energy Values						Val					
DE (MJ/kg ODM)	29.6		29.6	29.6	1						

Faecal Digestibility Coefficients

DM
OM
CP
CF
EE
NDF
ADF
Cell
GE

PIG DATABASE

FEED DESCRIPTION : **DRIED SKIM MILK** (Source 4)

Determination	Mean	SD	Min	Max	n	Determination	Mean	SD	Min	Max	n

General (g/kg ODM)

Ileal digestibility coefficients for amino acids

Determination	Mean	SD	Min	Max	n	Determination
ODM (fresh)	911.8		911.8	911.8	1	Ala
CP	356.5		356.5	356.5	1	Arg
CF						Asp
EE	38.1		38.1	38.1	1	Cys
AEE						Glu
TA	81.1		81.1	81.1	1	Gly
GE (MJ/kg ODM)	18.9		18.9	18.9	1	His
						Ile
						Leu
NDF ash						Lys
NDF unash						Meth
ADF ash						Phe
ADF unash						Pro
						Pro.OH
						Ser
WSC						Thr
Sugars	353.0		353.0	353.0	1	Tryp
						Tyr
						Val

Energy Values

Determination	Mean	SD	Min	Max	n
DE (MJ/kg ODM)	18.3		18.3	18.3	1

Faecal Digestibility Coefficients

DM
OM
CP
CF
EE
NDF
ADF
Cell
GE

371

PIG DATABASE

FEED DESCRIPTION : **FISH, ENSILED, MIXED** (Source 4)

Determination	Mean	SD	Min	Max	n	Determination	Mean	SD	Min	Max	n
General (g/kg ODM)						**Ileal digestibility coefficients for amino acids**					
ODM (fresh)	226.7	20.9	188.3	267.8	12	Ala					
CP	603.8	72.3	514.4	727.8	12	Arg					
CF						Asp					
EE	128.9	76.0	12.5	245.1	12	Cys					
AEE						Glu					
TA	92.0	17.0	63.6	116.7	12	Gly					
GE (MJ/kg ODM)	19.1	1.2	16.5	21.1	12	His					
						Ile					
NDF ash						Leu					
NDF unash						Lys					
ADF ash						Meth					
ADF unash						Phe					
						Pro					
						Pro.OH					
WSC						Ser					
Sugars						Thr					
						Tryp					
						Tyr					
Energy Values						Val					
DE (MJ/kg ODM)	18.3	1.7	14.4	21.1	12						

Faecal Digestibility Coefficients

DM
OM
CP
CF
EE
NDF
ADF
Cell
GE

PIG DATABASE

FEED DESCRIPTION : **FISHMEAL, CHILEAN** (Source 4)

Determination	Mean	SD	Min	Max	n	Determination	Mean	SD	Min	Max	n
General (g/kg ODM)						**Ileal digestibility coefficients for amino acids**					
ODM (fresh)	903.5	14.8	893.0	914.0	2	Ala					
CP	731.0	1.4	730.0	732.0	2	Arg					
CF						Asp					
EE	103.4	1.2	102.5	104.2	2	Cys					
AEE						Glu					
TA	162.1	9.3	155.5	168.6	2	Gly					
GE (MJ/kg ODM)	21.4	0.09	21.4	21.5	2	His					
						Ile					
						Leu					
NDF ash						Lys					
NDF unash						Meth					
ADF ash						Phe					
ADF unash						Pro					
						Pro.OH					
						Ser					
WSC						Thr					
Sugars						Tryp					
						Tyr					
Energy Values						Val					
DE (MJ/kg ODM)	18.8	1.6	17.7	20.0	2						

Faecal Digestibility Coefficients

DM
OM
CP
CF
EE
NDF
ADF
Cell
GE

PIG DATABASE

FEED DESCRIPTION : **FISHMEAL, HERRING** (Source 4)

Determination	Mean	SD	Min	Max	n	Determination	Mean	SD	Min	Max	n
General (g/kg ODM)						**Ileal digestibility coefficients for amino acids**					
ODM (fresh)	909.0	15.0	889.0	936.0	8	Ala					
CP	752.3	23.2	714.0	780.0	8	Arg					
CF						Asp					
EE	98.9	25.0	64.0	136.6	8	Cys					
AEE						Glu					
TA	141.8	26.7	111.9	178.2	8	Gly					
GE (MJ/kg ODM)	22.0	0.87	20.7	23.1	8	His					
						Ile					
						Leu					
NDF ash						Lys					
NDF unash						Meth					
ADF ash						Phe					
ADF unash						Pro					
						Pro.OH					
						Ser					
WSC						Thr					
Sugars						Tryp					
						Tyr					
Energy Values						Val					

DE (MJ/kg ODM) 19.3   1.1   16.9   20.4   8

Faecal Digestibility Coefficients

DM
OM
CP
CF
EE
NDF
ADF
Cell
GE

PIG DATABASE

FEED DESCRIPTION : **FISHMEAL, OFFAL MEAL WHITE** (Source 4)

Determination	Mean	SD	Min	Max	n	Determination	Mean	SD	Min	Max	n
General (g/kg ODM)						**Ileal digestibility coefficients for amino acids**					
ODM (fresh)	893.0		893.0	893.0	1	Ala					
CP	706.0		706.0	706.0	1	Arg					
CF						Asp					
EE	95.4		95.4	95.4	1	Cys					
AEE						Glu					
TA	214.1		214.1	214.1	1	Gly					
GE (MJ/kg ODM)	20.9		20.9	20.9	1	His					
						Ile					
						Leu					
NDF ash						Lys					
NDF unash						Meth					
ADF ash						Phe					
ADF unash						Pro					
						Pro.OH					
						Ser					
WSC						Thr					
Sugars						Tryp					
						Tyr					
Energy Values						Val					
DE (MJ/kg ODM)	18.7		18.7	18.7	1						

Faecal Digestibility Coefficients

DM
OM
CP
CF
EE
NDF
ADF
Cell
GE

PIG DATABASE

FEED DESCRIPTION : **FISHMEAL, PERUVIAN** (Source 4)

Determination	Mean	SD	Min	Max	n	Determination	Mean	SD	Min	Max	n
General (g/kg ODM)						**Ileal digestibility coefficients for amino acids**					
ODM (fresh)	889.0		889.0	889.0	1	Ala					
CP	709.0		709.0	709.0	1	Arg					
CF						Asp					
EE	121.6		121.6	121.6	1	Cys					
AEE						Glu					
TA	190.2		190.2	190.2	1	Gly					
GE (MJ/kg ODM)	22.0		22.0	22.0	1	His					
						Ile					
						Leu					
NDF ash						Lys					
NDF unash						Meth					
ADF ash						Phe					
ADF unash						Pro					
						Pro.OH					
						Ser					
WSC						Thr					
Sugars						Tryp					
						Tyr					
Energy Values						Val					
DE (MJ/kg ODM)	20.5		20.5	20.5	1						

Faecal Digestibility Coefficients

DM
OM
CP
CF
EE
NDF
ADF
Cell
GE

FEED DESCRIPTION : **FISHMEAL, WHITE** (Source 4)

Determination	Mean	SD	Min	Max	n	Determination	Mean	SD	Min	Max	n
General (g/kg ODM)						**Ileal digestibility coefficients for amino acids**					
ODM (fresh)	890.8	4.6	887.5	894.0	2	Ala					
CP	690.9	4.1	688.0	693.8	2	Arg					
CF						Asp					
EE	54.8	3.5	52.3	57.2	2	Cys					
AEE	72.4		72.4	72.4	1	Glu					
TA	238.8	38.1	211.8	265.7	2	Gly					
GE (MJ/kg ODM)	19.1	0.87	18.5	19.8	2	His					
						Ile					
						Leu					
NDF ash						Lys					
NDF unash						Meth					
ADF ash						Phe					
ADF unash						Pro					
						Pro.OH					
						Ser					
WSC						Thr					
Sugars						Tryp					
						Tyr					
Energy Values						Val					
DE (MJ/kg ODM)	17.4	0.96	16.7	18.1	2						

Faecal Digestibility Coefficients

DM
OM
CP
CF
EE
NDF
ADF
Cell
GE

PIG DATABASE

FEED DESCRIPTION : **GROUNDNUT MEAL** (Source 4)

Determination	Mean	SD	Min	Max	n	Determination	Mean	SD	Min	Max	n
General (g/kg ODM)						**Ileal digestibility coefficients for amino acids**					
ODM (fresh)	924.5		924.5	924.5	1	Ala					
CP	546.6		546.6	546.6	1	Arg					
CF	65.9		65.9	65.9	1	Asp					
EE	70.1		70.1	70.1	1	Cys					
AEE						Glu					
TA	63.3		63.3	63.3	1	Gly					
GE (MJ/kg ODM)	20.8		20.8	20.8	1	His					
						Ile					
						Leu					
NDF ash						Lys					
NDF unash						Meth					
ADF ash						Phe					
ADF unash						Pro					
						Pro.OH					
						Ser					
WSC						Thr					
Sugars	77.0		77.0	77.0	1	Tryp					
						Tyr					
Energy Values						Val					
DE (MJ/kg ODM)	17.9		17.9	17.9	1						

Faecal Digestibility Coefficients

DM
OM
CP
CF
EE
NDF
ADF
Cell
GE

PIG DATABASE

FEED DESCRIPTION : **MEAT AND BONE MEAL** (Source 4)

Determination	Mean	SD	Min	Max	n	Determination	Mean	SD	Min	Max	n
General (g/kg ODM)						**Ileal digestibility coefficients for amino acids**					
ODM (fresh)	911.7		911.7	911.7	1	Ala					
CP	555.0		555.0	555.0	1	Arg					
CF						Asp					
EE	47.4		47.4	47.4	1	Cys					
AEE						Glu					
TA	329.9		329.9	329.9	1	Gly					
GE (MJ/kg ODM)	15.6		15.6	15.6	1	His					
						Ile					
						Leu					
NDF ash						Lys					
NDF unash						Meth					
ADF ash						Phe					
ADF unash						Pro					
						Pro.OH					
						Ser					
WSC						Thr					
Sugars						Tryp					
						Tyr					
Energy Values						Val					
DE (MJ/kg ODM)	8.5		8.5	8.5	1						

Faecal Digestibility Coefficients

DM
OM
CP
CF
EE
NDF
ADF
Cell
GE

PIG DATABASE

FEED DESCRIPTION : **SOYABEAN MEAL, EXTRACTED** (Source 4)

Determination	Mean	SD	Min	Max	n	Determination	Mean	SD	Min	Max	n
General (g/kg ODM)						**Ileal digestibility coefficients for amino acids**					
ODM (fresh)	883.4	5.3	879.0	891.0	4	Ala					
CP	468.0	53.9	400.0	530.8	4	Arg					
CF	48.0		48.0	48.0	1	Asp					
EE	19.7	3.8	16.4	24.4	4	Cys					
AEE						Glu					
TA	68.9		68.9	68.9	1	Gly					
GE (MJ/kg ODM)	19.3	0.32	19.1	19.8	4	His					
						Ile					
						Leu					
NDF ash						Lys					
NDF unash						Meth					
ADF ash						Phe					
ADF unash						Pro					
						Pro.OH					
						Ser					
WSC						Thr					
Sugars	120.0		120.0	120.0	1	Tryp					
						Tyr					
						Val					

Energy Values

	Mean	SD	Min	Max	n
DE (MJ/kg ODM)	17.7	0.73	16.6	18.2	4

Faecal Digestibility Coefficients

DM
OM
CP
CF
EE
NDF
ADF
Cell
GE

POULTRY DATABASE

FEED CLASS 40

ENERGY FEEDS

POULTRY DATABASE

FEED DESCRIPTION : **BARLEY GRAIN, WINTER** (Source 3)

Determination	Mean	SD	Min	Max	n	Determination	Mean	SD	Min	Max	n

General (g/kg ODM)

Determination	Mean	SD	Min	Max	n
ODM (fresh)	850.4	34.8	792.0	909.5	10
CP	127.1	12.5	107.0	144.7	10
CF	45.8	6.0	40.3	58.2	10
EE	20.3	1.4	18.2	22.7	10
AEE	29.8	2.2	26.9	32.6	10
TA	22.5	1.4	20.5	24.0	10
GE (MJ/kg ODM)	18.5	0.14	18.3	18.7	10
NDF ash	164.7	17.1	140.0	196.5	10
NDF unash					
ADF ash	53.9	9.3	43.0	70.0	10
ADF unash					
Starch	598.8	16.8	571.4	625.3	10
WSC					
Sugars	14.1	4.6	7.6	21.0	10

Energy Values (MJ/kg ODM)

Determination	Mean	SD	Min	Max	n
AMEn	14.3	0.56	13.5	15.3	10
TMEn	14.5	0.57	13.7	15.5	10

Amino acid digestibility coefficients

Ala
Arg
Asp
Cys
Glu
Gly
His
Ile
Leu
Lys
Meth
Phe
Pro
Pro.OH
Ser
Thr
Tryp
Tyr
Val

POULTRY DATABASE

FEED DESCRIPTION : **CITRUS PULP, DRIED** (Source 3)

Determination	Mean	SD	Min	Max	n	Determination	Mean	SD	Min	Max	n

General (g/kg ODM)

Determination	Mean	SD	Min	Max	n
ODM (fresh)	896.5	9.8	888.5	912.5	5
CP	61.7	5.4	52.6	65.3	5
CF	125.3	7.7	111.6	130.3	5
EE	20.3	3.3	17.1	25.6	5
AEE	25.4	4.1	22.7	32.6	5
TA	60.9	2.0	59.0	63.0	5
GE (MJ/kg ODM)	17.4	0.07	17.3	17.5	5
NDF ash	194.2	7.8	184.5	203.0	5
NDF unash					
ADF ash	138.1	5.6	129.5	144.5	5
ADF unash					
Starch					
WSC					
Sugars	250.3	14.9	240.5	276.5	5

Energy Values (MJ/kg ODM)

Determination	Mean	SD	Min	Max	n
AMEn	5.8	0.31	5.4	6.1	5
TMEn	6.3	0.31	6.0	6.7	5

Amino acid digestibility coefficients

Ala
Arg
Asp
Cys
Glu
Gly
His
Ile
Leu
Lys
Meth
Phe
Pro
Pro.OH
Ser
Thr
Tryp
Tyr
Val

POULTRY DATABASE

FEED DESCRIPTION : **MAIZE GLUTEN FEED** (Source 3)

Determination	Mean	SD	Min	Max	n	Determination	Mean	SD	Min	Max	n
General (g/kg ODM)											
ODM (fresh)	891.9	20.6	856.0	906.0	5						
CP	216.7	7.1	205.7	222.0	5						
CF	72.5	5.2	64.3	78.8	5						
EE	34.3	4.6	29.4	39.7	5						
AEE	47.7	6.0	40.9	56.5	5						
TA	75.3	5.2	69.5	80.5	5						
GE (MJ/kg ODM)	18.8	0.23	18.5	19.0	5						
NDF ash	370.8	24.6	346.5	410.0	5						
NDF unash											
ADF ash	94.0	6.7	88.0	103.5	5						
ADF unash											
Starch	228.6	17.8	205.0	251.8	5						
WSC											
Sugars	20.7	7.4	11.1	31.3	5						

Energy Values (MJ/kg ODM)

Determination	Mean	SD	Min	Max	n
AMEn	9.2	0.51	8.6	10.0	5
TMEn	9.6	0.55	9.0	10.5	5

Amino acid digestibility coefficients

Ala
Arg
Asp
Cys
Glu
Gly
His
Ile
Leu
Lys
Meth
Phe
Pro
Pro.OH
Ser
Thr
Tryp
Tyr
Val

POULTRY DATABASE

FEED DESCRIPTION : **MAIZE GRAIN** (Source 3)

Determination	Mean	SD	Min	Max	n	Determination	Mean	SD	Min	Max	n

General (g/kg ODM)

ODM (fresh)	885.4	4.4	879.0	890.0	5		
CP	96.7	4.2	92.7	102.6	5		
CF	21.5	0.57	20.7	22.0	5		
EE	42.3	3.3	39.6	47.9	5		
AEE	46.5	3.4	43.6	52.2	5		
TA	14.4	0.55	14.0	15.0	5		
GE (MJ/kg ODM)	18.8	0.13	18.7	19.0	5		
NDF ash	110.6	7.0	102.0	120.5	5		
NDF unash							
ADF ash	21.8	3.5	18.5	25.5	5		
ADF unash							
Starch	723.9	8.5	711.3	732.0	5		
WSC							
Sugars	13.4	1.9	10.4	15.4	5		

Energy Values (MJ/kg ODM)

AMEn	15.9	0.16	15.6	16.0	5
TMEn	16.1	0.17	15.8	16.2	5

Amino acid digestibility coefficients

Ala
Arg
Asp
Cys
Glu
Gly
His
Ile
Leu
Lys
Meth
Phe
Pro
Pro.OH
Ser
Thr
Tryp
Tyr
Val

POULTRY DATABASE

FEED DESCRIPTION : **NAKED OATS GRAIN, SPRING** (Source 3)

Determination	Mean	SD	Min	Max	n	Determination	Mean	SD	Min	Max	n
General (g/kg ODM)											
ODM (fresh)	860.6	31.3	805.0	880.0	5						
CP	118.0	9.2	103.0	126.7	5						
CF	35.4	11.6	23.8	51.5	5						
EE	90.7	6.8	79.3	97.3	5						
AEE	104.9	6.3	93.9	109.5	5						
TA	21.8	3.0	18.0	25.0	5						
GE (MJ/kg ODM)	20.1	0.18	19.9	20.3	5						
NDF ash	113.2	27.3	90.5	153.5	5						
NDF unash											
ADF ash	45.6	19.5	26.0	75.5	5						
ADF unash											
Starch	562.1	22.6	545.5	602.0	5						
WSC											
Sugars	7.5	0.81	6.6	8.8	5						

Energy Values (MJ/kg ODM)

Determination	Mean	SD	Min	Max	n
AMEn	16.5	0.12	16.4	16.7	5
TMEn	16.7	0.12	16.6	16.9	5

Amino acid digestibility coefficients

Ala
Arg
Asp
Cys
Glu
Gly
His
Ile
Leu
Lys
Meth
Phe
Pro
Pro.OH
Ser
Thr
Tryp
Tyr
Val

POULTRY DATABASE

FEED DESCRIPTION : **OATS GRAIN, SPRING** (Source 3)

Determination	Mean	SD	Min	Max	n	Determination	Mean	SD	Min	Max	n

General (g/kg ODM)

Determination	Mean	SD	Min	Max	n
ODM (fresh)	857.5	10.9	840.0	869.0	5
CP	108.6	13.5	92.4	123.3	5
CF	112.1	11.6	105.5	132.5	5
EE	53.7	11.0	42.4	71.8	5
AEE	62.5	11.1	49.2	79.7	5
TA	28.9	5.3	24.0	37.5	5
GE (MJ/kg ODM)	19.6	0.36	19.3	20.2	5
NDF ash	280.4	26.1	254.5	323.5	5
NDF unash					
ADF ash	154.0	15.6	129.0	169.5	5
ADF unash					
Starch	455.6	24.5	419.7	478.0	5
WSC					
Sugars	8.6	0.47	8.1	9.2	5

Energy Values (MJ/kg ODM)

Determination	Mean	SD	Min	Max	n
AMEn	14.5	0.55	13.8	15.2	5
TMEn	14.8	0.55	14.1	15.5	5

Amino acid digestibility coefficients

Ala
Arg
Asp
Cys
Glu
Gly
His
Ile
Leu
Lys
Meth
Phe
Pro
Pro.OH
Ser
Thr
Tryp
Tyr
Val

POULTRY DATABASE

FEED DESCRIPTION : **RICE BRAN MEAL, EXTRACTED** (Source 3)

Determination	Mean	SD	Min	Max	n	Determination	Mean	SD	Min	Max	n

General (g/kg ODM)

Determination	Mean	SD	Min	Max	n
ODM (fresh)	902.4	4.7	897.5	909.0	5
CP	146.9	6.1	139.3	154.7	5
CF	165.1	12.9	152.9	186.0	5
EE	7.5	1.6	6.3	9.9	5
AEE	17.8	2.4	15.0	21.4	5
TA	16.2	1.2	14.5	17.2	5
GE (MJ/kg ODM)	16.6	0.12	16.5	16.8	5
NDF ash	428.7	25.2	401.0	465.0	5
NDF unash					
ADF ash	261.1	22.3	241.5	295.5	5
ADF unash					
Starch	263.1	29.8	226.0	301.5	5
WSC					
Sugars	19.2	4.4	12.0	24.0	5

Energy Values (MJ/kg ODM)

Determination	Mean	SD	Min	Max	n
AMEn	6.8	0.63	6.2	7.4	4
TMEn	7.3	0.63	6.8	7.9	4

Amino acid digestibility coefficients

Ala
Arg
Asp
Cys
Glu
Gly
His
Ile
Leu
Lys
Meth
Phe
Pro
Pro.OH
Ser
Thr
Tryp
Tyr
Val

POULTRY DATABASE

FEED DESCRIPTION : **SUGAR BEET FEED, DRIED, MOLASSED** (Source 3)

Determination	Mean	SD	Min	Max	n	Determination	Mean	SD	Min	Max	n
General (g/kg ODM)											
ODM (fresh)	875.7	13.7	860.0	888.5	5						
CP	105.3	5.0	97.2	109.7	5						
CF	136.8	6.8	126.5	145.0	5						
EE	3.8	0.71	3.0	4.8	5						
AEE	5.1	0.84	4.2	6.4	5						
TA	98.1	9.9	86.2	109.6	5						
GE (MJ/kg ODM)	16.7	0.11	16.5	16.8	5						
NDF ash	343.7	19.9	327.5	376.5	5						
NDF unash											
ADF ash	177.9	10.6	165.0	187.0	5						
ADF unash											
Starch	120.9	12.2	109.2	136.7	5						
WSC											
Sugars	235.4	14.6	211.9	248.6	5						

Energy Values (MJ/kg ODM)

Determination	Mean	SD	Min	Max	n
AMEn	5.7	0.41	5.0	6.0	5
TMEn	5.9	0.41	5.2	6.2	5

Amino acid digestibility coefficients

Ala
Arg
Asp
Cys
Glu
Gly
His
Ile
Leu
Lys
Meth
Phe
Pro
Pro.OH
Ser
Thr
Tryp
Tyr
Val

POULTRY DATABASE

FEED DESCRIPTION : **TRITICALE GRAIN, WINTER** (Source 3)

Determination	Mean	SD	Min	Max	n	Determination	Mean	SD	Min	Max	n

General (g/kg ODM)

ODM (fresh)	875.7	17.8	845.5	891.0	5						
CP	149.3	27.8	102.3	172.7	5						
CF	22.3	1.9	19.6	24.7	5						
EE	17.0	1.1	16.0	18.5	5						
AEE	23.9	1.1	22.2	24.8	5						
TA	20.4	1.1	19.0	21.5	5						
GE (MJ/kg ODM)	18.4	0.16	18.2	18.6	5						
NDF ash	128.1	11.5	109.5	137.0	5						
NDF unash											
ADF ash	35.6	4.5	30.0	42.5	5						
ADF unash											
Starch	625.4	35.5	604.8	688.3	5						
WSC											
Sugars	32.2	1.2	31.0	34.0	5						

Energy Values (MJ/kg ODM)

AMEn	14.0	0.26	13.9	14.5	5						
TMEn	14.4	0.35	14.1	15.0	5						

Amino acid digestibility coefficients

Ala
Arg
Asp
Cys
Glu
Gly
His
Ile
Leu
Lys
Meth
Phe
Pro
Pro.OH
Ser
Thr
Tryp
Tyr
Val

POULTRY DATABASE

FEED DESCRIPTION : **WHEAT BRAN** (Source 3)

Determination	Mean	SD	Min	Max	n	Determination	Mean	SD	Min	Max	n

General (g/kg ODM)

Determination	Mean	SD	Min	Max	n
ODM (fresh)	900.0	4.6	894.0	906.0	5
CP	177.6	8.3	168.3	184.3	5
CF	99.3	11.7	86.6	116.5	5
EE	35.4	1.8	32.7	37.1	5
AEE	52.1	3.2	46.7	54.5	5
TA	63.6	6.1	56.0	72.0	5
GE (MJ/kg ODM)	19.0	0.12	18.9	19.2	5
NDF ash	457.8	49.7	402.5	530.5	5
NDF unash					
ADF ash	126.4	15.6	110.5	149.5	5
ADF unash					
Starch	195.4	46.8	140.4	240.5	5
WSC					
Sugars	66.1	4.8	59.0	71.6	5

Energy Values (MJ/kg ODM)

Determination	Mean	SD	Min	Max	n
AMEn	7.4	1.0	5.9	8.5	5
TMEn	7.6	1.0	6.1	8.7	5

Amino acid digestibility coefficients

Ala
Arg
Asp
Cys
Glu
Gly
His
Ile
Leu
Lys
Meth
Phe
Pro
Pro.OH
Ser
Thr
Tryp
Tyr
Val

POULTRY DATABASE

FEED DESCRIPTION : **WHEAT FEED** (Source 3)

Determination	Mean	SD	Min	Max	n	Determination	Mean	SD	Min	Max	n

General (g/kg ODM)

Determination	Mean	SD	Min	Max	n
ODM (fresh)	906.3	14.9	881.0	918.0	5
CP	176.5	9.5	165.0	187.0	5
CF	83.1	4.8	77.5	87.9	5
EE	42.9	5.0	35.1	48.0	5
AEE	50.9	4.2	43.7	54.7	5
TA	51.6	3.4	48.0	55.0	5
GE (MJ/kg ODM)	19.0	0.10	18.9	19.1	5
NDF ash	388.1	26.8	353.5	428.5	5
NDF unash					
ADF ash	110.0	6.0	102.0	118.5	5
ADF unash					
Starch	275.4	38.6	227.0	326.5	5
WSC					
Sugars	56.6	6.1	49.8	64.8	5

Energy Values (MJ/kg ODM)

Determination	Mean	SD	Min	Max	n
AMEn	9.3	0.53	8.8	10.1	5
TMEn	9.5	0.53	9.0	10.3	5

Amino acid digestibility coefficients

Ala
Arg
Asp
Cys
Glu
Gly
His
Ile
Leu
Lys
Meth
Phe
Pro
Pro.OH
Ser
Thr
Tryp
Tyr
Val

POULTRY DATABASE

FEED DESCRIPTION : **WHEAT GRAIN, WINTER** (Source 3)

Determination	Mean	SD	Min	Max	n	Determination	Mean	SD	Min	Max	n

General (g/kg ODM)

	Mean	SD	Min	Max	n
ODM (fresh)	833.4	32.1	788.5	870.5	10
CP	124.3	12.0	106.1	139.7	10
CF	21.0	1.3	18.9	23.0	10
EE	15.9	2.9	12.0	19.2	10
AEE	22.2	2.8	17.6	25.6	10
TA	16.2	2.4	12.0	21.0	10
GE (MJ/kg ODM)	18.5	0.22	18.2	19.0	10
NDF ash	102.1	9.1	91.5	121.0	10
NDF unash					
ADF ash	26.0	1.7	23.0	28.0	10
ADF unash					
Starch	685.6	17.1	662.8	708.6	10
WSC					
Sugars	26.2	10.0	4.9	38.0	10

Energy Values (MJ/kg ODM)

	Mean	SD	Min	Max	n
AMEn	15.3	0.23	15.0	15.8	10
TMEn	15.5	0.22	15.3	16.0	10

Amino acid digestibility coefficients

Ala
Arg
Asp
Cys
Glu
Gly
His
Ile
Leu
Lys
Meth
Phe
Pro
Pro.OH
Ser
Thr
Tryp
Tyr
Val

POULTRY DATABASE

FEED CLASS 50

PROTEIN SUPPLEMENTS

POULTRY DATABASE

FEED DESCRIPTION : **BLOOD MEAL** (Source 3)

Determination	Mean	SD	Min	Max	n	Determination	Mean	SD	Min	Max	n

General (g/kg ODM)

Determination	Mean	SD	Min	Max	n
ODM (fresh)	914.8	16.7	894.5	937.5	5
CP	904.8	3.2	901.3	908.3	5
CF	2.3	0.31	2.0	2.8	5
EE					
AEE	12.0	2.2	9.4	14.4	5
TA	19.6	0.96	18.0	20.5	5
GE (MJ/kg ODM)	24.5	0.25	24.2	24.9	5

NDF ash
NDF unash
ADF ash
ADF unash

Starch
WSC
Sugars

Energy Values (MJ/kg ODM)

Determination	Mean	SD	Min	Max	n
AMEn	13.6	0.60	12.9	14.2	5
TMEn	13.8	0.60	13.1	14.4	5

Amino acid digestibility coefficients

Ala
Arg
Asp
Cys
Glu
Gly
His
Ile
Leu
Lys
Meth
Phe
Pro
Pro.OH
Ser
Thr
Tryp
Tyr
Val

POULTRY DATABASE

FEED DESCRIPTION : **COTTONSEED MEAL** (Source 3)

Determination	Mean	SD	Min	Max	n	Determination	Mean	SD	Min	Max	n
General (g/kg ODM)											
ODM (fresh)	959.6	11.2	945.5	976.0	5						
CP	382.1	18.0	362.4	400.9	5						
CF	165.1	24.3	132.5	188.5	5						
EE	61.7	4.1	56.4	66.0	5						
AEE	65.8	3.9	59.6	69.0	5						
TA	60.3	5.3	53.5	66.0	5						
GE (MJ/kg ODM)	20.6	0.24	20.3	20.9	5						
NDF ash	356.0	26.7	330.0	390.0	5						
NDF unash											
ADF ash	223.3	25.4	193.0	252.5	5						
ADF unash											
Starch	18.1	9.6	7.7	32.1	5						
WSC											
Sugars	50.8	2.8	46.2	53.5	5						

Energy Values (MJ/kg ODM)

Determination	Mean	SD	Min	Max	n
AMEn	9.1	0.34	8.6	9.5	5
TMEn	9.3	0.34	8.8	9.7	5

Amino acid digestibility coefficients

Ala
Arg
Asp
Cys
Glu
Gly
His
Ile
Leu
Lys
Meth
Phe
Pro
Pro.OH
Ser
Thr
Tryp
Tyr
Val

POULTRY DATABASE

FEED DESCRIPTION : **DISTILLERS DARK GRAINS, BARLEY BASED** (Source 3)

Determination	Mean	SD	Min	Max	n	Determination	Mean	SD	Min	Max	n
General (g/kg ODM)											
ODM (fresh)	913.9	20.2	880.0	930.0	5						
CP	278.2	9.4	263.3	289.2	5						
CF	118.2	13.1	99.7	129.5	5						
EE	67.8	9.2	53.0	74.2	5						
AEE	84.6	7.8	73.2	91.6	5						
TA	61.8	4.1	58.0	68.5	5						
GE (MJ/kg ODM)	21.3	0.30	20.9	21.7	5						
NDF ash											
NDF unash											
ADF ash											
ADF unash											
Starch	30.0	5.7	20.3	34.3	5						
WSC											
Sugars	38.9	18.0	23.1	65.9	5						
Energy Values (MJ/kg ODM)											
AMEn	9.6	0.58	8.8	10.2	4						
TMEn	9.9	0.58	9.1	10.5	4						

Amino acid digestibility coefficients

Ala
Arg
Asp
Cys
Glu
Gly
His
Ile
Leu
Lys
Meth
Phe
Pro
Pro.OH
Ser
Thr
Tryp
Tyr
Val

POULTRY DATABASE

FEED DESCRIPTION : **DISTILLERS DARK GRAINS, WHEAT BASED** (Source 3)

Determination	Mean	SD	Min	Max	n	Determination	Mean	SD	Min	Max	n

General (g/kg ODM)

Determination	Mean	SD	Min	Max	n
ODM (fresh)	906.4	35.1	851.5	932.5	5
CP	283.4	19.1	264.9	311.1	5
CF	89.1	16.4	68.0	104.0	5
EE	57.4	30.2	32.4	92.4	5
AEE	71.5	25.6	42.4	103.2	5
TA	50.5	13.4	41.5	73.2	5
GE (MJ/kg ODM)	21.3	0.69	20.7	22.1	5
NDF ash	359.9	115.1	230.0	462.0	5
NDF unash					
ADF ash	142.2	17.8	119.0	156.5	5
ADF unash					
Starch	44.9	19.8	26.0	68.5	5
WSC					
Sugars	63.2	8.1	50.3	69.9	5

Energy Values (MJ/kg ODM)

Determination	Mean	SD	Min	Max	n
AMEn	10.4	1.7	8.7	12.6	5
TMEn	10.6	1.7	8.9	12.8	5

Amino acid digestibility coefficients

Ala
Arg
Asp
Cys
Glu
Gly
His
Ile
Leu
Lys
Meth
Phe
Pro
Pro.OH
Ser
Thr
Tryp
Tyr
Val

POULTRY DATABASE

FEED DESCRIPTION : **FEATHER MEAL** (Source 3)

Determination	Mean	SD	Min	Max	n	Determination	Mean	SD	Min	Max	n
General (g/kg ODM)											
ODM (fresh)	906.8	12.3	885.0	914.5	5						
CP	891.7	2.1	889.3	894.7	5						
CF	4.7	0.21	4.6	5.1	5						
EE	64.0	0.73	62.7	64.4	5						
AEE	79.9	0.63	79.1	80.5	5						
TA	25.2	0.27	25.0	25.5	5						
GE (MJ/kg ODM)	24.0	0.08	23.9	24.1	5						
NDF ash											
NDF unash											
ADF ash											
ADF unash											
Starch											
WSC											
Sugars	1.8	0.93	1.0	2.8	3						

Energy Values (MJ/kg ODM)

Determination	Mean	SD	Min	Max	n
AMEn	13.7	0.57	13.2	14.4	5
TMEn	13.9	0.57	13.4	14.6	5

Amino acid digestibility coefficients

Ala
Arg
Asp
Cys
Glu
Gly
His
Ile
Leu
Lys
Meth
Phe
Pro
Pro.OH
Ser
Thr
Tryp
Tyr
Val

POULTRY DATABASE

FEED DESCRIPTION : **FISHMEAL, CHILEAN** (Source 3)

Determination	Mean	SD	Min	Max	n	Determination	Mean	SD	Min	Max	n

General (g/kg ODM)

ODM (fresh)	908.9	5.6	903.5	914.0	4
CP	689.7	39.6	631.1	716.5	4
CF					
EE	85.3	4.5	79.0	89.4	4
AEE	100.8	4.2	95.8	105.6	4
TA	163.5	9.8	149.5	171.5	4
GE (MJ/kg ODM)	20.6	0.17	20.4	20.8	4

NDF ash
NDF unash
ADF ash
ADF unash

Starch
WSC
Sugars

Energy Values (MJ/kg ODM)

AMEn	14.3	0.14	14.2	14.5	4
TMEn	14.5	0.14	14.4	14.7	4

Amino acid digestibility coefficients

Ala
Arg
Asp
Cys
Glu
Gly
His
Ile
Leu
Lys
Meth
Phe
Pro
Pro.OH
Ser
Thr
Tryp
Tyr
Val

POULTRY DATABASE

FEED DESCRIPTION : **LINSEED MEAL** (Source 3)

Determination	Mean	SD	Min	Max	n	Determination	Mean	SD	Min	Max	n

General (g/kg ODM)

Determination	Mean	SD	Min	Max	n
ODM (fresh)	884.9	1.0	884.0	886.0	5
CP	391.0	3.4	387.0	395.0	5
CF	74.9	0.92	74.1	76.4	5
EE	87.3	2.0	84.8	90.0	5
AEE	96.0	2.0	93.7	98.7	5
TA	51.0	0.0	51.0	51.0	5
GE (MJ/kg ODM)	24.2	0.09	24.2	24.4	5
NDF ash	192.2	8.6	183.0	206.0	5
NDF unash					
ADF ash	130.9	6.0	124.0	140.0	5
ADF unash					
Starch	52.3	1.3	50.4	53.6	5
WSC					
Sugars	42.4	0.73	41.3	43.2	5

Energy Values (MJ/kg ODM)

Determination	Mean	SD	Min	Max	n
AMEn	12.6	0.98	11.5	14.1	5
TMEn	13.0	0.99	11.9	14.5	5

Amino acid digestibility coefficients

Ala
Arg
Asp
Cys
Glu
Gly
His
Ile
Leu
Lys
Meth
Phe
Pro
Pro.OH
Ser
Thr
Tryp
Tyr
Val

POULTRY DATABASE

FEED DESCRIPTION : **MAIZE GERM MEAL** (Source 3)

Determination	Mean	SD	Min	Max	n	Determination	Mean	SD	Min	Max	n
General (g/kg ODM)											
ODM (fresh)	879.3	6.3	873.5	887.5	5						
CP	101.5	2.7	98.0	105.3	5						
CF	40.5	1.5	38.5	42.0	5						
EE	57.7	2.9	53.8	62.0	5						
AEE	63.9	2.9	60.3	68.3	5						
TA	19.7	0.97	18.5	21.0	5						
GE (MJ/kg ODM)	19.3	0.18	19.2	19.6	5						
NDF ash	191.4	11.2	178.0	203.0	5						
NDF unash											
ADF ash	51.4	2.5	48.5	55.0	5						
ADF unash											
Starch	620.2	3.7	616.3	624.3	5						
WSC											
Sugars	15.9	2.5	12.3	19.2	5						

Energy Values (MJ/kg ODM)

Determination	Mean	SD	Min	Max	n
AMEn	14.3	0.23	14.0	14.6	5
TMEn	14.8	0.25	14.4	15.0	5

Amino acid digestibility coefficients

Ala
Arg
Asp
Cys
Glu
Gly
His
Ile
Leu
Lys
Meth
Phe
Pro
Pro.OH
Ser
Thr
Tryp
Tyr
Val

POULTRY DATABASE

FEED DESCRIPTION : **MAIZE GLUTEN MEAL** (Source 3)

Determination	Mean	SD	Min	Max	n	Determination	Mean	SD	Min	Max	n

---

General (g/kg ODM)

Determination	Mean	SD	Min	Max	n
ODM (fresh)	903.3	12.5	883.0	915.5	5
CP	672.1	38.3	629.0	729.3	5
CF	8.3	2.7	3.6	10.5	5
EE	27.6	14.7	14.9	53.0	5
AEE	70.8	17.9	52.0	99.5	5
TA	9.7	2.9	7.0	13.5	5
GE (MJ/kg ODM)	23.5	0.51	22.9	24.1	5
NDF ash	20.4	7.1	12.0	31.5	5
NDF unash					
ADF ash	4.8	1.8	2.0	6.5	5
ADF unash					
Starch	194.1	45.4	146.8	244.5	5
WSC					
Sugars	2.8	0.80	2.0	4.1	5

Energy Values (MJ/kg ODM)

Determination	Mean	SD	Min	Max	n
AMEn	17.9	0.28	17.7	18.4	5
TMEn	18.2	0.26	17.9	18.6	5

Amino acid digestibility coefficients

Ala
Arg
Asp
Cys
Glu
Gly
His
Ile
Leu
Lys
Meth
Phe
Pro
Pro.OH
Ser
Thr
Tryp
Tyr
Val

POULTRY DATABASE

FEED DESCRIPTION : **MALT CULMS** (Source 3)

Determination	Mean	SD	Min	Max	n	Determination	Mean	SD	Min	Max	n

General (g/kg ODM)

Determination	Mean	SD	Min	Max	n
ODM (fresh)	914.8	28.9	888.5	964.5	5
CP	282.8	26.4	246.7	319.7	5
CF	136.5	12.6	115.0	146.5	5
EE	14.3	3.2	9.9	17.4	5
AEE	25.9	4.2	21.3	32.3	5
TA	65.3	2.4	61.5	68.0	5
GE (MJ/kg ODM)	18.7	0.35	18.2	19.0	5
NDF ash	462.9	34.9	425.5	510.5	5
NDF unash					
ADF ash	162.5	23.3	125.5	188.0	5
ADF unash					
Starch	63.3	36.0	26.3	121.7	5
WSC					
Sugars	107.2	47.9	65.2	184.4	5

Energy Values (MJ/kg ODM)

Determination	Mean	SD	Min	Max	n
AMEn	6.8	1.0	5.8	8.5	5
TMEn	7.4	0.78	6.8	8.7	5

Amino acid digestibility coefficients

Ala
Arg
Asp
Cys
Glu
Gly
His
Ile
Leu
Lys
Meth
Phe
Pro
Pro.OH
Ser
Thr
Tryp
Tyr
Val

FEED DESCRIPTION : **MALT CULMS** (Source 3)

POULTRY DATABASE

FEED DESCRIPTION : **MEAT AND BONE MEAL** (Source 3)

Determination	Mean	SD	Min	Max	n	Determination	Mean	SD	Min	Max	n

General (g/kg ODM)

Determination	Mean	SD	Min	Max	n
ODM (fresh)	971.8	0.82	970.5	973.0	10
CP	525.0	7.9	514.3	533.3	10
CF	19.7	2.5	16.5	23.0	10
EE	143.2	12.2	131.0	157.5	10
AEE	151.4	11.8	139.3	165.3	10
TA	277.3	4.8	273.5	287.5	10
GE (MJ/kg ODM)	18.7	0.18	18.5	19.0	10
NDF ash					
NDF unash					
ADF ash					
ADF unash					
Starch					
WSC					
Sugars	4.2	0.87	3.1	5.4	5

Energy Values (MJ/kg ODM)

Determination	Mean	SD	Min	Max	n
AMEn	11.9	0.40	11.3	12.4	10
TMEn	12.1	0.40	11.5	12.6	10

Amino acid digestibility coefficients

Ala
Arg
Asp
Cys
Glu
Gly
His
Ile
Leu
Lys
Meth
Phe
Pro
Pro.OH
Ser
Thr
Tryp
Tyr
Val

POULTRY DATABASE

FEED DESCRIPTION : **PEAS, FIELD** (Source 3)

Determination	Mean	SD	Min	Max	n	Determination	Mean	SD	Min	Max	n

General (g/kg ODM)

Determination	Mean	SD	Min	Max	n
ODM (fresh)	865.8	18.6	842.5	884.0	5
CP	246.6	12.4	226.3	259.7	5
CF	59.2	4.9	52.3	65.0	5
EE	14.1	1.7	12.4	16.2	5
AEE	24.5	2.1	22.0	26.3	5
TA	27.3	0.84	26.0	28.0	5
GE (MJ/kg ODM)	18.4	0.33	17.9	18.7	5
NDF ash	102.3	5.7	94.0	108.0	5
NDF unash					
ADF ash	65.2	2.6	61.0	67.5	5
ADF unash					
Starch	481.9	23.4	460.0	519.0	5
WSC					
Sugars	56.9	7.3	45.8	65.4	5

Energy Values (MJ/kg ODM)

Determination	Mean	SD	Min	Max	n
AMEn	13.6	0.40	13.1	14.1	5
TMEn	14.1	0.44	13.5	14.6	5

Amino acid digestibility coefficients

Ala
Arg
Asp
Cys
Glu
Gly
His
Ile
Leu
Lys
Meth
Phe
Pro
Pro.OH
Ser
Thr
Tryp
Tyr
Val

POULTRY DATABASE

FEED DESCRIPTION : **POULTRY OFFAL MEAL** (Source 3)

Determination	Mean	SD	Min	Max	n	Determination	Mean	SD	Min	Max	n

General (g/kg ODM)

ODM (fresh)	904.5	10.4	896.0	922.0	5
CP	544.9	31.6	497.0	584.3	5
CF	3.8	0.61	3.3	4.7	5
EE	346.9	34.2	322.8	407.3	5
AEE	354.5	32.5	331.3	411.8	5
TA	73.2	17.9	49.1	89.9	5
GE (MJ/kg ODM)	26.8	0.86	25.8	27.8	5

NDF ash
NDF unash
ADF ash
ADF unash

Starch
WSC

Sugars	3.4	1.1	1.8	4.4	5

Energy Values (MJ/kg ODM)

AMEn	18.0	1.3	17.0	19.9	4
TMEn	18.2	1.3	17.2	20.1	4

Amino acid digestibility coefficients

Ala
Arg
Asp
Cys
Glu
Gly
His
Ile
Leu
Lys
Meth
Phe
Pro
Pro.OH
Ser
Thr
Tryp
Tyr
Val

POULTRY DATABASE

FEED DESCRIPTION : **RAPESEED MEAL** (Source 3)

Determination	Mean	SD	Min	Max	n	Determination	Mean	SD	Min	Max	n

General (g/kg ODM)

Determination	Mean	SD	Min	Max	n
ODM (fresh)	900.4	18.3	883.0	929.0	5
CP	405.9	4.5	400.3	412.7	5
CF	91.8	17.7	70.9	113.5	5
EE	33.1	7.8	21.8	42.7	5
AEE	54.1	7.5	43.2	63.5	5
TA	68.2	1.2	67.0	70.0	5
GE (MJ/kg ODM)	19.8	0.17	19.5	19.9	5
NDF ash	260.2	8.2	252.5	269.5	5
NDF unash					
ADF ash	173.9	6.6	167.0	183.0	5
ADF unash					
Starch	47.3	3.6	43.0	52.8	5
WSC					
Sugars	106.8	1.7	105.3	109.5	5

Energy Values (MJ/kg ODM)

Determination	Mean	SD	Min	Max	n
AMEn	8.4	0.24	8.2	8.7	4
TMEn	8.8	0.22	8.6	9.1	4

Amino acid digestibility coefficients

Ala
Arg
Asp
Cys
Glu
Gly
His
Ile
Leu
Lys
Meth
Phe
Pro
Pro.OH
Ser
Thr
Tryp
Tyr
Val

POULTRY DATABASE

FEED DESCRIPTION : **SESAME CAKE** (Source 3)

Determination	Mean	SD	Min	Max	n	Determination	Mean	SD	Min	Max	n

General (g/kg ODM)

ODM (fresh)	951.7	2.1	949.5	954.0	5
CP	487.8	7.9	476.4	498.6	5
CF	56.8	0.67	56.0	57.6	5
EE	113.8	5.3	107.4	120.6	5
AEE	116.2	3.9	113.0	122.2	5
TA	140.8	1.6	138.5	142.5	5
GE (MJ/kg ODM)	19.9	0.10	19.8	20.0	5

NDF ash
NDF unash
ADF ash
ADF unash

Starch	14.8	2.3	12.2	17.4	5
WSC					
Sugars	38.3	1.3	36.8	39.8	5

Energy Values (MJ/kg ODM)

AMEn	11.4	0.18	11.2	11.6	5
TMEn	11.5	0.21	11.3	11.8	5

Amino acid digestibility coefficients

Ala
Arg
Asp
Cys
Glu
Gly
His
Ile
Leu
Lys
Meth
Phe
Pro
Pro.OH
Ser
Thr
Tryp
Tyr
Val

POULTRY DATABASE

FEED DESCRIPTION : **SOYABEAN, FULL FAT** (Source 3)

Determination	Mean	SD	Min	Max	n	Determination	Mean	SD	Min	Max	n

General (g/kg ODM)

Determination	Mean	SD	Min	Max	n
ODM (fresh)	895.3	5.9	890.0	902.0	5
CP	421.5	5.2	414.3	428.7	5
CF	50.6	2.8	47.8	55.2	5
EE	231.0	0.98	229.5	232.0	5
AEE	226.2	1.8	223.0	227.3	5
TA	55.1	0.23	55.0	55.5	5
GE (MJ/kg ODM)	23.7	0.15	23.6	24.0	5
NDF ash	120.6	4.1	116.5	126.0	5
NDF unash					
ADF ash	69.9	1.9	67.5	72.5	5
ADF unash					
Starch	15.7	2.0	13.4	18.4	5
WSC					
Sugars	76.4	4.2	71.4	81.3	5

Energy Values (MJ/kg ODM)

Determination	Mean	SD	Min	Max	n
AMEn	15.7	0.24	15.4	16.0	5
TMEn	16.2	0.29	15.8	16.5	5

Amino acid digestibility coefficients

Ala
Arg
Asp
Cys
Glu
Gly
His
Ile
Leu
Lys
Meth
Phe
Pro
Pro.OH
Ser
Thr
Tryp
Tyr
Val

POULTRY DATABASE

FEED DESCRIPTION : **SOYABEAN MEAL, EXTRACTED** (Source 3)

Determination	Mean	SD	Min	Max	n	Determination	Mean	SD	Min	Max	n

General (g/kg ODM)

ODM (fresh)	887.8	13.4	874.5	902.0	5
CP	508.9	6.9	502.7	518.3	5
CF	68.2	4.8	62.8	75.3	5
EE	16.3	3.8	12.7	22.8	5
AEE	26.6	3.2	22.7	31.7	5
TA	67.2	2.0	64.0	69.0	5
GE (MJ/kg ODM)	19.7	0.18	19.5	19.9	5
NDF ash	89.3	32.4	64.5	127.5	5
NDF unash					
ADF ash	55.0	20.8	38.5	78.5	5
ADF unash					
Starch	39.4	15.6	22.1	54.0	5
WSC					
Sugars	95.6	6.7	85.8	104.5	5

Energy Values (MJ/kg ODM)

AMEn	11.2	0.23	11.0	11.6	5
TMEn	11.6	0.25	11.2	11.8	5

Amino acid digestibility coefficients

Ala
Arg
Asp
Cys
Glu
Gly
His
Ile
Leu
Lys
Meth
Phe
Pro
Pro.OH
Ser
Thr
Tryp
Tyr
Val

POULTRY DATABASE

FEED DESCRIPTION : **SOYABEAN MEAL, EXTRACTED, DEHULLED** (Source 3)

Determination	Mean	SD	Min	Max	n	Determination	Mean	SD	Min	Max	n

General (g/kg ODM)

Determination	Mean	SD	Min	Max	n
ODM (fresh)	887.4	5.2	880.0	892.0	5
CP	547.1	5.6	538.0	552.0	5
CF	34.0	1.7	33.1	37.0	5
EE	20.0	7.1	10.2	25.2	5
AEE	31.2	8.6	20.8	38.3	5
TA	70.1	1.7	67.0	71.0	5
GE (MJ/kg ODM)	19.9	0.06	19.8	19.9	5
NDF ash	109.2	34.1	69.5	143.5	5
NDF unash					
ADF ash	67.2	25.3	36.0	92.0	5
ADF unash					
Starch	34.1	13.7	20.7	50.7	5
WSC					
Sugars	105.2	5.0	99.4	111.0	5

Energy Values (MJ/kg ODM)

Determination	Mean	SD	Min	Max	n
AMEn	11.8	0.17	11.7	12.1	5
TMEn	12.1	0.14	11.9	12.3	5

Amino acid digestibility coefficients

Ala
Arg
Asp
Cys
Glu
Gly
His
Ile
Leu
Lys
Meth
Phe
Pro
Pro.OH
Ser
Thr
Tryp
Tyr
Val

REFERENCES

Alderman G (1985) In: W Haresign and D J A Cole (Editors) Recent Advances in Animal Nutrition - 1985 Butterworths, London. pp 3-52.

Alexander R H and McGowan M J (1966). J.Brit.Grassld.Soc. 21, 140-147.

Anon (1985). Feedingstuffs Regulations, Sampling and Analysis (amendments) 1985, HMSO, London.

AOAC (1984) Official Methods of Analysis, 14th edition, Section 28.056-28.066

ARC (1984) The Nutrient Requirements of Ruminant Livestock, Supplement No 1, CAB, Farnham Royal.

Blaxter K L and Clapperton J L (1965). Brit. J. Nutr. 19, 511-522.

Dewar R and McDonald P (1961). J.Sci.Fd.Agric. 12, 790-795.

Goering H K and Van Soest P J (1970). Forage Fiber Analysis, USDA Handbook No 379. Washington DC.

Hall R J and Gupta P L (1969). Analyst (London) 94, 292-299.

INFIC (1980) International Feed Descriptions, International Feed Names and Country Feed Names. International Network of Feed Information Centres, Publication No 5, Utah State University, Logan.

Jones D I H and Hayward M V (1975). J.Sci.Fd.Agric. 26, 711-718.

MAFF (1984). Analysis of Agricultural Materials, Reference Book 427, HMSO, London.

MAFF (1986). Feed Composition, UK Tables of Feed Composition and Nutritive Value for Ruminants, Chalcombe Publications, Marlow.

McNab J M and Blair J C (1988). Brit. Poultry Sci. 29, 697-707.

Moore S, Spackman D H and Stein W H (1958). Anal.Chem. 30, 1185-1190.

Moore S (1963). J.Biol.Chem. 238, 235-237.

Nielson H K and Hurrell R F (1985). J.Sci.Fd.Agric. 36, 893-907.

Ørskov E R and McDonald I (1979). J.Agric.Sci.(Cambs), 92, 499-503.

Pons W A and Guthrie J D (1946). Ind. Engng.Chem. 18, 184-186.

Simmons W J (1975). Anal.Chem. 47, 2015-2018.

Tilley J M A and Terry R A (1963). J.Brit.Grassld.Soc. 18, 104-111.

INDEX OF FEEDS

417